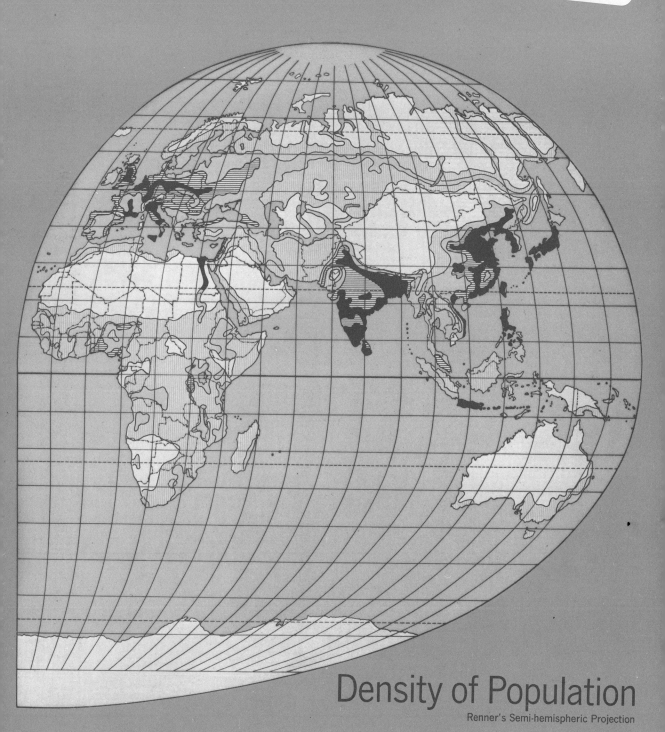

Density of Population

Renner's Semi-hemispheric Projection

GEOGRAPHY:
FACTORS
AND
CONCEPTS

Kirtley F. Mather, Editor

CENTURY EARTH SCIENCE SERIES

C. Langdon White
Stanford University

George T. Renner
Late of Columbia University

Henry J. Warman
Clark University

GEOGRAPHY:

FACTORS

AND

CONCEPTS

New York

APPLETON-CENTURY-CROFTS
Division of Meredith Corporation

ACKNOWLEDGMENTS

The following maps use Renner's semihemispheric projection, copyright 1945 by G. T. Renner:
Figs. 7-10, 7-12, 8-1, 9-1, 10-1, 11-2, 12-1, 13-1, 14-1, 15-1, 16-1, 17-4, 21-1, 22-2, 23-1, 24-2,
27-12, 28-7, 35-3, and 36-1.

The following maps use Renner's ocean-basin projection, copyright 1946: Figs. 7-5 and 27-4.

The map used as a basis for Fig. 30-1 is from Goode Base Map Series, Department of Geography,
The University of Chicago, publisher. Copyright by The University of Chicago.

Preface

The science of geography is a very old one; indeed, it sometimes has been called the "mother of sciences." When one goes back into the historical record in order to see which modern school of thought embodies the real meaning of geography, he encounters evidence from which a great variety of interpretations are possible. It is generally agreed, however, that a Greek scholar of old originated the term *geography* by combining two common words of the Greek language—*gē* (the earth) and *graphein* (to write). The resulting word, geography, therefore means literally to write concerning the earth, but it does not specify what is to be written. All through the subsequent centuries, the ideas of both geographers and laymen have differed as to what materials were geographic or nongeographic. One geographer would write mainly of the physical earth, another of the earth's human inhabitants, and still others of the earth's mathematical, astronomical, and locational aspects. Geographic words were, therefore, variously descriptive, philosophic, analytic, synthetic, and historical in character. All indicated a profound concern, often a driving, burning zeal to interpret the "writings" in, on, and of the earth's surface—writings done by man and society as well as by nature. Along with such interpretive accounts there was created a host of graphic devices, especially maps and globes. Through the ages the subject (and its accompanying visual and audio devices) grew slowly and evolved toward its present form. Its body of facts increased, its ideas and philosophies multiplied, and its principles became better understood. The evolution in meaning has by no means all been in the same direction. Today the thinking of American geographers has diverged so far as to produce several distinct schools of thought in geography. Among them the schools of human ecology, physiography, chorography (or land use), geonomics, resource development, and environmental measurement and perception seem to be most worthy of note.

POINT OF VIEW AND SUBJECT MATTER

The authors of this book believe that all the current schools of thought in geography are equally valid and, under certain circumstances, equally valuable. Indeed, they believe that all of them represent parts of the total science of geography. From long experience as educators, the authors believe that three very great needs of American citizens in general and American students in particular, are (1) to be capable of viewing themselves and all other peoples of the world in the light of their specific homelands, (2) to grasp through study the problems of peoples and their places, and (3) to understand the past and present solutions to these problems with a view to a better, more meaningful use in the future of a place's attributes and its people's abilities. This learning simultaneously about human affairs and the attributes of place almost invariably reveals to the student that human society is interrelated with earth characteristics, not independent of them. The exact nature of this relationship need not be deterministic in the sense of the social Darwinism of the nineteenth century, or even of the milder influences of the twentieth century. Rather it involves a sort of social pragmatism wherein human beings are viewed as living within a natural environment which varies strikingly from one part of the earth's surface to another. Human activities and cultural functions are regarded, as is the natural environment, as being active and dynamic. The latter, the natural environment, while active in its processes is only passively restrictive or permissive in the opportunities which it presents to the former, the man-culture milieu.

This study of men and place simultaneously is the essence of the human ecology school of geography. Its objective is to make people aware of places and resources and conscious of the relationships between the earth environment and the problems of living. On a world scale, it aims to enable people to think in global terms and to understand the strategy of men, their culture, space, and resources.

v

The subject matter of geography is therefore threefold. First are the social data drawn from the realm of human affairs; second are the physical materials drawn from the realm of nature; the third is the realm of abstract correlation, integration, and relationship between the two.

THE APPROACH TO GEOGRAPHY

While there are several methods of beginning geographic study, one logical way to approach it is to go into the field, observe the data firsthand, and geographically interpret those data. It is not difficult to train the beginning student to observe and even to map and otherwise record social data, but to interpret these in the light of the human ecology school requires possession of many of the tools and methods of classification from the natural as well as the social sciences. Such natural science tools and methods cannot be learned incidentally as a sideline to the study of social data in the field. However, even when time, funds, and adequate transport are available it is not especially advantageous to undertake extensive field work until the students are prepared to analyze geographically the data observed and researched, the classifications made, and the relationships (if any) revealed. Such geographic analysis consists in applying the general methodology of the natural sciences to the data of the social sciences, and in evaluating the results in terms of the philosophy of the ecological sciences. A beginning course in geography can provide the student with the general environmental tools needed for geographic analysis and with a general idea of how one thinks in geographic terms.

THE INTRODUCTORY-COURSE TEXT AND TEACHER

In North America it appears that to meet the needs of a beginning course in geography, a good textbook, presenting the materials and methodology of geography is indispensable. To meet these needs the authors of the present work have written certain general chapters dealing with the meaning of geography. Its scope, elements, major concepts, and the geographer's point of view appear in six chapters in Part I. The remainder of the forty chapters are grouped in Parts II to X. Parts II to VII present in detail the climatic, physiographic, hydrographic, edaphic, the three biotic, and the mineral factors. Part IX contains three chapters on major spatial factors—augmenting those dealt with primarily in Part I. The last Part, entitled Perpetual Transformation, treats the ecological succession within the region and essays to formulate, in tentative form, to be sure, a geographic theory of human society.

The best textbook cannot, however, produce by itself good geographic education. Nevertheless, the authors are hopeful that this book will assist both teachers and students in acquiring (1) a deeper interest in human affairs, (2) a keener perception of location factors, regional patterns, and space relations, (3) more perceptive power in the field, (4) an above-average competency to synthesize diverse data, and (5) the ability to distinguish between *causality* and mere *concomitancy* in dealing with human affairs.

ACKNOWLEDGMENTS

Many persons have contributed not only to this edition but also to preceding editions. Hence some of the material is indicative of the concern, reflection, and scholarly work of the early contributors. The authors wish to express their gratitude to them as well as to the more recent contributors. Thanks and appreciation are extended to the following: Miss Susan Linn of Middlebury College and Miss Nancy Abodeely of Clark University and University of Chicago who supplied student points of view in planning this book; Dr. Paul F. Griffin, Oregon College of Education, for criticisms bearing upon Chapter 1; Dr. Loyal Durand of the University of Tennessee for contributions to Chapters 13 and 23; Dr. James N. Wilson of Long Beach State College for critical reading of some material now in Chapters 2 and 6; Dr. Robert Chauvin of John B. Stetson University; Dr. George T. Renner, 3rd, of Arizona State University for a critical reading of earlier manuscripts and for many helpful comments; Dr. Julius Kaikow, City College of New York, for helpful suggestions as a result of using the book over a period of years; Professor Thomas Ladonsky, State University, Agricultural and Technical Institute, Stony Brook, New York, for careful reading of and frank comments on the entire project; Robert S. Weiner, Briarcliff College, for his incisive comments particularly on Parts I and II; and finally high praise to the Clark University Library staff for willing, efficient assistance in securing references and to departmental colleagues for encouragement, individually and collectively.

C.L.W.
H.J.W.

Contents

I

The Nature and Field of Geography

In the ecological-school approach to geography, taken by the authors of this text, it is difficult, in fact, almost impossible, to separate geography into neat compartments of physical and cultural. The human realm, the physical world, and the world of man-made creations, or institutions, are intricately entwined. The actions, reactions, and interactions are not the same everywhere. The significance of place and the varying attributes thereof call for a positioning of events on the earth's surface. Geographic position and geomatic position with all their ramifications, particularly of the former, when studied and used intently, give insight to the "life motif" of selected areas. Such areas are often called regions, and *regions are made by persons who have special reasons for creating them.* The creation of regions, or regionalizing, is a fundamental concept, the operational one, of all geography.

1

The Environment: Physical and Cultural

Geography is part of the great composite science of human society. It is, therefore, one of the seven so-called social sciences (anthropology, economics, geography, history, political science, social psychology, and sociology) whose common purpose is to study the structure and behavior of human society. While all of these have a common purpose, they possess unique points of view and they have evolved different techniques of studying human affairs. Each attacks social problems in its own individual manner, and the study of no two of them yields the same understandings.

PREMISE OF GEOGRAPHY

The major premise of geography is that nothing can be adequately understood apart from the place where it occurs. That is, no event, situation, or problem in human society has much meaning until it is examined against the characteristics of that part of the earth which constitutes the background for it. For instance, had a federal corporation like the Tennessee Valley Authority been established in the state of New York, had the Battle of Waterloo occurred at the approach to the Khyber Pass in Asia, or had the Magna Carta been signed on the banks of the Volga River, the significance of these happenings would have been greatly altered. Or if the Everlasting League had been formed on the plains of Poland instead of in the Swiss Alps, if the first civilizations had arisen in Scandinavia instead of Mesopotamia, or if the Industrial Revolution had first occurred in Spain rather

than in Britain, the meaning of these examples of behavior in human society would have been vastly different, even though the happenings themselves had remained the same. This connection between human affairs and the places where they exist or occur is the essence of geography, while the study of natural similarities and differences in the various parts of the earth and the examination of areal patterns and regionalism in the affairs of men are the raw materials.

BASIC GEOGRAPHIC CONCEPTS

The study of geography begins with two basic concepts—that of *human society* and that of *natural environment*. Of these two highly important concepts, the former is familiar to most Americans. The latter, however, is generally an unfamiliar one and therefore needs considerable explanation at the very outset.

NATURAL VERSUS SOCIAL ENVIRONMENT

It is generally known that an individual is born into this world with natural animal characteristics which are determined by heredity. It is known, also, that as soon as an individual is born he begins to live in, and be acted upon by, a whole set of surroundings which are commonly referred to as *environment*. What is usually meant by this term is only the social environment, consisting of home, school, playground, church, community, and state, together with group traditions, codes of behavior, and general "climate of opinion," made by other

3

people who were born into the world before him. This social environment plays a crucial role in affecting and shaping the individual's behavior and character.

Beyond and outside the social environment, however, is a much larger environment which the experts on human affairs usually overlook or ignore. This is the natural environment. It affects mankind perhaps even more than do the social surroundings, but in a different way. The social environment plays a major part in shaping the individual human being, whereas the natural environment affects him only secondarily and for the most part indirectly. Indeed, in a modern urban community such as New York City, the individual escapes almost all of the direct effects of the natural surroundings.

On the other hand, the natural environment affects large groups of people very directly and in a primary manner. Every community, tribe, state, nation, and empire on earth is affected by it directly, vigorously, and persistently. No major activity of human society is independent of its helps, hindrances, or directives. The natural environment does to human society what the social environment does to the human individual.

NATURAL ENVIRONMENT IS A COMPOSITE

The natural environment includes a great number of things—all the agents, forces, processes, and material resources of nature. The list of all these is unbelievably long. In fact, it is bewilderingly complex until one sorts and classifies its components and puts them into some simple arrangement. When this is done, the whole matter is easy to understand. For instance, the natural environment of any part of the earth's surface can be classified into the following sixteen elements (Fig. 1–1).

1. Geomatic position
2. Geographic location
3. Weather and climate
4. Landforms
5. Surface waters of the land
6. Underground waters
7. The ocean[1]
8. The coast zone[1]
9. Soils
10. Natural vegetation (flora)
11. Native animal life (fauna)
12. Microorganic realm
13. Rocks and minerals
14. Areal space or size
15. Regional form or shape
16. Natural situation

THE SIXTEEN NATURAL ENVIRONMENTAL ELEMENTS

Each of the elements of the natural environment listed above may be subdivided into two or more types, so that the student of geography must know and be familiar with not only the sixteen natural elements, but with more than seventy-five subdivisions of them as well. After he learns these, he uses them as criteria, or measuring-sticks, in social analysis. At the outset, then, it might be well to examine briefly each of the natural environmental elements.

GEOMATIC POSITION

When one examines a small globe representing the earth, he might conclude that a community's mathematical position on that globe would make little difference to its inhabitants. Nothing, however, could be further from the truth. If a community lies in latitude 5°, it experiences no seasons and the daily periods of sunshine and darkness are always approximately equal. If the community lies in latitude 75°, violent seasonal contrasts are experienced and the sun disappears entirely for several weeks each year. Geomatic position is one of the factors which helps to create differences in human society.

GEOGRAPHIC LOCATION

California, located on the western margin of the United States, has long been interested in Oriental affairs. Japanese war scares have been perennial. Before the war against the Axis, large numbers of Californians were in favor of stopping Japan before she got started in her attack upon America.

North Dakota, located in the heart of America, long pursued a policy of almost complete

[1] These elements are not present in all localities.

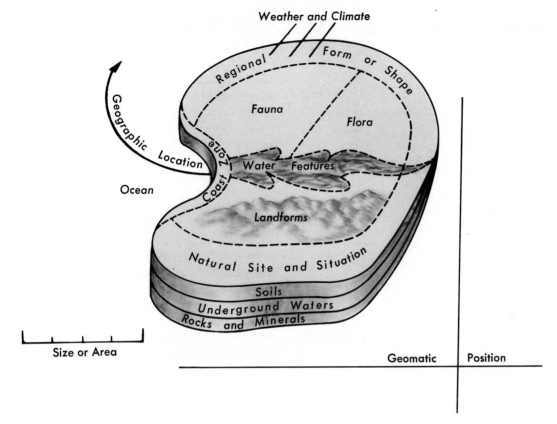

Figure 1–1 Conventionalized representation of several elements of the natural environment.

political isolationism. From her central location, immediate American affairs seemed of primary importance. Problems and threats which were visible along the margins of the nation were scarcely visible in North Dakota. Such is the effect of location upon society.

WEATHER AND CLIMATE

Weather is a condition of the atmosphere at any given time and place. It is the result of sun behavior, plus land-and-water distribution over the earth, plus topography of the lands. When the irregularities of weather are smoothed out by taking averages over a long period of time, we call it *climate*.

Climate is often the measuring stick of human society. For example, a great lowland plain stretches across the continent of North America without a break from the Gulf of Mexico to the Arctic Ocean. Logically, human society might be the same from one end of it to the other, but it

is not. Along the southern edge, men grow sugar cane and rice. North of this stretch there are many square miles of cotton. Next come several hundred miles of corn and oats; then an equal expanse of wheat; then hundreds of miles of forest and fur-bearing animals. Finally, there are a thousand miles of Arctic tundra, musk-oxen, and reindeer. From sugar cane to reindeer is largely a matter of climate. To be more exact, it is a matter of only one small part of climate, namely, the number of days without frost in each year.

The number of days without frost per year is merely another way of saying "length of growing season" or the number of days between the last *killing* frost in spring and the first killing frost in autumn for any given locality. In eastern United States, the average date of last killing frost in spring varies from February 15 in central Florida to June 1 in northern Minnesota. Figure 1–2 shows the relation between the plant-

Figure 1–2 Zones of the last killing frost in the spring over eastern United States.

ing of gardens and the zones of the last killing frost over eastern United States.

The amount of rain which falls during the year may be just as important to human society as is the length of the frost-free growing season. In some cases, the season of the year when the rain occurs, or the manner in which it falls, or the amount of snowfall, or the likelihood of drought periods, or some other aspect of climate may be the critical factor.

LANDFORMS

The physical relief features of the land, that is, the landforms of the earth's surface, are another measuring stick for human society. How this element of the environment operates is shown by an example from Kentucky. The eastern part of that state consists of two parts: one is a very rugged area of hills, the other is a fairly level plain. Both areas were settled by English, Scottish-Irish, and French Huguenot people. Indeed, the same families settled in both areas—a fact indicated by the common occurrence of the same surnames among the present-day inhabitants. The cultures of the two areas have, however, come to be highly different. The Kentucky Hills became marked by poverty, lack of education, wooden-shack and log-cabin homes, self-sufficing agriculture, drab people, and somewhat archaic

social conditions. Although conditions are improving considerably over portions of the Kentucky Hills, largely as a result of improved highway transportation, the region as a whole must still be regarded as the most seriously depressed densely settled area in the nation.[2] The Kentucky Bluegrass Plain, on the contrary, became a land of large estates, lovely homes, education, wealth, beautiful women, fine horses, and commercial tobacco growing. The character of the surface relief of the land was obviously the key to the difference.

SURFACE WATERS OF THE LAND

Surface waters, such as streams, ponds, lakes, and swamps, are familiar to everyone. But seldom does one take the trouble to observe the extent to which such features affect human destiny. The world is full of examples, but one from central United States will suffice. The chain of water bodies known as the Great Lakes provides an excellent transportation route for iron ore and other bulky materials. Lining the shores of the Great Lakes are industrial districts, busy industrial and commercial cities, and market gardens serving city markets. A few miles back from the lakes, society is agricultural and rural.

UNDERGROUND WATERS

Water occurs in the pores of the soil. Below this usually lies a water table. Still deeper, there is sometimes artesian water. All of this is mysterious to the average citizen, but ground waters constitute one of society's bank accounts, deposited through the ages by nature.

In the American Middle West, the early settlers could dig a well almost anywhere and get all the water they wanted. In the Southwest, however, man could find it only at widely separated points. In the former area, the land was first surveyed into standard 160-acre plots and distributed to families of homesteaders. Each family dug its own well and built a home adjacent to that well. In the Southwest, men first seized the points where water was available, and divided the land later—each farm or ranch reaching halfway to

[2] Harry M. Caudill, *Night Comes to the Cumberlands: A Biography of a Depressed Area* (Boston, Little, Brown and Company, 1963).

the next source of water. The two land-holding patterns were, therefore, radically different. Obviously, too, human society is quite different in the two areas today.

THE OCEAN

Most of the earth's surface is water, not land. No people, therefore, have altogether escaped the influence of the ocean. The degree of this influence varies markedly from region to region and from culture to culture—depending upon a number of factors.

One of those factors is distance from the ocean. For instance, the northern end of the British Isles, washed by the Atlantic, has an average January temperature of about 50° F.; eastern interior Siberia, in the same latitude but far from the reach of maritime influences, has a January temperature of 50° or more *below* zero. Similarly, the Amazon lowland of interior Brazil has an average July temperature of 30° F. or more; small islands in the same latitudes are rendered pleasant by cooling ocean breezes.

To the Norwegians, facing into both the Atlantic and the Arctic oceans, fish of all kinds are extremely important as food. The Kirghiz, Uzbeks, and Mongols of central Asia, on the other hand, are eaters of meat and animal products.

The ancient Punic peoples who lived on the Mediterranean Sea were consumers of sea food, and an important item in their commerce was the *Tyrian purple* dye, a product of one variety of shellfish. The closely related Hebrew tribes, however, developed religio-dietary laws against eating shellfish.

Some peoples, such as the ancient Greeks and Phoenicians, the medieval Venetians and Scandinavians, and the modern British, Dutch, Spanish, French, and Portuguese took to the sea and thereby obtained overseas empires. Other peoples, such as the Swiss, Hungarians, Siamese, and Chinese, seem not to have been able to make successful geographic adjustments to the ocean. The resources of the ocean are so large that if utilized they could probably support the entire existing population of the world. So far, however, the human race has succeeded in using only a few of the more obvious and easily accessible riches of the ocean.

THE LITTORAL

Not all nations and peoples have territorial frontage on the ocean. Where they do have such frontage, a great deal depends upon the extent and character of their littoral or coast zone.

For instance, in New England the coastline is exceedingly ragged and irregular. Deep-water harbors extend far into the land. New England, accordingly, has long been at work building ships. New Englanders have been going to sea in fishing craft, merchant vessels, and warships; they are deep-sea men.

The coast of New Jersey is low and sandy with a long sandbar offshore. A few shallow harbors provide haven for the small craft employed in the recreation and small fishing enterprises. The biggest pier on the Jersey coast south of Sandy Hook was built for recreation only. The New Jerseyite is a shallow-water man.

Southward, in Georgia, the coast zone consists of a maze of low swampy or sandy sea islands. There is an almost complete lack of harbors. The men of Georgia are landsmen; within a few miles of the sea, they are planters or farmers.

SOIL

Soil is a well organized and highly complicated layer of debris covering most of the earth's land surface. Weather, rocks, water, plants, animals, and bacteria have played a part in its making. Like grandmother's crazy quilt is the pattern of distribution of the many varieties of soil over the earth. Each variety is good for a different use. Therefore, soil differences often produce profound social differences.

For example, in western Washington much of the countryside is covered with a sandy gray-brown soil. In some of the stream valleys and other low, flat areas, however, there is black muck soil. If one clears the trees, stumps, and stones off the gray-brown soil and farms it, his income per acre is small. The black soils of the bottom lands, however, if planted with small fruits and truck crops, will produce much greater returns. The rent on an acre of the former is low, whereas on the latter it is very high. Anyone can rent the gray-brown soil, but only one who is willing to work his entire family from dawn to dusk can afford to rent the latter. Hence, the gray-brown soils have been occupied by Americans, Canadians, and Scandinavians, while Japanese farmers have tended to monopolize the black soil areas, especially those near the cities. The contrast in the social conditions on the two classes of soil has been truly striking.

World War II aroused anti-Japanese sentiment to a high pitch, and so all Japanese-Americans were uprooted and swept off the land. During the war, some of these areas of black soil lay idle; others were worked by Filipinos, Poles, and Mexicans. After the war, many of the Japanese returned. But whatever people occupy these soils, they must be willing to work long hours and accept a relatively low living standard.

NATURAL VEGETATION

It takes four thousand years for nature to build a giant sequoia; four hundred years to produce a fine Douglas fir; about forty years will make some varieties of pine, but four years will yield a pretty good alder or wild cherry tree. For this and other reasons, there are forests of many different kinds. Forests of one kind or another originally spread their shade over half of the United States. The well-watered eastern part of the country was almost solidly covered with forest.[3] West of the Mississippi, forest gave way to prairie grass half as tall as a man. Beyond the twenty-inch rainfall line, the grasses rapidly grow shorter until they become a feltlike mat no more than ankle high. Tall grass, medium grass, and short grass covered one-third of the country. Beyond the Rockies spreads the realm of hard desert and semidesert shrubs, adapted through the ages to little water and high evaporation. One-sixth of the United States was covered with such dry-land vegetation.

And so it is all over the world: forest, grassland, and desert shrub compose an intricate pattern of natural vegetation, which often differentiates human society in surprising ways. For instance, southern Illinois was originally forest; northern Illinois was prairie. In the early 1800's, men from Kentucky, Tennessee, and Virginia settled the forested portions of Illinois because, after the timber was cleared, they could easily plow the soil. They avoided the prairies of northern Illinois because their iron-shod wooden plows could not break the tough sod.

Several decades later, after the steel plow was invented, the prairies were settled rapidly by men of New England stock. Since there was more prairie than forest land, Illinois became dominantly an antislavery and Republican state. Had Illinois been all forest it might conceivably have become predominantly a proslavery, Southern Democrat state and eventually might have seceded from the Union.

NATIVE ANIMAL LIFE

The fish which inhabit the waters, the birds of the air, waterways, and hedgerows, the animals of forest, grassland and desert, the insects, and even lowlier living things make up the earth's fauna. This fauna has a geography all its own, because each kind of living creature seeks out and eventually becomes adapted to a special habitat. The distributional pattern of this fauna or native animal life is, in turn, a factor which helps to shape the geography of human society.

For example, buffalo were abundant in the region inhabited by the Sioux tribes of American Indians, whereas fish were very scarce. The Sioux accordingly developed a nomadic civilization. They lived in portable hide tepees and followed the buffalo herds in their annual migrations. The Salish tribes, on the other hand, found abundant salmon but no buffalo in their region. Accordingly, they built log houses and settled permanently near their fishing sites.

THE MICROORGANIC REALM

The world of microorganisms is exceedingly varied. Its members have only one trait in common—they are very small; many of them are invisible to the naked human eye. Some are tiny animals such as the amoeba, the vinegar eel, and the trichinella; some are very small plants like the yeasts and molds; some—the bacteria, rickettsias, and viruses—are neither plant nor animal.

Some members of this realm of small living things are useful to men, and a few, indeed, have been domesticated by mankind and put to work; but a great many varieties attack human beings and cause disease or debility. As such, they constitute a real and active element in man's environment. When Europeans went to tropical Africa

[3] Northern Illinois and a few smaller prairie areas were exceptions to this generalization.

and America (after Negro slavery was introduced), they were attacked by the yellow fever virus which caused widespread panic among them. Thousands died because they had no immunity against this organism. In return, the Europeans carried with them viruses, bacteria, and other microorganisms to the tropical lands, which wreaked even greater havoc on their inhabitants. Even today, there are large areas of the world where human settlement is largely impeded by the so-called "tropical diseases." It is dangerous for an American or Canadian to travel in many parts of the world unless he observes rigid rules pertaining to food, drink, and hygiene, and fortifies himself with vaccines and antitoxins.

ROCKS AND MINERALS

Beneath the surface of the earth, nature has been at work for two billion years or so, storing deposits of iron, copper, lead, zinc, gold, vanadium, and other metals; and more recently, laying down beds of coal, petroleum, phosphates and so forth. Nature, however, has been capricious, bestowing her mineral favors very unequally and irregularly.

The existence or absence of various kinds of rocks and minerals may cause human society to vary surprisingly from place to place. In the midst of the Appalachian Highlands, for instance, there is a long, narrow lowland underlain by limestone. It is known as the Great Appalachian Valley. One may cross it in Pennsylvania and see a fine landscape of "Pennsylvania Deutsch" farms. Far to the south, in Alabama, one may cross it and see a landscape of blazing blast furnaces, smoking mills, and black piles of coal. The reason is that the mineral resources of the two ends of the Great Valley are different.

AREAL SPACE OR SIZE

The mere bigness or smallness of a region affects the destiny of the human beings who live there. The space available to a people leaves a stamp on their industry and their psychology.

Holland is a small country. Not an inch of space is wasted. In order to save space and all the precious raw materials produced on their limited acres, the Dutch consume a great deal of time. Nearly every invention made in Holland is for the purpose of saving space and material. Meanwhile, Dutch society moves along leisurely.

The United States is a big country—a very big one. Americans waste space on a scale that would amaze a Dutchman. Americans also waste materials faster than any nation in the world's history. But thousands of Americans are killed each year in airplanes and by automobiles in a frantic effort to save time. Most of the inventions patented in America are designed to save time and labor. American society is anything but leisurely. The difference is not racial, because Americans and Hollanders are both predominantly Nordic (that is, dolichocephalic North European) peoples. Size, or space, as an environmental factor accounts for many of their apparent differences. This is a world example, not an isolated instance.

REGIONAL FORM OR SHAPE

The state of Iowa is a compact, unified bloc of land. Iowans, therefore, tend to think and feel alike. State loyalty is all in one piece. By way of contrast, California is markedly elongated or attenuated. The result of this is to develop two centers of sentiment and loyalty—one at each end. Californians divide into northern and southern Californians on many issues.

NATURAL SITUATION

The state of Mississippi possesses a small strip of coast on the Gulf of Mexico. The rest of the state extends back into the continent for nearly three hundred miles. Coastal or littoral Mississippi is interested in shipping and the winter-resort industry. Biloxi, Gulfport, and the other coastal cities are alert and progressive. Continental Mississippi, on the other hand, is predominantly agricultural in its economics, conservative in its politics, and often reactionary in its sociology. This is not an isolated example of social differences growing out of unlike kinds of natural situation. The world is full of examples.

UNITY OF THE ENVIRONMENT

The preceding discussion has been conducted as though each of these sixteen natural factors operated separately in its interaction with human society. Actually, however, human society pushes against all sixteen factors at once. No wonder that large human groups, even though they are thoroughly organized into social structures, cannot run roughshod over nature. Something has to give way, and a study of history shows that mankind yields more often than does nature.

The sixteen natural factors, then, are not separate considerations; they are component elements which, when combined, provide an omnipresent and persistent natural environment for human society.

In reality the physical environment is only a part of the study of geography. The physical realm forms a portion of our understanding of man in a region. The elements of the environment might be called the physical impactors. However, the elements of the cultural environment or the cultural impactors also have an important contribution to make to our understanding of man in a region (Fig. 2–1).

CIRCLES OF RELATIONSHIP

To this natural environment, mankind is related in several intertwined circles of relationships. First, there are local relationships. Included in these, are the ties between the human community and its locus, site, terrain, and local resources or what might be called the "life layer." Secondly, there are regional relationships or areal associations—the ties between the human community and the natural environment which spread out over a large related area. Finally, there are the global relationships or the world region—the affairs of the human community which ramify over the whole earth. The human community, to which each of us belongs, is a complex organism bound to a complex natural environment by complex circles of geographic relationships.

SUGGESTED USEFUL READINGS

Broek, Jan O. M., *Geography, Its Scope and Spirit* (Columbus, Ohio, Charles E. Merrill Books, Inc., 1965).

Dohrs, Fred E., Lawrence M. Sommers, and Donald R. Petterson, *Introduction to Geography Readings* (New York, Thomas Y. Crowell Company, 1967).

Dohrs, Fred E., Lawrence M. Sommers, and Donald R. Petterson, *Outside Readings in Geography* (New York, Thomas Y. Crowell Company, 1955). See especially Chapters 1, 2, and 3.

The Science of Geography, Report of the Ad Hoc Committee on Geography, Earth Sciences Division, National Academy of Sciences–National Research Council (Washington, D.C., 1965).

Wagner, Philip L., and Marvin W. Mikesell, *Readings in Cultural Geography* (Chicago, The University of Chicago Press, 1962). See especially Chapters 1, 2, 3, 4, 5, and the last chapter.

2

The Human Realm: Geographic Adjustment and Relationship

The previous chapter dealt primarily with the physical realm of man's environment. In a geographic sense, however, our understanding of man in a region involves not only a study of the realm of nature, but also a study of the human or cultural realm.

THE REALM OF NATURE

THE NATURAL ENVIRONMENT

In the succeeding chapters human society in various parts of the world will be examined against a background of location, space, and natural resources. In the course of that examination, large groups of human beings will be shown in their relations to the environmental elements—climates, soils, minerals, and others (Fig. 2–1). Out of this process there should begin to emerge in the reader's mind a fairly definite concept of the natural environment.

The natural environment consists of the entire realm of nature which impinges upon man—the forces, processes, and elements of the natural surroundings. The *forces* include insolation, global rotation and revolution, gravitation, volcanic action, earth movement, and the phenomenon of life itself. The *processes* include erosion, sedimentation, transmission of heat, air and water circulation, birth, growth, and death, evolution of organic species, and numerous others. The environmental *elements* include a group of factors which form the descriptive traits of the earth's surface.

The forces and processes are universal and

inherent in all earth environment. The elements, however, are extremely variable, differing from place to place over the earth in striking fashion. Moreover, they are, themselves, the products of the forces and processes of nature, and therefore imply the presence of the latter. Consequently, in a geographic sense, the elements may be thought of as synonymous with the natural environment. As pointed out in Chapter 1, the natural environmental elements consist of the following.

Physical Elements:
    1. Weather and climate
    2. Landforms
    3. Soils
    4. Minerals
    5. Surface waters
    6. Ground waters
    7. The ocean
    8. The coast zone
Biotic Elements:
    9. Flora
    10. Fauna
    11. Microorganisms
Abstract Elements:
    12. Size
    13. Form
    14. Position
    15. Situation
    16. Location

These sixteen elements are not discrete parts of the natural environment. Instead, they are

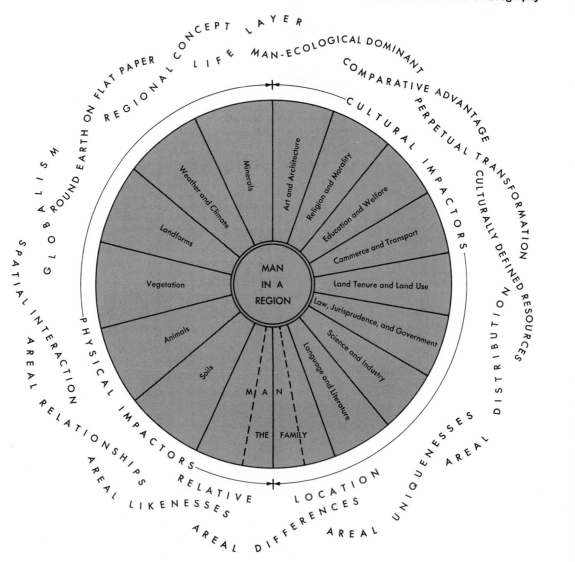

Figure 2–1 Diagram showing man in relation to the elements of the natural and the cultural environment.

actually inseparable ingredients in an integrated whole. It is with this composite whole that mankind must deal in occupying any portion of the earth. Its separation into elements is only academic and for the practical purpose of study. The natural environment, therefore, is ever-present, composite, and variable.

THE NATURAL LANDSCAPE

The natural landscape is the visible portion of the natural environment. It consists of landforms, soils, water features, natural vegetation, native animal life, coast forms, and so on. It also

includes the direct and indirect products of climate and some of those of ground water. It may or may not reveal some of the implications of rocks and minerals and natural situation. Thus, not all elements of the environment are visible in the natural landscape; the latter is composed only of those aspects of nature open to the eye of the observer (as, for instance, the vista in Fig. 10–5).

The natural landscape is relatively constant. Barring rare cataclysmic events of nature, it does not change much from year to year or even from century to century. Processes at work in the natural landscape produce constant changes, but the rate at which change occurs is so slow that for geographic purposes they can be largely ignored.

The study of geography involves man in a region. This region may be a physical region, such as the dry world, or it may be a cultural region, such as the eastern North American manufacturing region. In every case there is an interaction between both the physical and cultural impactors and man in the region (Fig. 2–1). As one studies man in a specific region, some of the physical and cultural impactors stand out as more important (or dominant) than others. This is the geographic approach to the study of the natural and cultural milieu. As the student proceeds through the book, constant reference should be made to the conceptual framework depicted in Figure 2–1.

THE HUMAN REALM

SOCIETY

Men are gregarious beings and hence tend to group themselves together. Such groupings are called communities. Collectively the similar and related communities within an area are termed *society.*

Human society is not a new invention; as far back as there is evidence, people lived in groups. Probably no great number of people have ever lived alone, even in earliest times. Man, therefore, has always been a social being, and the tendency through history has been an increase in the size and density of human groupings. All but a few antisocial people are members of one or more social groups—family, vocational, recreational, religious, political, or educational groups, and these limit, direct, and mold their actions, beliefs, and thoughts. Indeed, the life of the individual, both modern and primitive, is regulated in minute detail by group custom and sanction.

Thus, human society is more than the sum total of the individuals which compose its body. It is a living mass organism consisting of people (their race, numbers, and distribution[1]), social processes (such as migration, nutrition, reproduction, glomeration, conflict, and so forth), and the social environment (the patterns of human living).

THE SOCIAL ENVIRONMENT

The most dynamic part of society is the social environment. It is the regulator of human beings, and the director of social processes. It consists essentially of the three following man-made patterns of living:

First, there is the *pattern of social control.* This comprises folkways, customs, and mores and other simple controls of human behavior. It also comprises the organized and formal devices for control, namely, *institutions.* Some of these latter are government, church, marriage, police, law, war, school, and press. Rules for folk behavior and institutions form very different patterns from one society to another, but they invariably serve to control the individual toward desired ends.[2]

Second, there are the *activity patterns* of the social environment. An activity is merely something which people do. Some of the activities, of course, have no social significance to speak of. The significant activities of mankind include (1) the occupations or industries, (2) the political and military undertakings, (3) educational and cultural endeavors, (4) esthetic efforts, and (5) recreations.

Third, there are society's *construction patterns.* These are the various physical structures and arrangements created or laid out in the process of man's evolving his patterns of controls and activities. Unlike these latter, however, the pattern of constructions consists of physical and tangible things, not abstract and intangible values and forces.

THE CULTURAL LANDSCAPE

The pattern of constructions is the most obvious part of the social environment because it includes the whole vista of man-made creations which lies stretched out before the eye of the observer (Fig. 6–7). For this reason, this tangible and physical part of the social environment is often called the *cultural landscape.* When analyzed it is seen to consist of the following twelve elements.
1. Land subdivision system

[1] See Chapter 3.
[2] The control patterns are usually of more interest to the sociologist than to the geographer.

2. Canals, gradings, and other surface fittings of the land
3. Crop and animal husbandry patterns
4. Rural habitations and associated farmstead features
5. Urban and semiurban formations
6. Mineral-working establishments (mines, quarries, etc.)
7. Manufacturing developments
8. Docks, piers, wharves, and other port installations
9. Road and railway patterns
10. Reserved spaces (forests, parks, cemeteries, recreation areas)
11. Residual unused or waste areas
12. Boundaries, customs houses, and military fortifications

This cultural landscape is highly important because it differs strikingly from place to place and hence it reveals how man is using his natural environment. It is also the direct indicator or index of how effectively an area is being used by man. For these reasons, the cultural landscape is of great and immediate interest to the geographer.

GEOGRAPHIC STUDY

CHOROGRAPHIC STEPS

Mature geographic study consists of examining the cultural landscape and the natural landscape as they occur together in any particular part of the earth's surface. In other words, what the geographer is primarily interested in is the total geographic landscape comprising both natural and cultural features of an area. Often—indeed usually—he finds it necessary to map both the natural landscape and the cultural landscape, sometimes separately, sometimes together, so that the data are put in desired form, are made complete, and are reduced to a size small enough to be examined, compared, and described all at one time.

This study, mapping, and description of the geographic landscape is called *chorography*. It constitutes the first steps in geographical study.

ANALYTIC STEPS

The later steps in geographic study consist of weighing, correlating, and interpreting the data.

These steps combined constitute geographic analysis and synthesis.

Geography as landscape morphology

Although all geographers agree in general as to the methods of gathering, recording, and mapping geographic data, there is considerable difference of opinion as to the methods of interpreting these data. One group of geographers believes that the data should be interpreted and presented in such manner as to show how the geographic landscape has evolved to its present form, and then to classify that form in comparison with other forms of landscapes elsewhere. The purpose of doing this is to find a reliable and exact method of describing the various regions of the earth. This kind of interpretation is *morphological*. It would make of geography a relatively exact natural science.

Geography as human ecology

When the natural landscape and the cultural landscape are examined together, it becomes obvious that the former constitutes the foundation upon which the latter is built and contains the materials and resources from which it has been created. Obviously, therefore, there are important interrelations between society and nature.

Accordingly, a very much larger group of geographers, together with many educators, believes that geographic analysis should be *ecological* rather than morphological. Ecology is the study of organisms in relation to environment, and it may concern itself with plants or animals or people, depending upon the interest of the ecologist. If an ecological approach to geography is employed, there is implied that the primary objective of geography is to describe and explain human society against its natural environmental background in any part of the earth. The aim of geography is to discover and make known one very important aspect of human society—the interrelationships between the society and the natural environment. Geography aims to show how mankind has adjusted itself to the particular character of its region and, in turn, how it may have changed the character of that region. This would make of geography a social science rather than a natural science, concerned with qualitative social diagnosis rather than exact regional description. The key concepts in geography as human ecology are those of geographic adjustment and relationship.

GEOGRAPHIC ADJUSTMENT

As soon as human beings enter a region, they at once begin to adjust themselves to it. They, of course, bring with them language, religion, tradition, custom, institutions, arts, and technology—things which they had evolved in their previous environment. Most of these are misfits, or partial misfits, in the new surroundings. Consequently, the process of adjustment begins at once and continues until a new cultural equilibrium is reached. The social group commences the active exploitation of one or more of the environmental elements, drawing upon the stored natural resources in order to construct a cultural landscape and capitalizing upon those natural factors which aid in promoting social solidarity and political safety.

Not only do pioneers in a new region accommodate or adjust themselves and their activities to the natural landscape, but their adjustment may be so successful that their descendants become very numerous in the area. These descendants, by expending vast amounts of labor and energy, may transform so many of the surface aspects of the natural landscape that after a time it becomes obscured or even unrecognizable. (Compare Figures 10–5 and 6–7.) Man may dig the minerals, cut down the trees, destroy the wild game, harness the streams for power or navigation or irrigation, and cover the surface with farms, towns, mills, factories, and other items of his culture. But still, some areas seem destined to be rural, others urban; some seem to develop into regions of farming, others of pasturing, commerce, or manufacturing, in deference to deep-seated qualities of the natural environment as it impinges upon society. In addition to these physical works, man also erects a fabric of social, economic, and political institutions and creates a "climate of opinion," all of which become interwoven to create a social environment.

The process of geographic adjustment is, and has been since the earliest Stone Age times, essentially a process of building patterns upon the face of the earth. The primitive attempts to devise shelter, to discover what natural foods were edible, to chip and flake flints for tools, to domesticate wild animals, to provide group security, or to devise magic were the first steps in erecting cultural patterns; and the spread of these patterns created the first geography of human society.

Since that early time, man has altered his physical environment very little; the basic processes of nature he has not changed at all. He has, however, altered very drastically his science and technology, his social and political organization, and his economic methods of utilizing the natural environment. Consequently, his equipment for making adjustments to the natural environment has been enlarged and changed almost beyond belief. These adjustments are of three principal kinds, *economic, social-cultural,* and *political.*

ECONOMIC ADJUSTMENTS

The economic adjustments made by society are *work* patterns. The kind of work which men do depends in some measure upon the desires, ideas, and skills prevalent in a human group. In larger measure, it depends upon what resources are present in their natural environment.

In general, the economic adjustments of society are of some four types. First, there are the *extractive* industries: fishing, hunting, trapping, mining, logging, and so forth. In these activities, man takes various materials directly from nature. In so doing, he produces what the economist calls material or substance utility. Second, there are the *genetic* or refundive industries, where man uses various elements and processes in nature to produce more of certain substances which he already has, as in agriculture, stock rearing, and silviculture. Third, there are the *fabricative* industries, such as smelting, refining, processing, and manufacturing. In such activities as these, man takes the products of the extractive and genetic industries, applies power and design to them and creates form utility. Fourth, there are the *commercial* industries such as transporting, storing, exchanging, and financing. The purpose of such activities is to add time and place utility to the products of the other three classes of industry. Here might also be included the professional services (education, medicine, law, and others) and the personal services (domestic labor, barbering, street sweeping, and so forth). Such services facilitate economic production in the commercial and other types of industries.

THE SOCIAL AND CULTURAL ADJUSTMENTS

Human society also makes social and cultural adjustments to the natural environment. These include arrangements in population density, land ownership, social classes, kinship and group relationship, and the social status of labor. It also includes the kinds of community groupings employed and the habits of such groupings—whether nomadic or sedentary. Included, too, are clothing, diet, houses, manners, art, and religious forms.

THE POLITICAL ADJUSTMENTS

Human society likewise makes civic and political adaptations or adjustments to its natural environment. These include internal governmental arrangements (local, provincial, and national) and international governmental arrangements (empires, alliances, spheres of influence, and united nations). It also includes diplomatic and military strategies and undertakings and international law.

These three patterns of adjustment represent society's adaptations and accommodations to the realities of location, space, and resources. They are the external and measurable characteristics of society.

GEOGRAPHIC RELATIONSHIP

THE REALIZED ENVIRONMENT

In studying and describing the adjustments of society to its natural milieu, there are at every turn implied relationships between people and the various forces, processes, and elements of the natural environment. Indeed, the whole concept of adjustment and adaptation is predicated upon the idea of *geographic relationship*. This may sound like a vague abstraction, but actually in one sense it is the very essence of definiteness and concreteness.

Man has never known much about his natural environment, although modern scientific re-

search is rapidly revealing its secrets. The part of the environment which is known and adjusted to, at any specific time and place, may be called the "realized environment." It is with the various elements in this realized environment that man establishes his relationships. In general, these geographic relationships are of three kinds: (1) use relationships, (2) control relationships, and (3) idea relationships.

Use relationships

The use relationships are the most obvious and direct among the ties which man sets up between himself and nature. For instance, man uses soil, landforms, and climate to give him agricultural commodities; in arid regions he supplements this with surface or underground waters. He uses grassland, water features, and domesticated members of the fauna to provide meat, leather, fibers, and other pastoral products. He uses rocks and minerals to yield tools, weapons, building materials, and other necessities.

Such use relations vary, however, as man's knowledge and technology vary. The early farmer probably punched holes in the soil with a stick, dropped seeds into these holes, filled these up with his big toe, and waited for rain. Next, he learned to stir the surface of the earth with a digging stick after enriching the soil with ashes. Later, the hoe was invented and the use of manure was discovered. Finally, the steel plow, the harrow, the drill, and the cultivator were designed, the use of compost and commercial fertilizers developed, and the sciences of meteorology, genetics, biochemistry, and bacteriology were enlisted in the agriculturalist's aid. Throughout this process, the use relationships in agriculture have multiplied and expanded.

Control relationships

The richness of soil and the fertility of seed are matters belonging in the realm of nature. Man, however, has been slow in learning to understand them. In earliest times he conceived of deities whose province was that of controlling fertility. Accordingly he set up such goddesses as Demeter, Ceres, or Ma and worshiped them with sacrifices. As erudition increased, the control of fertility ceased to be purely religious and became a matter of ritual. For instance, in the period of rice blooming, the peasants of some parts of southeast Asia go to the paddies and there practice cohabitation in an effort to show nature how to be fertile in the matter of producing rice. Gradually such rituals cease to be required, and ideological relations to fertility survive only as superstitions. Among the Scottish peasants a tiny parcel of land is left to the brownie who watches over fertility. Among some American farmers the practice of throwing a handful of seed into the fencerow for good luck or of planting in certain phases of the moon is an analogous practice. As for modern society in general, the same purpose is accomplished by increasing the tax millage in order to establish and support state colleges of agriculture and agricultural experiment stations.

In ancient times, men propitiated a god of the winds with libations when they desired to insure a safe voyage. Ulysses, for instance, is said to have bargained for and obtained from the Aeolian temple a bag in which the winds were imprisoned, in order that he might hang it at his masthead. In medieval Europe, safe voyages were almost universally insured by having the priest bless the vessel. Modern man still breaks a bottle of champagne over a ship's bow as a libation, but he trusts more to radar and to radio reports from the Weather Bureau and the International Ice Patrol. An airplane may employ radar in addition to weather reports.

And so it goes, from Ceres to the state "aggie" school; from Aeolus to radar; from religion to magic to superstition to science, in countless aspects of human endeavor. The control relationships ramify into every phase of man's life.

Idea relationships

Many of the relationships between men and environment manifest themselves in the realm of ideas. When a Japanese looks at Mt. Fuji he regards it as the "venerable one." To the Salish folk, Mt. Ranier was the "mountain that was god." To the Norse, Jotunheim was the abode of the frost giants. To the Greeks, Olympus was the abode of the gods. The ancient Goths in their dark mast-rich beech and oak forests be-

lieved the gods kept pigs in Asgaard; the Semites on the dry grasslands referred to their god as the "Good Shepherd."

Similarly, the music of Polynesia echoes the refrain of the sea; that of tropical America is filled with the rhythm and untamed night sounds of the selva; that of the Scottish highlands records the moan of the winds on the heath.

Primitive peoples regarded iron with awe and shunned the smith. The medieval peasant regarded iron as an omen of good luck, usually suspending a bit of it (often in the form of a horseshoe) over his doorway. Modern man, on the other hand, regards iron very prosaically; he reduces the ore into pig iron which he then converts into steel. With steel he can make scientific equipment for probing further into the secrets of nature.

The sacrament of the nomadic warrior tribes of the Sudan consisted of bits of a dead human enemy. The sacrament of the ancient Chinese civilization of Shang consisted of rice and millet beer. The sacrament of Mediterranean Christianity consists of barley bread and grape wine. On all sides, the relation between human ideation and the character of the environment is apparent. In music, art, law, religion, science, and industry, these idea relations exist. They change in character from age to age, but the fact of relationship persists.

A GEOGRAPHIC THEORY OF HUMAN SOCIETY

By now, definite ideas concerning geographic causation and modification in human affairs have undoubtedly begun to take shape in the reader's mind, and out of them a tentative geographic theory of human society has probably been formulated.

THE THEORY STATED

A human society is a living organism characterized by a structure of customs and institutions and exhibiting a pattern of economic, social, and political activities. When human beings first enter a region, they bring with them an inheritance of biological traits and an accumulation of cultural equipment and behavior adopted by them in some previous environment or environments. At once they begin to adapt the new environment to their needs and habits as far as possible. Where this is not possible, they begin adjusting their own ideas, institutions, behavior, and activities to the new environment. The culture of a human group at any particular time or place is some sort of compromise between the past heritage of a people and the necessities of the present surroundings.

From the geographical or ecological standpoint, therefore, the institutions and activities of a society are not the essential traits of that society. They are purely extrinsic aspects. They are the external devices or forms adopted or evolved by man for the purpose of adjusting himself to his region.

Human society, therefore, in order to have real substance or basis finds itself obliged to adjust to the area which it inhabits. This is accomplished by the adaptation of its form, structure, and activity to the natural environment of that area. A society supports itself by suitable economic adjustments to the natural environment; it distributes, motivates, and integrates its members by harmonious social adjustments; and it maintains and controls itself by effective political adjustments.

These ecological adjustments to environment involve countless relationships set up between men and specific aspects and elements of the environment. In general, these are of three kinds: use relationships, control relationships, and idea relationships. All of these undergo constant change as science and technology evolve. It is these relationships which give a human group its geographic character; it is the adjustments made by a group which give it form and descriptive appearance.

The evolution of geographic relations and the perfecting of geographic adjustments are processes which culminate in the creation of a cultural landscape. As this latter is constructed, it is built upon, and more or less in harmony with, the preexisting natural landscape. Thus the nature-made and the man-made landscapes are integrated into a whole. The degree of harmony or disharmony, that is, the degree of integration,

is the measure of the geographic effectiveness of a society.

IMPLICATIONS OF THE THEORY

It is the geographer's contention, therefore, that human society can be understood only when its culture, makeup, and behavior are viewed against the background of its location, the space it occupies, and the resources which it utilitzes. More especially, the geographer contends that society can be understood adequately only when it is examined in the light of its adjustments to and relations with the factors of location, space, and resources. An understanding of these not only affords an insight into present-day society but provides a key to the historical past.

Moreover, since an understanding of society in terms of its adjustments and environmental relations reveals the basic underlying strategy of men, space, and resources, it also reveals the places where stresses are accumulating and where tensions and strains exist. Likewise, any study of adjustments is bound to strip bare the maladjustments which exist. All of this, therefore, offers a ready means of interpreting current events in the world and, indeed, of anticipating them before they transpire. Geographic understanding obviously provides a key to the future and affords a basis for regional planning in society.

MAN'S SO-CALLED CONTROL OVER NATURE

In contrast to these assertions of the geographer is the argument sometimes put forth by nongeographers. The gist of this argument is that the growth of science and the advances of technology in modern society are rapidly increasing man's control over nature, thereby leveling out environmental differences, and that in the end they will destroy the significance of geographic relations.

SCIENCE INCREASES GEOGRAPHIC RELATIONSHIP

Advances in civilization, however, involve an ever increasing exploitation of locational advantages, a fuller and more effective use of space, and closer and more efficient relations between man and his resources. Since this is true, it is unrealistic to say that science and technology are freeing man from dependence upon the very things which yield the advantages and materials for civilization's advance. Quite the reverse of the argument is true. Each advance in science, each forward stride in technology, multiplies the number of man's contacts with nature.

One specific example will suffice to show this. A wheat farmer is directly dependent upon the weather. When multiple plows are invented and more productive seed developed, this wheat farmer may no longer be needed in agriculture. Accordingly, he moves to the city and there may make his living dealing in wheat on the Board of Trade. He lives in a steam-heated, air-conditioned apartment and rides to work by heated bus or subway. Without thinking too deeply on the matter, we are inclined to say that he has been liberated from dependence upon the weather. The error in this is shown by the fact that he watches the latest weather reports feverishly, because weather fluctuations over half the world mean the difference between wealth and ruin to him in his market transactions.

Meanwhile, the wheat grower's neighbor who has remained on the farm has augmented and regularized his yields somewhat by means of increased science and improved machinery. Hence, weather fluctuations no longer affect his production quite so violently. But has he been thereby freed from dependence upon the weather? Quite the reverse: that same science and technology have extended wheat growing into new portions of the world and provided improved transportation for wheat into the world market. Weather over half the earth now affects the farmer far more than before because it controls the extent to which he will or will not have to face ruinous competition in the world's markets. This same multiplication of relations to nature applies to practically every other phase of human life. Wheat growing is merely an example chosen at random.

During the Cold War, Canada, the United States, and the U.S.S.R. all intensified their activities in the polar realm. But all learned that to be successful in cold-weather operations they had to work with natural forces. All those who have been successful in the Arctic—Peary, Stefansson, Amundsen, Nansen, Byrd—had one thing in common: they were proficient because of thorough preparations and study. Survival there depends more than anything else on meticulous attention to the ways of nature.

Obviously, scientific and technological advances do not give man an increasing *control* over nature. On the contrary, they multiply his contacts and relations with the environment.

SUGGESTED USEFUL READINGS

Leighly, John, ed., *Land and Life, A Selection from the Writings of Carl O. Sauer* (Berkeley, Calif., University of California Press, 1963). See especially chapters 9, 10, 12, 16, and 18.

Thomas, William L., Jr., *Man's Role in Changing the Face of the Earth* (Chicago, The University of Chicago Press, 1956). First two chapters of Part II, "Process" by Richard J. Russell and Paul B. Sears, expand on the material in this chapter.

Warman, Henry J., "Geography Teaching and the Structure of the Discipline," *The Journal of Geography*, Vol. LXIV, No. 5 (May, 1965), pp. 197–201.

3

Population Distribution, Density, Composition, and Trends

A glance at the population map of the world (inside front cover) reveals that human beings are distributed unevenly over the land. Approximately one-half of the population is concentrated in just a few densely settled areas comprising a mere 5 percent of the earth's surface, whereas enormous empty, or at least sparsely settled, areas aggregating 57 percent of the land surface support only 5 percent of the people.

To persons who are just beginning to think about population, this distribution may seem strange indeed. Why have not human beings scattered more widely and more evenly over the earth? Is this a matter of human preference or has the natural environment invited here and repelled there?

It is to supply the answers to these questions, that this book is written; for man's distribution over the earth is the most important, the most significant phenomenon in the entire field of human geography.

Population growth is as important as is population distribution. In A.D. 1800, approximately 900 million people inhabited the globe. In the 168 years since 1800, mankind not only doubled his numbers but added more units to the human total than in the entire previous span of his existence. Thus throughout 99 percent of human history, man's distribution was extremely sparse. During this great span of time, sustenance for the most part was gained through hunting, fishing, and the collecting of plant and animal products, pursuits which required huge areas for few people—sometimes as much as two hundred square miles for one person.[1] It was only some 15,000 to 20,000 years ago (at the beginning of the Neolithic era), with the advent of domesticated animals, farming, and the making of pottery and textiles, that greater density became possible. The real burst of population growth in the Western world came with the latest stage in cultural progress—the Industrial Revolution beginning about 1750 in Europe. The rapid diffusion of industrialization to other regions extended its influence around the globe. Since this change began first among European peoples and those of European stock, the slackening rates of growth characteristic of the late phases of the change have also appeared first among them.

The total world population is today roughly 3,750,000,000.[2] Henry Pratt Fairchild[3] insists that these figures are "the most important statistics in the world," for all human interests have meaning only as they are projected against the encompassing background of population and its growth. All others, he says, may be regarded as "mere embroideries upon this great central pattern."

[1] A. B. Wolfe, "The Fecundity and Fertility of Early Man," *Human Biology*, Vol. V (February, 1933), pp. 36–39.
[2] As of January, 1968.
[3] Henry Pratt Fairchild, *People: The Quantity and Quality of the Population* (New York, Henry Holt and Company, Inc., 1939).

20

WHERE THE PEOPLE ARE AND WHY

It is significant that 95 percent of the world's population dwells in the Northern Hemisphere, which possesses 80 percent of the total land area. It is significant, too, that for the most part dense population is to be found in those parts of the earth best endowed by nature. Unfortunately, these areas comprise but a fraction of the land surface of the globe: probably not more than one-fourth of the earth's surface receives sufficient precipitation for agriculture, and much of this one-fourth is too rough, too cold, too infertile, or too badly eroded for successful farming.

Since the dawn of recorded human history and on down until quite recently, man has owed his distribution primarily to the abundance of game and to the productivity of the soil. River valleys—the Nile, the Tigris and Euphrates, the Ganges, the Yangtze, the Hwang—have long been noted for their fertility and for the swarming humanity they sustain. More recently mineral wealth and power have played an important role. Thus, the three main population centers in the Northern Hemisphere are: the intensively cultivated farming regions of eastern and southern Asia and the highly developed industrial regions of Western Europe and of eastern United States.

WHERE THE PEOPLE ARE NOT AND WHY

The population density map (inside front cover) indicates those parts of the world which contain few people. With two principal exceptions,[4] they are the so-called restrictive environments—high mountains, deserts, ice caps and tundras, and the wet tropical lowlands. Any increased population there encounters serious obstacles, some of which at present appear insuperable. By and large, man has only outposts in these lands. Each of these types of restrictive environment merits some attention.

HIGH MOUNTAINS

Rugged surface, shallow stony soils, restricted flat land, and inhospitable climates keep population to very small numbers in mountains everywhere on earth, except in the tropics where elevation may lift the people into a temperate climate, as is the case at Mexico City and Quito. The farther man goes from the equator, however, the more inhospitable high mountains become as a permanent habitat, and in high latitudes they are wholly unoccupied.

DESERTS

The world's deserts are among the most sparsely populated of all lands. Only a fraction of most deserts is under cultivation, a situation that will persist for the most part, since there usually is little water—and in the desert water means life.

Thus, although Egypt (or the United Arab Republic) has a total area of 363,000 square miles, only about 13,000 square miles or a mere $3\frac{1}{2}$ percent are irrigable. In actuality, Egypt is the Nile—the valley and delta. Of the total population of 28 million persons, less than 5 percent dwell outside the oasis. In the irrigated area, the population density runs as high as 2,000 persons to the square mile. And each year the number of Egyptians increases by more than 800,000. The seriousness of the situation is apparent when we realize that in the past fifty years the population has more than doubled, whereas the arable area has expanded by approximately 12 percent. The population has been growing so fast that the per capita intake of calories has been declining in recent years.

Since expansion of the crop area is limited by the desert, and since industrial development is restricted by lean endowment in fuel and mineral resources and by the limited market for fabricated products due in large part to the biting poverty of the people, Egypt's growing population poses a very serious problem. With Russian financial and technological aid, the Egyptians undertook construction of the High Aswan Dam, some 430 miles south of Cairo. The dam forms

[4] The first notable exception is in parts of South America where enormous land holdings are in the hands of the few and hence are held out of full settlement; the second is in Inner Asia, where pastoral peoples, unwilling to farm, hold lands capable of agricultural settlement. Under the Communists, however, this system is breaking down in Mongolia, Turkestan, and Siberia.

behind it one of the world's largest man-made lakes, which supplies water to irrigate two million acres of new farm land. In addition, the project supplies Egypt with ten million kilowatts of hydroelectric power per annum. However, it is not expected that the project will solve Egypt's population problem.

Any appreciable increase in the present population of tropical deserts appears unlikely. Areas such as the Sahara are barely subsisting, since the number of human beings living there is limited by water for drinking, for oasis irrigation, and for grazing (some parts of the Sahara, however, do have deep reserves of water). But finding more people who can live permanently in the Sahara may prove to be as much of a problem as finding the resources to sustain them. No white people, particularly women and infants, are able to thrive during the torrid summers (May to October). Although Negroes can withstand the desert heat and sunshine better than whites, they do not do well during the cold winters and the diurnal temperature changes. Dry air is particularly hard on them.

THE ICE CAPS

Antarctica, most of Greenland, and other ice covered areas have practically no permanent inhabitants. Though Antarctica is almost twice the size of the United States, it has not one single permanent human inhabitant. Since it is the coldest place on earth and since it is virtually covered with ice and snow, it is difficult to see any economic basis for settlement ever.

THE TUNDRAS

Tundras cover millions of square miles in the Arctic, but human numbers are exceedingly small. Agriculture is close to impossible, for the growing season is too short, most soils are infertile, and isolation is appalling. Permafrost and poor drainage are also problems. No doubt the growing of crops will move farther north, but how far will depend on the results of future research and on national politics. Up to the present time neither the United States nor Canada has deemed it worth while to invest heavily in subpolar (tundra) agricultural enterprises. Both have left their lands largely in wilderness for the benefit of fur and other wildlife resources. Only

the Soviet Union has announced a policy of autonomy in agricultural production for the tundra. According to the Russians, they have achieved spectacular accomplishments at advanced agricultural experiment stations. Some farming is now being carried on along the coasts of the Barents Sea and the mouths of the Ob and Yenesei and points north of the Arctic Circle on the Lena, the Kolyma, and the Indigirka on lands once considered to be waste land. Spots are carefully chosen by farmers thoroughly familiar with the vagaries of the climate so as to be protected from cold north winds. Organic and mineral fertilizers are used and manure, besides serving as a fertilizer, is said to insulate plants from the cold rising from the frozen ground. Only quick-ripening crops are grown—cabbage, broccoli, turnips, spinach, lettuce, radishes, cucumbers, and the Arctic raspberry. In Finland and Sweden, farmers are now plowing land that had lain under ice for centuries. In 1956 Greenland began to experiment with quinoa, the grain that grows highest in the Andes of Peru and Bolivia. The United Nations announced in 1954 that a million acres of Arctic land are now producing food crops by scientific methods. It would be a mistake, however, to believe that man has made more than a dent in the tundra.

For the most part, man is engaged in hunting and fishing and his numbers are small, since seventy to two hundred square miles are needed to sustain each person. Because the pastures are poor and need resting, the grazier on the tundras is nomadic.

THE WET TROPICAL LOWLANDS

All of these lands are not unpopulated but many of them, as for instance the Amazon Basin, are very sparsely settled. This huge area's population averages less than one person to the square mile. On the other hand, Nigeria is moderately populated and Java, partly rainy tropical and partly lowland, teems with humanity. In most instances, however, the hot wet lands have repelled the European: perhaps he may win them in time. If he does, he must develop a very different mode of living. These lands at present are too hot and humid for human comfort. Additional handicaps are insect pests, a cover of dense tropical rain forest or jungle, a red clay soil that is for the most part leached of its soluble mineral elements and hence is infertile, constantly high temperatures, and diseases.[5] Hundreds of millions of people have been treated for and cured of tropical diseases by the World Health Organization (WHO), which wages incessant warfare against diseases in the tropical countries—particularly those in the rainy tropics. It is attempting to stamp out the 50 million cases of yaws from the world—half of which are in Africa. It has eliminated completely, by using penicillin, this disease from Haiti. WHO, also, is slowly driving the tsetse fly, slayer of cattle and killer of men, from the area where it is found in Africa—an area half as great again in extent as the continent of Australia.

Large numbers of people are not expected to migrate to the rainy tropics, however, until life can be much improved, transport modernized, public health service improved, and a safer water supply and better and larger quantities of food made available to the masses of people. All these require huge funds which the various governments lack. Outside funds are accomplishing much, but these can hardly be expected to continue forever.

The ill health resulting from poor food and water contributes to the low economic status of the people. When people are ill and weak from starvation or near-starvation, they cannot work and produce as they could if they were well and had a satisfactory diet.

The strongest argument against the wet tropics as a permanent home for Europeans is the trend in pioneering today. Even if science should prove its ability to cure or avoid the diseases which impede progress, Europeans certainly prefer a cool climate to a hot one. European people who plan to migrate will go into most portions of the nontropics before they venture to make a grand assault upon the wet tropics. What emigrants desire, and not what they can or could do, determines the trend of population.[6]

POPULATION GROWTH

There is no geographical area on the earth with favorable natural environmental conditions where population increase has not been substantial in the past half-century. The rate of growth during

the past three centuries has varied widely from continent to continent. For the world as a whole, the increase has been fivefold; for North America, 166; for Latin America, 23; for Oceania, $6\frac{1}{2}$; for Europe (including the Soviet Union), 6; for Asia, 5; and for Africa, 2.[7]

What of population growth now? That for the world is increasing at the fantastic and explosive rate of 60 million per year. What is even more awesome is the projection of population growth for the year 2000—about 6,280,000,000 people, and it may reach 10 or 12 billion by the year 2050.[8]

POPULATION DENSITIES
THE FUTILITY OF AVERAGE FIGURES

There are some 63 persons to the square mile over the land surface of the globe. This figure is often cited as evidence that the earth is not overpopulated. Such a figure actually means nothing, because population is not distributed in anything approaching the manner suggested by such a figure. When one considers population in relation only to cultivable land, which is about one-third of the total land area, the figure becomes 180 persons per square mile. Even this, however, does not give a correct picture.

Applied on a continental scale, an average figure is equally misleading. For instance, Asia (excluding the U.S.S.R.) averages about 115 persons to the square mile; but this figure obscures the fact that Japan averages 651, China 179, and Siberia probably less than 5 persons to the square mile. Even these figures are misleading, for six-sevenths of China's people are congested in one-third of her area. On some of the floodplains and deltas, the population density

[5] Air conditioning and tropical medicine are making sensational progress in this last sphere.
[6] See Joseph Tosi, Jr., and Robert Voertmann, "Some Environmental Factors in the Economic Development of the Tropics," *Economic Geography,* Vol. 40, No. 3 (July, 1964), pp. 189–203.
[7] Philip M. Hauser, "World Population Trends," *Sociology and Social Research,* Vol. XXXVIII (November-December, 1954), p. 75.
[8] Robert C. Cook, "World Population Growth," *Law and Contemporary Problems,* Summer issue, 1960, Duke University, School of Law (Durham, N.C., 1960).

approaches 7,000 to the square mile of arable land. And in Japan, if only arable land is considered, the density exceeds 4,600 to the square mile. Compare this with the 1,835 in the United Kingdom and 219 in the United States.

CULTIVATED LAND PER CAPITA

One of the better ways to picture density of population, except in countries highly industrialized and urbanized, is to note the cultivated land per capita (Table 3–1).

Australia	3.9	acres
Canada	6.46	"
China[9]	.39	"
India	.85	"
United States	2.9	"
U.S.S.R.	2.04	"

Even the term *arable acre*, however, is an abstraction, for it may mean little without reference to levels of living and to agricultural practices. Thus in the southern two-thirds of China, where the diet is based on rice and a minimum of meat and dairy products, several people per acre obtain a good life according to Asiatic standards. In the United States, on the other hand, at least two and a half acres of arable land per capita are needed to maintain the current standard of living.

CAN THE EARTH SUPPORT ITS FAST-GROWING POPULATION?

If surface features alone are considered, about two-thirds of the land area of the world is adapted to agriculture—95 percent of the plains, 75 percent of the plateaus, 25 percent of the hill country, and 5 percent of the mountains. But when climate and soils are also considered, only 25 percent of the earth's land area is suitable for farming.

Will this quarter of the earth's surface be adequate to supply man with the food he needs? There is much disagreement among authorities on this problem. One author[10] holds that nearly four-fifths of the world's people live close to the starvation line. There is not enough food and there is not enough arable land on which to grow more. A high rate of infant mortality, war, pestilence, and famine, still keep a check on China's millions. But in areas where "death control," sanitation, hygiene, public health, and modern medicine have played their humanistic roles, misery has multiplied. More people are alive and more people are hungry, wretched, and reduced to degraded poverty.

[9] Twenty-two provinces; excludes Sinkiang, Kwangsi, 9 provinces of Manchuria, Formosa, and Tibet.

[10] Robert C. Cook, *Human Fertility: The Modern Dilemma* (New York, William Sloane Associates, 1951).

Country	Population Density per Square Mile of Total Area	Country	Population per Square Mile of Cultivated Land	Country	Area in Square Miles (Thousands of Square Miles)
Australia	3	Australia	134	Soviet Union	8,571
Argentina	19	Argentina	164	Canada	3,846
Brazil	20	United States	219	China	3,745
Soviet Union	25	Soviet Union	231	United States	3,681
United States	49	France	526	Brazil	3,288
China	179	Brazil	794	Australia	3,158
France	211	Germany	1,336	France	213
Germany	525	China	1,625	Japan	143
United Kingdom	555	United Kingdom	1,835	Germany (E. & W.)	137
Japan	651	Japan	4,610	United Kingdom	94

Table 3–1   Note the sizes of these ten countries and the population densities per square mile, then see how the rank changes when square mile of cultivated land is used. Some ideas of the unused territory may be gained.

On the opposing side are authorities who are far more optimistic. They see the factory and the use of rock as the salvation, believing that as machine civilization spreads, the per capita requirements and the use of raw materials will be greatly multiplied. "The crux of the problem of survival for a growing world population in the next century is: where will the energy and the raw materials come from?" And their answer is *brain power:* "technology must use air, sea water, ordinary rock and sunlight. Some techniques are already known. Others must be devised."[11]

THEORIES CONCERNING THE RELATIONS BETWEEN POPULATION DENSITY AND THE STANDARD OF LIVING

Some 170 years ago (1798) Thomas Malthus wrote *An Essay on the Principle of Population* in which he stressed the fact that population growth was the principal cause of mass poverty. He asserted that production of the means of subsistence increases only in arithmetical ratio, whereas population tends to grow in geometric progression. Starting with the unit 1, population growth would normally be at the rate of 1, 2, 4, 8, 16, 32, 64; food supply at the rate of 1, 2, 3, 4, 5, 6, 7. Unchecked, a people might multiply within 150 years to 64 times its original size; but the food supply would increase only 7 times. Malthus believed that this population growth was being held within the limits of subsistence by the positive checks of war, pestilence, famine, and premature death. He believed the consequent misery of the masses could not be relieved by social reforms, for any benefits from that source would shortly be consumed by new additions to the population. Thus, according to Malthus, man was probably doomed to perpetual misery through overpopulation. He held out but one hope for improving the standard of living—the practice of "moral restraint," by which he meant prudential delay of marriage. A century of world expansion into new lands undreamed of by Malthus led to general disparagement of his thesis. His teachings became considered out-of-date.

What is the situation today? Was Malthus correct?[12] Actually he was too gloomy: Europe

not only tripled its population but raised its standard of living markedly. The great increase in population during the nineteenth century resulted from both a higher birth rate and a lower death rate. This latter resulted from the science of medicine, improved housing, better food, and the Industrial Revolution.

Many modern scholars, outside the socialist tradition, repudiate the oversimplified arguments of Malthus but agree that population increase in some circumstances hinders economic and social progress.

The review of scientific studies points clearly to this conclusion: the question how population growth affects the material welfare of the people, does not admit of any general answer that would be valid in all places and at all times ... the relevant circumstances are very different in different parts of the world.[13]

However, with the lessening incidence of the natural checks and with world population again pressing hard on world resources, and with overseas lands awaiting easy development no longer available, the truth of Malthus' basic assertion is undeniably applicable to the underdeveloped countries.[14]

THE WORLD'S HUNGER: SOME IMPLICATIONS

Hunger and overpopulation are undoubtedly two of the greatest, if not *the* greatest, world problems. The stark facts are that about one-half of the world's three and a half billion inhabitants receive barely enough food to maintain life at the minimum level and another one-fourth is seriously undernourished. More human beings have

[11] From a survey titled "Raw Materials, Energy, Population and the Spread of Industrialization" made by a team from the California Institute of Technology for major American corporations. (From *The New York Times,* May 21, 1956, p. C 19.)

[12] Ian Burton and Robert W. Kates, "Slaying the Malthusian Dragon: A Review," *Economic Geography,* Vol. 40, No. 1 (January, 1964), pp. 82–89.

[13] *Population Growth and the Standard of Living in Underdeveloped Countries* (New York, United Nations: ST/SOA/Ser.A/20, 1954), p. 2.

[14] L. Dudley Stamp, *Land for Tomorrow* (Bloomington, Indiana University Press, 1952), p. 28.

died from famine than have been killed in war. Most of the ill fed dwell in the overpopulated lands—eastern and southern Asia (Fig. 3–1), the Middle East, parts of Africa, eastern and southeastern Europe, and portions of Latin America.[15]

Although the world produces a surplus of food, the lands yielding these surpluses are not the ones where the populations are densest. Thus, North America normally produces not only enough food for its own population but has an appreciable surplus. Unless the people in the deficient food-producing countries can buy it (which they generally cannot do because of biting poverty), they face famine or must be fed from gifts by nations with surpluses. In short, the well fed continue to be well fed and the hungry get hungrier. Should this hunger situation continue, there will inevitably be a rising tide of unrest, revolution, and perhaps even war; for these people are today experiencing "a revolution of rising expectations"—that is, they no longer believe that poverty, illiteracy, disease, and premature death are inevitable. They fervently desire to alter their status. In short, as

Western standards are unfolded to them by improved means of communications, they are demanding that these standards be made available to them. Furthermore, hunger is the ally of Communism, which is anathema to the Free World. "Stomach Communism" cannot be halted with weapons of war.

CAN THE PROBLEM OF OVERPOPULATION BE SOLVED?

Assuming that the greater part of the world is today overpopulated in relation to its resource base, can the problem be solved? Three factors will be considered: *emigration, industrialization,* and *birth control.*

[15] When the expression "overpopulated" is employed, it can mean a country such as Greece, Spain, or Iran—one whose population per square mile would not be comparable with that, for example, of China, Japan, India, or Java, but whose population is too large for the resource base. Invariably the prosperous countries are those with small populations in relation to their resources—New Zealand, Australia, Canada, and the United States.

Figure 3–1 When drought strikes in India and brings famine to its people, the children are particularly hard hit. (Photo courtesy of CARE)

EMIGRATION

It is frequently asserted that problems created by density of population in particular regions can be alleviated by removing the so-called surplus population to economically undeveloped and sparsely settled areas. Thus in their "thunder wars" which antedated World War II, the Japanese, Italian, and German dictators demanded *lebensraum* for their "surplus population." Careful study of this problem, however, reveals that outlying dependent lands in the past have absorbed and, under normal conditions, can absorb only a relatively small fraction of the peoples from areas of great population density. Very small numbers of Japanese went to Manchuria and only a trickle of Germans and Italians ever migrated to the colonies under their flags. Investigations reveal that to a very great extent persons who have migrated to economically undeveloped areas came not from regions of population density in the countries from which they emigrated, but from relatively sparsely settled areas in their homelands.[16] It is not the underdeveloped but the economically well-developed regions which must absorb extra people and supply their needs. Possibly no better proof of the invalidity of the *lebensraum* theory is to be found than in the fact that no large country in modern times has solved its population problem by emigration. Invariably, when people move out, their places are soon filled. In the *Review of Demographic Studies of Selected Areas of Rapid Growth*,[17] the Round Table on Population Problems released the following statement: "Emigration will not check growth in the most important areas of population pressure at the present stage of their demographic evolution." Isaiah Bowman[18] in his *Limits of Land Settlement* says, "In our present nationalized world, in which the best lands have been occupied, and restrictive measures are in force, migration is no answer to economic and social strain induced by so-called overpopulation." And Warren S. Thompson[19] in his *Danger Spots in World Population* says:

It should also be recognized in connection with emigration as a solution of problems of population pressure that almost never does emigration actually reduce the numbers of the homeland.

Ireland is the only example of a European country in which the population has decreased since emigration set in on a large scale. Famine, emigration, and, more recently, the practice of birth control have reduced Ireland's population till it is now but little more than half of what it was in 1840. . . .

Emigration can, therefore, only be regarded as a temporary expedient for any people. It will keep the pressure on certain areas from growing much greater as long as there is abundance of new land, but it will not actually reduce the pressure to any great extent, especially among such large and dense populations as we find in the western Pacific.

It looks as though no effective redistribution of population via the migration route can care for the world's surplus populations.[20]

INDUSTRIALIZATION

The Western world's transition from agrarianism to industrialism has been singularly successful. Great Britain's shining example of transition through the Industrial Revolution functions as a beacon before the nonindustrial lands of the world, their peoples believing that what Great Britain did, their countries too can do. They fail to realize the extent to which the world has changed since then; no country ever again can repeat what Great Britain did. No country, of course, should pattern itself precisely after another, for each has its own peculiar demographic, economic, geographic, political, and social problems. In nearly all of the countries now overpopulated with respect to their resources base, industrialization as a panacea is limited by lack

[16] Isaiah Bowman, "Peace—The Business of Every Citizen," *Think* (October, 1944), p. 7.
[17] *Review of Demographic Studies of Selected Areas of Rapid Growth,* Proceedings of Round Table on Population Problems, 22nd Annual Conference of Milbank Memorial Fund (New York, 1944), p. 318.
[18] Isaiah Bowman, *Limits of Land Settlement* (New York, Council on Foreign Relations, 1937), p. 1.
[19] Warren S. Thompson, *Danger Spots in World Population* (New York, Alfred A. Knopf, Inc., 1929), p. 133.
[20] Migration today is in the form of a "drift to towns." See Ronald Freedman, ed., *Population: The Vital Explosion* (Chicago, Aldine Publishing Company, 1965). See especially Chapter 5, "World Urbanization: Trends and Prospects."

or paucity of fuel and power, by low wages, dearth of skilled workers, limited and all too frequently poorly developed transport, scarcity of capital and unwillingness of local capital to invest in manufacturing; hostile or at least unfavorable climates, lean raw materials base, and all kinds of social obstacles and man-made economic difficulties. Of the last, the caste system of India is an example.

Until recently, whether or not a region did or did not industrialize depended on whether it possessed the bases for manufacturing[21] and whether it could compete with the more favored regions, particularly those rimming the North Atlantic. Today this is less true. In Communist countries such as China and the Soviet Union, where nationalization has absorbed industry, the leaders are not interested in the people but in national power. Everything else is subordinated to this. Hence much stress is placed upon heavy industry. Other densely populated countries are industrializing, getting the capital through loans, taxing the already poverty-stricken people to the limit of endurance, and by playing one ideology against another, for example, the United States against the Soviet Union. Even in the United States the Cold War has to a certain extent dictated the dispersal of special types of industry into areas that would not have been selected if economic geographic factors alone had operated.[22]

However, it appears that such lands of teeming population as China, Japan, India, Java, and Egypt will not solve their population problem through industrialization. Commenting on this point a United Nations publication[23] states:

However important the benefits of industrialization might be, it would be a mistake to dismiss the population problem of the underdeveloped countries on the easy assumption that they will soon be solved in this way. It is a formidable task to develop large-scale industries in a predominantly agricultural country with a low level of income and little capital, even if the country is amply endowed with such resources as coal, oil, iron ore, and other sources of energy and industrial raw material. It is difficult enough to get the capital required for developing these resources and building the factories, railroads, and other facilities of an industrial economy.

Moreover, such countries experience difficulty selling their products in either the home or foreign market—in the former because of the limited size of the market which results from the inadequacy of income and purchasing power; and in the latter, because they have to compete with countries that already have efficient plants, skilled labor, and a reputation in world markets.

In the California Institute of Technology study, "Raw Materials, Energy, Population, and Spread of Industrialization," the assertion is made that the 10 billion or more people which the world may have by the year 2050 could be fed, clothed, and housed by factories feeding upon the most common substances available—air, sea water, ordinary rock, and sunlight.[24] By most students of population and natural resources, however, this conclusion would be regarded as highly theoretical and optimistic.

BIRTH CONTROL

We have noted that neither emigration nor industrialization appear capable of solving the population problem of the overpopulated countries. Each may contribute but many demographers insist that a vigorous campaign in favor of planned parenthood is imperative. This is not to say that birth control is an alternative to economic and social reforms: it is a supplement rather than a substitute (Fig. 3–2). Those who oppose birth control as contrary to religious doctrine or moral principle see a solution only through global cooperation for improving the conditions in overpopulated countries.[25]

One reason why birth control seems so important is that death rates have been declining

[21] C. Langdon White, Edwin J. Foscue, and Tom L. McKnight, *Regional Geography of Anglo-America*, 3d ed. (Englewood Cliffs, N.J., Prentice-Hall, Inc., 1964). See especially Chapter 2, "The City and Industrial Geography."

[22] C. Langdon White, "Industrialization: A Panacea for Underdeveloped Nations?," *Yearbook of the Association of Pacific Coast Geographers*, Vol. 17, 1955, p. 12.

[23] *Population Growth and the Standard of Living in Under-Developed Countries* (New York, United Nations, 1954), p. 5.

[24] *New York Times*, May 21, 1956, p. C 19.

[25] *World Population—1963*, Population Bulletin, Population Reference Bureau, Inc., Vol. XIX, No. 6 (October, 1963). This publication has an excellent, concise account of the birth rate, along with other pertinent information.

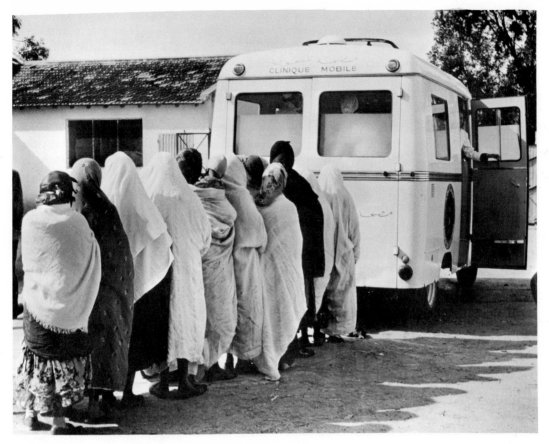

Figure 3–2   At a mobile birth-control clinic in a Tunisian village, women line up for an examination and service. (Photo by Frank W. Notestein, courtesy of the Population Council)

the world over even in those lands where birth rates are still high. In many such countries the death rates are now only about one-half as high as they were just before the outbreak of World War II. The birth rates in most of these countries, however, are generally as high as ever. In fact, in some instances, they have increased as a result of improved health conditions. The result is a spurt in population growth that surpasses what happened in Western Europe, the United States, and the British Dominions of Oceania during the nineteenth and early twentieth centuries. Thus in most of Asia, Africa, and Latin America, present birth rates exceed death rates by a margin sufficient to increase population at least 2 percent per annum.

The governments of some of the densely populated nations, for example, Japan and India, are trying to effect a reduction in the birth rate and Japan has done amazingly well.

HOW FAST ARE COUNTRIES GROWING?

Population growth rates differ throughout the world. Thus Egypt's population is expected to double in 40 years; Indonesia's in 44; Iran's in 46; Thailand's in 33; Japan's in 100; France's in 100; Italy's in 200; Belgium's in 200; the United Kingdom's in 143; and that of the world in 56. Surprising indeed to many persons is the fact that the population of Japan is now growing less rapidly than that of the United States.[26]

Some of the growth rates given above are alarming. Thus Dr. Vannevar Bush[27] emphasizing the need to understand world population

[26] Based upon annual rate of increase from 1958 to 1963 and calculated from *World Population—1963,* Population Bulletin, Population Reference Bureau, Inc., Vol. XIX, No. 6 (October, 1963), pp. 161–167.

[27] Population Reference Bureau, Inc., 1956.

trends and their significance, says: "War aside, man is still headed for trouble. The world's population is increasing at a rate which renders distress, famine, and disintegration inevitable unless we learn to hold our numbers within reason. . . ."

URBAN POPULATION AND GROWTH

Dense population usually leads to urbanism, and urbanism almost invariably is an index to industrialization. Antiquity was characterized by a paucity of great cities. Most are believed to have been small affairs. Rome, which was probably the largest, is believed by many to have had a population of 200,000, perhaps a million. The smaller figure appears to be the more logical, because fifty to ninety farmers were required to care for one urban resident. Moreover, transportation was poorly developed. The present in contrast with the ancient world is distinguished by an abundance of cities. Few, however, lie within the tropics, except at the higher elevations, in polar regions, or in true deserts. Most of the world's cities are located in middle latitudes in the densely populated regions already referred to.

Space does not permit here a detailed treatment of urban growth. But since this book will be used mostly by Americans, it is appropriate to present some of the salient facts concerning urban development in the United States.

In 1790, of the 24 urban places in the United States, only New York and Philadelphia had populations of 25,000 or more and only 5 percent of the total population was living in urban areas. In 1940, however, there were 3,464 urban places totaling more than 74 million people (or 56.5 percent of the total population). Moreover, there were 5 cities with populations exceeding a million and 92 with 100,000 persons or more. In 1950 there was a change in the definition as to what should be included in the terms *urban* and *rural*. People living under distinctly urban conditions in the immediate environs of the larger cities are now regarded as urban, whereas under the old definition they would have been included in the rural population. In 1960, under the new urban-rural definition, 125,268,750

persons, or 69 percent of the total population, were classified as urban. More than three-fourths of the urban population lived in the 263 urbanized areas in 1960. There were still 5 cities with populations exceeding a million but 125 with 100,000 inhabitants or more.

When countries become more urban than rural in their population makeup, the birth rate tends to fall. It is said that the "great cities" are not reproducing themselves. This is not because urban man is unable to increase but because once he becomes master of the birth rate, he appears to be unwilling to forego, for the sake of biological survival, the economic and social advantages of relative childlessness in the city environment.

Thus, since the majority of cities are the homes of manufacturing plants, it appears that the birth rate tends to drop as industrialization spreads.

THE POPULATION SITUATION IN SEVERAL SELECTED COUNTRIES

CHINA

No one knows how many people occupy China. This results in part from variations in the definitions of the country's boundaries and to the lack of accurate census data. An official estimate in 1950 gave the population as 475 million. The Population Reference Bureau has estimated the population of mainland China at 730.8 million for mid-1963, and that of Taiwan at 11.8 million.

It is believed by many demographers that the population of China proper is little, if any, larger than it was in 1850, the reason being that the high death rate nearly balances the high birth rate even in good years and rises above the birth rate in times of disaster. The Chinese Communist government maintains, however, that the population is increasing at the rate of 12 million annually.

The population is not distributed uniformly even in China proper, which has 40 percent of the total land area but 96 per cent of the total population. Outer China, which comprises 60 percent of the total land area has but 4 percent of the population. But even in China proper, most of the people are compressed into the restricted floodplains and deltas of the three great rivers, whereas the mountains are either uninhabited or but sparsely settled. In the more densely occupied lands, the population approximates 7,000 to the square mile of arable land.

It is possible that the population density is already near the maximum which can be supported under existing economic and social arrangements. However, the Communist government claims that the country's "Socialist" economic growth can keep ahead of the population increase; that there is a vast amount of virgin land; and that inasmuch as labor produces value, the more labor the better. Actually it is doubtful that much potentially productive virgin land exists in China proper; such land would have been utilized centuries ago. Moreover, it is well known that the present government is sending large numbers of farmers as permanent settlers to reclaim the barren lands of the border areas (Outer China)—lands devoted almost exclusively to pastoral activities in the past.

China is essentially agricultural and the farms in the past were very small—probably averaging about four acres. Rice is the principal crop in the southern two-thirds of the country, while millet, wheat, *kaoliang*, and soy beans predominate in the north. Nowhere are work animals numerous. Farm practices have been fixed by tradition and changes come slowly. Yields are small, methods antiquated, and farming intensive—so much so that every square foot of tillable land is used. Possibly there is no other area in the world where farming reaches the same levels of intensity as in the more favored parts of China. There is little evidence that the Communal Program of Communist China has altered this situation.

The level of living is low by any criterion—annual per capita wage, annual daily per capita calorie intake, and annual per capita consumption of inanimate energy. Small farms simply cannot produce enough above the food necessities of the family to permit the purchase of the multitude of things an industrial society can produce.

What about industrialization? Can it ameliorate the picture? Here again the future is uncertain. The Communists are trying to transform the rural and village economy into a centrally planned industrial state. Outside the Communist orbit, however, it is not believed that industrialization can appreciably improve the standard of living.

The majority of Western demographers apparently believe that the population pressure in China will increase unless something is done soon to lessen the birth rate. So huge a population in so restricted an area (the really favorable part) may produce important geopolitical pressures so that within a decade or two, China may be sorely tempted to expand into the somewhat emptier lands to the south—Burma, Vietnam, Laos, Cambodia, Thailand, Indonesia, and Malaysia.

JAPAN

In few countries did population increase more rapidly than in Japan. Whereas the population reached Malthusian equilibrium early in the eighteenth century and remained relatively constant until 1850, it doubled after 1860. When one realizes that Japan proper is no larger than the state of California and that three-fourths of the area is mountainous, her ability to sustain 96 million people is amazing.

The average size of a farm in Japan is approximately 2.4 acres and the population density per square mile of cultivated land is 4,610, counting the area of double-cropped land twice. This is about 7.2 persons per acre. The tillable area may be expanded somewhat, but only at unbelievably great cost in labor and capital. Most of it would have to come from reclaiming sea bottom and clearing forest from mountainsides.

Japan ranks as one of the world's best farmed countries. In the period between 1870 and 1920 (two generations), Japan increased her food supply 80 to 100 percent while her population increased by 60 percent. No country in Monsoon Asia has made such full use of its rice lands through scientific farming, including particularly the adoption of better seed and the widespread use of fertilizers. Japan's per acre yield of rice is double that of Burma and Thailand.

No country in Asia has become so thoroughly industrialized and no other is so close a

competitor of the industrial powers of the West.
Yet Japan shows no promise of duplicating the
manufactural achievements of the United States
and the Soviet Union, for like all nations in the
Far East, she lacks two essential elements for
outstanding industrialization: cheap and abundant raw materials, and easy access to markets
with large purchasing power. Nonetheless, her
achievements under the circumstances are positively astounding. Japan will continue to be, for
the time being at least, Asia's outstanding industrial nation, not because the bases for manufacturing are strong, but because of industrial inertia, the financial backing of the United States,
and Japanese initiative. Industrialization is contributing to the solution of the problem of overpopulation, but so is birth control.

While the annual natural increase in population approximates two million, the birth rate is
considerably lower than that of either China or
India. It is believed that Japan has reached the
end of the heavy growth phase as a result of increased urbanization, industrialization, education,
and birth control. Widespread publicity has been
given the fact that the country is overpopulated
and that smaller families are desirable. Even the
government has pronounced itself in favor of
smaller families. Hence, Japan is the only non-
white country in the world to be experiencing a
decline in the birth rate similar to that in Western Europe.

What of the future? With a population of
96 million and with limited natural resources,
there can be no doubt that Japan is overpopulated.[28]

INDIA

India ranks as one of the most densely populated countries in the world. In an area less than
half that of the United States, live more than
461 million people—more than the combined
populations of the United States and the Soviet
Union—two of the largest countries in the world.
The average population density is about six times
the world average, and the nation faces a dismal
population future growth of about 10 million
people every year—a staggering increment to an
already overpopulated land.

Many people believe India's rate of growth

to be extremely high; actually it is 2.2 percent
a year, slightly more than that of the United
States. But in so densely populated a land, even
a small percentage increase augments the total
number enormously.

The birth rate (41 per 1,000 for South
Central Asia) has been consistently high and the
death rate (24 per 1,000) has been falling steadily, thereby giving a continuous net increase. Improved medical facilities, a better check of epidemics, and control of famines all have played
their part in lowering the death rate.

Most of the population consists of farmers,
and the good farm lands are badly overcrowded.
One-third of the people live on less than 6 percent of the land and the average densities in
these areas exceed 650 persons to the square
mile. Actually, the densities are higher, for they
should be calculated not on gross area but on
cultivated area. On this basis the figure soars
from 1,000 to 2,500 per square mile, for example, in the Ganges Plain and in the coastal
areas. The average farmer has only about four-
fifths of an acre.

The level of living is low. Whereas the minimum daily food requirement for India may be
put at 2,100 calories per person, the quantity
actually available is only 1,600 calories.

Other discouraging conditions are that the
cultivated area probably has not substantially increased since the beginning of the century and
per acre yields are notoriously low. Too little
commercial fertilizer is used; even much of the
cattle dung is utilized for fuel. In the middle
1950's, twenty million persons were unemployed.
Half the rural population is idle except during
the summer monsoon season. Chances of attaining the aim of doubling the per capita national
income by 1977 are not promising.

Improved agriculture and industrialization
will not solve the population problem. India is
a comparatively rich country in natural resources
(the government claims it is the third richest)
and might ultimately become the leading industrial nation in Asia. Many Indian demographers

[28] Japan is the only Asian country classified in the
"fourth stage of population growth" today—experiencing birth rates between ten and twenty per thousand and death rates of eight to thirteen per thousand.

and sociologists, however, assert that without planned parenthood, to which the Hindu religion is not opposed, the level of living cannot be raised. The Indian government is establishing health centers in villages which are teaching birth control. Hence India is one of the few countries in the world to adopt birth control as a deliberate policy of government. Initial surveys indicate that 70 percent of the people favor family planning.

THE U.S.S.R.[29]

This huge country, clearly the major power of Eurasia, is growing much as did the United States several generations ago. It is adding annually almost as many inhabitants as all the Western European nations combined.

Nonetheless, it is a land characterized by a falling birth rate and death rate, particularly in the cities. It is believed that these will continue to fall with the progress in industrialization. Thus while the population continues to grow rapidly, the Russian people appear to be following the same reproduction pattern as in the West.

The total population is estimated at 225 million.[30] The yearly increase is about 3.8 million. The distribution of the population is far from uniform. Huge areas are almost empty, although the government has moved millions of people to the Ural area, Siberia, and the far eastern districts.

The planned relocation of population in the U.S.S.R. is accepted as a means of increasing the effectiveness of utilizing natural resources, of diminishing regional contrasts in the degree of economic development in the conditions of life and in the development of consumers' goods industries in the areas where the goods are consumed. The plan thus is to lessen the degree of centralization of economic activities and to disperse the population more widely than has been the case in the advanced industrial countries of the West. The movement of people from rural areas to cities has gone forward at a rapid pace. This, of course, has produced profound effects on the birth rate, with the urban, small-family pattern rapidly emerging. At present about half the population of the Soviet Union could be considered urban.

What of the level of living? It is low. The Soviet Union ranks intermediate in the classification of nations as *advanced, intermediate,* and *underdeveloped.* This subordinate rank results in part from the restricted area of first-class agricultural land and from the government's sublimation of everything to heavy industry. As pointed out earlier, the government has been more interested in national strength and technological advances than in raising the standard of living of its people. Communist ideology justifies this.

THE UNITED STATES

The population of the United States grew very rapidly almost from the beginning of white settlement. Emigrants from the crowded countries of Europe came to these shores in large numbers. Nearly all were land-hungry and restless, and since the most productive agricultural lands lay to the west of the Appalachians, the immigrants soon were pushing westward. In colonial times 85 percent of the people were engaged in farming; each farmer was able to supply his own needs and a third of those of another person. Large families were the rule. Then came logging and lumbering, mining, transporting, and finally manufacturing. Ere long the factory machine became the rival of the plow. People began to drift cityward and many a city grew to enormous size. As of 1960, only 6.6 percent of the total employed population were in agriculture, but by then each could feed himself and thirty-four others. To become so productive, the American farmer has largely become a machine tender and a power user. Whereas in 1910 there were only 1,000 tractors in the entire nation and 25 million horses and mules, in 1957 there were only 5 million horses and mules and 4 million petroleum-powered tractors—the latter having a force of 750 million horses. No other farmers in the

[29] Vital statistics on the U.S.S.R. are difficult to obtain. However, students of population are able to piece together information gathered from numerous sources and thereby determine the trend. The first all-union census was completed in 1959.

[30] Information Service, Population Reference Bureau, Inc., data sheet for 1963 lists U.S.S.R. population at 224.7 million (estimate) with 29.7 percent under fifteen years of age.

world are so highly mechanized. In 1965, there were slightly over 5.1 million tractors on farms in the United States. Europe by contrast had not quite one-third this number, and the rest of the world barely one-eighth of this number.

A century ago, five man-hours were required to produce a bushel of corn; today perhaps not more than two minutes are needed to do it. Mechanization is therefore the way in which the United States increased farm production 30 percent despite a labor loss of two billion man hours a year.

Today more than two-thirds of the population lives in 212 Standard Metropolitan Statistical Areas. From 1950 to 1960 the central cities of urbanized areas grew 19.8 percent, while the urban fringe areas grew 81.4 percent. Today about 60 percent of the population of urbanized areas live in the central cities and 40 percent in the urban fringe. Americans are truly becoming a nation of suburbanites.

The majority of the people live east of the 100th meridian, which coincides with the 20-inch rainfall line. Except in favored areas west of this line, population is indeed sparse. Population is densest, cities most numerous, industrialization most intense, and transportation best developed in the American Manufacturing Region, the parallelogram connecting Boston, Baltimore, St. Louis, Green Bay, and Boston. However, population is growing most rapidly on the Pacific Coast, with California now ranking as the most populous state in the nation.[31] The density of population for the country as a whole is only forty-nine persons per square mile, but many metropolitan areas rank among the most densely populated areas in the world.

So far as level of living is concerned, the United States is unique. Among the world's major peoples, Americans are almost alone in being satisfied with the status quo in contrast with the vast majority of mankind which is dissatisfied to the point of welcoming *any* change.

Industrialization has contributed much to the attainment of a high level of living. The population stood at 5 million in 1800 and at 190 million in 1963. Had the population remained stationary, that is, at the 1800 figure, it could never have supplied the labor force necessary to exploit the vast natural resources and to build and man the present industrial plant. Nor could the vast market have been provided to absorb the many products of the large-scale industries.

Thus the United States, with only 6 percent of the world's population and less than 7 percent of its land, produces and consumes more than 33 percent of the world's goods and services and turns out nearly 50 percent of the products of its factories. The purchasing power of its 200 million people is believed to be greater than that of the 667 million who inhabit Europe and the Soviet Union combined.

The United States now has over 200 million people. It is increasing at an average rate of 5 persons every minute. Births are booming at the rate of one every eight seconds and the life span inches up steadily. In 1970 the population is expected to reach 213 million based upon its annual growth rate of 1.7 percent since 1958. However, there is recent evidence that this rate might be lowering. Whether this is a temporary trend remains to be seen.

The population picture has changed much since 1940, and until recently the rate of expansion has exceeded that of many of the countries in Asia, which are usually cited as examples of unrestrained population increase. What is actually happening is in contrast with the views expressed by demographers during the 1920's and 1930's when it was believed that the population of the United States would soon reach a virtual peak and either level off or decline. The sharp increase since 1940, however, has been accompanied by marked advances in levels of living, particularly in the case of the "common man," despite World War II and postwar international burdens.

What would be the ideal population figure in the United States? Kingsley Davis,[32] eminent demographer, believes it possible to supply some

---

[31] See Figure 3 in article by Henry J. Warman, in *Journal of Geography,* Vol. LXIV, No. 5 (May, 1965). The cultural and physical attributes of the Eastern North American Manufactured Region are shown clearly.

[32] Kingsley Davis, "Ideal Size of Our Population," *The New York Times Magazine* (May 1, 1955), pp. 12–35.

300 million people at a high level of living. After carefully balancing all the variables, he would prefer that the population not exceed 220 million by the year 2000, though he surmises that it is more likely to reach 275 million. Howard Nielson,[33] on the other hand, estimates that the population will reach 220 million by 1975. Some estimates exceed 300 million!

THE UNITED KINGDOM

The United Kingdom, which is about the size of the state of New Mexico, has a population of some 54 million. This is the equivalent of 555 persons to the square mile—one of the densest in the world.

With 56 million acres of land, only 28 million are plowable. There is but one-half acre of cultivable land per person. Thus, given the best possible care, and in few countries do the people do as well in this respect, the land can satisfactorily support not more than 20 million people. This disparity between 20 and 50 million was not so serious when Britain was the world's leading trading nation and when the foreign investments guaranteed a large return from "invisible exports." In the pre-World War II period, Britain was actually producing less than 40 percent of her essential food requirements; she was becoming a land of idle acres. By 1938 the arable acreage was the lowest ever recorded. World War II brought about a reversal; and now Britain, whose farms are among the most highly mechanized in the world, produces more than 80 percent of the food consumed. Today the revenue from foreign investments is much less than formerly. Hence food must either be grown at home or bought in world markets at high prices.

Britain, of course, is an outstanding industrial nation and is highly urbanized. Even as early as 1880, 68 percent of the population was urban and in recent years the figure has stood at around 80 percent.

The standard of living is reasonably high, but at times the austerity of the British program results in the people's eating less well than those in some of the neighboring countries on the continent. However, Britain ranks high among the advanced nations.

As to the future population, it may be pointed out that in the 1930's population growth was slowing down. Following World War II there was a sudden rise in the birth rate. Other factors also may be operating to reverse the previous decline in crude birth rates, though no authorities anticipate much growth. The already dense population, the modest natural resources, the high taxes, and the rather dismal future do not augur well for large families. It has been estimated, moreover, that the optimum population for the British Isles would be less than one-half what it is now.

FRANCE

France, in an area about one and three-fourths the size of the British Isles, supports a population of 47,400,000. This means a population per square mile of over 200. For centuries, agriculture was the mainstay of France and the agricultural tradition still remains strong. The majority of the people, however, are no longer employed on the land. Nonetheless, the peasant farmer still is regarded as the backbone of the nation. France is essentially a land of villages and small towns. There is, of course, Paris with a population of 2,811,711, and there are thirty-one cities with populations exceeding 100,000. The urban population as a percentage of the total population is only 53—considerably lower than in Great Britain, Belgium, and Germany.

The rate of population growth in France has never been high—only 1 percent since 1958. Fertility was moderate in the first quarter of the nineteenth century but declined during the second quarter and then remained fairly constant at a relatively low level for several decades.

Concerned over Germany's rapid increase in numbers, France developed a full-blown population policy aimed in large measure at increasing numbers. Nothing sensational, however, has occurred. Nonetheless, the decline in the birth rate has been less than in many other European countries. Whether the family allowance system had anything to do with holding the rate more stable is not known. As to why this predominantly Catholic country should have long limited the

[33] Howard C. Nielson, *Population Trends in the United States Through 1975* (Menlo Park, Calif., Stanford Research Institute, 1955), p. 16.

size of families, the following reasons seem to be pertinent: the love of luxury, desire to advance in the social scale, and the desire to avoid the subdivision of property by inheritance.

Few countries show a more even distribution of population. The ecumene is virtually co-extensive with the area: in short, France lacks the empty areas that characterize so many countries. A major reason for this is that few countries have so large a proportion of their total areas so well suited to the practice of agriculture.

What of the future as far as population is concerned? Most authorities agree that France could well care for from 50 to 74 million inhabitants and that such a population might be a distinct advantage to the nation. The projected population for 1970 is put at about 51 million. In one respect France is quite unique among countries of Western Europe: she grows the bulk of the food required to feed her present population.

ITALY

Considering Italy's resricted area (about the same size as the state of New Mexico) and its preponderance of rough terrain, poor soils, destructive erosion, rainless summers (the boot), meager endowment in minerals and forests, and a heavy dependence upon agriculture, the nation is definitely overpopulated. Under Mussolini, the need for a large and growing population was emphasized as a means of helping the country attain a world position of importance. Accordingly, laws that aimed against voluntary control of births were instituted. Noting that the birth rate was lower in cities than in rural districts, the Fascists attempted to discourage the growth of the larger cities and thereby avoid the low birth rates prevailing in urbanized central and western Europe. Despite all efforts, however, the rate of population growth actually declined.

Italy's population is in the neighborhood of 50 million—a density of over 400 per square mile. On the basis of arable land there is four-fifths of an acre per capita. For a predominantly agricultural nation this is an extremely low figure. Moreover, Italy cannot be compared with France in percentage of arable land. Yet wher-

ever a piece of really suitable farmland is available, even if it be on a steep slope where the soil must be carried in buckets to construct terraces, the Italian farmer achieves enviable results through ingenuity and intensive cultivation. In fact, the Italian has been praised as one of the best farmers on earth—a praise well deserved.

From 1820 on Italy sent some 17 million of her sons abroad. Today one-third of the total population of Argentina and one-fourth that of Brazil are of Italian birth or descent. And in the 116 years between 1820 and 1936 almost 5 million Italians migrated to the United States. Yet during this period of heavy emigration, Italy's population growth in the homeland was one of the highest in Europe. Actually, Italy's mass migration during a century did not effectively relieve the population pressure nor the misery and poverty of most of the people. Yet the demand that other lands absorb the surplus millions continues.

Italy's one hope is that the declining birth rate which has been in progress for several generations will continue. In northern Italy the birth rate now balances the death rate. If this can happen also in southern Italy, perhaps the rate of growth will fall and the level of living can be raised appreciably. Migration has failed and industrialization cannot be expected to solve the problem.

OVERPOPULATION?

The populations of China and India continue to maintain their undoubted numerical superiority. Hence there may be danger that these nations may one day seek to dominate the earth. Yet, as has been pointed out, overpopulation is a relative matter. Whether it leads to war depends upon many factors other than mere population density. Overpopulation threatens the peace of the world only when a people feels that it is being confined in narrower limits (so far as land area and natural resources are concerned) than are its due, because other peoples are unjustly monopolizing too much of the earth's resources. This was the attitude of Japan, Italy, and Germany prior to World War II. It presently seems to be the mood in underdeveloped countries. The sheer impossibility of keeping production ahead of population growth in such areas as southern and eastern Asia, where more than 1.6 billion people live, is obvious. These lands are passing from the status of tradition in their modes of living and producing to a stage of determination in an effort to provide a better life for their downtrodden populations. Unless they succeed, they may well emulate Japan when she demanded larger resources in terms of land area and was willing to fight to get them.

No nation, once its people become literate and are allowed to know what is going on in the world, can be expected to accept calmly the increasing hardship its people will feel as they become more and more crowded and live, what seems to them, a more and more uncertain and precarious existence. Under these conditions outbreaks of war may initiate cycles of destruction which will raise the death rate until there is little or no increase in population.[34]

PROGRESS IN MAN'S CONQUEST OF DISEASE: RELATION TO THE POPULATION PROBLEM

Among the factors in the current "Revolution of Rising Expectations" is the determination of the millions of people occupying the underdeveloped lands to improve their health situation and extend the life expectancy which averages about thirty-five years in contrast with sixty-nine for the United States and seventy-two for the Netherlands.

Invariably high mortality is associated with low income per capita, high rates of illiteracy, a large proportion of male farmers, and a great number of persons per physician.

In areas of high mortality, communicable diseases account for a large part of the deaths. For example, in Egypt half the people are afflicted with bilharziasis, which reduces their productivity by 33 percent. Conditions as bad as these exist in scores of other lands throughout the world. Organization (WHO) was organized to see what could be done for humanity through the global control of disease. Since its inception WHO has waged global war on infectious diseases. That the organization accomplished wonders cannot be questioned: during just a five-year period, among other accomplishments some 400 million people —one-eighth of all mankind—benefited from modern methods of controlling malaria, tuberculosis, yaws, and numerous other diseases. Yaws, for example, has been completely eliminated from Haiti and is being attacked successfully in Africa and southern and eastern Asia.[35]

Looking at the other side of the picture, we cannot help but ask whether lives should be saved without opportunity for those saved to live with some degree of satisfaction; in short, are these people being saved from an early death simply to lead a life of lingering hunger? The disparity between the hungry and the well-fed nations grows wider.

SUMMARY AND CONCLUSIONS

It has been pointed out that widespread overpopulation is probably the most serious problem facing the world today. And since overpopulation is related to area and natural resources, it becomes a matter of high geographic importance. There is, of course, no more fundamental relationship than that between man and the land. The ratio of amount of land to the numbers of human beings is the fundamental consideration of life in any society.

Since there are only so much productive land and other natural resources, since intense nationalism prevails almost everywhere, and since there are even now too many people, it is certain that man cannot continue to multiply without limit. For all his superior qualities, particularly his "brain power," it would seem that he is no exception to the laws of nature. It must be admitted that it would be technically possible to feed a much larger population than the world

[34] Warren S. Thompson, "World Population Trends, Problems, and Policies," in J. F. Timmons and W. G. Murray, eds., *Land Problems and Policies* (Ames, Iowa State College Press, 1950), p. 42.

[35] See L. Dudley Stamp, *The Geography of Life and Death* (Ithaca, N.Y., Cornell University Press, 1964). Especially Chapter VI, "The Rulers of Africa."

Figure 3–3 A Peace Corps volunteer directs students at the Kolo Agricultural School in Niger. They are taught how to grow various crops such as rice, cotton, millet, peanuts, corn, and sorghum, as well as to care properly for oxen and to use oxen-drawn equipment. (Photo courtesy of the Peace Corps)

now has. The increases in production that are likely to be achieved in the foreseeable future, however, promise to be much smaller than those which are technically possible.

Fully three-fifths of the world's population is increasing as fast or faster than subsistence, and prevailing society and economic conditions appear to preclude hope of increasing subsistence adequately, even with Western technology.

If human numbers continue to soar, does the future hold in store for the bulk of mankind the alternative of warfare or starvation? It will depend on man himself. Certainly war is a possibility; for poverty, starvation, and overcrowding are among its major causes. Obviously no nation starves quietly!

However, man does know how to check population growth by limiting the number of births. Moreover, the birth rate is subject to individual control to a greater degree than the death rate.

Hundreds of millions of people, however, do not yet possess this information; and even if it were to be disseminated widely, even universally, possibly there would still be obstacles to the solving of the problem of excessive numbers, for birth control would require fundamental changes in the outlook and values of the people. Since these values are deeply imbedded and rigidly enforced by social sanctions, it is believed that they would change slowly even under the impact of rapidly changing conditions. Whenever efforts have been expended to arouse the peasants to improve their villages, their lands, and their systems of economy, progress has been slow and often heartbreaking because of the reluctance of the people to change. Many governments, too, resist the idea that fertility is a detriment.

The strong, prosperous, and well-fed nations must be sympathetic with the underdeveloped lands, become interested in world population trends and problems, and help solve such problems, if the people want help. In those instances, where advice and counsel are not wanted, there should be no pressure. We in the more advanced nations must not assume that we can give them better solutions to their problems than they themselves might find. Particularly we should beware of assuming that just because certain measures worked well in the West, they must necessarily do so in underdeveloped lands.

Nonetheless, the problem each day becomes more urgent. Poverty and degradation spread wider and deeper. To improve the subsistence of the masses in the underdeveloped countries would require much capital and technology, both of which they themselves lack. The per capita annual income in some countries is below $100. Certainly some of the science we offer them should be put to work not only to increase production but also to lessen the birth rate (Fig. 3–3). In the common world interest, the maximum population obtainable cannot be countenanced. Hence, despite optimism or indifference to the world problem of overpopulation, there must certainly come a time when the earth simply will be unable to support more than a certain number of billions of people.[36]

[36] Karl Sax, *Standing Room Only: Malthus and the Modern World* (Boston, Beacon Press, Inc., 1955).

SUGGESTED USEFUL READINGS

Clarke, John I., *Population Geography* (New York, Pergamon Press, 1965). Paperback.

Perpillou, Aime Vincent, *Human Geography* (New York, John Wiley & Sons, Inc., 1966).

Stamp, L. Dudley, *The Geography of Life and Death* (Ithaca, N.Y., Cornell University Press, 1964). Paperback.

Zelinsky, Wilbur, *A Prologue to Population Geography* (Englewood Cliffs, N.J., Prentice-Hall, Inc., 1966). Paperback.

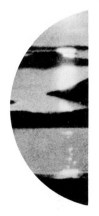

4

Geomatic Position and Its Significance

POSITION DEFINED

The term *position* as it is used in geography means the absolute occurrence of a point or of an area on the earth's surface. It is derived from the Latin words *ponere, positum* ("to put"). Since the earth is a sphere, it has no sides, corners, or guidelines on it, and therefore where a place really is on the earth (that is, its position) becomes literally a question of where one puts it.

DISTANCES AND BOUNDARIES

ORIGINS

In ancient land surveys, distances and boundaries were usually expressed in terms of various kinds of landmarks, but since these latter were never wholly permanent, their use was often confusing. Position in military operations also was, and today still is, usually stated in terms of landmarks. Such a practice is satisfactory for local and temporary purposes. Navigators, from very early times, determined their position at sea by observations of stars, sun, and planets. The method is fairly satisfactory but rather complicated for the untrained individual.

MEDITERRANEAN ERA

In antiquity, Western civilization centered in and about the Mediterranean Sea, and hence the known world of the period was coextensive with the basin of that sea. Position was, therefore, reckoned in terms of the length and width of the Mediterranean. The idea of determining position from two base lines perpendicular to each other seems to have originated with Eratosthenes

about 200 B.C. The terms *latitude* and *longitude* which are in use today derive from the Latin words *latus* and *longus*, and originally referred to the width and length of the Mediterranean Sea (Fig. 4–1).

The two sets of lines which Eratosthenes used for expressing position were purely arbitrary. To achieve a regular mathematical system of coordinates, one must know the shape and size of the earth and possess a proper method of dividing a circle into units of arc. Eratosthenes succeeded in proving that the earth was a sphere, and calculated that its circumference was a circle approximately 25,000 miles around. In his day, however, the present method of dividing a circle into degrees was unknown.

Hipparchus (about 125 B.C.) seems to have been the first to divide the circle into 360 degrees.[1] Ptolemy (A.D. 150) adopted Eratosthenes' method of determining latitude and longitude from two base lines at right angles to each other, and of using parallels to show position. He also adopted Hipparchus' system of circular degrees. But he, like others who came after him, made a serious error in computing the size of the earth; and therefore the value of his degree was incorrect. It was not until after the voyages of Columbus that the spherical shape of the earth came to be universally accepted and the actual length of a degree came to be generally known.

[1] Where he got the idea is not known. It may have been influenced by the duodecimal system of the Middle East. At an early date in the Far East, the Chinese were known to have divided the circle into 365¼ degrees—to correspond with the days of the earth year. Perhaps Hipparchus' 360° was a simplified approximation of this.

WORLD ERA

After the time of Columbus, the globe and world map were rapidly perfected. Since that time, too, the occurrence of any point or area has been conceived of in terms of the earth as a whole. It is no longer a matter of Mediterranean position but of global position. Today, position is expressed by means of a system of earth coordinates, mathematically fitted to the earth's shape and size (Fig. 4–2). Expressed in this manner, posi-

Figure 4–1 Ancient geomatic coordinates based upon the Mediterranean Sea.

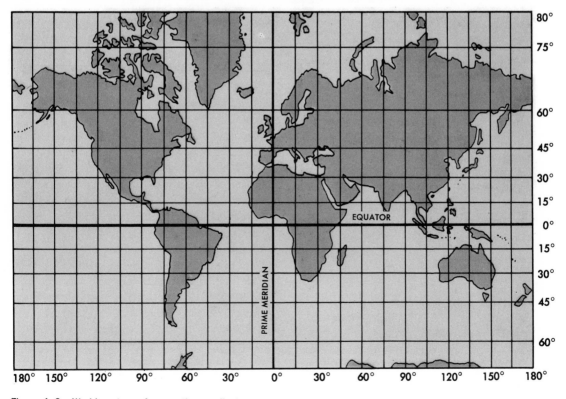

Figure 4–2 World system of geomatic coordinates.

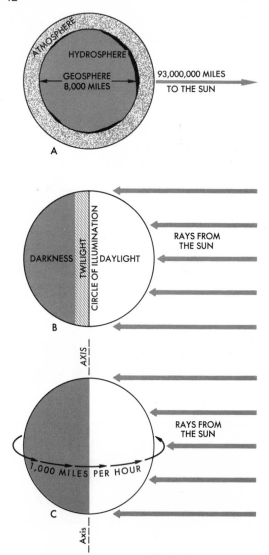

Figure 4–3   The earth as a planet. A, the composition of the earth; B, the earth receives its heat from the sun; C, the earth rotates on an axis.

tion becomes a matter of geomatics[2] (geomathematics). Thus, the position of Moscow on a map is seen to be 55° 45′ N., 37° 40′ E.

THE EARTH AS A PLANET

The earth is a large ball or sphere of mineral matter, some 8,000 miles in diameter, the depressions on which are filled with water. The whole is set inside a shell of gaseous atmosphere (Fig. 4–3A). It is suspended in space and tied to a near-by large star known as Sol

(the sun) by the enormously strong but invisible bonds of gravitation. The distance at which the sun holds the earth averages about 93 million miles.

Sol itself is a sphere bigger than the earth —nearly a million miles in diameter—which is so hot that its surface temperature is more than 10,000° F. This hot sun gives off waves of energy or force which radiate outward in all directions at a speed of 186,000 miles per second. About one-billionth of this energy falls on the earth. The amount of energy continually pouring onto the earth is about 100 trillion horsepower, or about one horsepower continually on each square yard of earth surface. Of course, the sun shines upon only one-half of the earth at any one time, the other half of the earth lying in darkness or twilight.

EARTH MOVEMENTS

IF THE EARTH WERE STATIONARY

Suppose that the earth were perfectly stationary in space, at a distance of some 93 million miles from the sun. If that were the case, the half of the earth facing the sun would be perpetually drenched in sunlight and very hot, but the other side would be perpetually dark and bitterly cold. On such a world it is probable that life would be possible only in the twilight zone between the light and dark hemispheres (Fig. 4–3B).

ROTATION AND REVOLUTION

Fortunately, the earth is not stationary, but instead it has two important motions: axial rotation and orbital revolution. The earth rotates at an equatorial speed of more than 1,000 miles per hour—taking twenty-four hours to complete one turn (Fig. 4–3C). At the same time, following an elliptical orbit about the sun, it travels at a velocity of nearly 67,000 miles per hour to complete one revolution in 365¼ days (Fig. 4–4). The rotation establishes the earth's axis or axial diameter. This axis wobbles a little, but nevertheless remains remarkably constant. Rotation serves a useful purpose because it compels the earth's surface to move through alternate periods

[2] A term probably originated by the Dutch geographer, Senstius, about 1920.

of light and darkness, thus producing the effect of nighttime and daytime (Fig. 4–3C). This tends to distribute the heat resulting from the sun's rays (insolation) which fall on the earth's surface in such a manner as to make the greater portion of the earth habitable. The rotation of the earth is partly responsible for the length of the earth's day. The revolutional velocity determines the length of the earth's year. The number of rotations the earth makes during the time required to complete one revolution around the sun is 365¼. This divides the year (one revolution) into days (rotations).

INCLINATION

If the earth rotated on an upright axis,[3] it would simply rotate round and round, producing the same length of day and night no matter on what side of the sun it was.

Fortunately for mankind, the earth's axis is inclined out of a vertical position by an angle of 23½° (Fig. 4–5). The earth rotates in this tipped-over position and does not swerve from it, even while revolving around the sun. The earth's axis remains constantly parallel to itself in all positions on its orbit. This is known as parallelism (see Fig. 4–4).

PARALLELS OF LATITUDE

The rotation of the earth on an axis establishes two fixed points on the earth's surface, known as the poles. For the sake of convenience, one is known as the North Pole, the other as the South Pole. The poles cannot be seen by the human eye, but a surveyor can find their location with instruments; and hence they are real things. Midway between the two poles, the mathematician can draw a line known as the equator (equal divider). Between the equator and each pole there are 90 *degrees*. The degrees are numbered (0 at the equator to 90 at either pole) in order to measure latitude or curved distance north or south from the equator. These parallel circles of latitude then serve as reference lines (Fig. 4–6).

SIZE OF A DEGREE OF LATITUDE

The earth is commonly described as a sphere, but this is not strictly correct. The centrifugal force created by rotation causes the earth to bulge slightly in its equatorial portion. This, in turn, causes a slight flattening near the poles. As a consequence, the length of a degree of latitude varies. Near the equator, 1° is equal to 68.7 land miles; at latitude 45° it is equal to 69.0 miles; while near the poles it is equal to 69.4 miles. An average value is approximately 69 miles. To say, therefore, that Philadelphia lies in latitude 40° north is to imply that it lies about 2,760 miles north of the equator.

PERIODS OF LIGHT AND DARK

The combined effect of rotation, revolution, and inclination can be seen from the diagram in Figure 4–7. This shows the earth in four main positions about the sun during the course of a year. First, examine the earth in its June 21 position (Fig. 4–7A). As the earth turns in this position, point E on the equator passes through

[3] That is, if its axis were perpendicular to the plane of its orbit.

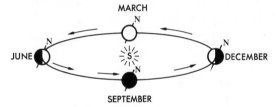

Figure 4–4   The earth revolves about the sun annually along a huge elliptical path or orbit.

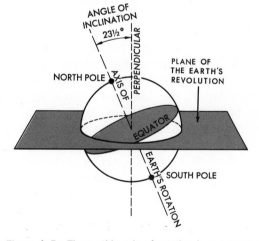

Figure 4–5   The earth's axis of rotation is not perpendicular to the plane of its revolution. Instead it is tipped at an angle of 23½ degrees out of a perpendicular position.

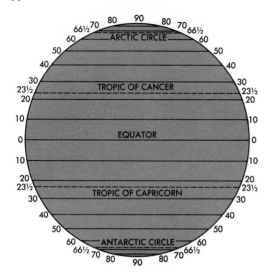

Figure 4–6 Parallels of latitude at 10-degree intervals over the earth, showing also the equator, the tropic circles, and the polar circles.

APPARENT MOVEMENT OF THE SUN

Most people have observed that each morning the sun appears to rise in the east, to follow a generally semicircular path across the sky, and then to set in the west. They have probably also deduced that during the nighttime period, the sun completes the circle in order to be in position to rise on the following morning. As spring comes, the sun rises higher in the sky at noonday and stays above the horizon longer. Each day the sun mounts higher and higher until the summer solstice, after which it declines day by day until the winter solstice. After that it once more begins to increase in elevation.

This annual cycle in sun elevation produces marked variation in the amount of heating obtained from sunlight in any given place. This in turn produces marked changes in temperature. When these are added to the cycle of change in length of daytime and nighttime shown in Figure 4–16, the changes in temperature through the year in some parts of the earth are truly great.

During the course of a year, the sun is not always directly overhead at noon on the equator, but shifts first to the north of the equator, then south of it, and then back again. The tilt of the earth's axis controls how far north or how far south of the geographic equator this "sunshine equator" will shift in the course of a year. The extreme limits of vertical sun enable the mathematician to trace out two more reference lines on the earth—the Tropic of Cancer and the Tropic of Capricorn.[5] Outside these two limits, the sun at noon never reaches an overhead position.

sunlight and darkness[4] an equal number of hours each day. A point T turns through sunlight longer than darkness. A point X turns round and round in the sunlight. South of the equator, point C is in darkness longer than in sunlight. Point Y turns round and round unable to get out of darkness.

The circular patch of continuous sunlight about the North Pole and the patch of continuous darkness around the South Pole are especially worth noting. Their outer boundaries determine two more earth reference lines—the Arctic Circle (66½° North) and the Antarctic Circle (66½° South).

As the earth moves in its orbit, the Arctic patch of continuous sunlight shrinks daily. So does the patch of darkness in the Antarctic. By September 22 they both have disappeared and daytime and nighttime are equal (12 hours each) all over the earth (Fig. 4–7B). After that date a patch of continuous light appears about the South Pole and a patch of dark appears about the North Pole. Day by day these grow larger until they reach a maximum on December 22 (Fig. 4–7C). By March 21, the equinoctial condition (equal night and day) is again reached (Fig. 4–7D). By June 21, the original condition is once more attained (Fig. 4–7A).

NORTH-SOUTH REFERENCE LINES

Thus, the fact that the earth rotates on a tipped axis and revolves about the sun establishes the poles, the polar circles, the tropic circles, and an equatorial line. These together with the 178 parallels of latitude form a north-south reference system for the earth (Fig. 4–6).

[4] Including twilight.

[5] Cancer is the sign of the zodiac for June 21; Capricorn is the sign for December 22.

MERIDIANS OF LONGITUDE

Running across these latitude circles at right angles, a second set of circles is drawn on the earth by the geomathematician. These are not parallel to each other, but instead are laid out so as to intersect at each pole. Stated in another manner, they radiate outward from the North Pole, curve about the globe, cross the equator at right angles, and again intersect at the South Pole. Each half-circle, extending from one pole to the other, is known as a meridian. There are 359 meridians—dividing the distance around the earth into 360 equal parts (there are 360 degrees in a complete circle). Actually, only one meridian out of every ten, fifteen, or twenty is ordinarily shown on a map or globe (Fig. 4–8).

SIZE OF A DEGREE OF LONGITUDE

The equator is a perfect circle, so that all degrees of longitude along the equator are equal (approximately sixty-nine land miles). Since the meridians are not parallel to one another, they converge away from the equator and finally intersect at either pole. Thus a degree of longitude, as measured in miles, becomes less and less as one goes poleward. The following table gives the approximate values.

At latitude 0 = 69 miles
At latitude 20 = 65 "
At latitude 40 = 53 "
At latitude 60 = 35 "
At latitude 89 = 1 mile
At latitude 90 = 0 miles

From this, one can see that an area of land enclosed by two parallels and two meridians is not quite a square. Near the equator it is very nearly a square, but as one goes toward the pole it grows narrower and narrower in east-west extent. Even then, it is not a rectangle, because the poleward side is always narrower than the equatorward side (Fig. 4–9). Instead, it is an

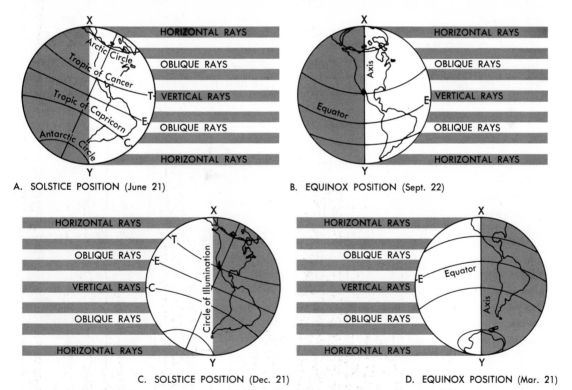

A. SOLSTICE POSITION (June 21)

B. EQUINOX POSITION (Sept. 22)

C. SOLSTICE POSITION (Dec. 21)

D. EQUINOX POSITION (Mar. 21)

Figure 4–7 Four seasonal positions assumed by the earth as it revolves about the sun throughout the year. Note that the sun's rays fall vertically on the equator at the equinoxes, at the Tropic of Cancer in June, and at the Tropic of Capricorn in December.

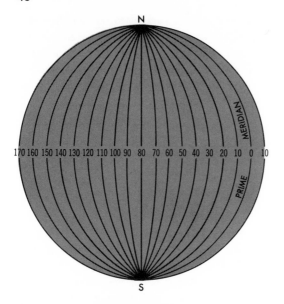

Figure 4–8   Meridians of longitude. The Prime Meridian was arbitrarily selected so as to run through the Greenwich Observatory in London.

isosceles trapezoid; the last one nearest the pole is a triangle.

GLOBAL COORDINATES

The two sets of lines (parallels and meridians) compose the earth's grid or coordinate network. By means of it, places on the globe can be located accurately. Since all of the meridians are alike, it has been necessary to select one of them arbitrarily as a starting line. The one running from pole to pole through Greenwich, England (a suburb of London) has been chosen as the zero line or Prime Meridian. The other half of this circle (longitude 180°) is mathematically the International Date Line.

RECTANGULAR LAND SURVEY

REFERENCE LINES

Very early in the history of the United States, Congress enacted laws providing for a rectangular land survey of the unsettled public domain west of the Appalachians. Position on the globe generally is measured from the intersection of the equator and the Prime Meridian. In a detailed survey of American lands into small plots, however, such a reference point was too far away to be practical. Accordingly, north-south lines

known as *principal meridians* were run by surveyors, the First Principal Meridian now serving as the western boundary of Ohio (Fig. 4–10). Later, more than thirty other principal meridians were surveyed at intervals westward to the Pacific.

At the same time, certain parallels or east-west lines were also surveyed. These were known as *base lines.* North-south strips of land, approximately six miles wide, were laid out on both sides of each principal meridian. These are known as ranges. East-west strips of land, six miles wide, were also laid out parallel to the base lines. They are known as township tiers (Fig. 4–11).

CORRECTION LINES

These two systems of intersecting lines divide the land into square units of land called *congressional townships,* 6 miles on each side and therefore containing an area of 36 square miles. They are not, however, true squares. They are 6 miles long on their base, but as one goes northward their sides converge because of the curvature of the earth. In latitude 40°, this convergence is about 40 feet for 6 miles. Every four tiers (24 miles) therefore, one side of the range is offset or jogged over about 120 feet in what

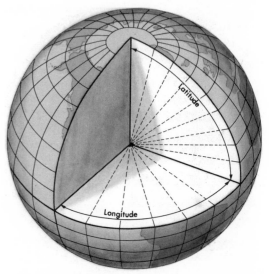

Figure 4–9   A globe with a section cut away to show that latitude and longitude are arcs of central angles. These central angles are formed by earth radii as they move through successive positions around the equator or from equator to pole.

is known as a *correction line*. In this way the areas of townships are kept at approximately 36 square miles (Fig. 4–11).

TOWNSHIPS AND SECTIONS

Each township is surveyed into thirty-six land sections, approximately one mile square (640 acres), and numbered on a standard pattern (Fig. 4–12).

Each section is subdivided into quarter sections (160 acres). Each quarter section is further subdivided into halves (80 acres) and quarters (40 acres). Thus a land title may identify Mr. Brown's 40-acre farm as "The N.W.¼ of the S.W.¼ of section 28, Township 3N., Range 2W., of the Fifth Principal Meridian" (Fig. 4–13). Thus is the matter of geomatical position carried into the daily lives of millions of Americans.

THE EFFECTS OF LATITUDE

SEASONS

Geomatic position has many more spectacular effects than that just described in connection with land survey. For instance, the latitude of a place is directly related to the elevation of the sun which that place experiences. The higher the latitude, the lower the noon altitude of the sun becomes.

Near the equator, where the noon sun is always high in the sky, an increase or decrease of a few degrees in sun elevation does not make much difference in temperature. At latitude 40°, where the noon sun is lower in the sky, such changes produce marked results. Near the poles, where even at its highest, the sun never rises far above the horizon, a few degrees make a vast difference.

The reason for this is at once apparent from Figure 4–14. In this diagram, the sun's rays are falling vertically at A on the surface, and their heating effect is concentrated on a small area. At B they are falling obliquely and hence their heating effect is scattered over a large area. This principle applies to all parts of the earth.

Figure 4–7B shows the earth at one of the equinoxes. The sun's rays fall vertically on the equator and hence produce hot temperatures. They fall more slantingly in middle latitudes and

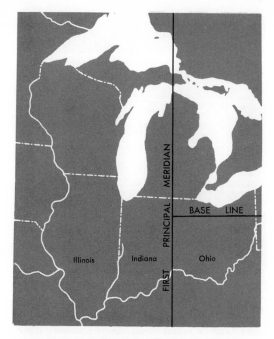

Figure 4–10 The First Principal Meridian and the base line for the first general rectangular land survey.

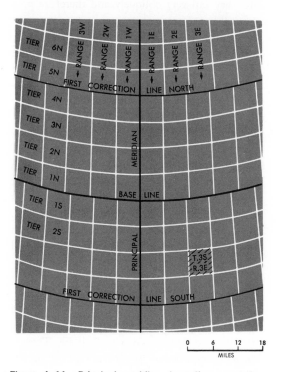

Figure 4–11 Principal meridian, base line, correction lines, and township lines in a typical area of rectangular survey. Note how the townships are aligned into tiers and ranges for the purpose of identification.

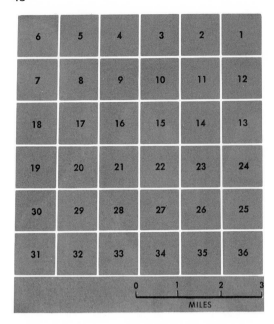

Figure 4-12 A typical survey township showing standard numbering of the 36-square-mile land sections.

hence produce less hot temperatures. Near the poles they fall very obliquely and therefore produce still lower temperatures.

The latitude of a place is also related to its daily duration of sunlight. In low latitudes, the daily periods of sunlight and darkness do not vary much from twelve hours each. As one goes poleward in summer the hours of sunlight in a day rapidly lengthen (Fig. 4-15), with a corresponding decrease in length of darkness. Similarly in winter, the length of daytime rapidly becomes shorter with increase in latitude, with a corresponding increase in nighttime. The effect of this is to create greater and greater contrasts in the seasons as one goes into higher latitudes. The summer increase and winter decrease in sun elevation only serve to accentuate these seasonal contrasts in the higher latitudes (Fig. 4-16).

GREAT GEOMATIC ZONES

As a result of these relationships, the latitude of a place (its geomatic position) determines the climatic zone within which it shall lie. That is, it determines whether its general climatic regime shall be a Tropical, Subtropical, Cyclonic, or Polar regime. This, however, is *not* tantamount to saying that the specific type of climate occurring in the place in question is the result of

geomatic position; that is a function of topography, land and water configuration, and other factors.

In ancient times, this division of the earth into great geomatic zones made little difference because few men ever journeyed from one zone to another. Up to comparatively recent times, it was of only limited significance. Surface travel was slow at best, and hence, although many of the products of the zones are different, only the nonperishable ones could be transported from one to the other. During recent times, fast ships and mechanical refrigeration have improved conditions markedly.

CONTRASTING HEMISPHERES

One geomatic peculiarity of the earth is that the Northern Hemisphere has summer while the Southern Hemisphere has winter, and vice versa. With rapid transportation this has produced some interesting results. Both piston-driven and jet planes have revolutionized relations between zones and between the hemispheres. They enable quick shifts of people and certain products from midsummer to midwinter or from spring to autumn. For instance, the United States imports grapes from Argentina, during the off-season for California production. Similarly, there is considerable travel between zones by tourists and health seekers.

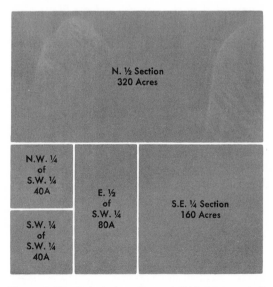

Figure 4-13 A typical section subdivided into a half section, a quarter section, an "eighty," and two "forties."

GREAT CIRCLES

Another geomatic peculiarity of the earth is that between two places in the same latitude, the shortest distance is not a route along the parallel connecting them. For example, Columbus, Ohio, and Philadelphia, Pennsylvania, both lie on the 40th parallel. To fly from Columbus to Philadelphia, however, one does not go eastward. Instead he first flies northeastward and then gradually turns southeastward (Fig. 4–17).

The reason for this is, of course, that the shortest distance between two points on a sphere follows the arc of a great circle (a maximum circle or equator) drawn around the world in such manner as to pass through both of them. It is a truism that any great circle around a sphere can be considered an equator, but obviously no two such circles can be parallel. Since the circle of latitude 40° is parallel to that of latitude 0° (which is the standard geographic equator and therefore a great circle) it follows that the 40th parallel is smaller than a great circle. Hence, in flying between the two points named, the navigator must plot a new and shorter circular arc between them.

The same principle applies to ships crossing the ocean. These latter do not follow the latitude circles, but pursue courses on great-circle arcs. Such a practice appears perfectly reasonable to a person with a globe before him, fairly reasonable to one with a conical map before him, but wholly unreasonable and mystifying to one who is looking at a Mercator map.

THE EFFECTS OF LONGITUDE
WHAT IS A DAY?

The average citizen thinks of the time of day as something fundamental and fixed. He may be surprised, therefore, to learn that time has no practical meaning except in terms of geomatic relationships. A day is only the period required for one earth rotation, and a year is only the time required for the earth to make a trip around the sun. Even the hour of day and the date are the products of geomatic position on the globe.

ROTATIONAL SPEEDS

In this connection it should be recalled that the earth turns on its axis from west to east; a point on the equator moves around a circle through a distance of more than 24,000 miles in twenty-four hours. During the same twenty-four hours, the points known as the poles merely turn around on themselves. Also during the same twenty-four hours, a point in latitude 60° moves around a circle some 12,000 miles in circumference. Therefore the point in question on the equator is moving eastward at a rate of about 1,000 miles per hour, the point in latitude 60° is moving about 500 miles per hour, and the points at the poles are moving 0 miles per hour[6] (Fig. 4–18).

In the light of these facts, it is obvious that if a pilot flies a plane westward at the same speed

[6] The way to compute these speeds is to find the cosine of the angle of latitude of the place in question and multiply it by the equatorial speed of rotation.

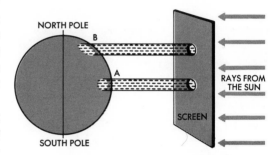

Figure 4–14 The heating effect of vertical and oblique sun rays. Note the scattering of the rays when they fall at a slant.

Figure 4–15 The midnight sun. Within the polar circles during the season of twenty-four hours of daylight, the sun describes a path in the heavens but does not set. In taking this photograph, the plate was exposed at intervals of every thirty minutes from 11 P.M. to 1 A.M. (Photo courtesy of the Swedish Information Service)

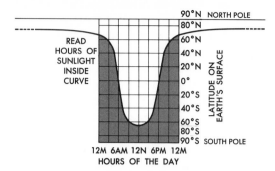

Figure 4–16 Sunlight graph showing the duration of sunshine over the earth for June 21. To use it for December 22, reverse the latitudes, that is, interchange the Northern Hemisphere for the Southern Hemisphere. For the two equinoxes the graph becomes simply two vertical lines coinciding with the 6 A.M. and 6 P.M. ordinates. Then with the duration of sunshine known for the two solstices and the two equinoxes, one can by a process of interpolation compute the approximate duration for any day desired.

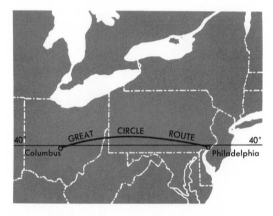

Figure 4–17 Great circle flying route between two cities located on the same parallel of latitude.

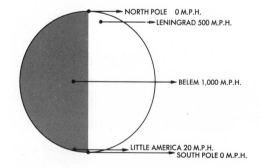

Figure 4–18 Rotational speeds of some selected points on the globe.

at which the earth is turning eastward in that particular latitude, he can stop the passage of day and night altogether. If he flies his plane eastward he can speed up the passage of day and night. This shows that time on the earth is a relative matter.

The rotational speed of the earth is of some help in the launching of space capsules from Cape Kennedy. "Down range" is to the east toward Africa. The rotational speed of the earth in Florida gives the launch an additional "thrust" since the capsule is going out beyond the atmosphere of the earth.

PRIME MERIDIANS

Man's device for fixing time is a system of meridians. In 1675, a British royal observatory was established at Greenwich in order to aid navigators in determining longitude and time at sea. A meridian was run through Greenwich which the British called the *Prime Meridian*, and they reckoned time and longitude from it (Fig. 4–2). The French, however, surveyed a Prime Meridian through Paris. The Germans used Berlin and the United States used Washington. In 1884, the Greenwich meridian was adopted by international agreement as the zero line and its noon as standard noon. Since then, most of the world has used this standard time.

THE TIME VALUE OF LONGITUDE

The sun makes an *apparent* passage around the earth in twenty-four hours. Hence, 360° of arc represent twenty-four hours of time. Therefore, one hour is represented by 15° of arc, or four minutes is represented by 1° of arc, one minute of time is represented by 15″ of arc. Another way of saying this is that six o'clock in the morning moves westward around the earth at an average rate of 15° of longitude each hour. Noon or midnight or sunset moves around the earth at the same average speed.

INTERNATIONAL DATE LINE

This being true, when it is noon in London, it has already become 1:00 P.M. in longitude 15° East, but it is as yet only 11:00 A.M. in longitude 15° West. Carrying this a step further: on, say, July 1, when it is noon in London it is 11:00 A.M.

in longitude 15° West, 10:00 A.M. in longitude 30° West, 4.00 A.M. in longitude 120° West, and 12 midnight in longitude 180°. Fifteen degrees beyond this (at 165° East Longitude), however, it would be only 11:00 P.M. on June 30. But this cannot be, because figuring eastward from London, one finds that July 2nd is due to dawn within an hour, at longitude 165° East. Obviously, no place could have a time of 11:00 P.M. June 30 and yet be getting ready to start July 2 at the same time. Hence, longitude 180° was fixed by international agreement (in 1884) as the place where the date changes. It is known as the International Date Line.[7] Obviously, time is a matter of geomatic position.

LONGITUDE AND TIME

The effects of longitude as regards time may be summarized as follows.
1. Each calendar day is begun at longitude 180° (the I.D.L.).
2. Noon at longitude 0° (London) is set as a standard for the world.
3. When one travels westward, time gets earlier (1 hour for every 15° of longitude).
4. When one travels eastward, time gets later (1 hour for every 15° of longitude).
5. Crossing the Date Line westward, one enters the following calendar day (because while the next day has already started there, it has not yet moved around the earth and caught up with the observer). Hence one adds a day.
6. Crossing the Date Line eastward, one enters the previous day, and hence one drops a day.

STANDARD TIME BELTS

Because time of day (noon, for example) is a *condition* which moves around the earth from east to west, no two places (unless they lie on the same meridian) would have the same time. In a world of rapid communication, this would lead to endless confusion. Therefore, by international agreement, the world has been divided into twenty-four north-south strips or standard time belts. Each time belt centers on a standard meridian such as 0°, 15°, 30°, 45°, that is, the meridians of 15° or multiples thereof. Each time zone extends roughly 7½° on either side of its meridian. All places within a zone use the time of its central meridian. In crossing North America

from east to west, for instance, one passes through successively, Atlantic Time, Eastern Time, Central Time, Mountain Time, Pacific Time, Northwest Time, Alaskan Time, and Aleutian Time.[8] Thus, when it is noon in Halifax, it is only 5:00 A.M. on Attu Island (Fig. 4–19).

KINDS OF TIME

Dividing the world into time belts, however, does not altogether end the complexity, because not all nations have adopted the system. Even within the United States, not all people use it. Farmers, for instance, commonly use sun time,[9] the government and the railways use standard time, while the cities frequently use daylight saving time—at least during the summer.

THE GLOBE

Man's efforts in exploring and studying his earth have gradually enabled him to develop a grid or coordinate network of lines (parallels and meridians) by means of which the position of places on the earth can be given with remarkable accuracy. This achievement has also given man two tools of very great usefulness, namely, the model globe and the map.

The model globe is a sphere in shape and it has two poles, two polar circles, two tropical circles, and an equator. Usually, but not always, it is mounted so as to turn on its axis, and to rotate at an angle of 23½° inclination from a vertical position.

The globe also has a system of coordinate lines—parallels and meridans—carefully numbered north and south from the equator and east and west from the Prime Meridian. Over these lines is drawn the tracery or outline of the land and water bodies of the earth. Since the shape and arrangement of the parallels and meridians on the globe are exactly like those on

---

[7] For practical purposes, the International Date Line departs from longitude 180° in three places.

[8] Official Alaskan time was fixed by an Act of Congress in 1918 as that of the 150th meridian west, 10 hours earlier than Greenwich time. Actually, however, four times are in use in Alaska: 120° W, 135° W, 150° W, and 165° W—8, 9, 10, 11 hours earlier than Greenwich respectively.

[9] Where noon is determined by the shadow of a pole or the reading on a sundial.

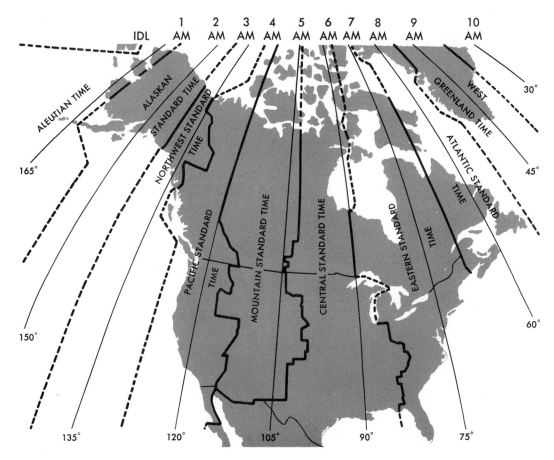

Figure 4–19   The time zones across North America. The central meridian of each zone is fixed, but the boundaries of the zones are changed from time to time for reasons of local convenience.

the earth itself, the land and water bodies on the globe are shown in true shape, true relative size, and in true space relation to one another. These are something which no flat map can show accurately.

Upon the outline, in turn, are printed the data of the globe. Rivers, lakes, and oceans are usually shown in blue; the land is often shown in buff or sand color. Political boundary lines are shown in broken black lines or narrow ribbons of color. Or, if the globe is primarily designed to show political divisions, each individual country is printed in a different color. Or again, if the globe is primarily to show physical relief, the lands are colored according to their general elevation above sea level. Cities are indicated by dots, and place names are printed usually in black. Other data are indicated by special symbols.

Each globe has a scale or ratio. The earth is about 8,000 miles in diameter and, therefore, on an eight-inch globe (one that is eight inches in diameter) one inch represents about 1,000 miles on the real earth globe. On a sixteen-inch globe, one inch represents 500 miles, and so on for each size of globe.

DISADVANTAGES OF GLOBES

Globes are relatively costly to make. They are also of relatively small size. Some possess the disadvantage of being clumsy to handle, and almost impossible to carry about with one. Another shortcoming of the globe is that it never enables one to see all of the earth at one glance. Nor does it enable one to see any one section of the globe in great detail. All of these shortcomings make it necessary to use a map rather than a globe for most purposes.

THE MAP[10]

THE NATURE OF MAPS

A map is a diagram of the earth's global surface, or some part of the earth's surface, drawn on a flat piece of paper (a plane). "The real problem of the map makers is that when one projects any considerable area of a globe on a plane, one sacrifices either true distance or direction, or area, or all three."[11] For instance, when one makes a world map on which directions are true, shape is sacrificed. When one tries to get true shape, then area or size is sacrificed. If one makes the shape true, then distance and direction are sacrificed, and so on.

If one makes a map of a very small piece of the earth's surface, the errors are small—too small to make any difference usually. But the larger the area represented, the greater the errors. Therefore, there is no accurate map of the world as a whole except that on the surface of a miniature or model globe.

MAP ELEMENTS

A map is therefore simply the product of an attempt to transfer the curved surface of the globe to a flat surface. The difficulties in doing this have already been pointed out, but the resulting product is highly useful nonetheless.

There are three elements to the map—the *projection*, the *outline*, and the *data*. The spherical grid of lines on a globe cannot be reproduced upon a flat surface, but there are various ways of projecting it onto a flat surface. Therefore, in the process of map making, the grid of the globe is transformed into a map's "projection." The projection of a map is one of its identifying features. The shape of the outline of land and water on a map depends wholly upon the projection used. This is true because every point of the outline must fit the lines of the projection, regardless of how warped or twisted the shapes become. The reason for this is that every point on the earth has an exact latitude and longitude. Two cities lying on two different meridians may actually be relatively close together on the earth. But if, in the process of projecting the meridians onto a map, they become pulled far apart, then the cities must be placed equally far apart on the

map in order to keep their true longitudes. A narrow lake lying between these same two meridians must be elongated enough to reach from one meridian to the other on the map. A parallel is a circle on the globe, but if the parallel becomes distorted in the process of projecting it onto a map, then a relatively straight river, railway, or boundary line following that parallel must be curved on the map. If all these distortions are not made in entering the outline and the data on a map, then the outline and data do not fit the mathematical facts of the grid or projection; whereupon the map is inaccurate and largely unusable. Despite these distortions, the shapes of land and water bodies, political units, and other data are still recognizable, but obviously they cannot be exactly the same as the shapes on the globe itself. A geographer, or one who studies areas, must be able to recognize areas, shapes, and data no matter upon what projections they are placed.

The same is true with regard to directions. Regardless of what appears or seems to be north or south on a map, that seeming appearance cannot guide one in map reading. The lines which make up the projection determine the directions, regardless of what is the top, bottom, or sides, of a map. The only safe rule to follow is that true north and true south on a map are always measured along the meridians, whereas east and west are measured along the parallels.

MAP SCALES

Maps often distort size as well as shape and direction. In reading a map, therefore, careful attention must be paid to the scale or ratio of the map. On some projections, two or even more scales must be used. On the Mercator, indeed, a different scale must be used for every latitude. The same is true for equidistant pole-centered maps.

Maps which use one scale throughout are known as *homolographic* or equal-area projections. On such a projection, one square inch of surface represents the same area of earth as does a square inch anywhere else on the map.

[10] See also Henry J. Warman, "Map Meanings," *Journal of Geography,* Vol. LVIII, No. 5 (May, 1959).
[11] R. Peattie, *How to Read Military Maps* (New York, George W. Stewart, Inc., 1942), p. 62.

At this point it should be recalled that the earth's diameter is roughly 8,000 miles, and that the distance between the poles along the surface of the earth is approximately 12,500 miles. A world map, therefore, which is twelve and a half inches from pole to pole may be said to have a scale of one inch to 1,000 miles because one inch on the map represents 1,000 miles in nature. Another way to state this is to put it in the form of a fraction, 1/63,360,000, because one inch on the map represents 63,360,000 inches (1,000 miles) in nature. Or it can be expressed as a ratio—1:63,360,000. Still another way is to express it graphically as follows:

```
|_____|_____|
0             1,000            2,000
                miles
```

KINDS OF MAP DATA

The third element on a map is the data. Maps are invariably classified by the user on the basis of what data they may show. For instance, the user refers to a map as a population map, a wheat map, a rainfall map, a relief map, a daily weather map, or an outline map. The legend or title of each carries an explanation of its data.

There are many ways of representing data on maps. Some common methods are color designs, black-and-white designs (often known as Ben Day patterns), or concentrations of dots. Sometimes the things to be shown are actually depicted by pictorial symbols. For the most part, however, map data are highly symbolic and conventionalized.

KINDS OF MAP PROJECTIONS

The number of different map projections is large; so large, indeed, that the layman is often bewildered. The matter can be greatly simplified, however, by realizing that there are really only three main classes of projections. These are (1) *globe-skin maps,* (2) *eye-perspective maps,* and (3) *geometric-figure maps.*

GLOBE-SKIN MAPS

The skin or surface of a globe is actually a world map if it could be peeled off and pressed flat. In the peeling process, however, it will be torn into pieces, unless the skin is slit along the meridians. If the latter be done, the skin will come off in gores or segments connected in their equatorial portions. This might then be called a *gore projection.* The first one was probably made about the year 1500, when the making of globes began (Fig. 4–20A).

If some of the gores are pinched together so as to show each continent in one piece, the result is the *interrupted homolographic projection,* first made by Goode in 1916 (Fig. 4–20B).

If more of the gores are pinched together, more warping is produced, but it is possible to get them into two hemispheres. Mollweide made a *hemispheric projection* of this kind about the year 1800 (Fig. 4–20C).

Still more pinching together gives Renner's *semihemispheric projection* of 1928 (Fig. 4–20D). Finally, if all the gores are pinched together, it gives Mollweide's *homolographic elliptical projection* of 1805 (Fig. 4–20E).

EYE-PERSPECTIVE MAPS

A wholly different method of making maps is that of drawing the two halves of the globe as the eye would see them from various positions. The *orthographic projection* (Hipparchus 130 B.C.) shows the near side of the globe as seen from a great distance (Fig. 4–21A). The *globular projection* (Fournier, 1645) shows the earth as seen by the eye at a distance from a transparent globe equal to the radius times sin 45°, looking through to the far side (Fig. 4–21B).

The *stereographic projection* (Hipparchus, 130 B.C.) shows the earth as seen if the eye were placed against one side of a transparent globe, looking through to the far side (Fig. 4–21C). The *gnomonic projection* (the basic idea for which is said to have been suggested by Thales about 600 B.C., although probably such maps were not actually constructed until the seventeenth century) shows the earth as it would look to an observer at the center, inside the globe. In short, this map represents a gnome's-eye view of the earth (Fig. 4–21D).

GEOMETRIC-FIGURE MAPS

The commonest maps in use are made by placing the globe inside or against some other geometrical body or figure (usually tangent to it) and then projecting the grid from the globe onto the latter. The surface of the tangent solid is then split and unrolled, giving a world map. If the spherical globe is projected onto a cylinder, the result is a *cylindrical projection.* The commonest map of this general type is the Mercator projection (1569), named after Gerhard Krämer who made maps under the pseudonym of Mercator (Fig. 4–22A), although it is not a true cylindrical projection but a modified form of one.

If the globe is projected onto a cone, the result is the *conic projection* (Ptolemy, A.D. 150), one type of which is illustrated in Figure 4–22B.

If the globe is projected onto a tangent plane the result may be the *azimuthal equidistant projection* (Postel, 1581). Figure 4–22C shows the global grid projected onto a plane tangent at the North Pole, giving a north polar equidistant projection of the azimuthal type.

OTHER TYPES

Numerous other types of maps have been made, but most of them are modifications of the three classes described, as for instance Denoyer's semi-elliptical projection (1921) or Goode's homolosine projection of 1929 (Fig. 4–23). Others are combinations of the two or more standard varieties. A few are "freak" projections of great interest but small usefulness.

REPRESENTING DATA ON MAPS

There are many ways of plotting data on a map, many of them so conventionalized as to require explanation. A road, railway, river, or airway may be represented by a certain kind of line. If so, one may easily interpret it by referring to the legend of the map. A map of land relief is sometimes made by sketching the relief in detail or by using plastic shading. A map of this kind is so graphic as to be readily interpreted.

More commonly, however, relief is shown by one of three symbolic methods. Figure 4–24A shows land relief represented by fine lines known as *hachures.* Figure 4–24B illustrates the contour line method of showing relief. Figure 4–24C

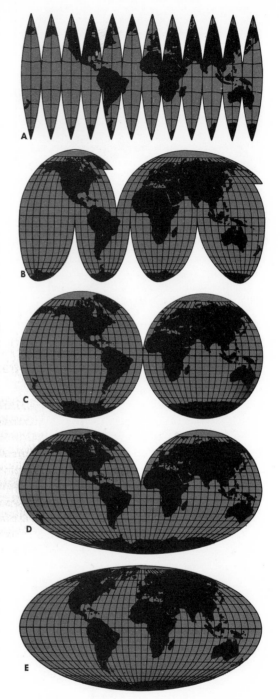

Figure 4–20   Globe-skin maps. A series of five maps showing 23, 5, 3, 2, and 1 interruptions.

employs the very common method of indicating relief by the interval or layer method. In this last-named method, the intervals or levels of

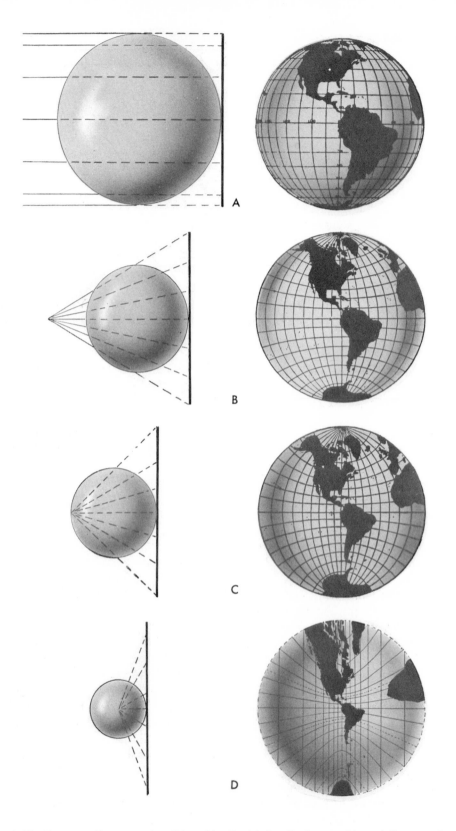

Figure 4–21   Eye-perspective maps. A, orthographic; B, globular; C, stereographic; and D, gnomonic.

elevation, intensity, or magnitude are represented by different colors or by different black-and-white Ben Day patterns.

Where one wishes to show only the separation of an area into sections, as on political or regional maps, the sections are simply colored differently or covered by different black-and-white patterns. Sometimes, indeed, they are merely separated by boundary lines and then named or numbered.

In cases where it is desired to show accurate distribution of some data, such as telephones or wheat production or population, the dot method is used. If, for instance, one dot represents 1,000 bushels of wheat produced and the dots are entered on their proper places, the location of the dots shows at a glance where wheat is produced. At the same time, the density of the dots reveals the places where production is sparse and where heavy.

SELECTION OF MAPS

Each map projection and each method of representing data has its own merits and demerits. Moreover, one projection is useful for certain purposes but useless for others. For instance, a geographer knows that the Mercator map is excellent for showing world trade routes, the conic map is excellent for showing the countries of Europe, and the north polar equidistant map is excellent for showing certain air-age relations. But no geographer would use Goode's homolosine map (as shown in Fig. 4–23) to show ocean trade routes, Mercator's map to show air-age relations, or a gnomonic map to show colonial empires. The selection of the proper map for each use requires considerable discrimination. Meanwhile, new kinds of maps continue to be designed, and new uses are daily being found for both old and new maps.

CONCLUSION

LATITUDE

By way of summary, it may be pointed out that the latitude of a place determines its seasons and hence the general climatic zone within which it falls. This, in turn, helps to determine the

amount of heating and lighting which must be used and the kind of housing and clothing which will be employed. It also for the most part determines the dates for planting and harvesting crops.

LONGITUDE

Longitude determines the time of day which a place has at any given moment. It, therefore, is related to the standard time belt which prevails. As a result, two places a mile apart in distance may be an hour apart in time or have the same time. Longitude is also related to the calendar day which a place has. As a result, Americans can sit at their radios on Saturday and listen to Sunday events as they transpire in Japan or Australia. Arguments over whether the Sabbath shall be the sixth or seventh day of the week become merely academic when one sees that the two days in question really exist simultaneously on the earth.

LATITUDE AND LONGITUDE

Lines of latitude and longitude (parallels and meridians) together form a world network which serves as a set of coordinates in terms of which global position is expressed. This network also serves as the basis for map making and land surveying.

MAPS AND GLOBES

The map and the globe are products of latitude and longitude and the geomatical relations underlying them. As such, they are among the most important of the geographer's tools. The chief reason why geography leans so heavily on maps has been aptly stated by Preston James,[12] one of America's leading geographers. Said he, "In geography, the phenomena to be described and analyzed are so much larger than the observer ... that they can only be studied or described by reducing them to observable size on maps." Geography is on the earth, not in books; but the geography we see about us is made up of only the infinitely small details, not the important relationships which these details illustrate or exemplify. For instance, one could live all his

[12] P. E. James, *An Outline of Geography* (Boston, Ginn and Company, 1935), p. viii.

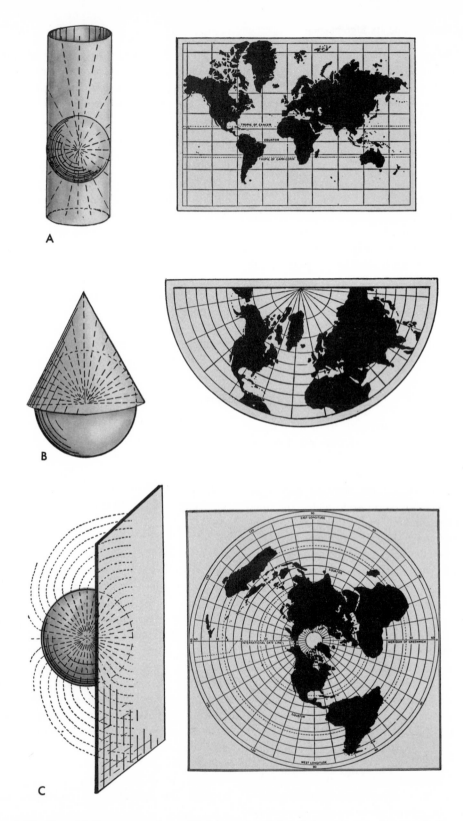

Figure 4–22 Geometric-figure maps. A, modified tangent cylinder; B, tangent cone; C, tangent plane.

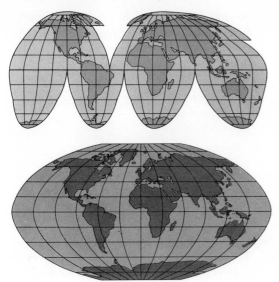

Figure 4–23   Other types of maps. Above, homolosine; below, semielliptical.

lifetime in a Midwestern community without discovering the Corn Belt. Similarly, one could live out his life in a New England town without discovering the American Manufacturing Region. But plot the relevant data on a map of the United States, and the Corn Belt and the American Manufacturing Region immediately become obvious, whereas the two communities in question are revealed as inconsequential details in the big pattern of things. Without the use of the map, most of the large important things in geography would remain unknown and many generalizations would be impossible.

For some reason or other, a great many Americans hold the curious notion that maps are essentially geographic; indeed, that maps and geography are synonymous. Equally common is the belief that skill in making, or even in reading, maps denotes competence as a geographer. A knowledge of great numbers of place locations on the map also is frequently mistaken as a sign of geographic erudition. Actually a map is one of the means to an end—geographic analysis and synthesis—and not an end in itself.

THE MAP AS A GENERAL INSTRUMENT

The map is a visual instrument of general nature. It belongs equally to all educational subjects— history, botany, geology, economics, and so forth.

It also belongs to the military man, the engineer, the stockbroker, and the journalist. There is nothing geographic about the map as such.

CARTOGRAPHERS

Nor are maps ordinarily made by geographers. They are made by men trained in mathematics and map-making processes. An artistic sense and a flair for design are definite assets. Men who make maps are called *cartographers*, and if a geographer happens to be a cartographer, it is merely a coincidence.

Despite what has just been said about maps and geography, it is perfectly true that geography makes greater use of maps than any other subject and that geographers as a group are usually more skillful users of maps than men in other profes-

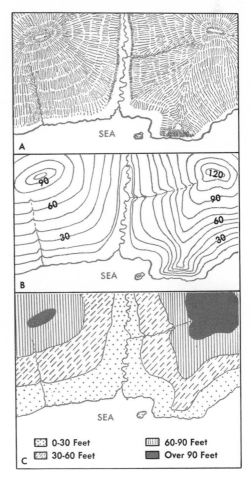

Figure 4–24   Three methods of showing relief on a map. A, hachures; B, contours; C, layers.

sions. In general, all phases of visual education have been seriously neglected in most fields of learning. Geographers, long before students in other fields did so, began using on a large scale visual instruments of all kinds—pictures, models, graphs, and plain sketches, as well as maps.

The fact that geography began very early to develop the map, and to use it for so many of its purposes, probably explains why the layman so often identifies one with the other. It is certain that the student of geography must be prepared to accept the map as one of his major tools and must be willing to train himself to understand and use it.

SUGGESTED USEFUL READINGS

Carpenter, Helen McCracken, ed., *Skills in Social Studies*, 24th Yearbook of National Council for the Social Studies, National Education Association (Washington, D.C., 1953). See especially Chapter VIII, "Interpreting Maps and Globes," pp. 146–177.

Greenhood, David, *Down to Earth* (New York, Holiday House, 1944).

Harrison, Lucia Carolyn, *Sun, Earth, Time and Man* (Chicago, Rand McNally & Company, 1960).

Strahler, Arthur N., *Introduction to Physical Geography* (New York, John Wiley & Sons, Inc., 1965). See especially Chapters 1 and 2, and Appendix II, "Topographic Map Reading."

5

Geographic Location

THE MEANING OF LOCATION

Almost the first question asked about an industry, a city, a region, or a country is: "Where is it?" Geographic location provides the greater part of the answer.

DERIVATION

The term *location* is derived from the Latin word *locus*, meaning place, order, or rank. From these several meanings of the word, it is rather obvious that the word implies relative rather than absolute occurrence. Applied to geography, therefore, the term *location* expresses relative occurrence in space, that is, space relationship. Stated in somewhat different words, the meaning of the location of any given place depends not upon the virtues of its own site but upon other surrounding locations with which it has relations; and these latter, in their turn, depend upon the significance of still other locations. This is a concept of great importance, because it sets up a wide pattern of space relationship wherein the occurrence of any place can be evaluated in terms of travel-time distance, readiness of access, and ease of communication.

SIGNIFICANCE

This location of a place or area as seen in relation to other places or areas is an important element in man's natural environment. An American geographer, Ellen Churchill Semple, believed that "the location of a country or a people is always the supreme geographical fact in its history."[1] In its more expanded sense, this statement is undeniably true; but even in a more restricted sense, it can scarcely be questioned that geographic location is a factor of great and continual moment in human affairs.

GEOGRAPHIC CENTER OF GRAVITY

There is, in each region, country, and continent (and, indeed, for the globe as a whole) a climax place. This place becomes, during any period in history, the locational culmination (that is, where human affairs come to a head) of the area in question. It becomes, figuratively speaking, the area's geographic center of gravity—the part of the area where it is, in general, most profitable or advantageous to be. The location of all other parts of the area are evaluated or measured in terms of or in relation to this geographic center of gravity. This measure has been variously called *locus, mediate location, relative location, vicinal location,* and *space relation.* All these terms imply one thing: the relationship in space of the different parts of an area to the whole, or of a point or area to neighboring points or areas.

AN ABSTRACT AND IMPONDERABLE FACTOR

From this it is clear that geographic location is largely an abstraction, an intangible element of the natural environment; not a concrete element like climate, minerals, or surface features. This is not to say that it is unimportant or negative, however. The very opposite is true: it is dynamic and positive in its effects upon human society.

Geographic location is, to a certain extent, imponderable and immeasurable. At best it can be measured quantitatively only in terms of some particular single factor or relationship. The geographer can, however, express geographic location in rather general terms with, at the same time, enough accuracy to be exceedingly useful.

[1] E. C. Semple, *Influences of Geographic Environment* (New York, Henry Holt and Company, Inc., 1911), p. 129.

LOCATION IN REGIONAL TERMS

TYPES OF LOCATION

When any region is studied, it soon becomes evident that a certain part of it has a high degree of centrality; that other parts have less of this characteristic of centrality; and that still other parts have none of this quality, but instead lie out on the edge of the theater of human events. The geographic locations or space relations of all parts of any region, therefore, fall into the following four classes: (1) strategic, (2) central, (3) adjacent, and (4) peripheral.

These four types of location denote four different degrees of relationship to some common geographic center of gravity, and are equally applicable whether one be thinking in global terms (relative to the earth as a whole) or in regional terms (relative to some particular part of the earth).

LOCATION IN TERMS OF A SINGLE REGION

To show how geographic location is determined and how it operates within the confines of a single natural region, one might use the North German Plain in Europe as an illustration (Fig. 5–1). This region extends from the Strait of Dover to the Bug River and from the central European hill country northward to the sea. It is crossed from southeast to northwest by numerous sub-parallel rivers.

Within this region, the area consisting of

Hannover, Lower Saxony, and Brandenburg is centrally located. It is the cultural and political "heart" of Germany. Around this lies an adjacent or marginal zone consisting of Lower Silesia, Westphalia, Oldenburg, the Baltic coastlands, and western Poland. This zone is less German than the central area, containing Poles, Mazurs, and Frisians as well as Germans. Outside this is an area of peripheral location inhabited by Dutch, Flemings, Danes, and Poles. Although all of this periphery has at times been under German political control, practically all of it has now become detached from Germany.

Within the North German Plain itself, there are a number of points which possess special or strategic location. Among these, Berlin is a noteworthy example. It stands near the center of the plain and serves as a focusing point for roads, railways, and airways. To a lesser extent Brussels in the west and Warsaw in the east are also strong focal points. In addition, there are several strategic sites which serve as portals or gateways to the region. These are Antwerp at the mouth of the Scheldt; Rotterdam at and Amsterdam near the mouth of the Rhine; Emden at the mouth of the Ems; Bremen on the Weser; Hamburg on the Elbe; Stettin on the Oder; Danzig at the mouth of the Vistula; and Koenigsberg on the Pregel.

Where ancient east-west land routes and modern railways cross these rivers, a set of strong nodal locations is created. These include Breslau, Posen, Frankfurt-am-Oder, Magdeburg, Bruns-

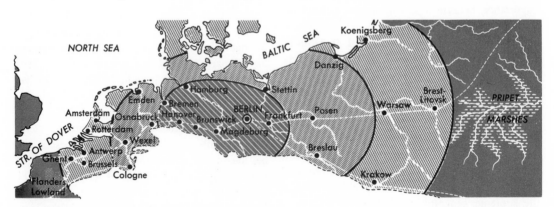

Figure 5–1 Location values on the North German Plain. Note the areas of central, adjacent, and peripheral location. Note also the focal locus of Berlin, the portal loci at or near the mouths of the rivers, and the nodal loci at the river crossings. At either end, the Flanders Lowland and the Pripet Marshes evince strong interstitial locus.

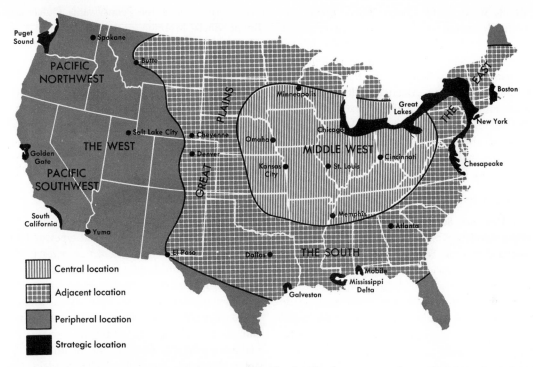

Figure 5–2 Geographic location in the United States. The locational names are those which have become attached to the several sections through common usage.

wick, Hannover, Cologne and several lesser points. In addition to these, the Flanders Lowland at the west end of the region and the Pripet marshes at the eastern end are strategic because of military and political reasons: the former because it is interstitial[2] between the North German Plain and the Paris Basin; the latter because it lies between the North German Plain and the Russian Plain. There are periods in the history of a single region, such as the North German Plain, when man disrupts the locational pattern. This particular region has been going through such a period since the end of World War II. The so-called Iron Curtain of the Communist world has almost completely divided this plain in two. Berlin's former strategic location is virtually nullified, not only by the recently erected wall, but also because of its present status as a Western enclave in Communist territory.

LOCATION IN TERMS OF A COUNTRY

What has been indicated in the preceding section as applicable to a natural or geographic region (for example, the North German Plain)

is equally valid when applied to a nation. This is true because a national state is merely a region in an expanded, political sense of the term. The same considerations of locational advantages and disadvantages, therefore, apply to it as to a geographic region. A good example of this is afforded by the United States (Fig. 5–2).

Central location

The geometric center of coterminus United States lies in north central Kansas. On the other hand, the population center of the nation lies in Illinois, the industrial center in Ohio, and the urban center of gravity in Pennsylvania. When these four facts are weighed against one another, it can be readily seen that the composite geographic center of gravity is displaced or skewed eastward from the true geometric center of the United States. The informal names which Americans bestow on the great sections of their nation reflect this rather accurately. For instance, most of what in common parlance is known as the

[2] This term is derived from the Latin word *interstare*, meaning to stand between.

Middle West (or the Central States) is not geo-metrically central at all; it is all east of center. Geographically, however, it is centrally located. Here, roads and railways reach an optimum de-velopment, and willingness to travel reaches a maximum. Here too, American culture attains its most uniform and most representative character. The Middle West, or American Midland, feeds much of the nation because its products easily reach the market through the simple process of overflowing the boundaries of the producing area.

Adjacent location

The East, the South, the Great Plains, and the upper Great Lakes area possess an adjacent or marginal location. Such regions share some of the economic and social advantages of the central area, but these are modified by certain disad-vantages. Politically, however, they tend to de-velop sectional or bloc interests on what would appear to be a disproportionately large number of national issues.

Peripheral location

The far western regions (the Pacific Northwest and the Pacific Southwest), the intermontane West, northern Maine, peninsular Florida, and a few other small areas are peripheral in their location. As a rule peripheral areas are able to sell staple articles in central markets only with great difficulty. For example, Utah potato growers cannot compete with those from Minnesota, Michigan, or Long Island. Idaho producers can do so only by developing a special type of potato; northern Maine producers can do so only through intense specialization and cooperative effort. Simi-larly, flour milled in Spokane can offer no more than local competition to the product of Minne-apolis, Buffalo, or Kansas City. Lumber from the Pacific Northwest can enter central markets only since the depletion of more adjacently lo-cated forests. These peripheral parts of the United States and some of the adjacent portions as well have tended to produce provincialism. Accordingly, it is sometimes said "To know the real America, one must make the acquaintance of the Middle West." It is true that the New Englander, the Southerner, or the Westerner, taken by himself, is but little more representative

of America than is the Pennsylvania Dutchman, the provincial Mormon, or the cosmopolitan New Yorker. The United States is, however, a youth-ful nation and sectional modification has not progressed far. Spain, a much older nation, il-lustrates in far more striking fashion the cultural differentiation between periphery and central area. There, the area of purest Spanish blood, speech, and culture lies in the central Castilian section, while Catalans, Andalusians, Portuguese, Gallegos, and Basques form an almost solid rim of marginal types.

Strategic location

Over and above the three regional types of loca-tion just described, there are certain sites in the United States which possess a high degree of strategic importance. The strategic virtues of these latter, however, arise from several sources. Boston Bay, New York Harbor, Chesapeake Bay, Mobile Bay, the mouth of the Mississippi, the Galveston-Houston Harbor, the Southern Cali-fornia Lowland, the Golden Gate District, the Columbia Estuary, and Puget Sound are the portals or gateways to the nation. These sites, therefore, possess extraordinary naval and com-mercial-maritime importance. In contrast to these, is the strong strategic location of Chicago where railways, highways, and lines of communication from nearly all parts of the country come to a focus. Lesser foci may be seen at Atlanta, Dallas-Fort Worth, and Denver.

Strategic location of a third kind is also in evidence, namely, at nodes in major lines of transcontinental transit. Such nodal sites are the important river-crossing cities of Cincinnati, St. Louis, Memphis, Omaha, Kansas City, and Minneapolis-St. Paul. It is also seen in the desert-crossing terminals of El Paso and Yuma and in the mountain-crossing terminals of Cheyenne and Salt Lake City, Butte and Spokane.

One of the world's most remarkable ex-amples of strategic location is revealed in the interstitial or corridor area of northeastern United States. This consists of the lower Hudson Valley, the Mohawk Trench, and the Lake Erie Lowland. It forms a continuous lowland corridor of transit from the Atlantic seaboard to the central plains (Fig. 5–3). New York and Chicago are the

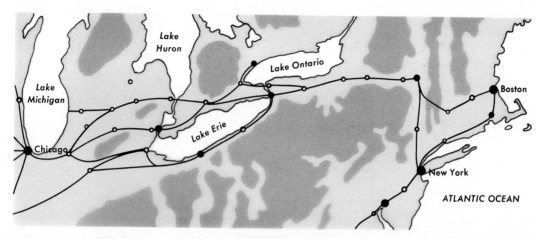

Figure 5–3 Interstitial location of the Hudson-Mohawk-Erie Corridor. New York (portal) and Chicago (focal) are the end points. Intermediate cities are located at nodal points. Land above 1,000 feet elevation is shaded. The Penn-Central follows a lowland or water-level route all the way, reaching its highest elevation at Little Falls, N.Y., at an elevation of only 370 feet above the sea.

terminal points, while Albany, Buffalo, Cleveland, and Detroit-Windsor are important nodes. So great is the flow of goods through this "bottleneck" of trade that it has developed into an almost continuous line of cities (Fig. 5–4).

LOCATION IN TERMS OF A CONTINENT

The same contrasts in relative location which occur in geographic regions and in countries are also observable in the continents. This is true because a continent is only a region in the most expanded and general sense of that term. This is strikingly obvious in Europe (Fig. 5–5).

Central location

In Europe, the area enclosed by a line drawn from Moscow to Paris to Marseille to Odessa to Moscow possesses a central location. This area is displaced somewhat westward or southwestward from geometric center because of historico-geographic reasons. Central location of this kind within a continent is both a danger and an advantage. Centrality so multiplies the points of contact between an area and its neighbors that where coupled with open accessibility, it threatens politically all but the strongest national groups. Formerly strong nations such as Austria-Hungary and Burgundy have disappeared from the map partly as a result of their central location. Centrality has harmed Romania and Poland, and today threatens Hungary, Austria, and Germany.

For a long time, Germany adopted a violent militarism in order to preserve its national existence in the face of central location and open accessibility.

However dangerous central location may be politically, it is usually advantageous economically. The Danube Valley plays a large role in feeding Europe; Germany and Czechoslovakia have long supplied European markets with manufactures. Switzerland, which has survived in a central location despite small size, is able to market its scenery, resort facilities, dairy products, and scientific manufactures.

Adjacent location

Spain, Italy, the Balkan states, central Russia, southern Scandinavia, the Low Countries, Britain, and most of France lie adjacent to the central area of Europe. They are washed by the main streams of European affairs without being subjected to the full force of the disruptive influences which have assailed Germany, Poland, and the Danubian states in the years gone by.

Prior to World War I, most of adjacent Europe was rapidly drifting toward economic subservience to the centrally located industrial districts of the Ruhr, the Ardennes, Silesia, Bohemia, and Saxony. Shortly after 1918, Europe partially avoided this situation by excessively high national tariff walls. During World War II, adjacent Europe was almost completely absorbed,

Figure 5–4   Scene in the Mohawk Valley—the one outstanding route through the Appalachian barrier. The early railroad surveyors explored the mountains of New York, Pennsylvania, and Virginia in a desperate effort to locate other natural avenues to the West, but learned that nature had left only this superior one. Note the concentration of parallel transportation facilities; from left to right are the two-track route belonging to the Penn-Central, the New York State Barge Canal, the Mohawk River, a four-lane highway, and the four-track main line of the Penn-Central.

politically and economically, by the central German-dominated area. It remains to be seen whether this centralizing tendency can be prevented during the decades to come.

Britain, being an island, has thus far been able to prevent military invasion from the central area. She has also been able to prevent economic domination from it by expanding along the sea lanes and trading with her world-girdling Commonwealth and other non-European regions.

The economic unity now being sought in Europe has the potential of disrupting the central locational aspects of the past, even though the potential appears to be somewhat diluted when one views the present distributional pattern of the European Economic Community (the Common Market) and the European Free Trade Association (EFTA or the "Outer Seven").[3]

The Common Market countries present a strong resemblance to a new central location, while the "Outer Seven" countries would represent an adjacent location. If Britain were to join the Common Market this pattern might be slightly disrupted. On this step she has held a vacillating position for a number of years. When the decision was finally made to join, France virtually "vetoed" the move.

Peripheral location

Portugal, Ireland, Iceland, northern Scandinavia, Finland, and Greece form a politically weak periphery about the kernel of Europe. These countries exist in relative safety despite their

[3] J. W. Nystrom and P. Malof, *The Common Market: European Community in Action* (New York, Van Nostrand Searchlight Book #5, 1962), p. 95.

lack of military strength. Indeed, most of them have owed their independence, at least in part, to the support of British sea power.

Strategic location

Many points and small areas in Europe are possessed of strategic location. Berlin, Milano, Warsaw, and Moscow are strong focal sites. Strategic also are the portal or gateway sites of Le Havre, Hamburg, Marseille, Liverpool, London, Odessa, Trieste, Leningrad, Riga, and Glasgow.

Strong nodal land sites are exemplified by Prague and many of the German and Russian river-crossing cities. Maritime nodes are represented by Gibraltar, Malta, the Kiel Canal, the Sund Channel between Sweden and Denmark, and the Dardanelles-Bosporus.

The most strategic location in Europe, however, is the area lying between the Strait of Dover and the Ruhr Valley. This crucial site is the lowland gateway for land routes from eastern to western Europe. It is also a major commercial outlet and inlet for the center of the continent. Furthermore, it is the military locus where land power meets sea power. Within this area the decisive battles of the Napoleonic War, the Franco-Prussian War, and World Wars I and II were fought.

REGIONAL LOCATION SUMMARIZED

CENTRAL LOCATION

Central location is an immense advantage economically and socially, but it is apt to be dangerous politically. Only the strongest of nations can survive under the conditions of open access usually provided by central location. Centrality is, therefore, frequently the undoing of small nations. Some weak nations, however, manage to

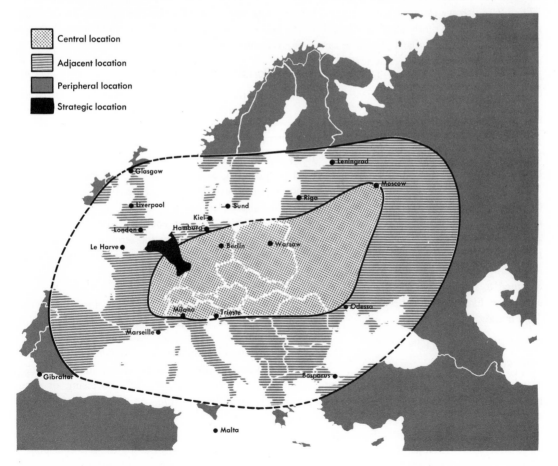

Figure 5–5   Geographic location in Europe.

survive despite central location, because of a poor local accessibility provided by high mountains or the comparative ease with which they may be defended. Switzerland, Ethiopia, Nepal, Afghanistan, and Bolivia furnish examples.

ADJACENT LOCATION

Adjacent location confers many of the benefits of centrality without, however, its full exposure to encroachment. Countries located adjacently are usually relatively accessible, so that their cultural and economic relations to the central area are close. Canada, for instance, juxtaposed to the United States along a 3,000-mile boundary, is to a certain extent an economic appendage. Economic nationalism, however, is so strong that every effort is being made to impress the world that Canada has come of age. When in the 1950's a prominent American suggested annexation to Lester Pearson, Canada's Secretary of State for Foreign Affairs, the latter replied: "Trouble is that we can't decide whether Canada is to be the forty-ninth state or America the eleventh province." Similarly, Cuba, at one time, and Mexico have attracted American investment capital and have been fertile fields for cultural diffusion.

PERIPHERAL LOCATION

Location upon the periphery of a continent is often a political advantage to a country. It is, however, usually not an asset economically. Isolation is often intense and centrifugal forces tend to disrupt relations with the central area. Peripheral areas, if their situation is a maritime one, are able to develop fishing and perhaps to enter the carrying trade, but their manufacturing efforts are usually chiefly confined to fabricating articles designed to meet local needs. Their agricultural enterprises likewise suffer because of remoteness from markets.

STRATEGIC LOCATION
Four categories

Many localities are possessed of an exceptionally high degree of accessibility, that is, they may be severely exposed to the crosscurrents of national or continental affairs and events; or they may be so situated as to render them capable of controlling a major trade route or of politically or economically commanding a large tributary area. Such points are of great naval, military, political, or commercial significance. For this reason, their location may be termed strategic. Carefully scrutinized, such strategic locations may be divided into four subclasses—*focal, portal, nodal,* and *interstitial.*

Focal strategic location

Wherever two or more routes of trade and travel converge or cross, there focality is produced. The centers of mountain valleys, river basins, coastal plains, and other naturally defined areas often possess such strong focality that they come to be the sites of political and commercial cities. Moscow, Chicago, and Winnipeg are impressive examples of the focusing of railroads.

Focality is also produced by the convergence of sea routes as at Colombo, Honolulu, Suva, and Singapore, and of air routes as at Dakar, Honolulu, New York, and Paris. The spokelike arrangement of highways or caravan routes may also create strong focality as at El Fasher, Delhi, Denver, and Samarkand.

Portal strategic location

The heads of large bays, sounds, and estuaries, the mouths of great navigable rivers, or coastal sites lying at the seaward ends of lowland routes to the interior may be described as portal or gateway locations. Boston, Seattle, Buenos Aires, Shanghai, and New York are commercial cities which have developed respectively in these kinds of sites. Such portal locations derive their strategic significance almost entirely from foreign trade, since they are at once the termini of ocean trade lines and the end points of land routes.

Nodal strategic locations

Nodality is possessed by all points where the continuous flow of trade is broken. Whenever goods are stopped in transit or where bulk is broken, opportunity for commercial transaction arises. Moreover, goods halting in transit may be temporarily diverted for processing or even for final manufacture. As a consequence, both commercial and manufacturing cities arise upon such sites.

Nodality is possessed by the terminal points of caravan routes crossing desert regions. Thus

Palmyra and Damascus, Kalgan and Yarkand, are pairs of terminal nodes of great antiquity in Asia. In Africa, the four great caravan routes across the Sahara have produced similar pairs of cities: Timbuctoo and Tuggurt, Kano and Tripoli, Abeshr and Benghazi, El Fasher and Asyut. Desert railways show the same geographical effects. In America, El Paso and Yuma, Salt Lake City and Sacramento, and in Australia, Coolgardie and Port Augusta illustrate the same principle. In like manner, pairs of nodal cities often arise at the opposite ends of mountain passes, as Beirut and Damascus, Prague and Dresden, Seattle and Yakima, Trento and Innsbruck.

Constrictions or "bottlenecks" in ocean trade routes are also nodal sites. They do not often occasion the rise of cities, but they do constitute strategic loci of great naval value. The Panama and Suez canals, the Malaccan Straits, the Sund, the Strait of Bab-el-Mandeb, and Gibraltar all exemplify such constrictions.

Islands lying along major ocean routes also become strategic in their nodality. This is well illustrated by the importance of Malta, Ceylon, Singapore, Hong Kong, and Hawaii. Within a large land mass, on the other hand, the head of navigation in a river or great lake, the outer bank of a large river bend, the confluence of two navigable rivers, the crossing of a land route over a large river, and even division points on a trunk railway may all assume the characteristics of a nodal location.

Interstitial strategic location

Localities sometimes possess strategic value because they stand directly between two important regions. An example of this is furnished by Palestine which, for four thousand years, formed a corridor between Egypt on one side and the various seats of civilization in Mesopotamia and Asia Minor on the other. Its ownership was contested by a score of powers, but no one people ever succeeded in occupying it for long. In somewhat similar manner, ancient Greece was interstitially located between Europe and the Middle East. Contest for its possessions resulted in centuries of bitter warfare. Later the quality of interstitial or strategic mediate location was largely transferred to the site of Istanbul. This, in turn, has been bitterly contested by Roman,

Byzantine, Viking, Turkish, Balkan, and British power. It finally fell to Turkish control, and there it has remained, not because the Turks have been strong enough to hold it but because its control was so important in world politics that the Great Powers considered Turkish hegemony to be the simplest arrangement.

Interstitial sites also have considerable social importance. For example, Spain for a long time served as a land bridge between Europe and Africa. Accordingly, the armies of Rome and Carthage, Visigoth and Vandal, Saracen and Moor, crossed and recrossed the land. For more than a thousand years, Spain was little more than an armed camp; industry languished and agriculture was relegated to the hands of a nondescript peasantry—circumstances which have left an indelible imprint upon modern Spanish national character.

The quality of interstitiality also has important economic results. For example, Malaysia is a relatively thinly populated area standing midway between the densely populated Far East and India. Despite its low state of economic development, the Malay Peninsula became, within a period of less than two decades, the world center of rubber production. This represented, in large part, a capitalization of abundant land and exposed accessibility; but in considerable measure it was the result of geographic adjustment to a location interstitial to two regions containing enormous reserves of surplus labor. The four categories of strategic location are not meant to be the basis of an iron-clad classification of cities or strategic locations. As one can see from the examples used, a particular city can be placed just as well under one category as another. These subclasses should be used as a guide in analyzing a region rather than as a framework for a topology of location.

GEOGRAPHIC LOCATION IS A CHANGING QUALITY

Positive though it be in its effects upon human affairs, geographic location is not a fixed quality. For instance, Rome was once located at the focus of the civilized world. When civilization moved northward and westward, Rome became a back eddy in European affairs. To cite an example closer home, Ohio a little more than a century ago lay upon the remote periphery of the United States; today it enjoys the benefit of a central location.

In many respects, geographic location is the most important environmental factor in the world. It affects not only the spread of human settlement and economic patterns of development, but it guides the building of roads, railways, canals, and communication lines, and the routing of airways.

These man-made things, in their turn, then become factors which help to create or modify the previous values of geographic location. For example, from 1775 to 1825, Cumberland Gap (in the Southern Appalachian Hill Country) was highly strategic as a gateway to the interior. After the construction of the Erie Canal, it lost almost all of its significance, and the lowland corridor from New York Harbor to Lake Erie far surpassed it in importance. Similarly, when pioneers crossed the Great Plains in covered wagons, Independence, Missouri, was a strategic point. When they were able to cross the Plains by transcontinental railways, Chicago became preeminent.

When commercial life centered in the Mediterranean Basin, Venice, located at the head of the Adriatic Sea, was the gateway to an important part of Europe, and the Brenner Pass was the doorway between north and south Europe. When commerce moved to the North Atlantic, the mouths of the Weser, Elbe, Rhine, and Thames rivers became Europe's chief portals. The value of the locations of Venice and the Brenner Pass dwindled rapidly. Today Venice is only a tourist's paradise; Brenner Pass is a gap in the mountains where railway trains crawl through, and otherwise its major claim to fame is as a place where the pseudo-Caesars, Hitler and Mussolini, met for their tub-thumping antics in a "war of nerves."

When sailing vessels were the vogue, the Azores, Canaries, and the Virgin Islands were strategic loci. Later the advent of the steamship made the isthmuses of Suez and Panama so important that gigantic canals were cut through them. Now transoceanic and world air service is lending importance to such points as Miami, Caracas, Natal, and Pasadena.

And so it goes, on every portion of the earth. Geographic location, being a matter of relative values, seldom remains fixed. Instead, it ebbs and flows in accordance with the tide of human affairs, with the streams of man's ideas and values. But it is nonetheless real at any specific time and place.

LOCATION IN GLOBAL TERMS

Any discussion of geographic location on a global scale must embody all the essentials treated in connection with location on a small regional, a national, or a continental scale. In addition, however, it must treat those aspects of location which affect the world struggle for power and domination, and which help to shape the interrelations among nations which are aimed at peace and cultural intercourse.

CATEGORIES OF LOCATION

In view of these latter considerations, the world exhibits four types of geographic location. First, there is an area of *pivotal* location, possession of which bestows upon the nation or nations occupying it an actual or potential position of security and relative military invulnerability. Second, there is a *marginal* zone where world conflicts occur. Third, there is an outer zone of *remote* location—an area of military importance. Fourth, there are a few *strategic* loci, possession of which yields effective world control.

THE AEGEAN ERA

When Western civilization centered in the basin of the Aegean Sea and more especially in ancient Greece, the central pivotal area lay in Macedonia. This was true because from it not only could the Greek Peninsula be commanded, but radial military blows could be delivered landward in several directions. Control points lay in southern Italy, Sicily, Crete, Corcyra, Rhodes, and at the Hellespont and the Isthmus of Corinth (Fig. 5–6).

THE MEDITERRANEAN ERA

When civilization spread over the entire Mediterranean Basin, its natural focus developed at Rome (Fig. 5–7). The area of pivotal location consisted of a large area at the base of the Italian Peninsula. This included northern Italy (Cisalpine Gaul), much of France (Transalpine

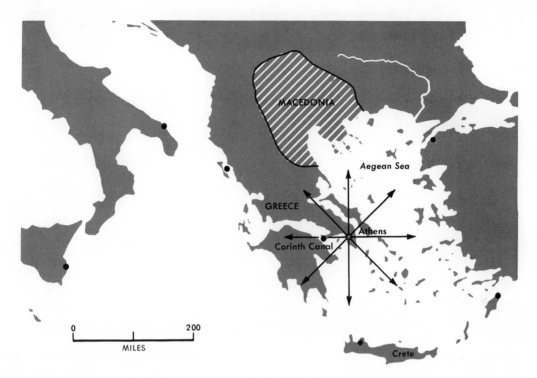

Figure 5–6 World location in the Aegean Era. The pivot area is ruled. Strategic world control points are shown by black dots.

Gaul) and Switzerland (Helvetia). Strategic control points lay at Gibraltar, Tunis, the Nile Delta, the Cilician Gates (in Asia Minor), the Dardanelles-Bosporus, the Danube and Rhine crossings, and the Rhone Valley.

THE WORLD OCEAN ERA

When civilization burst its Mediterranean bounds, it spread quickly over Europe. Soon, indeed, it took to the oceans and became worldwide.

Pivotal location

In the period of world history from 1492 to 1939, naval power was dominant in world affairs and the warship was a sort of lowest common denominator of geographic location. In such a world, nations possessing naval power could control, or at least reach into, all lands except the interior of the World Island—the land mass of Eurasia. This latter area, partly protected by mountain walls, partly by the frozen Arctic Ocean, and partly by the narrow gateways to the Baltic and Black seas, therefore, enjoyed *pivotal* location in world terms. It has accordingly been

called the "World Heartland."[4] Any strong military power holding it could have withstood all the navies of the world. In addition, from it, both western Europe and the Orient could have been dominated (Fig. 5–8).

Marginal and remote locations

Around the pivotal area of the Heartland lay the "World Borderlands," a zone of *marginal* location, into which sea power could reach and contest with land power for world control. Out beyond this, lay a zone of *remote* location, the "World Fringelands," completely dominated by sea power. All through this period, Russia, the nation holding most of the Heartland, was young and relatively weak. Germany, lying at the western gateway to the Heartland, conducted two world wars partly in the hope of gaining control of the pivotal area, but was defeated in both attempts by Anglo-American sea power.

[4] H. J. Mackinder, *Democratic Ideals and Reality* (New York, Henry Holt and Company, Inc., 1919 and 1940).

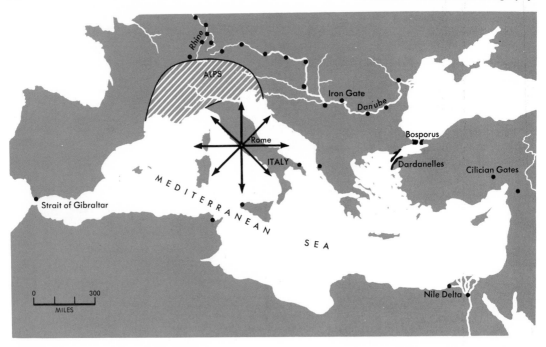

Figure 5–7 World location in the Mediterranean Era. Pivot area is ruled. Strategic world control points are shown by black dots.

Control-point location

The control points during this period of world history consisted of thirteen naval base sites at the sea gateways or "bottlenecks" between oceans. Ten of these were in British hands, five of which lay along the British Empire Lifeline which followed the Borderlands around Eurasia. The

other three naval base sites were in American and Dutch hands.

THE GLOBAL AIR-AGE ERA
Pivotal location

The coming of the long-range military jet planes carrying nuclear weapons or intercontinental

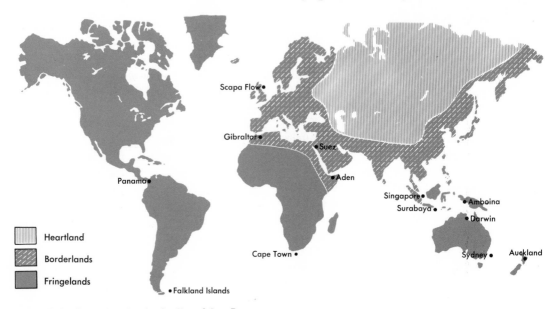

Figure 5–8 World location in the Era of Sea Power.

Figure 5–9   World location in the Air Age.

ballistic missiles has, however, modified the qualities of global location considerably, because it has freed war strategy from some of the controls of land and water arrangement. The new global relations can best be seen on a North Pole-centered world map.[5] On such a map (Fig. 5–9), Eurasia is seen curved about the Arctic "Mediterranean" in a colossal semicircle. North America and its two outliers, Greenland and Iceland, nearly complete the circle. In the world of air power, the area of pivotal location, or World Heartland, consists of the vast spaces of the U.S.S.R. and western China and the somewhat smaller but still vast spaces of Canada and interior United States, facing one another across the narrow Arctic. These lands constitute a world core or heartland, now occupied by the two strongest nations on earth, approachable with difficulty over the land, inaccessible by ship, but centrally located in a world of air power. The two heartland nations, if united, are therefore invulnerable to all the rest of the world combined, but they are vulnerable to each other across the small polar sea. Whoever holds this pivotal area in the future must, therefore, play a dominant role in world affairs.

Marginal and remote locations

Encircling this central pivotal area is a disconnected zone of World Borderlands or Coastlands enjoying marginal location. These include western Europe, Mediterranean Europe, the southern and eastern margins of Asia, seaboard North America, and Caribbean America. Out beyond these is a zone of remote location or World Fringelands.

[5] G. T. Renner, *Human Geography in the Air Age* (New York, The Macmillan Company, 1942).

Control-point location

Within the framework of this new world pattern, most of the old strategic locations are losing their importance and a new set of Global Control Points is assuming importance. Up to now, global strategic location has been measured in terms of seaways. The new control points are sites from which bomber patrols can transect all sea and air traffic plying between the continents, and at the same time oversee the World Borderland or Coastland zone. Such points are Miami, Natal, Dakar, Baghdad, Karachi, Calcutta, Talien, Petropavlovsk, Anchorage, Frederchab, and a few other sites. Some of these are in the process of declining in importance as world control points as new weapons systems are developed—such as ICBM's and nuclear submarines, which can remain at sea for prolonged periods of time.

CONCLUSIONS

Geographic location, embodying as it does the qualities of space relationship and relative de-grees of accessibility and isolation, is an all-pervading factor in human geography. Cities are the creatures of geographic location. Even real estate values and the pattern of economic functions within a city are the outgrowths of internal locational factors. Geographic location enters into the growth of commercial nations and underlies the development of national policies and ideals. Indeed, it accounts for the very existence of certain nations and certain political arrangements. It enters, too, into questions of political boundaries, culture contacts, and race relations.

Differences in geographic location are thus highly important, even crucial in the affairs of peoples and regions, but they are not necessarily permanent differences. Consequently, a nation must constantly resurvey its locational factors because a correct current appraisal of these must underlie a nation's trade, its public improvements and works, and its international policies. It must guide its national defense, its military and naval undertakings, and its hope for world peace.

SUGGESTED USEFUL READINGS

Semple, Ellen Churchill, *Influences of Geographic Environment* (New York, Henry Holt and Company, 1911, reprinted, 1941). Chapter V has many thought-provoking statements, to be judged in the light of today's knowledge.

Thomas, William L., Jr., *Man's Role in Changing the Face of the Earth* (Chicago, The University of Chicago Press, 1956). See especially the chapter by E. A. Gutkind, "Our World From the Air: Conflict and Adaptation."

6

The Region and Regionalizing

KINDS OF AREAL UNITS

In perusing the succeeding chapters of this book, it should become obvious that one of geography's main concerns is studying the earth's surface as a background for human society. But since the earth's surface is both very large and extremely varied, it is impossible to study it as a whole in anything other than a very general reconnaissance fashion. It is possible, however, to divide the earth's surface into separate areas and to study these individually. Accordingly, it has long been recognized that geography involves a study of areas.

Although geography's concern with area is obvious, the kind of areal unit to be selected for study is not so obvious. In the past, there has been considerable disagreement among geographers as to the kind of areas which they should employ as units of study.

POLITICAL DIVISIONS

Political divisions were perhaps the first areas generally to be studied by geographers. They have the advantage of being obvious units and of being areas of unified sovereignty and political behavior. Moreover, they can be handled with greatest facility because census statistics of all kinds are gathered on the basis of political divisions. Their shortcomings for geographic study are that political boundary lines are usually artificial—internal boundaries being the product of legislative vagary and gerrymandering, whereas international boundaries are largely the result of diplomatic horse trading or the compulsion of war. As a consequence, a political unit often includes two or more kinds of geographic areas;

or what is more complex, a political boundary often quite artificially divides areas of great similarity. For example, if the state of Missouri is selected as a unit for geographic study, one quickly finds that northern Missouri is simply an extension of the geography of Iowa, Illinois, Nebraska, and eastern Kansas. At the same time, one finds that southern Missouri is geographically similar to northern Arkansas and eastern Oklahoma. As a unit for geographic study, therefore, Missouri is confusing and inadequate. The same can be said for most other American states. It is also true in regard to most other political units such as countries, provinces, counties, townships, and metropolitan districts.

PHYSIOGRAPHIC OR NATURAL AREAS

Geographers next employed natural or physiographic areas as units of study. These were of several kinds—river drainage basins, soil provinces, landform areas, climatic areas, vegetation areas, and others. The assumption underlying the use of such so-called regions was that the cultural landscape needs must be the same throughout any area which has physical unity. Such an assumption is understandable because most early geographers had originally been physiographers. Actually, however, the *geography of people* seldom coincides with any single physiographic factor.

An attempt to improve the various kinds of physiographic units was made when geographers began to devise a *composite natural region* as their unit of study. Natural regions are units of area demarked not on the basis of some one physiographic factor, but on the basis of considering as many physiographic factors as possible at the same time. Such areas are, therefore, characterized by a high degree of unity throughout and are delineated by natural boundaries. Composite natural regions thus are an improvement upon single-factor physiographic regions for purposes of study and description; but they are still inadequate because the geography of human society does not always coincide with unity which exists in the natural environment.

HUMAN-USE REGIONS

Finally, as the philosophy of geography developed toward maturity, geographers began to divide the surface of the earth into human-use regions. This came about as a result of redefining geography as a study of the interaction of man and environment in the various areas of the earth, rather than simply as a study of areas per se.[1]

THE THREE TYPES OF UNITS COMPARED

This changed definition of geography came about when scholars ceased to regard geography as purely descriptive and began to regard it as human ecology. Motivated by this new point of view, geographers soon recognized that parts of the same natural area might be covered by quite different kinds of cultural landscape; or that the same general type of cultural landscape might spread over several somewhat different kinds of natural environment. In short, no variety of natural environment can compel man to develop any particular kind of cultural pattern in society. Allegorically speaking, nature, in any area, draws up a list of things which man can and cannot do. From this list, man can and does make a choice of what he will do; but he must stay within the limits set by the natural environment in making his choices.

Thus, natural areas represent lists of possibilities drawn up by nature, political divisions represent man's attempts to override the limits set by nature, human-use units represent the results of man's conformance to the limitations of nature. The last named, therefore, are the only kinds of areas which are *regions* in the ecological sense of the word. Indeed, from the standpoint of the student of human society, geographic or

human-use areas are the only divisions of the earth's surface meriting the name of regions.

WHAT MAKES A REGION?

UNIFYING PRINCIPLE

Any region is distinguished by two traits: it possesses some *unifying principle*, and it possesses *boundaries* which limit its areal extent. The unifying principle usually has its roots in the economic adjustments which mankind has made locally to the environment. If, for instance, society has capitalized upon its climate, soil, landforms, and other related natural factors in such a way as to live by means of a distinctive type of crop production, that society may accordingly be said to be agriculturally adjusted to its environment. The type of agriculture practiced and the specific elements of the environment utilized by that type of agriculture may be said to constitute the unifying principle in the region. The region extends as far as that particular kind of agriculture prevails.

BOUNDARIES

The boundaries of the region in question are drawn where that type of agriculture ceases to be the dominant means of support for society, and gives way to some other kind of agriculture or to manufacturing or to grazing or to some other kind of group economy.

SOME SAMPLE REGIONS

The unifying principle which creates geographic regionalism operates in many different ways and therefore results in a great variety of regions over the earth. These regions, however, are of seven principal kinds, depending upon what general group of resources are utilized by them. The seven kinds of regions are illustrated by the examples which follow.

[1] Preston E. James, ed., *New Viewpoints in Geography,* 29th Yearbook, National Council for the Social Studies, National Education Association (Washington, D.C., 1959). See especially Chapter X, "The Use of Cultural Areas as a Frame of Organization for the Social Studies."

A HUNTING AND FISHING REGION— SOUTHWESTERN GREENLAND

People will engage in various types of hunting, fishing, and other forms of exploitation of the wild fauna—either when they are so low in cultural development as to be unable to support themselves in any better way, or where the stern nature of their environment prevents them from following more advanced economic pursuits, or in a few instances, to supplement an inadequate food supply.

Southwestern Greenland is a hard land with a restrictive environment (Fig. 6–1). The Godthaab district, which is typical of the region, is a rugged, fiorded littoral. The land is one of hummocky rocky hills, cut by a veritable labyrinth of channels, straits, bare rocky islands, and reefs. There is practically no soil, even glacial

moraine being absent. Fog shrouds the coast much of the time. The shore is washed by a cold current and is treeless. There is good shelter for small boats almost everywhere along the coastline.

Traditionally, the Greenlanders were hunters depending largely upon the seal and walrus and to a smaller extent upon fish, caribou, and seabirds. The distribution of settlements was attuned to this economy. Some fifty years ago, however, the number of seals and walruses began to decline, accompanied by a slight increase in the temperature of the sea water. Simultaneously cod and halibut began to appear in the coastal waters off west Greenland. Accordingly, the Greenlander has become essentially a fisherman, preparing codfish for the world market. No longer is he a hunter with a self-contained subsistence economy. His needs are now filled in the main by imported

Figure 6–1 A typical community in the Godthaab district. It lies at the foot of low hills on Godthaab Fiord, adjacent to waters rich in cod, which are caught and sold in world markets. (Photo from DeWys, Inc.)

goods. Thus, the natural economy has gradually been replaced by a monetary one.

The population in the region has been increasing quite rapidly considering the inadequate natural resources. There is definitely an upper limit beyond which numbers cannot go without reducing dangerously the level of living. There are about forty thousand people occupying west Greenland. The people, known as "Greenlanders," are part Eskimo, part European.

Considering the change in customs and the loss of traditional skills as a consequence of the reduction in hunting, one wonders whether the economy could again revert to that formerly followed if the temperature of the coastal waters is only temporary.

The Danish government of Greenland has been a model of colonial administration: the welfare of the native has ever been the sole criterion of success.

In such a milieu, only a relatively small number of people can support themselves and only the hardy survive. Society is plain and simple.

A FOREST-EXPLOITATION REGION—AMAZONIA

The vast selva of the Amazon Basin was the original habitat of the *Hevea* rubber tree and for long almost the sole source of the world's rubber supply. Competition from plantations in southeastern Asia has reduced Amazonia to relatively small importance in rubber production, but still a considerable proportion of this region's sparse population is engaged in the rubber business (Fig. 6–2).

Most of the rubber production comes from forests near the rivers, because only the trees near the rivers are accessible. The dense, rapidly growing vegetation and the superabundance of noxious insects confine all major human traffic to the streams.

During the period of heavier rains, the rubber gatherer lives in some city, such as Iquitos or Manaos. During the so-called dry season, he resides on a rubber estate. A typical rubber estate consists of a two- or three-mile-wide strip of forest fronting on some stream for fifty to seventy miles. It has a central collecting station and a

Figure 6–2 Amazonian rubber gatherer or *seringueiro* filling a gourd with latex from a rubber tree. The life of the collector is not pleasant; he faces frightful hardships. The mortality rate is high. Rubber is collected only during the so-called *dry season*, for the rains during the *wet season* (November to May) cause enormous floods over thousands of miles of territory as the Amazon and its numerous tributaries overflow their banks. And then the rubber gatherer must penetrate far into the dark forest to collect his latex, since it is estimated that the *Hevea brasiliensis* does not average more than one per acre. (Photo courtesy of FAO)

quay for river steamers. The estate is divided up among the workers who erect temporary shelters of poles and palm thatch. From May to October, these workers chop paths through the forest, locate wild rubber trees, and make half-day circuits from tree to tree. Each tree is gashed, the latex is collected and coagulated over fire and smoke into balls or "biscuits."

In so unhealthful a region, it is not expected that the collector will work every day. Few, indeed, escape fever, and few average more than three or four days of actual work per week. When the worker has enough rubber biscuits to make a load, he puts them in a small boat and delivers them to the central office of the estate. He is paid for them after the cost of the supplies which he has purchased has been deducted, following which he usually drifts back to some town for the wet season.

A PASTORAL REGION— THE KIRGHIZ STEPPES

The Kirghiz Steppes comprise a part of the great lowland of central Eurasia which stretches between the Caspian Sea and the Tien Shan highlands. Because of the interior continental situation of this vast area, the climate varies from arid to subhumid and the natural vegetation is scanty, short, steppe grass. The easternmost portion of the area lies adjacent to Chinese Sinkiang and is comprised in the Kirghiz Soviet Socialist Republic.

Through the northern and central parts of Kirghizia (that is, the Ki.S.S.R.) runs the high Tien Shan. Along the southern edge tower the front ranges of the Pamirs. In the west lie the hot desert lowlands, but these rise toward the east into some twenty-seven million acres of alpine pasture. The land is densely populated only in the valleys of the Chu and Talas rivers and around the margins of the big lake, Issyk Kul. Prior to 1919, nomadic herding was almost the sole human activity in this grassland. The life of the Kirghiz at that time, therefore, well illustrated the close geographic relationship between pastoral man and grass.

Domestic animals, if they are at all numerous, eat all the grass around an encampment within a few weeks, and hence they must graze a different tract of land each day. The Kirghiz were, therefore, "constantly on the move," as the forage within easy traveling distance was soon grazed. The short moves were planned so as to arrive in the mountains in summer and in the lowlands in winter. Obviously the density of population was low, for the carrying capacity of the land for human occupants depended upon the ability of the natural vegetation to support live-

stock, which in turn depended directly upon the rainfall.

All phases of Kirghiz life were adjusted to the wanderings. Food for rich and poor alike consisted almost entirely of sour milk, cheese, and a little meat from sheep, cattle, horses, and camels. Bread and tea were luxuries and fruits and vegetables conspicuous by their absence. Necessaries of life were few indeed: the shelter, known as a *kibitka* or *akoi*, was a tent constructed from strips of warm felt from sheep's wool stretched over a lattice of willow poles and tied in place with thongs. This was probably the most substantial dwelling to be found anywhere in the world among nomadic graziers; in this climate, a tent must shed rain and snow and protect its owners from the biting cold. The kibitka's warmth was especially important because of the paucity of fuel (which consisted almost entirely of the dried dung of animals and of sticks from scrubby bushes). Furniture was absent among people constantly on the move. Utensils, too, were few and made principally of leather and wood. Clothing consisted essentially of materials from the flocks and herds, supplemented by cotton procured through barter.

When the pasture in a certain area was completely grazed or when animal pollution threatened public health, the Kirghiz moved. The men would round up the animals and start on ahead; the women would break camp and perform all the routine work. The few possessions were placed upon the backs of camels or oxen; horses carried only human burdens. By evening, a new camp would have been established and the move apparently forgotten. Thus from time immemorial had the Kirghiz roamed seasonally from pasture to pasture following their flocks and herds. And so might they have continued to live during future generations were it not for a revolution in far-off Europe.

Since the Russian revolution, the government planners of the Soviet Union have expended great effort to break up nomadism and to get the inhabitants of Kirghizia settled on the land. The government has persistently encouraged agricultural adjustments and considerable areas have been incorporated into state and collective farms. More than half the plowed land is reported as being under irrigation, producing cotton, fruits and vegetables, hemp, poppies, rice, and tobacco. Much of the farm land in the northern part of the area is of only marginal value for dry farming and is mainly included in state-owned farms.

Stock breeding is being put on a scientific basis, with veterinary hospitals, artificial insemination stations, bacteriological laboratories, quarantine posts, and meat inspection points.

Considerable mining is carried on and the region contributes a large amount of copper, coal, gold, iron ore, lead, manganese, petroleum, silver, and zinc. Much of the region, however, has not as yet been explored and completely new discoveries are to be expected.

A modern capital city of considerable size has been built at Frunze, which is connected by rail with many of the principal cities of the Soviet Union.

However, most of the region is desert and the available water supply can irrigate only a small proportion of the total area. Even dry-farming over extensive areas is submarginal and fraught with danger. Accordingly, a large proportion of the Kirghiz still are pastoral nomads (Fig. 6–3), contributing to the outside world their surplus of karakul, wool, skins, and rugs. For generations the Kirghiz have been regarded as being the most exemplary pastoral nomads on earth. It is difficult indeed to see how they can change so very much in the future.

Figure 6–3   Two Kirghis farmers and a pensioner (left) discussing plans for their winter trek. Kirghiz life is closely attuned to the rhythm of the seasons: moving is so planned that the flocks arrive in the mountains in summer and in the lowlands in winter. These farmers are tending the flocks of the Shamsi state farm located seventy kilometers from the Kirghiz capital of Funze. Although they have a radio, they still live in the traditional type of dwelling suited to the nomadic life. (Novosti photo from Sovfoto)

Figure 6–4 Butte, Montana, one of the world's outstanding copper centers. Butte, considered by geographers as typifying mining, differs from many mining communities in having assumed an aspect of permanency. Hence, in all respects it is far in advance of the average mining camp or city. (Photo courtesy of the Butte Chamber of Commerce)

A MINING DISTRICT—BUTTE, MONTANA

Butte, Montana, and its environs constitute what is probably America's most typical mining district and one of the world's great copper producing areas (Fig. 6–4). It forms a small district in the Rocky Mountain Region—a region characterized by mines, ranches, forests, and recreation areas. More than two billion dollars' worth of metals has been removed from this district since 1869, and the end is not yet in sight. In 1955 the Anaconda Copper Mining Company announced that it foresaw at least sixty years of profitable mining in Butte. The mineral deposits here are extremely abundant and in addition to these, there are huge reserves of low-grade copper-bearing material in and around the larger veins. Carefully controlled experiments indicate

that 150 million tons of this material can be mined to yield approximately twenty pounds of fine copper per ton plus substantial amounts of precious metals.

In addition to the impressive output of copper, the district's mines yield also gold, manganese, silver, and zinc. It is reported that today 95 percent of the manganese mined within the United States comes from Butte mines.

The population of this section of Montana, including Butte, Anaconda, Great Falls, and Helena, is dependent largely upon the copper industry. Butte, the largest urban center in the state, is a substantial and prosperous city, although it has its ups-and-downs in accordance with the price of copper. Anaconda Hill, on which the city of Butte was built, has long been known as "the richest hill on earth." Butte, however, is really two cities—one below and one above ground. Activity is ceaseless, for shifts work day and night. The district lies in Summit Valley in a broad intermontane depression. It presents a desolate picture: the granite mountain slopes are bare and gray; mines and prospect holes literally pepper the hills; at numerous places stand red, odd-shaped mine buildings, steel hoists, tall smokestacks, trestles, shops, railway yards, and other adjuncts of subterranean mining. Great heaps of gray mine waste are conspicuous features of the landscape. The underground workings include 40 miles of vertical shafts, together with 2,420 miles of other passageways. Adding the excavation from slopes brings the total length to 8,666 miles.

Formerly not a tree, not a flower, not even a blade of grass grew here, for the poisonous arsenic-sulfur fumes from the smelter stacks and fired "stink piles" destroyed everything green. Since the removal of the smelters twenty-three miles distant and the electrification of the railways and hoisting machines, however, the city has become practically free from smelter fumes and green spots have made their appearance. Gardens have become numerous and trees line almost every street; and now Butte is not an unattractive city. It languished commercially until the arrival of the railroads, for its freight had to be hauled 400 miles by wagon. At present, it is served by no less than four rail lines.

AN AGRICULTURAL SUBREGION—THE SALT LAKE OASIS

The Salt Lake Oasis, part of the Intermontane Basins and Plateaus Region, is an excellent example of an agricultural subregion. It is a strip of human habitation about 120 miles long and from 2 to 18 miles wide along the western foot of the Wasatch Mountains.

A series of small and fluctuating streams flow in canyons down the west side of the mountains and debouch onto alluvial fans, making irrigation possible. Here on the deep soils of the piedmont slopes, on the benchlands, deltas and terraces of ancient, long-vanished Lake Bonneville, and in the lower mountain valleys live three-fourths of the population of Utah.

At the mouth of nearly every canyon stream which emerges from the Wasatch lies a pleasant village or city girdled by green fields and adorned by orchards and lines of shade trees. Such locales are favorite sites because of the ease of controlling water. Each town is separated from its neighbor towns by from five to ten miles of field or desert. Small holdings, cultivated thoroughly, characterize the Oasis (Fig. 6–5). Their small size is the result of a scarcity of arable land, a limited amount of water for irrigation, and the early land system devised by the Mormon Church.

The biggest single obstacle to enlargement of the farming area is the scarcity of water. More water can be provided by storage and by transbasin diversion but this will be costly. It is inconceivable that transbasin diversion could be done except by the federal government.

Only 3 percent of the state is used for agriculture: 2 percent for irrigation, 1 percent for dry-farming.

Possibly 90 percent of the Oasis farmers are town-dwellers. The Church, the desert, and the canyon stream have conspired to produce this village concentration. Farms lie from one to five miles from town. Home and farm are linked together by broad shady roadways. Every town has its church and school buildings, its public hall and its stores, and is compact and practically self-sufficient.

Crops are so diversified that farms resemble gardens (Fig. 6–5). Notwithstanding this marked diversity, approximately three-fourths of the cropped land is devoted to sugar beets, alfalfa, and wheat, and the remaining one-fourth to fruits and vegetables. Most farmers concentrate on crops which give a high return per acre and which can be sold locally. If distant markets are sought, however, crops that can travel in concentrated form are grown, for these can better stand the high transportation costs which are the burden of this remote and relatively isolated area.

A MANUFACTURING DISTRICT—GARY, INDIANA

Probably no manufacturing district so well typifies America's eastern and central industrial regions as does the Gary area. Most urban areas which have become industrialized have done so through trial and error. The great manufacturing plants at Gary, on the other hand, were care-

Figure 6–5 Agricultural landscape in an irrigated Utah valley. Small farms, such as the one shown, abound throughout the Salt Lake Oasis and are intensely cultivated. (Photo from DeWys, Inc.)

fully planned and laid out on a scientific basis, both as regards general location and specific site (Fig. 6–6). Unfortunately, however, the design of the city itself, and of housing in particular, was left out of the planning and these are therefore of the usual dismal, sordid, and exploitative variety. For more than sixty years, the great steel industry has been built up step by step and is still in the process of being rounded out.

In 1905, the United States Steel Corporation, needing a new plant to serve the rapidly growing Midwestern market, selected an area of sand dune and swamp and built Gary, now a city of more than 178,000 inhabitants.

Gary's general location is unexcelled, for it lies near its raw materials: ore and limestone are transported economically to the blast furnaces by lake carrier. Coking coal is delivered at considerable expense from Kentucky and West Virginia, but steam coal is easily and cheaply brought by rail from Illinois and Indiana. Moreover, Gary is situated strategically with reference to markets, for nearby are automobile- and machinery-manufacturing centers. Chicago-Gary is the best balanced district in the country with regard to production and consumption. Gary's proximity to

Chicago is of particular significance. It is near enough to deal conveniently with Chicago companies but lies far enough away to escape high land values and ruinous taxes. The dense population of the tributary area insures adequate labor of the right sort. Ample cold, clear water of good quality is available from Lake Michigan. The topography is level and there is, consequently, almost unlimited room for industrial and residential expansion. This is in marked contrast to Cleveland, Pittsburgh, Youngstown, Wheeling, and many other steel-making districts.

The Gary-Indiana Harbor-South Chicago district now ranks as the nation's leading iron and steel-making center, having recently eclipsed Pittsburgh. It is interesting to note that when the industry as a whole falls in production, this district nearly always operates at from 90 to 99 percent of its capacity.

A COMMERCIAL SUBREGION— METROPOLITAN NEW YORK

New York, which handles approximately 40 percent of all commerce entering and leaving the United States, is the world's outstanding example of a commercial area (Fig. 6–7). Its preeminence is owing to its strategic location, its superb littoral site, and the advantageous character of its coast zone. It is the chief portal to the North American continent, it is a powerful nodal point formed by the junction of land and sea routes, and its access to a vast and productive hinterland is without parallel. It has, accordingly, become the outstanding market and financial center of the continent.

New York has one of the best harbors in the world. Its direct water frontage is approximately 771 miles, about half of which is developed; the depth is sufficient to accommodate the largest ships afloat. Moreover, the waters of the Hudson River, East River, Harlem River, Long Island Sound, Newark Bay, Jamaica Bay, and New York Bay mingle without a single bar-

rier; the channel leading to the Atlantic is direct; the tidal range is so narrow that ships may come and go at any time; ice never blocks the harbor, though fog does occasionally hold up transportation. Of all Atlantic ports, New York alone has access via easy grades to the interior where many of the articles of commerce are grown, manufactured, and consumed. For years New York had no actual advantage over Boston, Philadelphia, and Baltimore. In fact, in colonial times Philadelphia, because it had behind it the largest tract of fertile farm land east of the Appalachian barrier (a very significant factor prior to the railroad era, when the growth of a city depended in large part on the food potentialities of the immediate hinterland), was America's largest city and an outstanding port. But the Hudson-Mo-

Figure 6–6   Part of the U.S. Steel Corporation plant at Gary, Indiana—a capital example of modern, scientific industrial location. Few places have so many natural advantages for iron and steel manufacture: the property conformed admirably to the requirements of a mill site, lacking only a harbor, which was later constructed without difficulty. Prior to Gary's development, the land, despite its proximity to Chicago, was purely a waste of sand dune and swamp. It is fortunate indeed that such was the case, for had the area been subdivided, its purchase as a huge single block for industry would have been impossible. Raw materials are delivered via lake carrier almost to the blast furnaces and coke ovens (note ship channel). Although the many steel plants resemble one another externally, internally each is a distinct unit, well fitted to the highly specialized needs of the industry. The maze of railroad tracks mutely testifies to the importance of transportation in the manufacture of iron and steel. (Photo courtesy of U.S. Steel)

Figure 6–7 Manhattan Island and its immediate tributary area. Here is one of the greatest concentrations of human beings in the world. The contest for space is so severe that real estate prices and rentals have reached fantastic levels. Here the skyscraper is an adjustment to insufficient ground space. Manhattan Island contains the greatest concentration of tall buildings in the world. The size, prosperity, and congestion of New York City are the results of commercial adjustments to advantageous coastal features, strategic location, and superior transport connections with a productive hinterland. (Photo courtesy of The Port of New York Authority)

hawk depression, by means of the Erie Canal and the New York Central Railway, gave New York a superior connection with the interior and the entire Great Lakes Region became its hinterland (Fig. 5–3).

The population is distributed largely on Manhattan and Long Island and on the peninsulas of the Bronx and Bayonne. Most of the business is concentrated in the southern half of Manhattan in an area not more than six miles long and one and a half to two miles wide. Exporters and importers from all parts of the country located of necessity in New York. The small extent of land and the many water barriers prevented expansion and crowding became a menace. Hence the skyscrapers, which are, in a sense, monuments to man's efforts to counteract this handicap. Nowhere else in the world is there such a collection of tall buildings; in 1945 the city had nearly two hundred buildings of more than twenty stories and the number has greatly increased since. Ferries, bridges, and tun-

nels have been built to carry millions of people to and from the city each day. This lack of space leads to a congestion of transportation (a daily traffic jam of 1,400,000 vehicles) which has become the greatest single problem facing the city.

From atop one of the city's higher buildings, one may look down upon the commercial life of New York and upon an area in which from fifteen to twenty million persons live and work. Closer inspection discloses miles and miles of piers jutting out into the water, offering anchorage to all kinds of craft. Some ten thousand vessels pass through the port of New York each year.

HOMOGENEITY OF REGIONS

REGIONS VERSUS STATES

From the preceding examples, as well as numerous others, it may readily be seen that what characterizes a region is its *homogeneity* in economic and social life. In addition, a region is usually

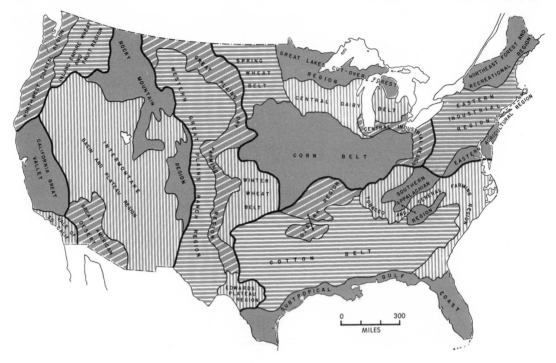

Figure 6–8 Generalized pattern of geographic regions in the United States.

fairly homogeneous in its natural environment. Figure 6–8 shows the coterminous United States divided into twenty-four rather generalized human-use regions. The location and boundaries of these regions do not even remotely resemble or coincide with the forty-eight states. In contrast to the latter, these twenty-four regions represent the largest areas which exhibit any great amount of homogeneity in their economic and social life. As such, these regions are distinctly geographic units.

REGIONS VERSUS SECTIONS

Regions often show an interesting tendency to cluster together into *sections* or major provinces. This is the result of various factors such as political interests, general cultural traits, social problems, similar dialect or language traits, or common sociopsychological attitudes (Fig. 6–9). In the United States there are some seven of these sectional or provincial clusters of regions—the East, the South, the Middle West,[2] the Great Plains, the Intermontane West, the Pacific Southwest, and the Pacific Northwest.[3]

Sectional groupings such as these should

not, however, be confused with regions; they are more vague, usually larger, and delineated on the basis of quite different considerations than regions. They are more the products of political, cultural, and historical factors than of direct geographic relations between man and area. Moreover, they lack most of that homogeneity in socioeconomic patterns which demarks regions. The loyalties, political motivations, and cultural peculiarities which mark the inhabitants of sections is commonly referred to as *sectionalism*. This phenomenon is regarded by many students as undesirable. Sectionalism, insofar as it represents a clustering or grouping together of somewhat similar regions, however, is both normal and natural and therefore can scarcely be condemned as undesirable. If it be utilized as a basis for the planning and carrying out of programs of resource conservation, material development,

[2] Also known as the Midwest and the Midlands.

[3] Sometimes the latter two combined are referred to as the Far West. It should be noted that these terms merely locate the regions but do not "characterize" them.

and the preservation of cultural assets, it is actually very desirable.

POLITICAL BLOCS AND BLOCISM

Unfortunately, the term *sectionalism* is often used to cover quite a different sort of cleavage in national life. This is the tendency of certain groups of states or provinces within a nation to act in concert politically—to the detriment of the whole. The voting together on the question of bimetalism by the western states, the secession of slaveholding southern states, the "isolationism" toward international responsibilities on the part of certain interior states, and the endorsement of "machine politics" by certain highly urbanized states are examples of this phenomenon in the United States.

This, however, is not a peculiarity of American life: Canada is marked by a cleavage along linguistic and religious lines which at times causes great problems in the Dominion. Czechoslovakia has at times been torn asunder by the conflict between the democratic liberalism of the Czechs and the political clericalism of the Slovaks. Cleavage between Prussians, Austrians, and

Swabo-Bavarians has long disrupted German unity. Divergence between north China and south China produced for decades almost endless civil war among the Chinese.

Such cleavage in national life might better be called political "blocism" rather than sectionalism. Whatever name be applied to it, however, it is the basis of social confusion, economic deterioration, and political uproar. It is beyond question undesirable in all of its aspects.

A SECTION IS A CLUSTER OF REGIONS

If any one of the great sections of the United States be examined, it will be seen to consist of several distinct component regions. The Middle West for example consists of five regions—the Spring Wheat Belt, the Corn Belt, the Central Dairy Region, the Interior Industrial Region, and the Great Lakes Cut-Over Forest Region (Fig. 6–10). These five regions are clear and distinct units, each marked by a large degree of homogeneity. By way of contrast, the Middle West as a whole possesses only a small degree of homogeneity and there is even considerable argument as to what constitutes its actual boundaries.

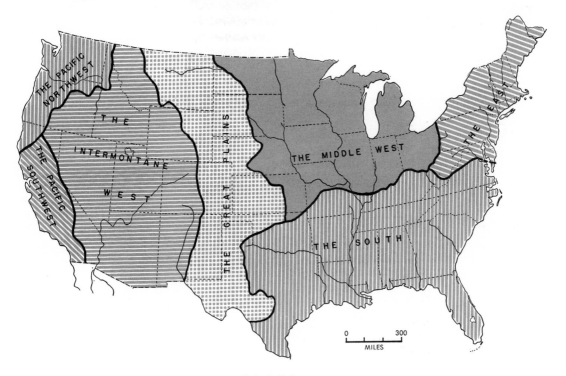

Figure 6–9 The seven great sections of the United States.

Figure 6–10 The Middle West section divided into geographic regions.

SUBDIVISIONS OF REGIONS

SUBREGIONS

The homogeneity and geographic uniformity of any one of these regions is only a relative matter. Close scrutiny of any sample region shows that it may be clearly divided into subregions. The Corn Belt, for example, may be subdivided into no less than 11 such units. Figure 6–11 shows these as follows.

1. Corn and hog subregion
2. Corn, alfalfa, and livestock subregion
3. Livestock and dairy subregion
4. Corn and livestock-pasturing subregion
5. Iowa cash-grain subregion
6. Illinois cash-grain subregion
7. Nebraska cash-grain subregion
8. Livestock feeding and industrial subregion
9. Corn and crop-specialty subregion
10. General farming and livestock pasturing subregion
11. Corn and general farming subregion

The presence of all these distinct subregions within a universally recognized region such as the American Corn Belt shows that even the most closely knit region is only relatively homogeneous.

DISTRICTS

Subregions are, in the very nature of things, more homogeneous and uniform than the region of which they are parts. The principal reason for this is that they are smaller in extent and hence there is less chance for them to include unlike patterns of human activities. Despite this, they often differ from portion to portion sufficiently for subdivision into districts. For example, the Corn and Oats Cash Grain Subregion of central

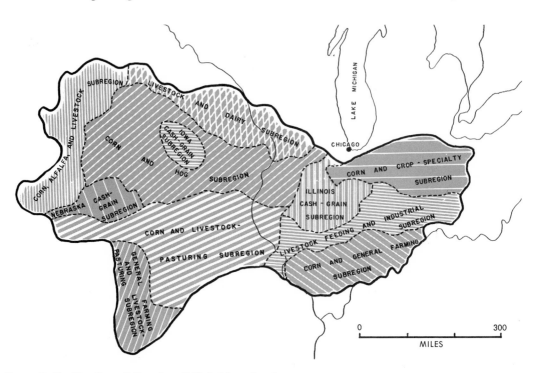

Figure 6–11 The Corn Belt region divided into subregions.

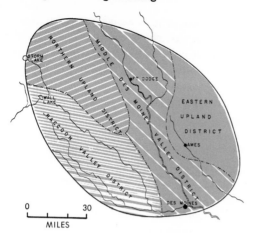

Figure 6–12 Geographic districts of the Cash-Grain subregion of Central Iowa.

Iowa can be subdivided into four districts: (1) the Eastern Upland District, (2) the Middle Des Moines Valley District, (3) the Raccoon Valley District, and (4) the Northern Upland District (Fig. 6–12).

LESSER SUBDIVISIONS

Any one of these may be further subdivided into localities. For instance, the Des Moines Valley District (Fig. 6–13) may be separated into the Des Moines, Boone, Webster City, Ft. Dodge, and Dakota City localities. Each of these localities in turn may be divided into communities; each community may be divided into neighborhoods; and each neighborhood into sites.

The site is, of course, the smallest geographic unit of space, beyond which subdivision cannot proceed. The site is completely homogeneous. Neighborhoods, communities, localities, districts, subregions, and regions are simply larger and larger groupings of sites. The larger the scale of the grouping, the less the homogeneity or geographic unity. The region is the largest grouping of sites which has any real degree of homogeneity, although for some purposes the section or province may be considered as a still larger grouping.

REGIONALISM IN OTHER COUNTRIES

The United States is not the only country which exhibits sections, regions, subregions, and minor divisions of area. Canada parallels the United States to a remarkable degree. Mexico does like-

wise. Russia exhibits a highly diversified pattern of regions. In fact, practically every country on the face of the earth manifests regional or subregional differences to some extent.

TRAITS OF REGIONS

SHIFTING BOUNDARIES

The boundaries of regions are never sharply defined, although the geographer finds it convenient to show them as definite lines in order to mark out regions for reference purposes. Actually, one region usually shades into another by gradual degrees, through a zone or band of appreciable width. Nor are these border zones fixed as to their location. For instance, in 1914, the western boundary of the Winter Wheat Belt lay in western Kansas. By 1929, it had been extended westward almost to the Rocky Mountains. It is now in the process of gradual retreat eastward.[4]

REGIONS NOT NECESSARILY PERMANENT

Even regions themselves are not necessarily permanent phenomena. For instance, it seems likely

[4] For a very detailed study see John Weaver and others, "Livestock Units and Crop Combinations in the Middle West," *Economic Geography,* Vol. 32, 1956, pp. 237–259.

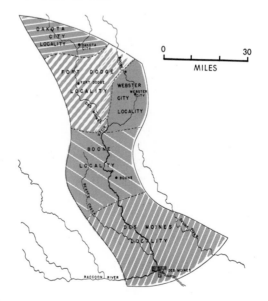

Figure 6–13 The Middle Des Moines Valley District divided into geographic localities.

that the region known as the Spring Wheat Belt will evolve away from its present pioneer wheat culture and eventually become an integral part of the adjacent Central Dairy Region (Fig. 6–8). Inventions of new agricultural machinery, development of new varieties of seed, extensions or retractions in transport facilities, changes in world markets, and numerous other factors cause the boundaries of regions to advance or recede.

EVOLUTIONARY CYCLE OF REGIONS

Regions, themselves, do not spring full-fledged into existence. Rather, they evolve through a life cycle somewhat like that of a living organism. A region, therefore, passes through stages of youth, submaturity, maturity, and old age in accordance with the development of the human society which occupies it. A youthful society, as for instance one composed of nomadic food-gatherers or pastoralists or one composed of mining, fishing, or trapping communities, produces only a scattered pattern of occupancy or resource utilization within a region.

A submature or adolescent society, such as one based upon pioneer agriculture or ranch pastoralism, produces a discontinuous and interrupted pattern of human settlement in a region. Colonization outposts of land utilization indicate that the region is being extended. As society becomes mature, more and more diverse and interrelated adjustments to environment are made and settlement becomes continuous and compact over a region; and the boundaries of the region reach their maximum extent. Finally, in senescence or old age, a region tends to shrink in size, leaving relict outlying islands of its occupance pattern. Meanwhile, the residual region itself tends to subdivide into a greater and greater number of subregions and other smaller areal units as its main geographic pattern breaks down.

THE USE OF REGIONS

SCIENTIFIC USE

The use of regions as units of study and analysis in geography serves two primary purposes. The first of these is the purely scientific purpose of organizing geographic facts and ideas. The world is so huge that almost no comments can be made about it *as a whole* except statements regarding its size, shape, and motions. Even the United States is so large and so varied that almost the only general statement which can safely be made concerning it is that it is populated by Americans. In a great country like the United States, stretching as it does across a continent, "with its varied topography, climate, plant and animal associations, regional diversities are of the greatest importance and need to be recognized and intelligently utilized."[5] Any student of human society, therefore, finds the region an indispensable tool for either the study of an area or for the presentation to others of the geography of an area.

SOCIAL ENGINEERING USE

The second usefulness of the region is for practical political and civic purposes. There are many people today who regard human society as so complex, so varied from place to place, and so vigorously in process of change, that to organize it for peace, stability, or greater permanence and order would seem to be impossible. It is not impossible, however. The very complexity, rapid change, and varied character of human society are what the geographer or human ecologist wishes to study, and the laws governing these things are what he wishes to seek out. The instability and change in present-day society are the evidences of geographic maladjustment and the varied pattern of society is the manifestation of regional differences. As Adams[6] points out:

New discoveries and inventions which help to cause social confusion must now be supplemented by new social discoveries and social inventions, in order to restore the relative balance; and this problem must be studied ecologically if a solution is to be found. It is just here that ecological methods have something to contribute to the new order.

The regional method of segregation and analysis is obviously one of the major contributions of geography to social science.

During the great economic "Depression" of

[5] Charles C. Adams, "A Note for Social-Minded Ecologists and Geographers," *Ecology,* Vol. 19, No. 3 (July, 1938), pp. 500–502.
[6] *Ibid.*

the 1930's, American agriculture reached such a state of collapse that the nation was compelled to spend enormous amounts of money and energy devising and carrying out a program of agricultural-adjustment planning. In 1935, Foster F. Elliott[7] stated that:

The first approach to production adjustment was entirely on a commodity basis. Now the problem is to adapt commodity programs so that they fit the special conditions of the various regions and localities. Farmers have suggested that if the problem were approached on a regional basis . . . decentralized planning would be possible.

This example from the field of crop reorganization in agriculture merely serves to illustrate the need of the regional approach to governmental planning and resource development of all kinds. Land use, water use, housing, population problems, race relations, transportation, city planning, and other such vast segments of public enterprise and administration are essentially regional problems and can be intelligently handled only through regional understanding. Over-all programs and policies may be formulated by the government for certain social and economic functions in general, but detailed physical planning must always produce plans which have been designed to apply to specific areas.

Thus, during times of peace, conservation and wise use of national resources, patterns of public works and improvement projects, industry, trade, urbanism, including megalopolitanism, demand detailed regional surveys and a vast deal of accurate regional planning.[8] During wartime, strategies for national defense, mobilization of labor and industry, and the deployment of weapons, supplies, and manpower are equally matters of regional knowledge, analysis, and public planning.

As we continue our study of the earth's surface and how man has used it we will regionalize it in several ways suggested in this chapter. The first regionalizing attempt will be made by using temperature and rainfall statistics to block off the world into Climate Regions. The role of the Climate Factor will be followed by those of the Physiographic, Hydrographic, Edaphic, Biotic, and Mineral Factors.

[7] Foster F. Elliott, *Regional Problems in Agricultural Production* (Washington, D.C., Government Printing Office, March, 1935), p. 3.

[8] J. M. Gaus, J. Crane, M. E. Dimock, and G. T. Renner, *Regional Factors in National Planning and Development* (Washington, D.C., Government Printing Office, 1935), 215 pp.; and Donald J. Bogue, *State Economic Areas* (Washington, D.C., Department of Commerce, Bureau of the Census, 1951).

SUGGESTED USEFUL READINGS

Bogue, Donald J., and Calvin L. Peale, *Economic Areas of the United States* (New York, The Free Press of Glencoe, Inc., 1961).

Bollens, John C., and Henry J. Schmandt, *The Metropolis. (Its People, Politics and Economic Life)* (New York, Harper & Row, Publishers, 1965). See especially Chapter 2, "Nature and Dimensions of the Metropolitan Community."

Gottmann, Jean, *Megalopolis: The Urbanized Northeastern Seaboard of the United States* (New York, Twentieth Century Fund, 1961). This book provides an insight into a new kind of "regionalism."

Higbee, Edward C., *American Agriculture: Geography, Resources, Conservation* (New York, John Wiley & Sons, Inc., 1958). This book is essentially regional in approach; it contains numerous types of farm studies.

II

The
Climatic
Factor

Climate affects everyone. Hence it seems logical to follow the chapters dealing with population, location, and regions with information about that physical impactor experienced by all peoples. The treatment will be within the framework of climate regions. The maps of population and climate reveal some interesting relationships. The succeeding chapters will attempt to bring these out as well as establish other associations, some physical, some cultural.

7

Weather
and Climate:
Elements
and Controls

Of all the elements in man's natural environment, weather and climate affect him most often and most persistently. The weather touches human life and behavior at every turn, and all of man's invention and science have not made him, and do not promise to make him, less dependent upon it. For this reason, the U.S. government, like that of every other civilized nation on earth, maintains a weather bureau (in the United States known as the Environmental Science Services Administration). Its function is to provide hourly, daily, monthly, yearly, and long-time reports on weather and climate. It serves business, industry, commerce, agriculture, and the professions almost as universally as does the postal service.

The study of geography involves weather and climate as an element of the environment almost at every turn; and hence it is advisable at the outset to gain a clear idea of the earth's atmosphere and of the fundamentals of weather and climate. The present chapter, therefore, presents some of those fundamentals as an introduction to the several chapters that immediately follow.[1]

THE ATMOSPHERE

COMPOSITION

The "shell" of atmosphere around the earth's solid sphere is probably hundreds of miles thick. This outer layer of the planet is almost invisible because it is composed mostly of invisible gases, but it has substance and weight. It is tied to the solid earth by gravitation and rotates with it. Roughly, it is a mixture of nearly 78 percent

nitrogen gas, 21 percent oxygen gas, and 1 percent rare gases and a varying amount of water vapor, drops of water or ice spicules, and of dust. The oxygen supports life and combustion; the nitrogen dilutes the oxygen and furnishes most of the substance of the wind. The water vapor forms clouds, acts as a thermal blanket to slow down the loss of heat from the earth into outer space, and constitutes the immediate source of rainfall. Dust acts as a diffusing agent for sunlight, yielding soft daylight, and produces the ordinary sky colors. Along with other minute particles of impurities, dust plays an important role as hygroscopic nuclei upon which vapor can condense as tiny droplets of water to form clouds.

DIVISIONS

The atmosphere, being a mixture of gases pulled downward by gravitation, is more and more compacted in its lower levels. Half of its total mass lies in the first 18,000 feet above sea level; one-fourth lies in the next 18,000 feet; the remaining one-fourth lies above 36,000 feet.

The atmosphere is divided into three fairly distinct layers: (1) the *troposphere,* (2) the *stratosphere,* and (3) the *ionosphere.* Of these, the troposphere, or lowest layer, is the only one of much interest to most people, for in it occurs practically all physical disturbances of the air and almost all of the manifestations of weather.

---

[1] The authors wish to emphasize the fact that this chapter is not a synopsis of meteorology and climatology, but instead gives merely those facts which seem to be of most immediate use to the student of geography.

TEMPERATURE

INSOLATION AND HEAT

Although the sun is the source of heat for the atmosphere, nevertheless the air is heated from the bottom upward. The reason for this is that the sun's energy in the form of short waves of light penetrates the atmosphere. These light rays strike the surface of the earth; some are reflected back into space and are lost, but about half of them are absorbed and transformed into heat at the earth's surface. This heat warms the atmosphere. Some of the heat is *radiated* upward in the form of long heat waves and is *absorbed* by the air. The lower layer of air touches the earth and is therefore also heated by *conduction*. The air layers above this are heated by vertical ascent and circulation of the warm air known as *convection*. Thus, the incoming radiant energy of the sun (insolation) is absorbed by the earth's surface and changed into heat, after which much of it is transmitted to the atmosphere. Gradually this heat is reradiated to outer space and eventually is lost by the earth.

The loss of heat goes on at all times, but the gaining of solar heat on any particular part of the earth occurs only when the sun is above the horizon of the place in question. The more nearly overhead the sun is, the greater its heating ability. Thus, the level of heat normally rises during the daytime and falls during the night. The level of heat is known as *temperature* and may be measured by a thermometer.

THE THERMOMETER

When a good thermometer is hung in the shade and protected from reflection, the true air temperature is obtained. If the thermometer is read hourly, the temperature is usually seen to climb from its lowest reading just after sunrise to its highest reading about 3:00 P.M. because insolation exceeds radiation during these hours due to the lag in the conversion of short-wave energy to long-wave energy. From about 3:00 P.M. to sunrise, the temperature customarily falls because radiation then predominates. Thus, each day has a maximum and minimum temperature, and from these, a mean or average daily temperature may be computed. From the daily averages, the monthly (Fig. 7–1), yearly, and longtime averages may be computed. The difference between the highest and lowest temperatures is known as the *range of temperature*—daily, monthly, or annual.

FROST

Keeping a continual record of temperature is useful because the trend of such a record sometimes shows the approach of certain critical temperatures. Perhaps the most important among these is the freezing point of fresh water (32° on a Fahrenheit thermometer or 0° on a Centigrade thermometer). All living things contain water, and hence the occurrence of a frost may harm or even destroy them. When water freezes, it not only changes from a liquid to a solid but it also increases its volume. When this occurs, a jug, water pipe, leaf, blade of grass, green ear of corn, or a cell of animal matter may be shattered.

Some parts of the earth, of course, never experience frost, but most parts of the United States experience it frequently during the winter. Conversely, they are usually free of frost during the summer or high-sun part of the year. Such being the case, the average duration of the frost-free season in any region is highly important. It influences the kinds of crops grown and the dates of planting and harvesting in agriculture. It also has a bearing on numerous other human activities.

RELATIVE HEATING OF LAND AND WATER

So far, the heating and cooling of the surface of the earth and of the atmosphere above it have been discussed as though they were a uniform process. This, however, is far from true. For example, given the same amount of solar heating (insolation), the surface of a lake, a sea, or an ocean heats up much more slowly and does not reach as high a temperature as does a body of land. The contrast arises out of the difference in behavior of a solid and a liquid when heat is applied to them. If a bar of iron and an equal weight of water are placed on a stove, the iron will reach a given temperature (150° F., for instance) much sooner than the water. Conversely, if the iron and a hot-water bottle (containing an equal weight of water at the same temperature)

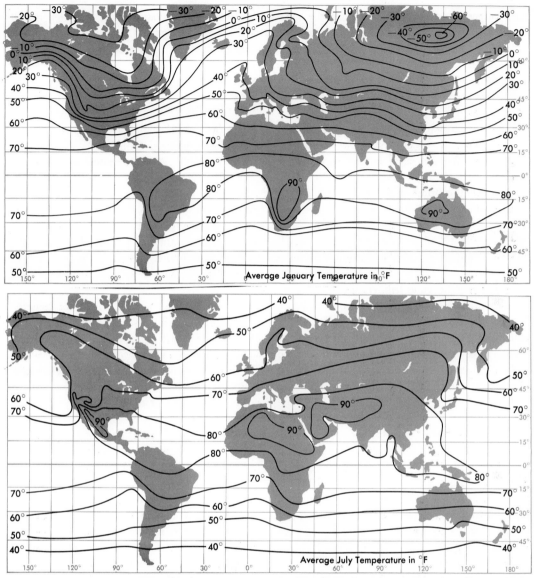

Figure 7–1 World temperatures: January (above) and July (below) means corrected to sea level. (Maps from William E. Powers, *Physical Geography*, New York, Appleton-Century-Crofts, 1966)

are placed in a hospital bed, the iron will soon be cold whereas the hot-water bottle will remain warm for several hours.

Similarly, as spring comes on, the surface of a continent and the air above it soon become warm. The coming of summer over an ocean is greatly delayed and summer temperatures never rise as high as on land. Conversely, as autumn advances, land soon cools; but over a body of water, winter is long delayed and temperatures do not reach such low levels as over land. Many

are the climatic results over the earth of this difference in heating behavior of land and water.

VARIATION WITH LATITUDE

On both land and water, however, there are important local differences in the rate of heating and cooling. There are several causes for this, but the most important is distance from the equator. The average sun elevation is greatest in equatorial regions, less high in middle latitudes, and lowest in polar or high latitudes. Because of this, temperatures average highest near the equator and lowest near the poles. There is not, however, a complete correspondence between temperature and latitude, hence it is desirable to make maps which will show the actual distribution of temperatures over the earth. The most common maps of this kind show average annual temperatures, average summer temperatures, and average winter temperatures. From them, one may obtain for any area facts regarding the severity of the seasons, annual range of temperature, and contrast with other areas in the same latitude.

ISOTHERMS

The usual way of showing temperature on maps is by means of *isotherms* or lines connecting places having the same temperature. On a temperature map, the isotherms are seen to run in a generally east-west direction. Where they pass from a continent to an ocean or vice versa, or cross a lake or ocean current, isotherms often make important jogs in a northerly or southerly direction as a result of the difference in heating of land and water, already mentioned.

VARIATION WITH ALTITUDE

Not only does the effectiveness of sun heating vary with latitude, but it varies in an upward direction as well. Places at high altitudes are normally cooler than those nearer sea level. Records made during balloon ascents show that on the average the temperature at the height of a mile is about 16° F. lower than at sea level. In other words, the temperature falls about 1° F. for every 330 feet of altitude. This is true because the main source of atmospheric heat is, as already mentioned, radiation from the surface. On a plateau or mountain the rate of decrease with altitude is somewhat less than in free air. The sun shines just as hotly on a mountain as on a lowland, but the thinner air at high altitudes is less effective in retarding the loss of heat by radiation. For this reason, the tops of high mountains even in equatorial regions are snow-clad although their bases are clothed in hot, humid rain forests. Between the hot base and the frozen summit lie most of the temperature zones found on earth, arranged one above the other in narrow belts. Highlands near the equator, therefore, produce many "temperate" crops, are often densely populated, and serve as health and pleasure resorts for some of the lowlanders.

AIR PRESSURE AND WIND

AIR PRESSURE

The gases which comprise the atmosphere are real substances, even though they are invisible. They have mass and are pulled downward by gravitation. This gives them weight. Anything which has weight exerts pressure, and the atmosphere certainly does so. The air normally presses down on every square inch of surface at sea level with a weight of 14.7 pounds. As one goes upward into higher altitudes, the pressure becomes lower because there is less of the air above him.

Human beings are ordinarily not conscious of this pressure because their bodies are built to withstand it and to adjust readily to moderate variations. It is only when subjected to sudden changes in pressure that people become conscious of the weight of the atmosphere, as for instance, when they ascend or descend rapidly in an elevator or airplane.

The figure of 14.7 pounds per square inch, however, is only an average value. In any place the pressure varies constantly, hour by hour. At two places a few hundred miles apart, the pressure may be markedly different at the same moment, even though their altitude above sea level is the same. Because each appreciable variation in atmospheric pressure normally brings a change in weather, it is important to have an instrument that will measure such variations.

THE BAROMETER

The instrument which reveals and measures changes in air pressure is the barometer. In its simplest form it is a long glass tube nearly filled with mercury and placed alongside a ruler. The mercury-filled tube is placed open end down in a cup of mercury. The mercury is prevented by air pressure from flowing entirely out of the tube into the cup. The vacuum which forms near the closed end of the tube exerts no pressure on the mercury, whereas the air on the surface of the cup exerts 14.7 pounds per square inch, enough to hold the mercury high in the tube.

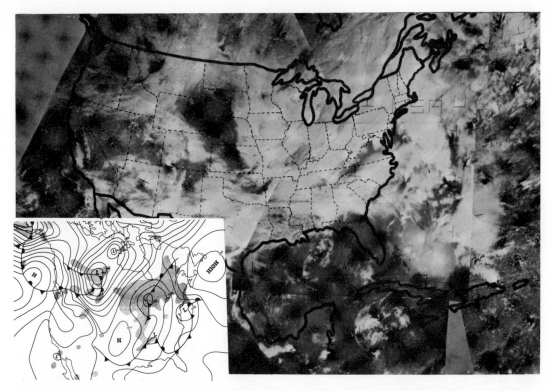

Figure 7–2 A photomap of the United States. Lower left: the U.S. weather map showing centers of high and low barometric pressure for the same day. (Photo and map courtesy of the Environmental Science Services Administration)

Under normal conditions, the air at sea level can push the mercury in a barometer to a height of about thirty inches. As the air pressure falls or rises the height of the mercury column varies, being usually between twenty-nine and thirty-one inches at sea level. Carried to higher altitudes, the mercury falls to twenty inches, to ten inches, or even less, depending upon the elevation. Indeed, an aviator can tell approximately how high he is flying by looking at a barometer.

BAROMETRIC PRESSURE MAPS

Since the pressure of the atmosphere is constantly varying all over the earth (and thereby bringing constant weather changes), it becomes highly desirable to show the differences in pressure from place to place. Accordingly, the Environmental Science Services Administration makes daily maps which show these (Fig. 7–2). Barometer readings are taken at hundreds of stations over the nation and on ships at sea. These are telegraphed to Washington and entered on a base map, each in its proper position. After these

readings are studied, places on the map with corresponding barometric pressures are connected by lines known as *isobars*. The arrangement of these isobars shows where the air pressure is low and where it is high (Fig. 7–3).

PRESSURE DIFFERENCES CAUSE WIND

The areas of high and low air pressure on the weather map may, in one sense, be likened to the hills and valleys, domes and basins of the earth's land surface. Acually, they represent variations in the air's density rather than irregularities in the surface of the air. Where the air is relatively dense and compacted, it exerts greater than average pressure per square inch; where it is less dense and expanded, it exerts lower than average pressure. *Wind* is air flowing from areas of high pressure toward areas of low pressure, and therefore represents nature's attempt to equalize pressure differences in the atmosphere. The velocity of a wind depends upon the amount of pressure difference between adjacent areas and the distance between the places in question.

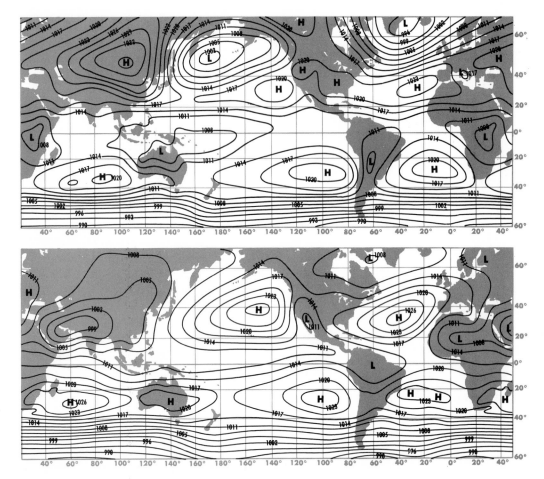

Figure 7–3 January (above) and July (below) mean sea-level pressure in millibars. (Maps after Mintz and Dean, Geophysical Research Paper No. 17, Air Force Cambridge Research Center, 1952, from William E. Powers, *Physical Geography*, New York, Appleton-Century-Crofts, 1966)

The primary cause for differences in air pressure is the unequal rates at which various parts of the earth's surface heat up through insolation and cool off through radiation. An important secondary cause of the differences is the earth's rapid rotation, which causes a deflection in the winds and interferes with the prompt equalization of pressure differences; indeed, the atmospheric whirls set up may locally have the opposite effect, that is, increase differences in pressure.

AIR DRAINAGE

Nowhere is the relation between heating, air density, and wind better observed than in hilly regions. On a clear night an exposed hilltop radiates its heat rapidly and the air upon it becomes relatively cold, dense, and heavy. This heavy cold air then flows down the slope and comes to rest on the lowland (Fig. 7–4). This forces the lighter warm air to flow upward. Thus, during winter nights frosts may occur on the low

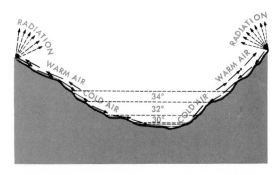

Figure 7–4 Cross section of a valley showing air drainage.

areas but not on the slopes. In California, for instance, in response to such *air drainage*, orchards of tender fruits are placed on the slopes, whereas barley, wheat, alfalfa, and sugar beets are planted on the valley bottoms.

OCEANIC WIND SYSTEM

PLANETARY CONVECTION AND PRESSURE BELTS

This same principle operates on a colossal scale to produce a planetary circulation of the atmosphere or world wind system over the oceans (Fig. 7–5).

It should be recalled at this point that the air over equatorial regions is heated by the sun more than over other parts of the earth. This air expands, becomes less dense, and after spreading out at high altitudes, exerts relatively low pressure per square inch. Heavier air from either side moves in and forces the expanding warm air to rise. The portion of the world's atmosphere near the equator, therefore, is known as the *doldrum belt*, or *belt of equatorial calms*, or the *low-pressure calm belt* (Fig. 7–6). During spring and autumn, the doldrum belt lies directly along the equator. In July, however, it moves a few degrees north of the equator, and in January it moves to a position south of the equator.

At the poles of the earth, where sun heating averages least, the air remains dense and heavy and therefore exerts relatively high barometric pressure.

The rising air over the doldrum belt reaches its ceiling at about thirty thousand feet. At that altitude, the air sometimes flows laterally toward either pole.

Not all of the air from the equatorial region reaches the polar regions. Much of it settles back to earth between latitudes 20° and 40° in both the Northern and Southern Hemispheres. The relatively heavy compacted air formed by this settling is responsible for the *belts of subtropical high-pressure calms*. From these belts, wind blows diagonally poleward (the westerlies), and diagonally equatorward (the trades).

Over the Antarctic there is a trough in the atmosphere extending around the world. Over the North Atlantic and the North Pacific, there are two separate "basins" or oval-shaped areas of low pressure.

PREVAILING WINDS OVER THE OCEANS

As might be expected, the belts of pressure just described give rise to a vast system of winds along the earth's surface. From these belts, air flows equatorward into the equatorial low-pressure belt. The earth's rotation has the effect of deflecting the course of this air toward the west. Thus are produced the *northeast trade winds* and the *southeast trade winds*.[2] The air flowing poleward from the subtropical calm belts into the subpolar lows creates the *southwesterly winds* and the *northwesterly winds*. Here again one sees the effect of the earth's rotation in the right-hand deflection of these winds in the Northern Hemisphere and the left-hand deflection in the Southern Hemisphere. Some of the results of this may be seen in Figure 7–6.

ANNUAL SHIFTING OF THE WIND SYSTEM

The sun's noonday rays, however, seldom fall exactly vertically at the equator. Instead, the "sunshine equator" migrates from the equator northward to latitude 23½° N., then back to the equator, then southward to latitude 23½° S., and then back again. This shifts the position of all the pressure belts and the entire wind system back and forth annually. Thus, an island in latitude 35° N. experiences the trade winds in summer, the high pressure or horse latitude calms in autumn, the westerlies in winter, and the calms again in spring.

OCEAN CURRENTS

The prevailing winds which exist over the oceans exert a "brushing" effect on the ocean water itself, urging the water into definite drifts or currents.[3]

In the Atlantic Ocean, for example, the trade winds push the white caps of the waves of the ocean in a general westerly direction. As

---

[2] A wind is always named for the direction *from* which it blows.

[3] The rotation of the earth is, of course, a primary cause of both water and air flow, along with heat differentials.

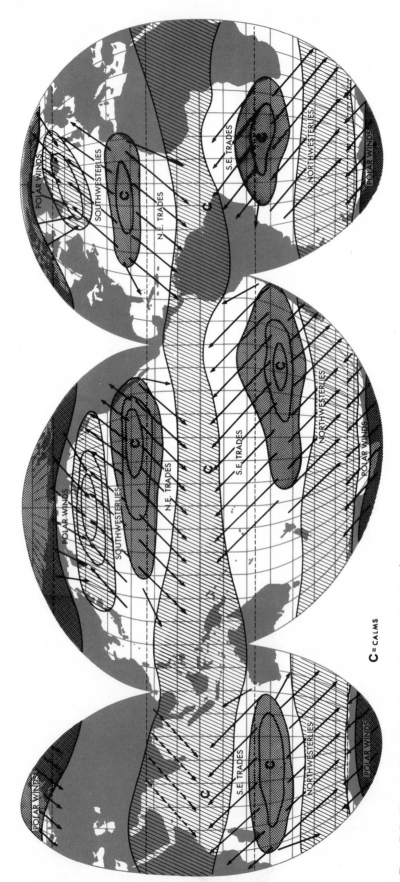

C = CALMS

Figure 7–5 The prevailing wind system of the earth. Note that the prevailing winds are confined to the oceanic areas and do not characterize the continental areas. Compare this map with those showing the periodic monsoon winds.

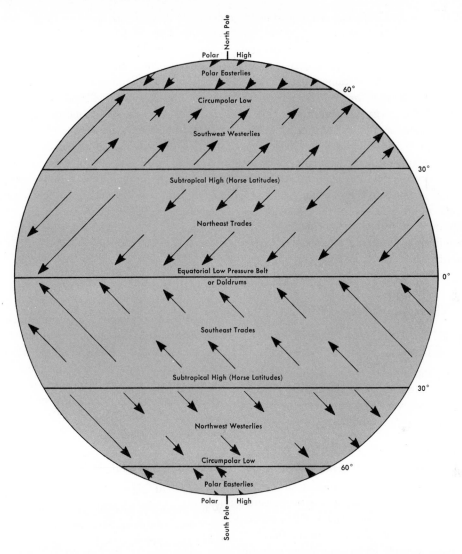

Figure 7–6 Generalized diagram of atmospheric pressure zones and world air movements as they would be if the earth's surface were smooth and uniform and there were no seasonal changes. (From William E. Powers, *Physical Geography*, New York, Appleton-Century-Crofts, 1966)

a result, a current flows westward on both sides of the equator (the "solid" part of the earth moves from west to east). Between the two equatorial currents, an *equatorial counter-current* flows eastward. This "counter-current" cannot return all the water carried by the two warm currents, and hence the excess flows poleward along the western edge of the Atlantic. In the southern part of the North Atlantic, this is known as the *Gulf Stream;* in the northern part of the South Atlantic, as the *Brazilian Current*. These waters, urged on by the westerly winds, then recross the

ocean in an easterly direction as west wind drifts, and return equatorward as cold currents. In the North Atlantic, this cold current is called the *Canaries Current;* in the South Atlantic, the *Benguela Current*.

Thus each ocean contains two enormous eddies, those of the Northern Hemisphere revolving clockwise and those of the Southern Hemisphere revolving counterclockwise.

Corresponding warm currents in other oceans are the *Kuro Siwo* (*Japan Current*), *Mozambique Current*, and the *East Australian Current*. Other cold currents are the *California, West Australian,* and *Peru (Humboldt) Currents.*

Into the Arctic Ocean, a branch of the warm *North Atlantic Drift* enters polar waters north of Norway. Two cold streams, the *Labrador Current* and the *Bering Current,* flow out of the Arctic. All of these ocean currents are important because the warm ones carry tongues of milder temperature poleward and usually create ice-free harbors in subpolar latitudes. Similarly, cold currents carry lower temperatures far closer to the equator than is normal. The cold *Labrador Current* influences the fogginess of the Grand Banks, and shipping and fishing there. The cold *Peru Current* influences northern Chile greatly, playing an important part in its aridity and its nitrate deposits.

CONTINENTAL WIND SYSTEM

CONTRASTS WITH THE OCEANIC WIND SYSTEM

Because of the rapidity with which great land masses heat up during summer and cool off during winter, the wind system above the oceans is not found over the continents.

SUMMER MONSOON WINDS

During the summer the air above the continents soon heats, expands, and becomes relatively less dense. A great area of low barometric pressure, therefore, forms over land masses which experience a summer season. The surplus air thus displaced rises to high levels and flows outward over to the oceans. Onto each of the continents, therefore, oceanic or maritime air flows (Fig. 7–7). This flow of moist air from the oceans onto the continents is known as a *summer monsoon.* Such summer monsoons are rainy. Where they blow up steep slopes, they produce heavy rains. In some exceptional cases, a total of three to four hundred inches of rain may fall in the warm half of the year.

WINTER MONSOON WINDS

During winter, the continents in middle latitudes cool off and the air above them contracts. Soon each continent is covered with relatively cold, dense air which forms an area of high barometric pressure. Out of this, a mass movement of air takes place in the direction of each of the oceans. This movement is known as the *winter monsoon.* It is a land wind and, therefore, is normally dry.

While "summer wet" and "winter dry" generally prevail, there are significant local exceptions to this rule. The exceptions are due to a combination of such factors as the configuration of the coast; smaller bodies of water such as seas, gulfs, or bays; orographic barriers; winds parallel to the coast; and upwellings of cold water just offshore.

CONTRASTS AMONG CONTINENTS

The larger the land mass in middle and high latitudes, the greater the seasonal contrasts in temperature and air pressure will be. Accordingly, Asia, the largest continent, has very strongly marked monsoon winds. In North America, the monsoon circulation is much disturbed by irregular cyclonic winds, and both the summer warming and winter cooling are interfered with by the Great Lakes and Hudson Bay. Nevertheless, the monsoon is often fairly well discernible for weeks at a time. This is particularly true over the Gulf and South Atlantic States.

HUMIDITY AND PRECIPITATION

WATER VAPOR

Water vapor, an invisible gaseous form of water, is present in varying amounts in all parts of the lower atmosphere.

EVAPORATION

Three-fourths of the earth's surface is ocean, and on a large part of this, the sun's energy is at any moment causing evaporation. Winds are also constantly at work transporting this water vapor onto the continents, upon which much of it falls as rain or snow.

SATURATION

The capacity of the air to hold vapor varies with the temperature. The higher the temperature, the more water vapor a given amount of space can hold. When it can take up no more water vapor at its existing temperature, it is saturated. Raising

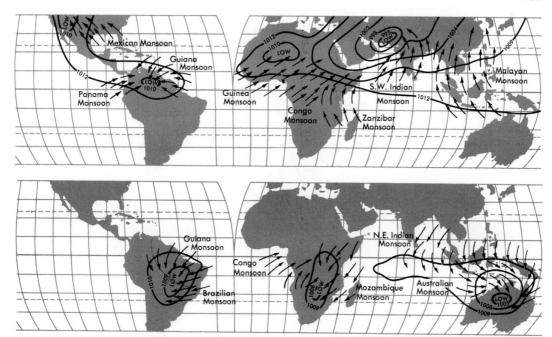

Figure 7–7 The monsoon winds of the earth. Above, during the high-sun period north of the equator; below, during the high-sun period south of the equator.

the temperature will, of course, create a new and higher saturation point.

DEW POINT AND CONDENSATION

Air will, if cooled sufficiently, reach saturation. The temperature at which this occurs is known as the *dew point*. When air is cooled below its dew point, the water vapor which it contains begins to condense as small droplets, and the more it is cooled, the more such condensation takes place. Water vapor condenses into dew, frost, fog, cloud, rain, snow, sleet, or hail.

PRECIPITATION

When the particles of moisture become large as a result of the cooling of a large volume of air, precipitation occurs. Precipitation is the fall of moisture in the form of rain (drops of water), snow (flakes of water crystal), sleet (pellets of ice), or hail (balls of ice).

LATENT HEAT

Heat, derived from solar energy, is required for the evaporation of water. Later, when this water is condensed to visible form once more, the heat used in evaporation is returned to the atmosphere. The heat thus liberated is known as *latent heat of condensation*. Its effects may be quite marked. For instance, during a snow- or rainstorm latent heat may supplement the primary source of heat in the atmosphere. One of its major effects is to intensify a storm once unstable air reaches the point where condensation takes place. The latent heat released has the tendency to increase the instability of the air causing it to rise to greater heights where further cooling takes place resulting in more condensation. This may be noted in the summer thunderstorm. An example of the effect of latent heat is furnished by the coasts of southern Alaska and western Europe. There, moisture-laden west winds blow off the ocean and onto the land. These produce an almost daily rainfall from autumn to spring. The latent heat liberated by this steady winter rainfall helps these lands to be twenty to thirty degrees warmer than is normal for their latitude.

PROCESSES OF PRECIPITATION

Other than simple cooling of air in place through radiation of its heat, there are three main

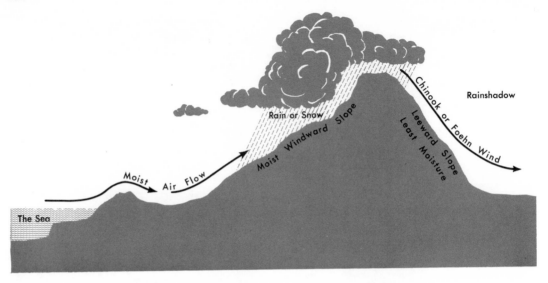

Figure 7–8 The windward and the leeward sides of a mountain range contrasted.

processes which account for cooling, condensation, and precipitation. These are *convectional, orographic,* and *cyclonic*.

Convectional process

Heated air becomes less dense and unstable. It rises and is replaced by cooler and denser air at the surface. As air rises it expands. As it expands, it automatically decreases in temperature.[4] As this occurs its vapor condenses, often into cumulus clouds. If condensation continues, precipitation takes place, often as thundershowers.

Orographic process

Where wind blows against a mountain barrier, a plateau edge, or even a steep hill, its momentum, plus the force of the oncoming air behind it, carries the air over the obstruction. Once started upward, it may rise much higher before gravity pulls it down again. As it is forced upward clouds form (if the air is moist), and rain falls on the windward side (Fig. 7–8). On the leeward side, the air descends and is thereby compressed and warmed. Accordingly, no rain falls. The dry area to leeward of high elevation is known as a *rain shadow*.

Cyclonic process

Over large portions of the earth, especially between latitudes 35° and 60°, moving formations of high or low barometric pressure in the atmosphere are common. Such areas of light or heavy air with a generally easterly motion are known as *lows* and *highs* or *cyclonic* and *anticyclonic storms*. A cyclonic formation is a large area of low pressure into which warm and cold air currents are moving as into a vortex (Fig. 7–9). In the front or eastern half of a cyclonic area, warm moist air tends to flow up and over a cold mass of air. Condensation takes place and widespread rain or snow occurs. In the rear or western part of a cyclone, cold heavy air sweeps down from the northwest, causing a sharp drop in temperature. The cyclonic process is rather intricate and involved. It will therefore be treated at more length in Chapter 15.

TROPICAL AND POLAR AIR MASSES

The cyclonic storms just discussed result from the coming together of two groups of air masses. Air masses develop when the atmosphere remains stationary over large areas for a sufficiently long time to acquire characteristics appropriate for those areas. Thus a polar air mass in North America might take on the cold and dry characteristics of central Canada or be cool and moist if it forms over the north Pacific Ocean. In contrast, an air

[4] The process of cooling by expansion (even though no heat is lost) is known as *adiabatic cooling*.

mass might assume the warm and moist qualities of the Caribbean and the Gulf of Mexico.

When polar continental air pushes out from its source region and flows southward and eastward across Canada and into the United States, it frequently collides with the lighter and moister air advancing from the Gulf of Mexico or the Atlantic, which, being lighter, is forced to ascend and yield moisture by precipitation (Fig. 7–3). Most of the rain received in eastern North America is caused by the interaction of these air masses. Although air is invisible, the air masses possess certain properties that enable their movements to be traced across the country. The Environmental Science Services Administration has an Air Mass Division which carefully studies air masses and indicates their positions for the daily weather map.

As our knowledge of the atmosphere increases we find that to indicate the middle latitudes as a zone of cyclonic storms is not enough. For example, meteorologists now designate a "polar front" as a discontinuous boundary between tropical and polar air which shifts with the seasons. Generally, this front marks the equatorward extent of polar air masses. Less is known about the "arctic front" which marks the boundary between less contrasting air masses such as maritime polar and continental polar or polar and arctic air masses. This would also apply to an "antarctic front." Much attention of late has also been given to an "intertropical zone of convergence (ITC)" which indicates the boundary between two tropical air masses. Much research is still needed to give us further understanding of these, but precipitation is usually associated with each of them.

DISTRIBUTION OF PRECIPITATION

Precipitation is very unequally distributed over the earth (Fig. 7–10). Areas of heavy rainfall occur on lowlands along the equator, and on windward mountain sides in both the trade wind and the westerly wind belts. Southern Chile, western British Columbia, and northwest Europe are excessively wet.

The world's dry lands include most of the trade wind belts in the tropics (except steep

Figure 7–9 Wind directions around a "high" and a "low." Note that air movement is outward from a "high" and inward to a "low."

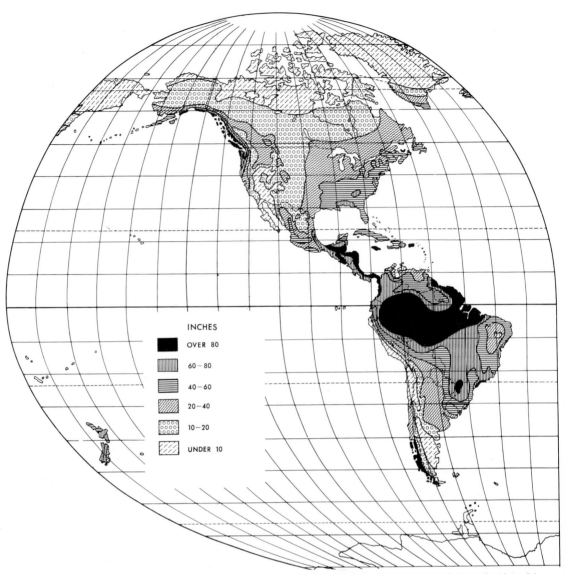

Figure 7–10 Average annual precipitation over the earth's lands. (After the Environmental Science Services Administration)

windward coasts) and regions behind mountain ranges in the interiors of continents in middle latitudes. In polar regions, because of cold and limited evaporation, the water vapor content of the air is usually low and these areas therefore receive little precipitation, though they are not dry.

CLIMATE

CLIMATE AS AVERAGE WEATHER

Weather is the condition of the atmosphere at any given time and place. Climate is for the most part average weather. The climate of an area or of a single place cannot be adequately known until such things as monthly temperatures throughout the year, annual precipitation, seasonal distribution of precipitation, length of growing season, and so forth have been averaged over at least twenty or thirty years. Climate, in addition to being the average weather, includes also the departures from normal. The extent and frequency of the departures cannot be determined until its records have been kept for many years.

TWO CLASSES OF CLIMATES

In general, there are two distinct "families" of climates—the *marine* and the *continental*. The former are characterized by the steadying, equalizing influence of the ocean. The latter are marked by irregular and seasonal extremes of the land

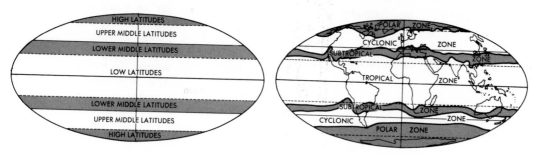

Figure 7–11 Zonal divisions of the earth. Left, ideal geomathematical divisions; right, actual geoclimatic divisions.

Figure 7–12 Climatic regions of the continents. Unclassified: (0) highlands where climates vary with altitude. Tropical Zone: (1) Rainy Tropical—tropical forest, (2) Monsoon Tropical—tropical savanna, (3) Semiarid Tropical—tropical grassland, (4) Arid Tropical—tropical desert. Subtropical Zone: (5) Mediterranean Subtropical—sclerophylous woodland, (6) Humid Subtropical—broadleaf and coniferous forest, (7) Dry Subtropical—steppe and desert. Cyclonic Zone: (8A) Humid Continental with Long Summers—deciduous forest and prairie, (8B) Humid

masses themselves. The following quotation portrays well the contrast between them.[5]

MARINE VERSUS CONTINENTAL CLIMATES

a. The Uniform Marine Climate of the Lofoten Islands.—Let us compare an extreme *marine* climate with an extreme continental climate in the same latitude. The southern Lofoten Islands off the coast of Norway, and Verkhoyansk in Siberia, probably furnish the greatest contrast to be found anywhere between places lying at equal distances from the equator. Both are within the Arctic

Circle. Yet in winter the winds blowing from the ocean prevent the Lofoten Islands from suffering the usual Arctic severity of such latitudes. Grass remains green and cattle are pastured out-of-doors all the year. In summer, however, although the weather is milder than in winter, the temperature of the ocean is so nearly the same as in winter that the islands are raw and chilly. So cool is the air that practically no trees and crops will grow, and the people wear the same thick, warm woolen

[5] Ellsworth Huntington and Earl B. Shaw, *Principles of Human Geography* (New York, John Wiley & Sons, Inc., 1951), pp. 132–133.

Continental with Medium Summers—coniferous forest and prairie, (8C) Humid Continental with Short Summers
—taiga, (9) Dry Continental—short grass (semiarid phase), shrubs and bushes (arid phase), (10) Temperate
Marine—coniferous and beach-oak forest. Polar Zone: (11) Subpolar—tundra (Arctic pasture), (12) Polar Ice
Cap—ice fields. (Large copies of the map of the climatic regions of the continents, suitable for coloring, can
be purchased in packages of twenty-five from the publisher.)

clothing summer and winter alike. The great characteristic of the marine climate of the Lofotens is its
uniformity.

*b. The Extreme Range of the Continental
Climate at Verkhoyansk.*—Verkhoyansk is so different from the Lofoten Islands that one can scarcely
believe that both places are in the same latitude and
and no farther apart than Portland, Maine, and Portland, Oregon. At the Siberian town the range from
the average January temperature to the average of
July is 120° F., while in the Lofotens it is only
20°. At Verkhoyansk the temperature has been
known to fall to 90° below zero, and almost every

year it goes down to −70 or −80°. In fact the
average for the whole month of January is about
−60°. It is so cold that a steel skate, so it is said,
will not "take hold" of the unmeltable ice, but
slips on the surface.

Strange as it may seem, the summer at Verkhoyansk is warmer than in the islands off the
Norwegian coast. This, of course, is because the
land of the continental interior yields quickly to
the summer sun. The *average* temperature in July
is 60°, or as high as the *highest* ever known in the
Lofotens, where the July average is only 51°.
Temperatures as high as 85° have been recorded at

111

Verkhoyansk, while 75° to 80° is common during the long days of summer. Hence some trees grow in spite of the intense cold, and crops can be raised, although none will grow on the Norwegian islands. To be sure, the ground never really thaws. If a man digs down a foot or so in his vegetable garden in July or August he comes to frozen soil, for only a thin layer on the surface ever melts.

In a place like Verkhoyansk not only the changes from season to season but from day to night are often extreme. Out of doors on a March night one wants all the fur coats he can get, and even then one's nose may freeze during a short walk. The next noon, however, the warm sun and still air make it possible to chop wood with bare hands. By day in August light clothing is sufficient, but at night frosts may occur.

Verkhoyansk and the Lofoten Islands represent the extremes of continental and oceanic climates, but many other regions show somewhat similar conditions. In the typical continental climate the winter is long and cold, and the summer long and hot, with brief transition periods in fall and spring. The typical oceanic climate has a mild winter and a cool summer, with no sharply marked transition seasons.

THE FOUR GREAT ZONES

From the discussion presented in this chapter, it is obvious that the distribution of insolation, atmospheric pressure, winds, ocean currents, and land and water bodies over the earth produce an intricate global pattern of rainfall, temperature, seasonal contrasts—in fact all varieties of weather.

When one examines this global pattern carefully, four great pairs of zones of temperature are recognizable—*tropical, subtropical, cyclonic,* and *polar* (Fig. 7–11). The *Tropical Zone* is characterized by continuously high lowland temperatures and notable uniformity of the length of the day. Such seasonal changes as occur are between wet and dry. Its boundaries are formed approximately by the limits of the natural growth of the palm tree. The *Subtropical Zone* is characterized by a long, almost tropical summer and a short mild winter. The *Cyclonic Zone* extends roughly from latitude 35° poleward to the limit of tree growth. It is characterized by a hot or warm season, a cold season, and two intermediate seasons; and in addition exceptionally variable weather, associated with much variation in the

winds, which are cyclonic. The *Polar Zone* is characterized by low average temperatures and by great variation in length of day from season to season.

TYPES OF CLIMATE

Within each of these great zones, there are such significant differences in rainfall, temperature, humidity, wind, and sunshine that it is desirable to divide each zone into several *types* of *climate*.

The number of different climates in the world is great. But when data on all parts of the world are assembled and classified, it becomes evident that climatic conditions are somewhat comparable over large areas. Indeed, the same general kind of climate recurs not only in the Northern as well as Southern Hemisphere, but on different continents. Thus, if one overlooks many climatological details, the world's climates may be classified into only twelve types, as follows.

Tropical Zone:
1. Rainy Tropical
2. Monsoon Tropical
3. Semiarid Tropical
4. Arid Tropical

Subtropical Zone:
5. Mediterranean Subtropical
6. Humid Subtropical
7. Dry Subtropical

Cyclonic Zone:
8. Humid Continental
9. Dry Continental
10. Temperate Marine

Polar Zone:
11. Subpolar
12. Polar Ice Cap

CLIMATIC REGIONS AND MAN

The regional occurrence of these types of climate is shown in Figure 7–12. These climatic regions are so different, as places for man to live and work, that one might almost say that mankind lives in several different kinds of world rather than in one world. The climate in each region largely determines what kind of natural vegetation, native animal life, and soil will be available to the human inhabitants. Climate plays a dominant role in man's distribution over the earth. In addition, climate directly affects man's industries (his ways of making a living) and has considerable bearing upon his health, mental and physical energy, and bodily comfort. Accordingly, the next ten chapters in this book will present mankind in his various climatic settings over the earth.

SUGGESTED USEFUL READINGS

This list is the most comprehensive of all those following other chapters. It can be used for Chapters 7 to 19 inclusive.

ATLASES

Brooks, C. F., and others, *Climatic Maps of North America* (Cambridge, Mass., Harvard University Press, 1936).

U.S. Department of Agriculture, *Atlas of American Agriculture*, Part 2, "Climate" (Washington, D.C., Government Printing Office, 1936).

Visher, Stephen S., *Climatic Atlas of the United States* (Cambridge, Mass., Harvard University Press, 1954), 403 pp.

GENERAL REFERENCES

Ackerman, Edward A., "The Koppen Classification of Climates in North America," *Geographical Review*, XXXI, 1941, pp. 105–111.

Blair, Thomas A., and Robert C. Fite, *Weather Elements; a Text in Elementary Meteorology*, 5th ed. (Englewood Cliffs, N.J., Prentice-Hall, Inc., 1965), 364 pp.

Blumenstock, David Irving, *The Ocean of Air* (New Brunswick, N.J., Rutgers University Press, 1959), 457 pp.

Brooks, Charles E. P., *Climate in Everyday Life* (New York, Philosophical Library, 1951), 314 pp.

Bulletin of the American Meterological Society, Vol. 47, No. 5 (May, 1966). A challenging article by Professor Athelstan Spilhaus, "Goals in Geo-Technology" deals with, among other goals, weather control.

Critchfield, Howard J., *General Climatology* (Englewood Cliffs, N.J., Prentice-Hall, Inc., 1960), 465 pp.

Geiger, Rudolph, *The Climate Near the Ground*, 2d ed., translated from German by Milroy Stewart (Cambridge, Mass., Harvard University Press, 1957), 494 pp.

Gentilli, Joseph, *A Geography of Climate*, 2d ed. (Perth, University of Western Australia Press, 1958), 172 pp.

Hare, F. Kenneth, *The Restless Atmosphere* (New York, Hillary House, 1961).

Haurwitz, Bernard, and James M. Austin, *Climatology* (New York, McGraw-Hill Book Company, 1944), 410 pp.

Sewell, W. R. Derrick, ed., *Human Dimensions of Weather Modifications*, Research Paper No. 105, Research Papers, Department of Geography (Chicago, University of Chicago, 1966).

Kendrew, Wilfred George, *The Climates of the Continents*, 5th ed. (Oxford, Clarendon Press, 1961), 608 pp.

Kendrew, Wilfred George, *Climatology*, 2d ed. (Oxford, Clarendon Press, 1957), 400 pp.

Koeppe, Clarence E., and George C. DeLong, *Weather and Climate* (New York, McGraw-Hill Book Company, 1958), 341 pp.

Stewart, George R., *Storm* (New York, Modern Library, 1947). This is the story of a cyclonic storm and how it affected the lives of certain people.

Thornthwaite, C. Warren, "An Approach toward a Regional Classification of Climate," *Geographic Review*, XXXVIII, 1948, pp. 55–94.

Thornthwaite, C. Warren, "The Climates of the Earth," *Geographical Review*, XXIII, 1933, pp. 433–440.

Trewartha, Glenn T., *An Introduction to Climate*, 3d ed. (New York, McGraw-Hill Book Company, 1954), 402 pp.

Trewartha, Glenn T., *Earth's Problem Climates* (Madison, Wis., University of Wisconsin, 1961), 344 pp.

U.S. Department of Agriculture, *Climate and Man,* Yearbook of Agriculture, 1941 (Washington, D.C., Government Printing Office, 1941). 1248 pp.

8

Rainy Tropical Climate Regions

RAINY TROPICAL REGIONS

Rainy Tropical climate occurs on every continent with the exception of Europe and Antarctica. In general, it is found in two sorts of locations. The most extensive occurrence is in the doldrums or equatorial calms which occupy a belt of variable width usually extending not more than five to eight degrees on either side of the equator. Within this equatorial belt, the air is hot and damp, and winds are feeble or absent for long periods of time. Rainfall is supplied almost entirely by convection circulation. Under the direct or nearly direct rays of the sun, the air begins to rise usually about midday. Ascent causes the air to expand and cool to its dewpoint. The resulting condensation produces local convection showers which fall torrentially. They are, however, of short duration because they soon cool the air and automatically weaken the process of convection. Regions which experience such conditions are the Pacific Coast of Colombia and the Amazon Basin in South America; the Guinea Coast, and the Congo Basin in Africa; certain insular and peninsular portions of Asia, northeastern Australia, and most of the northern islands of Australasia (Fig. 8–1).

Actually, however, few parts of this great area exhibit continuously *true equatorial* conditions. This is because the seasonal swing of the world's pressure belts, consequent upon the sun's annual migration from northern tropic to southern tropic and back again, permits the invasion of monsoon winds and trade winds.

The second type of location where Rainy

Tropical climate occurs is on windward coasts between latitudes 5° and 25°. In such areas, land is exposed to almost constant sea breezes from the northeast, east, or southeast. Wherever such land is hilly or mountainous, copious rains are produced by the cooling of the winds as they are forced to rise over these physical barriers. Areas which experience this phase of the Rainy Tropical climate are the Philippines, Hawaii, most of the South Sea Islands, the windward shores of some of the West Indies, and the eastern coasts of Central America, Brazil, Madagascar, and Vietnam.

DISTINGUISHING CHARACTERISTICS

Regions with this type of climate have the sun overhead or nearly so throughout the year; hence the sun's rays are almost vertical at all times, and days and nights are practically equal the year round. While such places are undeniably hot, they do not have the extremely high temperatures that characterize the marginal portions of the Tropical Zone or even the summers in the continental interiors of the Intermediate or so-called "temperate" Zones. This is a consequence, no doubt, of the high percentage of cloudiness and water vapor[1]; plus the fact that near the equator

[1] "Several years ago I was sent by the Government to Colon, on the Isthmus of Panama, to establish a weather station. I left Washington in July. The capital was sweltering in the worst hot spell of the summer, and its inhabitants—except those who had lived in the tropics—were telling one another that

Figure 8–1   Rainy Tropical regions.

the heat was 'tropical.' I remember that I was an object of commiseration on the part of relatives and friends because duty compelled me to enter the equatorial regions at that season of the year. These kind people, no doubt, had the impression that, as the mercury was hovering around 100 in the shade along Pennsylvania Avenue, it must have climbed clean out of the thermometer down on the Isthmus.

"I spent nine months keeping tab on Colon weather. During all this time my instruments never registered as high as 90!" From the *Realm of the Air*, by Charles Fitzhugh Talman, 1931, p. 238. Used by special permission of the publishers, The Bobbs-Merrill Co., Indianapolis.

"To say that the tropics are always hot, the 'temperate' regions neither hot nor cold, and the polar regions always cold, satisfies the mind's craving for simplicity and saves the time of the teacher, who gets an idea into the minds of his pupils with very little effort. The only trouble is that the idea is not correct—for any of the zones. The error of this simplified idea regarding the two former zones has been well put by Mark Jefferson, 'What a suggestion of burning heat has the phrase "torrid zone" and how unwarranted! And how pleasing is the name "temperate" applied to our own zone! . . . so intemperate in fact that the only sound description of it that applies at all times is that every season is exceptional.' " From V. Stefansson, "Some Erroneous Ideas of Arctic Geography," *The Geographical Review*, American Geographical Society of New York, Vol. 12, 1922, p. 267.

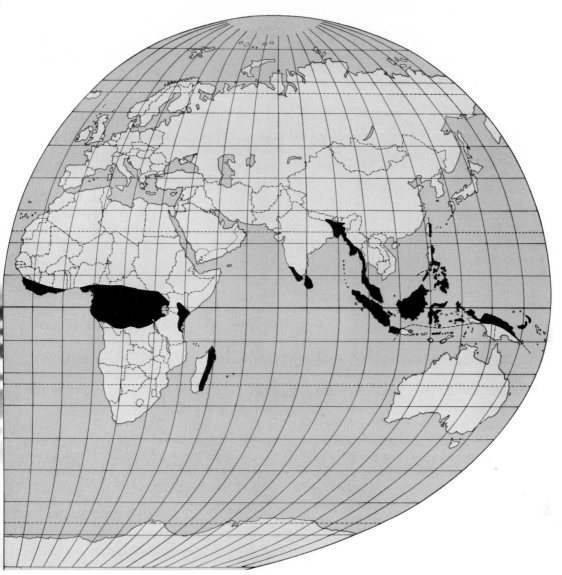

the sun shines only about twelve hours a day throughout the year as compared with fourteen to fifteen hours during the summer at the higher latitudes. Freezing temperatures are unheard of; here, as nowhere else, except in the polar regions, seasons in the true sense do not exist. The coolest temperatures occur at night, though the difference between day and night seldom exceeds a few degrees. Even so, night is the only *winter* that Rainy Tropical regions ever know.

The air is steamy, like that in a greenhouse, the relative humidity being high throughout the year. Hence, even without extraordinarily high temperatures, the continuous moist heat becomes unbearably oppressive. In short, the *sensible temperature* is high. By the sensible temperature is meant the degree of heat or cold *felt or sensed by the human body*, not that recorded by a thermometer.

Cloudy weather prevails; indeed many places are cloudy almost continuously. Heavy rain falls every month in the year and on at least four or five days of every week; there is no true dry season, and what is called *dry* must really be construed to mean *less rainy*. Thus no native of Belém (Para), Brazil, can remember the day when it has not rained. On the other hand, it should not be inferred that the rainfall is evenly distributed throughout the year (Fig. 8–2). The so-called *dry season* never is of sufficient intensity or duration to result in leaf fall.

The equinoctial seasons (when the sun is directly over the equator) are usually rainier than other parts of the year. These rainy periods

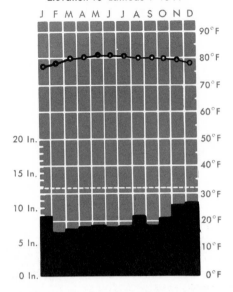

Figure 8–2 Climate graph for Singapore.

coincide with the passing of the intertropical convergence zone over the equator. The rains ordinarily come in the afternoon when the heated air is ascending most vigorously. This afternoon shower is such a regular occurrence that it is often used in place of a clock for dating engagements for business or pleasure. It is invariably of torrential character, is often accompanied by thunder and lightning (Java, for example, is the most thundery place in the world), and is of short duration, frequently lasting not more than half an hour, though occasionally continuing into the night as a drizzle. The cloud cover with its accompanying downpour of rain cools the air temporarily, but as soon as the sun reappears, the oppressive conditions prevail.

Taken as a whole, the Rainy Tropical climate is concident with the world's heaviest belt of precipitation. The *average* precipitation of the doldrum belt is estimated at approximately one hundred inches.

PLANT GEOGRAPHY

League upon league of monotonous virgin forest,[2] tall trees growing close together and bound one to another or festooned by hanging lianes (woody creepers), which shut out most of the light from the ground and make it so dark as to appear like twilight,[3] an impressive quietude[4] and a depressing monotony that make one happy to get to a stream where the sun may be seen again— this is the equatorial rain forest or *selva*, the product of high temperatures, heavy rainfall, high humidity, and retarded evaporation.

The natural vegetation consists of a three-story forest; the upper one of huge trees, monsters frequently 15 to 20 feet in girth and 125 feet high; an intermediate one, consisting of less tall trees; and a low one, comprising small trees and bushes (undergrowth). Where streams are present, the trees lean far out over the water. They support countless parasitic plants and climbing vines, which stretch across them in pendant loops, wrap themselves around the trunks like huge snakes, or hang down like ropes from the canopy overhead. The branches and trunks support parasitic ferns, lichens, and mosses in great abundance. Sometimes the floor of the rain forest or selva is surprisingly unobstructed so that one may walk over it quite unhampered; again, the floor, though not densely grown, is to a certain extent obstructed by vine-like plants, enormous roots of trees, and fallen trees.

It is the *jungle*, however, that constitutes the real barrier to human movement in this type of climate. Jungle occurs along the edges of the rain forest, along streams and rivers, on the steep slopes of mountains, and in occasional areas that have been cleared by man or have been burned over—*areas now reached by the sun.*

[2] P. W. Richards, *The Tropical Rain Forest* (Cambridge, England, Cambridge University Press, 1952), p. 5.

[3] How dark it is beneath the canopy may be appreciated when it is realized that photography takes as much as twenty thousand times longer than in the open.

[4] This quietude characterizes only the day. At night the forest is anything but quiet. A Marine corporal at Rendova had this advice for newcomers to the jungle: "Get used to weird noises at night. This jungle is not still at night. The land crabs and lizards (and tree frogs) make a hell of a noise. . . . And there is a bird here that sounds like a man banging two blocks of wood together. There is another bird that makes a noise like a dog barking."

When one walks through the jungle, one must constantly cut his way through the undergrowth; thus the *machete* is indispensable (Fig. 8–3). Even keeping open the constantly used dark tunnels of the jungle paths is a difficult task, for jungle growth is exceedingly prolific and soon obstructs all openings.

Since no cold or dry season interrupts growth, the trees, though broad leaved, are green all year, do not develop annual growth rings, and carry blossoms, green fruit, and ripe fruit at one time.

All vegetation desperately strains skyward and where the crowns of the trees come together the branches become interlocked, forming a canopy. This canopy, which attains an average height of about 125 feet, is of irregular outline because the crowns coalesce in bunches rather than in compact masses. From the ground one can see practically nothing of what lives in the tree tops since the forest is relatively dark. To look down upon this canopy from an airplane, however, is like looking down upon a vast billowy green plain—resplendent with color and teeming with animal and insect life.

Such forests differ greatly from those in middle latitudes. They contain a bewildering array of plant species—possibly 2,500 in the Amazon basin and as many as 150 on a single acre. This is a result of the keen struggle for existence which practically precludes the survival of seeds and makes extremely precarious a tree's success in finding room nearby for its offspring (Fig. 8–4).

Another conspicuous feature of the vegetation is the mangrove forest, which monopolizes the low coastal swamps and lagoons and deltas of rivers that are inundated at high tide. Attaining heights of twenty-five to seventy-five feet, these trees are adjusted to living in water and appear to stand on knee-shaped stilts which emerge from the slimy blue-black mud.

It would, however, be a mistake to believe that only forest characterizes the vegetation in the Rainy Tropics. Extensive savannas also are to be found. Most plant ecologists do not attribute these savannas to climate. They believe them to be biotic climaxes due to fire, or edaphic climaxes due to soil conditions hostile to trees.

SOILS

The soils which develop under the selva, except where they are covered at intervals by alluvium, are not fertile. The mature soils here are known

Figure 8–3 Difficulties confront people as they move and work in the jungle. Every step must be cut from the dense vegetation with a machete. (Photo courtesy of the Creole Petroleum Corporation)

Figure 8–4 The equatorial rain forest—a nonseasonal forest consisting almost wholly of woody plants. The trees are extremely numerous in species and varied in size. The taller trees are not so high as travelers would have readers and listeners believe. Most of them attain heights of 150 to 180 feet—considerably less than the California redwoods and the Australian gums. The richness of the flora is the most important characteristic of the equatorial rain forest. Due largely to the similarity and somber coloring of most of the leaves and to the absence of marked seasonal changes, it is a monotonous forest. It is also a several-layered forest—"a forest above a forest." (Photo courtesy of the United Nations)

as *laterites* (Fig. 8–5C). These soils receive organic matter that falls from the trees and forms humus. This humus must return to the forest. If man removes the tree cover, thus laying the soil bare, the humus decomposes rapidly and in the hot, wet climate is not renewed. Rather it is reduced to soluble mineral salts, which the rains leach away.

ANIMAL GEOGRAPHY

The Rainy Tropics constitute zoologically one of the richest regions in the world. The Rainy Tropics of Southeast Asia alone are known to have at least 650 indigenous species of mammals, 2,000 species of birds, 624 species of reptiles (of which 318 are varieties of snakes and 254 are species of amphibious or frog-like animals), well over a quarter of a million insect species, and hundreds of species of fish. This region, of course, is unique in that it has many unusual types of its own, and also draws upon the two very distinctive faunal types of Asia and Australia.

Because of the abundance of native animal life in the Rainy Tropics, most people imagine these climatic regions to be veritable paradises for big game hunters and to a limited extent this is true, for large mammals are present. They are less numerous, however, than in the parkland savanna of the Monsoon Tropical and in the steppe of the Semiarid Tropical climates, which sometimes border the doldrum belt on either side. It is in these two climates that mammals—both herbivores and carnivores—are most abundant and it is to these lands that most hunters who are after big game go. The tropical forest is a barrier to all but local movements of mammals.

The animals differ considerably on the several continents. Africa appears to be the richest. Among the forest-dwelling ground and water animals here are the buffalo, elephant (even the pygmy elephant), forest duiker, okapi, rhinoceros, and wart hog, and in the rivers the crocodile and hippopotamus (Fig. 8–6). Strangest, rarest, and shyest of all Rainy Tropical animals is the okapi, which lives in the deep gloomy forest of the Congo. It is about the size of a horse, has the horns and anatomical structure of the giraffe,

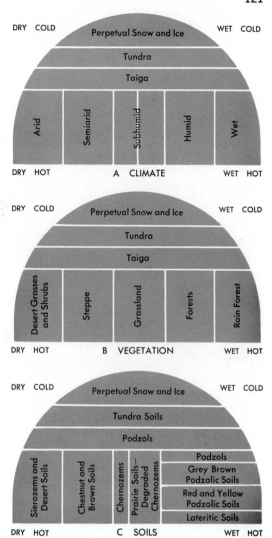

Figure 8–5 Schematic representation of: A, the distribution of climatic types; B, the distribution of vegetative formations, on a climatic base; C, the distribution of the major zonal soil groups on a climatic base. From left to right in each diagram climate varies from dry to wet, and from top to bottom it varies from cold to hot. (After the Environmental Science Services Administration)

the legs of the zebra, the hooves of the ox, the trunk of the antelope, the freely revolving eyes of the chameleon, and an extraordinary blue tongue which is exceeded in length only by that of the anteater. The okapi's exceptional strength and cunning enable it to vanish even through the thickest entanglements of vegetation at the slightest alarm.

In the South American rain forest, large

Figure 8–6   Hippopotami in a river in the Congo. These animals, found only in Africa, spend most of their time in the water and despite their huge bulk (a large one may weigh four tons) are excellent swimmers. Hippopotami are herbivorous, living principally on grasses and weeds. (Photo courtesy of Belgian Information Service, New York)

ground animals are not numerous. Among the more abundant are the anteater, armadillo, ocelot, and peccary. In Asia the ape, bear, buffalo, deer, elephant, monkey, rhinoceros, and tiger are important.

In the rain forest, native animal life is mainly arboreal, consisting essentially of apes, bats, birds, frogs, lizards, monkeys, snakes, and sloths (South America). This last is among the sideshow animals and probably is the most completely arboreal of all mammals, since it is positively helpless when removed from a tree. It obtains all the food it requires in the trees—buds, fruits, leaves, and young shoots. Even water can be supplied from the moisture in the trees.

Among the reptiles are various snakes, lizards, alligators, and crocodiles. Some of the snakes are strictly arboreal, are long and slender and thus find it easy to reach from tree to tree.

They live largely on birds or animals which they can swallow without too much inconvenience. The python, for example, can swallow prey four times larger than the normal diameter of its throat because the articulations of the jaws are very loose and allow a wide spread of mouth.

The anthropoid apes, bats, birds, and numerous varieties of monkeys are largely fruit-eaters. The gorilla, one of the rarest of Africa's jungle animals, frequently attains a size of four and a half to five feet and is said to dominate the forest; at least the natives fear him more than the elephant. Gorillas do considerable damage to gardens and fruit trees.

No discussion of Rainy Tropical animal life should fail to mention the piranha of the Amazon —probably the world's most dangerous fish. Only about a foot long, it possesses teeth so sharp and jaws so strong it can slice a piece of flesh from a man as neatly as a razor and reduce him to a skeleton in ten minutes. Afraid of nothing, it will attack like lightning any animal regardless of size. The piranha always attacks in schools of a hundred or a thousand. When "it smells blood, it turns into a raging demon!"[5] This fish is feared as no other animal throughout the entire length of South America.

Insects of many species abound, for the year-long frostless season enables them to breed continuously. Just a few of these may be mentioned. The Congo cockroach eats the backs of books and the paint off picture frames. Termites cover the country with hills eight to fifteen feet high, with a dozen or more to the acre (Fig. 8–7). They eat anything containing cellulose, leaving usually only the shell of the object; hence one may pick up what appears to be a solid object, as for instance, a chair, and find it crumbling into a heap of dust. Then there are the driver ants, most interesting of all insects and deadly enemies of the termites. They are about one half to three fourths of an inch long, and charge along like black streams, one half to three fourths of an inch wide. They move along like a vast miniature army, guarded by squadrons of "soldier ants." Nothing—neither elephants nor men—can stand against them; all life retreats before their ferocious attacks.

Many of the insects are blood-suckers and some carry the germs of deadly diseases from person to person. Among the most pestiferous, possibly, is the leech, which is about an inch long when empty and can penetrate one thickness of cotton cloth to get at his victim.

DISTRIBUTION OF POPULATION

With few exceptions the Rainy Tropics constitute some of the largest blank spaces on the population map of the world. Great tracts of almost continental immensity, such as Amazonia and Congoland, have scarcely more persons per square mile than some of the notoriously barren and inhospitable deserts. Where nature is too lavish or too niggardly, man struggles to obtain a foothold and to maintain it.

Population is small in both hemispheres in this type of climate because tribal wars, unsanitary

and unhygienic modes of living, and periodic migration levy a heavy toll of life among the young and old,[6] and because the chief occupation, patch-agriculture supplemented by miscellaneous hunting, never tolerates a dense population. To these should be added such environmental handicaps as enervating climate, dense forest, annoying insects, and deadly diseases.

Most of the people dwell along the streams which afford an important source of food (fish and turtles), an effective avenue of transportation, connection with the outside world, and fertile soils (recently deposited alluvium) for

[5] George S. Myers, "A Monograph on the Piranha," *The Aquarium Journal* (February, 1949), p. 52.

[6] Travelers see very few old people among so-called primitive tribes anywhere in Rainy Tropical regions. In many areas women are old at forty.

Figure 8–7   Termitary in Katanga. (Photo courtesy of Belgian Information Service, New York)

the few subsistence crops. Settlements tend to cling to the bluffs which are well drained and constantly exposed to river breezes.

Java, southern Nigeria, Ceylon, and parts of the Philippine Islands are densely populated, Java having the highest density in the world for a strictly natural area of its size dependent primarily upon agriculture—more than one thousand persons per square mile in an area only slightly larger than the island of Cuba. This is possible, however, only because the country possesses the most fertile soils (volcanic) in the Rainy Tropics.

NATIVE INHABITANTS AND STAGE OF CIVILIZATION

People outside the Rainy Tropics commonly believe that these regions consist entirely of vast tracts of impenetrable, fever-laden jungle inhabited by fierce savages and great beasts. To be sure some of them are precisely this, but many too are not. Not all the inhabitants can be lumped together as being backward and uncivilized, for on the banks of some of the larger rivers dwell natives who are relatively advanced. The interior of Africa has ceased to seem a dreary waste of uniform, unbroken savagery. The so-called primitive savages occupy the more remote sections where several elements of the natural environment have united to hinder, if not prevent, human advancement. Such primitive folk as the Pygmies of the Congo, certain Indian tribes of Amazonia, and the Punans of Borneo, wander about in small bands, wear little or no clothing, live in crude shelters of branches, or grass, or leaves on the ground or in trees and occasionally in natural caves or on rock ledges (the lowest savages may have no homes at all), and know little or nothing whatsoever of agriculture. They survive only because of the genial climate and the ease of gaining a hand-to-mouth existence. Hard work is unknown, for the combined high temperatures and humidity have helped to make the people sluggish and inert. Many too are ill. A scientific observer noted that a group of Negroes engaged in building a railroad in the former French Congo rested two minutes for every one minute's effort. And yet, why should they work when they can get every-

thing they need without too much effort? The incentive to work is not strong where clothing is not essential, where a rude hut, which may be made in several days, affords ample shelter from rain and sun's rays (Fig. 8–8), and where a small patch of beans, corn, and manioc and a few banana plants supply what food is needed.[7] After hundreds of years of human occupation, Amazonia continues in its pristine state, having been changed negligibly by man. It was estimated several years ago that in this area, which is as large as Argentina, not more than one hundred square miles of cropped land exist. The figure would be greater today.

Civilization, it will be recalled, has developed only in those parts of the world where a cold or a dry season (a time of rest) has forced man to produce a surplus for the dormant period. Places characterized either by extreme poverty of plant and animal life or by extreme abundance have proved equally unfavorable for human progress.[8] Wherever man dwells, he must conquer or at least tame all plant life; but where it grows continuously, he experiences extreme difficulty in doing either.

Progress in the Rainy Tropics has been impeded also by the difficulties coincident with the rearing of domestic animals—especially those for draft purposes. Nearly all domesticated animals, except the indigenous semiaquatic carabao and the elephant, find the Rainy Tropics unfavorable: they soon die of disease or deteriorate either because of the scarcity of forage or because of the harsh, rank, and unnutritious character of that

[7] Contrast this with the situation in the United States, where 73.3 percent of the total cost of living in 1967 went for food (24.5 percent), housing (28.9 percent), and clothing (19.9 percent). In short, the people of the Rainy Tropics, by performing a minimum amount of labor have the three basic human needs (though the three are by no means comparable), for which the American toils many hours a day.

[8] Rainy Tropical peoples are often accused of being improvident and happy-go-lucky—living only for today and permitting tomorrow to care for itself. One reason for this, not commonly appreciated, is the lack of storage facilities to carry over surpluses and thus give greater stability. Most native products deteriorate with amazing rapidity in the tropical, insect- and bacteria-ridden environment.

Figure 8–8 Congolese natives building a hut with "raw materials" taken directly from the forest. Such a hut can be constructed in several days and affords ample shelter from the rain and the rays of the sun. (Photo courtesy of Belgian Information Service, New York)

which does grow. In parts of Africa, the survival of domestic animals is positively doomed by the tsetse fly, a messenger of death which transmits the trypanosomes that cause the fatal nagana as well as sleeping sickness among human beings. Whole settlements have thus been depopulated. Some progress in controlling the tsetse fly and sleeping sickness (African Trypanosomiasis) has been made, but much still remains to be done.[9]

The development of a progressive civilization is halted also by the type of food available. Considering the small variety and poor quality of food, it is little wonder that the people are undernourished (the food is nearly all starchy and sugary—yams, bananas, maize, and cassava). Frequently natives eat one kind of food over a protracted period; moreover, they eat at any time; the result, of course, is poor digestion.

Progress anywhere depends largely upon effective communication, for only in this way can people get new ideas and new products.

Communication in the dripping equatorial forest is obviously seriously hampered.

Finally there is the matter of health. A doctor stationed in the Amazon Basin, who examined natives from over a large area, stated that 90 percent of them have more or less marked anemia and that this, along with chronic malaria, verminosis, secondary anemia, and splenomegaly, causes the natives to have "universal lethargy."

In another region—the Congo—whole tribes were wiped out by plagues before the coming of the white man. Today, areas where formerly nine-tenths of the people died of disease are greatly improved and the people live there in comparatively good health. In fact, it was once believed that these lands might have to be abandoned. Former British West Africa was much the

9 Jacques M. May, *Studies in Disease Ecology* (New York, Hafner Publishing Company, Inc., 1961), pp. 231–260.

same. Until the white man arrived, the people depended upon medicine men and witch doctors. Sleeping sickness, yellow fever, dengue, yaws, and especially malaria (commonest of all) took a heavy toll. Now the white man's knowledge of medicine and hygiene is replacing the witch doctor's "hokum." Much of the territory in the Rainy Tropics was formerly colonial territory of middle-latitude countries which provided medical aid and sanitation. Today, the World Health Organization (WHO) of the United Nations actively assists the many newly developing countries. The late Dr. Albert Schweitzer, among others, made notable contributions to tropical medicine and health.

To be sure, there still are wide areas over which conditions have improved little if at all. Millions of inhabitants, attached to the soil and to their tribal practices, still live under conditions similar to those prevailing centuries ago. Probably the major cause of this unsatisfactory situation is the unwillingness to depart from the daily habits and the conceptions of life based upon ancient immutable rites. The end of the great epidemics—an exclusively medical success —has not greatly altered the way of life of the indigenous masses.

"To the attempts to destroy the causal agents . . . must now be added hygiene education, health education, transformation of living conditions, triumph over nature of economic and social progress. Wells and latrines in villages, and shoes for the inhabitants, would equal the most sensational scientific discovery."[10]

WHITE SETTLEMENT AND THE MENACE OF INSECTS

Middle-latitude people, even with their phenomenal advance in science, have thus far made little progress in a determined effort to conquer the Rainy Tropics, which persist as one of the least hospitable environments for them. Usually the European becomes debilitated and falls victim to some endemic malady transmitted by insects, which besides causing such dreadful diseases as malaria, yellow fever, and sleeping sickness, lay their eggs beneath the skin, irritate by bite and sting, and even pollute the food.

Can the white man conquer these enemy insects? DDT is considered by many to be the panacea for absolute freedom from insect pests in the Rainy Tropics. Entomologists, however, despite their enthusiasm for this war-developed killer, fear that malaria-carrying mosquitoes, for example, are developing immunities against DDT. Since several years are necessary to develop this resistance, scientists believe that if they are to win this battle, they must intensify their efforts during the next few years before such resistance has developed. Many insecticides have been developed since DDT, but some questions have been raised as to whether or not their liabilities outweigh their assets.[11]

CLIMATE AND MAN

Can man adjust himself effectively to this type of climate? Recent advances in human and animal physiology, in tropical housing, and in sanitary engineering indicate that, based solely upon climate, there is no reason to believe that he cannot do well.

In future chapters, we shall see that climate *is* significant to human life but that it is a *limiting rather than a determining factor*. Several areas in the Rainy Tropics that were hostile to man's occupancy at the turn of the century, now are regarded as eminently suitable habitats. Hence if most parts of this climate realm are not regarded highly as human habitats, it would seem that other factors, perhaps a combination of them, are more responsible than climate per se.

ECONOMIC ADJUSTMENTS

Not one civilized country on earth can lay claim to being completely self-supporting. All nations have become interdependent and the countries of the Northern Hemisphere need many products which can be produced only in the Rainy Tropics. Accordingly, in backward regions which were

[10] Dr. M. Vaucel, "The Challenge of the Tropics," *World Health Organization News Letter,* Vol. VII (April, 1954), p. 2.
[11] Rachel L. Carson, *Silent Spring* (Boston, Houghton Mifflin Company, 1962).

richly endowed by nature but occupied by tribes apathetic to economic development, middle-latitude people stepped in and created a system whereby they ruled while the natives toiled. If there was a paucity of labor, machinery was set in motion for rounding up the requisite number of aborigines. Broadly speaking, the local people displayed little interest in the new order, because they saw few advantages accruing to them for their labor. A notable exception existed in what was the Gold Coast (now Ghana), where cacao was grown on the small holdings of the Negroes by themselves.

Throughout the Rainy Tropics, exploitation will go forward and nothing can stop it. Great corporations with ample capital and technological know-how can hope for commercial success; sanitation, clearing (Fig. 8–9), planting, the development of transportation, all demand this. The equatorial rain forest seems no place for individual enterprise at present. It will progress economically only if outside aid is forthcoming and if political stability takes place.

Figure 8–9 A jungle-brush leveler at work. Note the heavy bar in front and the rear-wheel steering device. The corrugated "tread" helps to crush the leveled vegetation into a matted bed. (Photo courtesy of R. G. LeTourneau, Inc.)

ADJUSTMENTS TO THE FOREST

Among the greatest forests in the world are those in the Rainy Tropics. Brazil's "Green Hell" or "Green Paradise" (depending upon the individual's reaction) is the most extensive, stretching 2,500 miles from the Atlantic to the eastern slopes of the Andes. Both hard and softwood trees grow here, though the former apparently predominate. Of the 2,500 tree species in Amazonia, 50 are high-grade cabinet woods, and many of the others are comparable with such well-known American trees as maple and yellow poplar. Some of the woods are easily worked; some can scarcely be worked at all; some split too easily; some are attractive to insects and hence are in little demand, while still others are resistant to insects—even to termites.

Despite the vast storehouse of valuable timber to be found in all Rainy Tropical regions, logging and lumbering are relatively unimportant. Exploitation is difficult because of the following.
1. Inadequate transportation facilities
2. Dearth of labor
3. Great distance from markets
4. Lack of pure stands (social species are in most cases exceedingly rare and the few commercially valuable trees are invariably scattered among many unutilizable ones)
5. High specific gravity which prevents many woods from floating
6. Unwise export duties

A bright future doubtless exists for these forests, among which are many trees that grow rapidly and afford a limitless supply, even though they are inferior to those of cyclonic regions for structural purposes.

It must be remembered that the principal market for wood is for lumber for construction purposes. Lack of a pure stand necessitates selective small-scale logging, with attendant higher costs, and prevents the steady flow of a *uniform* raw material, which is essential to maintain lumber operations and efficiently to supply market demand. Europeans long ago became accustomed to and now demand the softwoods[12]—pine, spruce, fir, and cedar. These, unfortunately, grow

[12] The terms *hardwood* and *softwood,* while in general use, are definitely misleading, since no definite degree of hardness divides woods falling into the two groups.

in very few places in the tropics. At present only the so-called precious woods of most Rainy Tropical lands have found much of a market, because only they bring high enough prices to warrant costly transport charges to export markets. If Amazonia, for example, can develop soon a large export trade with timber-starved Europe, logging might conceivably be carried on profitably. This would necessitate cutting the bulk of the species and these would have to be standardized in name, grade, and method of measurement of the various kinds of logs, timbers, and sawed lumber.

In Africa, as in tropical America, the forests contain innumerable species of valuable trees. Possibly the most important commercially is the mahogany.

Wild rubber

At one time the Amazon Basin was the center of the world's raw rubber production. In 1912, 49,000 long tons were produced—the maximum amount ever to come from the region. While rubber-gathering still is an important economic activity of Amazonia, production is dwarfed in comparison with that of southeastern Asia. Only 1 to 2 percent of the world supply originates here. Wild rubber just cannot compete with that grown on plantations in southeastern Asia. This was admirably demonstrated during World War II, when the Japanese held the principal rubber-growing lands, and the Western Allies, desperate for rubber, strove to have production increased in South America. The United States, particularly, was willing to pay a high price and even to help in protecting the health of the workers and to cooperate in increasing the local deficient food supply. Though it was believed that these measures would stimulate production and result in possibly 50,000 new workers migrating into the basin, not more than 25,000 did come, and production in 1943 in all Amazonian countries reached only 13,000 long tons. Moreover, little change is to be anticipated in the immediate future.

Plantation rubber in the Amazon Basin

To date, rubber has not been successfully grown[13] on plantations in the Amazon Basin. This has resulted partly from the paucity of low-cost, efficient labor and partly from the South America leaf blight—major foe of the plantation Para rubber tree. However, plant scientists waged an intensive and successful battle against the blight.

As is well known, the Amazon Basin is the native habitat of the Para rubber tree (*Hevea brasiliensis*). In this forest the *Hevea* tree and the South American leaf blight lived peacefully together for centuries—a consequence of forest conditions which prevented a parasite from multiplying and spreading with sufficient speed to overwhelm the host plant. Wild *Hevea* trees in the forest do not grow in pure stands, there being usually not more than half a dozen trees to the acre, and some authorities estimate the *average* for the entire Basin to be only one tree. Thus, each is screened from its neighbors by the foliage of trees of other genera and, as these other trees are not susceptible to leaf blight, they serve as barriers to the passage of spores from one *Hevea* tree to another. Accordingly, there is only moderate damage to the wild rubber trees.

Southeastern Asia has not been similarly plagued by the leaf blight because when the *Hevea* tree was introduced there, the disease was left behind. Subsequently, the great distance over which wind-borne spores would have to be carried, together with strict quarantine measures, has kept it free.

When it was once realized that the rubber business of the Amazon Basin with its wild trees could not compete with southeastern Asia with its plantations, attempts were made to grow plantation rubber in Amazonia. But plantations were unsuccessful largely because the leaf blight spread from scattered wild trees to most of the plantings—ultimately reaching epidemic proportions. Accordingly, mass defoliation and dead trees resulted.

In order to control this disease, scientists finally developed a "three-part tree." It is produced by grafting a bud from a high-yielding tree onto one having a strong root system, the grafted bud being placed near the ground and forming a new trunk. In order to give the grafted tree more resistance to leaf disease, a third strain of

---

[13] On a commercial basis.

tree, not susceptible to the disease, is added by top-budding at a height of 6 to 7 feet to form a new crown.

The lack of a suitable labor supply appears to offer the biggest single problem now. There is little chance that Brazil can solve this problem because of low population densities, poor health, and disinclination to work in Amazonia.

Plantation rubber production in southeastern Asia

In 1876, Henry Wickham smuggled seventy thousand seeds of *Hevea brasiliensis* out of Brazil and thereby laid the basis for the rubber plantations in southeastern Asia.

Environmental conditions in southeastern Asia are excellent for the growth of the rubber tree. The climate is constantly hot, the annual rainfall varies from 70 to 120 inches with no month receiving less than 3 inches, the soils are loose and well drained and adequately fertile, the plantations are located on relatively small islands or close to the coast if on the mainland (a significant advantage over Amazonia, where the cost of getting rubber a thousand miles out of the forest is great), and location of the plantations on the important trade route from southeastern Asia to Europe and the United States.

Economic conditions are equally favorable. Especially is southeastern Asia fortunate in having an abundance of native laborers who not only perform *more* work at lower cost, but are *more* skillful than those in Amazonia.

Here on plantations running into thousands of acres the trees are planted close together, so there is heavy production in a limited area. This enables a single gatherer to collect latex from as many as 400 trees (Fig. 8–10), whereas the collector in Amazonia can visit usually only 100 to 150 in the jungle.

Synthetic rubber

Because southeastern Asia, the source of 98 percent of the world's natural rubber, fell under the sway of the Japanese army; because Amazonia proved to be a stunning disappointment; and because the United States had to have rubber to carry on the war, the government poured 750 million dollars into a new synthetic rubber indus-

Figure 8–10 Tapping a **Hevea tree** on a rubber plantation in Malaysia. A thin shaving of bark is removed every other day at the base of the tapping area. The latex then oozes out of the tubes in the bark and runs down into a porcelain cup. Because the plantation industry gave the world a large and dependable supply of rubber at low cost, it now dominates natural rubber production. (Photo courtesy of Uniroyal)

try. By 1945 production had reached one million tons. In some respects it is superior and in some inferior to natural rubber. Synthetic rubber fills about 60 percent of the new rubber needs of the nation. In price, synthetic rubber has been underselling the natural variety.

Collection of Brazil nuts

The collection of Brazil nuts is the second most important activity in the Amazon forest. The tree grows wild as far inland as Bolivia. The trees, usually growing in groups of six or more on clayey soils 50 to 100 feet from streams or swamps, attain heights of 75 to 150 feet and have extremely large trunks.

The fruit of the tree is the large woody-shelled capsule which contains twelve to twenty triangular nuts. The harvest period usually lasts six or seven months—from November to May.

Because of the immense size of the tree, the laborers never collect the pods by climbing the trees. Instead they wait for the wind to break them loose and then gather them from the ground. They never work on windy or rainy days, for they know that they could easily be knocked out or even killed by a pod weighing two to four pounds falling from a height of 150 feet at the rate of 800 to 1,000 feet per minute. After collecting the pods, the workers carry them to their camps where they and their families crack them open with large knives. The nuts are placed in baskets or on mats until enough have been collected to deliver to the local trader who, in turn, sends them down the Amazon by boat.

Hunting and fishing

Natives who live by hunting and fishing alone typify the most primitive type of society. Yet in the Rainy Tropics there are tribes who know nothing of any other pursuit and who look with contempt upon those adjacent peoples who live by means of agriculture. The Pygmies of Congoland (Batwas and others) are professional hunters and subsist for the most part upon their kill and upon the wild honey and roots they collect. They exchange meat for the vegetables and fruits, especially manioc and bananas, of the neighboring tribes of big people. They understand the forest as do few other Africans and are woodsmen par excellence. They possess an uncanny sense of direction and are as keen of ear and eye and as agile and alert as a wild beast. It is fortunate indeed that they are, since large animals are none too numerous and birds and monkeys dwell in the treetops and hence are difficult to kill. Moreover, many of the animals are so colored as to blend perfectly with the vegetation and are therefore difficult to locate and kill.

The Pygmies hunt with spears and bows and arrows, the tips of which are dipped in a poison which paralyzes the nerves of the animals but does not affect the meat (Fig. 8–11). They even kill with spears such large animals as elephants, though much of their game is entrapped in nets or in pits skillfully covered with vegetation and placed along the runways of the animals which invariably lead down to drinking places. These little people, who are only four feet tall,[14]

Figure 8–11   Pygmy using a bow and arrow. (Photo courtesy of Belgian Information Service, New York)

catch fish in streams with nets and baskets, or with spears in pools which become isolated from the rivers. The Pygmies are nomadic, constantly shifting from place to place in search of game and as a sanitary measure. When a large beast is killed, instead of taking it to their camp, they move to it. This is the easier, inasmuch as they have no impedimenta save bows and arrows, spears, and a few clay pots.

A large proportion of Amerinds in the upper Amazon Country are primarily hunters, though they do some fishing occasionally and carry on a half-hearted, haphazard agriculture. They hunt with the blowgun and the throwing spear. They show uncanny dexterity in winding in and out of the almost impenetrable vegetation and can move almost without making a sound. Should the game become aware of the hunter's presence, he will remain motionless for an unbelievably long period of time.

When the hunter spies his quarry, he pulls several darts from a container and wraps the blunt end of each with a small amount of wild cotton. He then inserts one in the blowgun and approaches the game in a zigzag line so as to prevent the animal from seeing him until he is within effective shooting range, which varies with his individual skill, the size of the animal, and the prevailing wind. He can bring down a small

[14] The men average about four and a half feet high and weigh about eighty pounds. The women are several inches shorter and weigh ten to fifteen pounds less.

bird usually with a single shot from a distance of about twenty-seven yards.

In hunting peccary, the men go in groups, encircle the feeding animals, climb into nearby trees, and then let go with their darts. They may kill as many as thirty-five before the herd is aware of what is happening. After the animals have fled, the hunters descend to the ground and kill the paralyzed pigs with their spears.

The Yagua employ a large variety of traps, the most common of which are snares and pitfalls. They display extraordinary intelligence in selecting the area where the trap is to be built and manifest great familiarity with the habits of the animals they seek.

The only time they do much fishing is when large schools of fish ascend the rivers. They use poison in the form of mashed or crushed barbasco roots, which they throw into stagnant pools or behind dams. As the sap of the barbasco penetrates the water, the stupefied fish rise to the surface and are collected in knitted bags.

Where hunting and fishing are the dominant occupation in this type of climate, population is always sparse, for any marked increase in human numbers would shortly bring about a corresponding decrease in fish and game. Seldom does the population exceed eight persons to the square mile and frequently it is not more than two.

AGRICULTURAL ADJUSTMENTS

To generalize on so varied a topic as agriculture is a most difficult task, because the Rainy Tropics occur over so wide a sweep of territory and contain peoples of such varying habits and abilities—native, white, and mixed. Moreover, while it is true that all regions with a given type of climate are similar, they do, nevertheless, vary considerably.

Because of the heavy rainfall, the continuous heat, the high humidity, the dense vegetation, the insect pests, the virulent diseases, and the paucity of domestic animals, agriculture is spotty, for it is nothing short of an Herculean task to make a clearing in an equatorial forest. The work of the American pioneer, hard as it was, was child's play by comparison. Here growth was not continuous, the trees were smaller and softer, and

autumn, winter, and spring were so bracing as actually to goad a man to work rapidly, hard, and long. Not so in the steamy withering Rainy Tropics, where the vegetation grows the year round, springs up immediately after it has been cleared (trees grow as much as twenty feet in a single year), and chokes all openings.

Rainy Tropical agriculture is considered here under three headings: (1) *shifting agriculture*, (2) *small-scale sedentary native agriculture*, and (3) *plantation agriculture*.

SHIFTING AGRICULTURE

Milpa, fang, ladang, taungya all are terms used in different parts of the world for shifting or migratory farming. This type of farming is followed by backward peoples in all those parts of the world having this type of climate. On a small area of heavy forest the smaller trees are felled. The larger ones are left standing, though occasionally they may be girdled. This kills them and permits light to reach the ground, thereby enabling crops to grow. A great bonfire or even a series of bonfires is made as soon as the felled material is sufficiently dry to burn. The large trees do not burn. The ashes are used to fertilize the soil, which often is deficient in minerals.[15] The ground is then broken up with clubs; seeds and cuttings are dippled in with pointed sticks among the charred trunks in the partial shade. Manioc[16] is the principal food crop, but bananas,

[15] Most people believe that Rainy Tropical soils are extremely rich. This is a myth difficult to dispel. The lack of fertility results from the high temperature and humidity which favor rapid decay—decay that prevents the accumulation of partially decayed organic matter left over from the year before. Moreover, the constant rain throughout the year results in *leaching* the soils of their soluble mineral elements. By this process the descending vadose water dissolves the soluble minerals and carries them in solution down into the zone of saturation and thence out through the rivers to the world ocean.

[16] Manioc or mandioca (Brazil) is known as *yuca* in the Spanish-speaking countries and as *cassava* elsewhere. It is the staple food of the Rainy Tropics and means to the people there what corn means to the Mexicans, rice to the Orientals, and far more than both wheat and potatoes to Americans. Its starchy, tuberous root is boiled like potatoes; occasionally it is fried. Most frequently it is grated, squeezed dry,

papayas, yams, rice, corn, and sugar cane along with certain fish-poisoning plants all are important crops. There is no real cultivation either before or after planting.

After taking two crops, or at most three, from the land, the people abandon it and clear a new field, fire it and begin the cycle anew. If a third crop is grown, it is invariably inferior to the first and second. In short, the soil is depleted and weeds become exceedingly difficult to control. It is actually easier to clear a new area somewhere else than to attempt permanent tillage.

Disused plots are quickly swallowed by the jungle and most are never tilled again, though in some regions they are reclaimed after lying fallow for ten to twenty years. The soil, however, gets progressively poorer. Grasslands usually take the place of the original forest and to prepare grasslands for agriculture with primitive tools is far more difficult than removing the forest, so that shifting agriculture carries with it the "makings" of its own destruction.

Obviously only a small scattered population can secure support from this system of farming. In some parts of southeastern Asia where this kind of farming is followed, some one hundred to two hundred acres are required per family. In more advanced stages, the soil can support only one family for every five hundred to one thousand acres.

In occasional spots the natives practice a more elaborate type of migratory farming than that just depicted. Equipped with better tools, they really clear the forest except for certain trees they intentionally save—trees that supply them with fruits and nuts. In this system, these trees tower above the bananas, the next tallest, below which is a haphazard confusion of manioc, corn, dry-land rice, peanuts, and sugar cane. Finally on the ground itself are yams, beans, and other varieties of vegetables. Despite the apparent lack of system and careless methods of farming, a surprisingly large amount of food is actually grown on a given acre, but the staying power of the land is limited and hence the families must move from time to time.

Small-scale sedentary agriculture

Except in those lands in the Orient where dense populations have relatively complex culture and

hence a superior rice-growing agriculture, this is a form of farming that resembles in nearly every way the shifting type, except that the farmers are sedentary—remaining on the same land year after year. Conditions leading to fixity of abode include the following.

1. Refuge from stronger tribes may force certain weaker groups to maintain themselves on poor, islated tracts.

2. Europeans and North Americans may influence small groups of natives to take up sedentary agriculture. An example of this are the barbasco growers at Lagunas, Peru, the leading production center of the world for this crop, whence comes the much-demanded insecticide *rotenone*. Though the people here knew nothing about the chemical properties of rotenone, they did know that juice from the rope-like roots would kill fish. In preparing the land, they do exactly what is done in shifting agriculture—they clear and burn the forest cover and then plant the crop promptly in an effort to get the jump on weeds. In addition to barbasco, certain food crops are grown.

3. Long ago various items from all over the Rainy Tropics, such as spices from southeast Asia, dyewoods from the Guinea Coast, cinchona from the east flanks of the Andes, rubber from Amazonia, and many others, led the natives to become sedentary farmers in the neighborhoods of the major collecting and shipping points.

4. Wherever there are mines, sedentary farmers crowd nearby in order to supply some of the needs of the miners.

5. Better, improved soils make moving unnecessary.

One of the best examples of successful sedentary agriculture is the cacao production in West Africa. Cacao beans were not native to Africa but were introduced into the Gold Coast (Ghana) about the end of the nineteenth century. In colonial government nurseries, seedlings were produced and distributed to the chiefs. Whereas in

---

and lightly toasted in pans over log fires to make a hard, gritty and almost tasteless but preservable staple—*farina*. Manioc is tied to the low tropics by its need of eight to eighteen months for growth. One of its chief advantages in this climate where few products can be stored is its self-storage quality; it can be kept in the ground until needed.

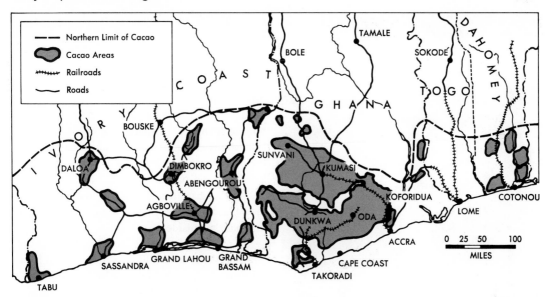

Figure 8–12 Approximately one-third of the world's cacao output comes from the region north of the Gulf of Guinea. The northern boundary of production results from the increasing length of the dry season and the decrease in the average annual rainfall. Nearly all the crop is grown on peasant holdings. The farms are small, irregular in pattern, and widely scattered. (Map after William Van Royen, *Atlas of the World's Resources*: Vol. I, *The Agricultural Resources of the World*, copyright 1954, by Prentice-Hall, Inc., New York, and published for the University of Maryland)

1891 the Gold Coast export amounted to eighty pounds, that of today runs into hundreds of thousands of tons. The crop is grown on tens of thousands of little African farms which honeycomb what was formerly equatorial rain forest (Fig. 8–12). It is authoritatively reported that the quality of the beans is low and would be greatly improved if the crop were grown more scientifically under the plantation system.

In Latin America, Africa, and Asia the methods of farming are similar: hoe culture prevails and some fertilizer is used. Clearing is done more carefully than in shifting agriculture. The actual clearing of the forest is the work of men; the planting and care of the fields is the work of women.

In eastern Bengal, Pakistan, largely in the lower Ganges-Brahmaputra delta, is raised 98 percent of the world's jute. This crop normally supplies the cheapest of all fibers and hence is in great world demand for bagging and for the manufacture of rugs and carpets, linoleum and twines. The natural environmental conditions favor production as does the dense population, which provides an abundance of cheap skilled labor (Fig. 8–13). Only two crops, rice and jute, are important in this poorly-drained region—rice

being the subsistence crop, jute the money or cash crop.

Figure 8–13 Natives loading jute in a boat in East Pakistan. (Photo courtesy of the Pakistan Mission to the United Nations)

Figure 8-14 Worker sprays cacao tree on a Central American farm. Cacao is one of the leading crops of the Rainy Tropics. The crop is confined largely to the doldrum belt because the trees cannot thrive where strong winds blow. When grown outside the doldrums, the trees are confined to wind-sheltered valleys. (Photo courtesy of the United Fruit Company)

PLANTATION AGRICULTURE

When the white man engages in agriculture in the Rainy Tropics, he invariably carries the plantation system with him. Tropical plantations are organized primarily for the production of money crops that will be shipped to the progressive countries of Europe and North America. Thus, it is probably a rubber plantation in the Malay Peninsula, Indonesia, and Liberia; a quinine (cinchona) plantation in Java; a coconut plantation in the Philippine Islands; a banana plantation in Honduras or Guatemala. Everywhere, however, the essential features are the same—the plantation is geared to supply distant markets, the tropical labor, except in parts of Malaysia and Indonesia, is not so very efficient, and white men supervise the work. The products, with the exception of sugar, do not compete with those grown in middle latitudes (Figs. 8-14 and 8-15).

The tropical plantation exists only because the industrial nations of the middle latitudes demand certain tropical products which will grow nowhere else and, since the natives are disinclined to produce on their own, irrespective of prices, the white man goes to the tropics and attempts to stimulate production. This is beginning to change somewhat as the newly independent nations attempt to better their economic position. However, the difficulty of overcoming the inertia of the past still exists. Capital, technical staffs, industrial machinery, clothing, fertilizers, medicines, and even part of the food are brought in from the outside.

Tropical plantations are highly localized; most of them lie within one hundred miles of the ocean and the great majority are within sight of the coast. Thus, islands rather than mainlands are the preferred locations—Ceylon, Java, Sumatra, and the Philippines, together with the Malay Peninsula, which in many respects resembles an island, and Central America contain many of the world's plantations. This distribution is consequent upon the fact that coasts are more healthful and freer from insect pests, they are more accessible to ships, more level land is available,

Figure 8-15 Bananas on a plantation on the Caribbean coast of Central America. (Photo courtesy of the United Fruit Company)

and the coco palm thrives best where there is a touch of sea salt in the air.

If a plantation is located on the mainland, it invariably is placed on the banks of a navigable river, since railways and roads are difficult and expensive to build and maintain. Throughout the Amazon and the Congo, roads and railroads are but short links built to connect navigable streams above and below falls and rapids and to connect ports with their immediate tributary areas.

DOMESTICATED ANIMALS

On maps showing world distribution of domesticated animals—particularly cattle, horses, mules, donkeys, sheep, and goats, and to a lesser extent even swine and poultry—the Rainy Tropics are unimpressive. This is because (1) the climate is unfavorable, (2) the animals soon die of disease or (3) they deteriorate either because of scarcity of forage or because they cannot thrive on the harsh, rank, unnutritious type that does grow, and (4) wild animals and snakes are a constant menace.

Only the water buffalo or carabao definitely *thrives*. His optimum climate is warm and moist and he works best in flooded rice fields, where most animals find it extremely trying to work at all. Moreover, his digestive system is attuned to coarse, watery vegetation and his thick hide, plus a coat of mud with which he customarily encases himself, assures considerable immunity against insects. In southeastern Asia the native humped cattle of India and the related *banteng* of Java are employed in growing crops other than rice, but they are relatively small, inefficient, unintelligent, and suffer from insects.

The elephant serves as a beast of burden in Rainy Tropical Asia and Africa. While well suited to the climate, the elephant is restricted in use because he is a voracious eater and hence can live and work only where forage is abundant. Furthermore, the elephant is used for only a few tasks—carrying logs and passengers, building roads and occasional plowing and harrowing. To but a limited extent is he utilized for pulling plows and wagons.

Cattle are raised in some areas with fair success. On Marajo Island, at the mouth of the Amazon, considerable numbers of cattle are raised by white cowboys who are reputed to live active, healthy lives. Where cattle are raised in Rainy Tropical America, the so-called "native" animals are crossed with Zebu or Brahma bulls, which results in larger, hardier, and generally more vigorous animals. Zebu and Brahma cattle have a higher heat tolerance than European cattle and this characteristic carries over to the progeny. They also show greater resistance to insect pests.

In the fly belts of Africa, however, it is virtually impossible to introduce cattle; if bitten by the tsetse fly, they get nagana and usually die.

MANUFACTURING ADJUSTMENTS

The Rainy Tropics stand out as producers of raw materials and foods rather than of manufactured goods. The machine scarcely touches the lives of the majority of the people, whose wants are relatively simple and whose purchasing power is pitifully low. Most of the commodities which enter foreign trade from the Rainy Tropics are but slightly processed. The Calcutta area is the principal exception. Its great modern mills turn out many kinds of commodities. The manufacture of jute products is one of its outstanding industries. Yet nearly 80 percent of the world's jute is grown in Eastern Pakistan (in 1947 the Empire of India came to an end and in its place were created the two self-governing dominions of the British Commonwealth of Nations— India and Pakistan). This partition brought many serious problems to both countries, one of which was the fact that Pakistan possessed most of the jute acreage but had until recently no spinning and weaving mills, whereas India with more than one hundred mills grew very little of the fiber. Today each country both grows and manufactures jute and there is overproduction. Eastern Pakistan had a small number of cotton and woolen mills also.

Some manufacturing is springing up in the heart of equatorial Africa, particularly in the Republic of the Congo where an important smelting industry has been established along with textile mills and a sulfuric acid plant.

All Rainy Tropical countries are underdeveloped countries and all underdeveloped countries desire to industrialize, believing that manufacturing will solve many of their problems. Space does not permit expansion of this topic, but industrialization alone is not the panacea for their ills, even if such lands could carry on modern machine industry.

COMMERCIAL ADJUSTMENTS AND TRANSPORTATION

The Rainy Tropics have practically a monopoly on such raw materials as bananas, cabinet woods, cacao, copal, dyewoods, ivory, manila hemp, quinine, rubber, spices and condiments, tin, some vegetable oils, and certain kinds of nuts—all of which are in great demand in middle latitude countries. Hence trade is inevitable despite the many obstacles. Commerce, of course, is handicapped by poor transport facilities. In many parts streams serve as the highways; thus the Amazon, which dwarfs all other world rivers, is navigable for small ocean vessels as far inland as Iquitos, Peru, 2,300 miles from the mouth. Hence, trading centers (towns) naturally are located upon waterways: Belém, Manaos, and Iquitos, on the Amazon; and Boma, Brazzaville, Kinshasa, Matadi, and Stanleyville on the Congo.

It was essentially trade that brought the white man to the Rainy Tropics. But trade demands improved transportation. Today there are some railways throughout equatorial Africa, though the total mileage is small.

The tsetse fly doomed domestic animals as beasts of burden in equatorial Africa, and human porters carried burdens where water transportation was unavailable. Obviously head porterage was costly, and only burdens having high value could be so handled. The commercial exploitation of this part of Africa had to await the railroad, construction having begun only after 1890. There was no coordination, however, and no single gauge. Modern highways did not come into existence in equatorial Africa until after World War I. Here commerce must continue to depend upon railways and waterways with highways as "feeders." In the Amazon Basin, railway mileage is small—approximately 500 miles. Most of it is built around the 250 miles of falls in the

Madeira River. Hailed as one of the great triumphs over a hostile nature, the Madeira-Mamoré Railway of Brazil, completed in 1913, was hardly built before the world's rubber production was shifted from Amazonia to Malaysia. In recent years it has been all but abandoned with only two trains per week each way; economically speaking, it is a "white elephant."

For the most part, roads are not numerous nor very good (Fig. 8–16). Parts of Indonesia and the Congo are exceptions. The American finding himself in the Amazon Basin is staggered to find almost no roads. The cost of building and maintaining highways in this region would be prohibitive.

The airplane is especially effective in overcoming the obstacles of great distance, of mountains, of jungle, and of lakes and rivers. Moreover, it is fast. Thus, in New Guinea, Africa, and South America, where all these factors, but particularly where immense distances separate the various population and economic nuclei, the airplane is bringing the twentieth century to the Stone Age. Detached areas that were asleep, forgotten, and abandoned are now getting some of the amenities of civilization. Internal services are being rapidly extended and improved in all these

Figure 8–16 Workers clearing forest area to permit construction of a road in Liberia. Forests cover a large part of Liberia, making road construction a difficult and costly operation. (Photo courtesy of the United Nations)

lands as are services with the outside world. There are, however, many difficulties; the fast-growing vegetation and the frequency and constancy of torrential rains make extremely laborious the maintenance of air strips. The impossibility of accurately forecasting the exact time of convectional rains is serious. The danger of crashing in the forest is obvious. Then there is on the economic side the small population and its biting poverty, as well as the fact that many of the products are not valuable in proportion to weight. To date, aviation has hardly affected the aborigines.

POLITICAL ADJUSTMENTS

In 1939 there were some 700 million people living under one or another variety of colonial rule established by Western powers. Well nigh all Rainy Tropical lands in the Eastern Hemisphere were so classified. But even then changes were under way. The really rapid changes, however, have come only recently when lands occupied by about 750 million people have acquired a new status—complete independence or self-government with voluntary "commonwealth" ties. Such Rainy Tropical lands are the Philippines, India, Pakistan, Ceylon, Indonesia, Burma, the two Congos, Ghana, Nigeria, Malaysia, and many others.

Liquidation of colonialism, after a slow start, has been rapid recently, perhaps too rapid in some cases. Many of the inhabitants are not yet ready "to stand by themselves under the strenuous conditions of the modern world," as the United Nations states it. What is needed is a planned development toward liberation. Even such countries as Indonesia, the Republic of the Philippines, India, and Pakistan face tremendous problems. Pakistan, for example, has been considered by some as economically impossible and politically absurd. Among its major problems is its division into two sections (lying as far apart as Massachusetts and Missouri), which are about as different as two regions can be.

In parts of equatorial Africa, utter political and economic chaos exists. Particularly has this been true of the Republic of the Congo. Part of the trouble lies in the myriad of tribes which occupy these new political areas. In the third quarter of the twentieth century one finds the tribal wars of past history still a strong force with which the new governments must reckon. Beside this, outside forces of two types have added to the confusion. First, there are the big powers of the Western World which desire to continue economic relations with these new countries and the Communist Bloc countries with their own form of "imperialism," which wish to add more territory to their already vast area of control. Second, there are the new leaders of Africa who have condemned nineteenth century imperialism, but by their present action are seeking similar control.

Even if these internal-external forces did not exist there would still be problems. There are simply too many countries, too small in area and without the basic resources necessary to survive in the modern world of today. After the first wave of the emotional "we are now free" passes and clearer heads of mature leadership begin to take hold and seriously cope with the problems of reality, then and only then will Africa move into the twentieth century. Hopefully, intelligent federation or union of some of the smaller countries will bring political stability to the African continent.

In Amazonia, which is largely wilderness, government is ineffective, except with the whites and *mamelucos* (mixed bloods), who dwell mostly in river towns. As far as the Indians are concerned, the government passes them by and will continue to do so until the region becomes more highly developed.

In Central America most Amerindians shunned the wet, gloomy, unhealthful lowlands of the Caribbean periphery, preferring to dwell on the cool, healthful plateau. Nor did the Rainy Tropical part become occupied until the establishment of the banana business in the nineteenth century. The work is done largely by Negroes introduced from Jamaica.

SOCIAL ADJUSTMENTS

Excepting Java, the Malay Peninsula, West Africa, and the Philippine Islands, the Rainy Tropics are but sparsely peopled. Yet because of the great amount of land in the aggregate, the total population (mostly native) is considerable.

Almost everywhere there is a bewildering diversity and complexity of race, language, religion, costume, custom, occupation, progress, and outlook. Particularly interesting in this respect is Africa, which presents to the world little of unity. One of the great lines of cleavage is that between the predominantly Islamic North Africa and the pagan (now partially Christianized) area to the south, of which equatorial Africa is an important part.

Everywhere the natives are grouped into tribes which comprise the social unit. Tribes supply the natives' fundamental needs as well as protection against enemies. Tribal organization is in some places extremely primitive, in others well systematized.

Each tribe is under a chief and each lays claim to a definite area which it occupies. Seldom does it interlope upon the territory of a neighboring group. Formerly each tribe lived for itself alone and warred occasionally against its neighbors. For many years slave-trading was common in some areas, particularly in Africa, which was treated as a human game preserve. It did not actually end in the Moslem world until the 1890's. But the slave trade was not restricted to Africa; it also existed intermittently in Amazonia and southeast Asia.

As in everything said regarding the peoples of equatorial lands, no generalization applies to all of them. Particularly does this hold for religion, which differs from tribe to tribe, from country to country, from island to island, and from continent to continent. The Africans, for the most part, are deeply religious and believe in a Supreme Being, which exists in the air, the trees, the stones, and the rivers. They also believe in the spirits of ancestors and in witchcraft and magic.

For a long time the witch doctor dominated equatorial Africa, since he combined genuine skill in herbalism, sleight-of-hand, and force of personality. The white man has compelled the witch doctor to abandon his more dubious practices. Primitive Africa, notwithstanding, still uses charms as protection against every conceivable kind of misfortune. In all probability much of what the European introduces in social organization is nothing more than a veneer, the natives

retaining *sub rosa* what they want of their own society.

In the Amazon Basin some of the savage Indian tribes do not believe in any gods and make no sacrifices to any spirit or god. There are no special places of worship and no idols for the protection of families. Myths deal largely with hunting and reproduction.

In Southeast Asia it is believed that except for small groups along the fringe of Melanesia and, perhaps, for some remnant Marquesans, all the Polynesian peoples have been converted to Christianity. So too have the majority of Micronesians.

Left solely to themselves, the natives would change little and would remain much as they were when first encountered by white men. They had adjusted themselves quite effectually, if simply, to their natural environment; their wants of food, clothing, and shelter were meager and easily satisfied. They were happy and contented and knew no mode of life superior to their own. But the white man almost everywhere profoundly disturbed this normal adjustment, plunging the natives into economic distress, social chaos, and despair. In many Rainy Tropical regions new diseases and strange ways of living began a cycle of rapid depopulation, a cycle that has for the most part now been arrested. Less and less the aborigines depend upon their immediate surroundings for a complete living. In many areas pure Amerinds, pure Polynesians, Melanesians, or Micronesians,[17] or pure Negroes are decreasing in the racial makeup.

Disease has already been discussed. Suffice it to say that a major factor tending to keep many whites from close association with natives is the fear of contracting disease, intestinal parasites, and other kinds of infection. The natives, too,

[17] *Polynesia* includes the widely scattered groups of islands in the Central Pacific—from New Zealand north to Hawaii and as far east as Easter Island. Its peoples represent a race of complex origin; they are a mixed people with bronzed skins. *Melanesia* includes the islands from New Guinea eastward to the Fijis, inhabited by natives who are of basic Negroid stock; *Micronesia* includes the islands lying east of the Philippines and north of New Guinea and its adjacent islands, and inhabited principally by short, dark peoples.

have learned to their cost that the white man is frequently a carrier of destructive maladies. Thus, the health problems of whites and natives are intertwined.

In some areas contagious or endemic diseases are now under control or are definitely coming under control. In large parts of Central and South America and in equatorial Africa, yellow fever shots have halted the epidemics that in the past periodically sowed panic among the people, making necessary the closing of ports, the quarantining of ships, and the stopping of trade. In Haiti, the terrible disease, yaws, which cripples and disfigures and which affected nearly one-third of the inhabitants, was almost wiped out with injections of penicillin. Malaria, which has struck as many as 300 million persons, killing three million annually, and which has been long considered man's number one enemy in the tropics, becomes less important by the year.

The most common and possibly the most important question under "social adjustments" is: Are the natives better off or worse off as a result of their contact with the white man? Unfortunately there is no single simple answer that is applicable to the peoples in all Rainy Tropical lands. It is well known that wherever and whenever primitive people have been brought under control of the white man, the indigenous social structure has been disturbed. Often, too, the natives, when confronted with an entirely different set of values, substitute certain vices of the new civilization for some of the virtues of the old. Hence native society in many instances has disintegrated before the white advance.

Yet slavery has been stopped; tribal wars have been prohibited; occasional cannibalism has been wiped out, as have ritual murder and the pawning of children. Confidence has been won from suspicious chiefs. The administration of justice was founded to protect both the person and property of the colonial. A subsistence form of economy, in some fractional part at least, has been transformed into an export or money economy; and a genuine battle against diseases and insect pests is in process. If minerals are present (Fig. 8–17), governments reasonably stable, and the investment climate favorable, foreign capital will develop them.

Figure 8–17 New Guinea natives working hand-powered rotary drilling rig in the jungle. This rig drills from one to three meters a day, has mud circulation, and hand-powered drawworks. (Photo courtesy of the Standard Oil Company, New Jersey).

Looking into the distant future, it is quite probable that white contact will have been for the best; in the process of accomplishment, however, much has happened and much will still happen that will be definitely detrimental in the lives of millions of people.

THE FUTURE

There are two dominant schools of thought regarding the geography of man in the Rainy Tropics: (1) the optimistic and (2) the pessimistic. If forced to be on one side or the other, the authors would align themselves with the second group. To be sure, the white man will accomplish much economically, politically, and socially in certain favored portions of the Rainy Tropics; but with what knowledge we now possess, such lands appear by and large to be relegated to the role of "underdeveloped" nations. After careful study of the excellent reports of the field technicians of the United States Rubber Development Corporation, Edward C. Higbee[18] says of the Amazon Basin:

Over so vast a territory as the Amazon modern transportation facilities, public-health services and other desirable improvements cannot be economically sustained without more intense economic activity and greater settlement. Malaria, poor roads, impure water supplies, inadequate hospital facilities, poor public services of all kinds, insufficient food supplies are all symptoms of economic distress. So often they are regarded as the cause of retarded develop-

ment, not as the products of unwise political and economic practices. Thus they are loudly proclaimed by government agencies that would promote grandiose programs financed with funds obtained partly from the United States or international organizations. Such programs can scarcely become self-supporting. They will continually require subsidies and will lapse into oblivion whenever the outside funds are exhausted unless the basic conditions are corrected that made the backward regions sick in the first place.

[18] Edward C. Higbee, "Of Man and the Amazon," *Geographical Review,* Vol. XLI (July, 1951), p. 415.

SUGGESTED USEFUL READINGS

Aubert de la Rue, Edgar François, and Jan-Paul Harroy, *The Tropics* (New York, Alfred A. Knopf, 1957), 208 pp.

Carson, Rachel L., *Silent Spring* (Boston, Houghton Mifflin Company, 1962).

Eyre, S. R., *Vegetation and Soils: A World Picture* (Chicago, Aldine Publishing Company, 1963), pp. 195–215.

Gourou, Pierre, *The Tropical World: Its Social and Economic Conditions and Its Future Status,* 3d ed., translated from the French by E. D. Laborde (London, Longmans, Green, and Company, 1961), 159 pp.

Lee, Douglas, *Climate and Economic Development in the Tropics* (New York, Harper & Brothers, 1957), 182 pp.

Mohr, Edward, and F. A. Van Baren, *Tropical Soils; a Critical Study of Soil Genesis as Related to Climate, Rock, and Vegetation* (New York, Interscience Publishers, 1954), 498 pp.

Phillips, John, *The Development of Agriculture and Forestry in the Tropics: Patterns, Problems, and Promise* (London, Faber and Faber, 1961), 212 pp.

Richards, Paul W., *The Tropical Rain Forest; an Ecological Study* (Cambridge, Cambridge University Press, 1952), 450 pp.

Stamp, L. Dudley, *The Geography of Life and Death* (Ithaca, New York, Cornell University Press, 1965). See especially Chapter V, "Living in the Tropics," and Chapter VI, "The Rulers of Africa."

Tempany, Sir Harold A., and Donald Henry Grist, *An Introduction to Tropical Agriculture* (New York, Longmans, Green, and Company, 1958), 347 pp.

United Nations Educational, Scientific, and Cultural Organization, *Problems of Humid Tropical Regions,* Humid Tropics Research (Paris, UNESCO, 1958), 102 pp.

Wrigley, Gordon, *Tropical Agriculture, the Development of Production* (London, Batsford, 1961), 291 pp.

9

Arid Tropical Climate Regions

No element of the natural environment is so important in human geography as is climate. And yet, in spite of this, the layman possesses less exact knowledge about climate than perhaps of any other aspect of nature. For example, the average man very commonly uses the term *tropical climate* when referring to the climatic characteristics of that part of the world which lies in low latitudes. Actually there is no tropical climate per se, but rather there are several kinds of tropical climates which upon examination evidence very strikingly different characteristics. Tropical climates vary all the way from the type with rain at all times of the year (which was discussed in the preceding chapter) to the type which is almost rainless (which forms the basis of discussion in the present chapter).

THE SEVEN TROPICAL DESERTS

Areas within the Tropical Zone which are almost rainless possess Arid Tropical climate, and are commonly called tropical deserts. There are seven of these in the world: the Sahara and the Namib in Africa; the Thar and Arabian in Asia; the Victoria in Australia; the Atacama-Peruvian Coastal in South America; and the Colorado-Sonora bordering the Gulf of California in North America (Fig. 9–1).

WHAT IS A DESERT?

There has not been and there is not now agreement as to the precise meaning of the word *desert*. In the United States *desert* has referred to

everything from the lands west of the forest to the arid core of the Southwest. Obviously botanists, climatologists, and geographers from all over the world must try to arrive at common agreement on the term. By superimposing small-scale world maps of climate, natural vegetation, population distribution, and agricultural regions, Benjamin E. Thomas[1] has made a map showing dry lands of the world (Fig. 9–2). It shows the approximate location and extent of the extreme deserts, such as the Atacama, Libyan, Empty Quarter of Arabia, and the barren parts of Australia.

In true deserts the precipitation is usually less than five inches; in semideserts it is seven, ten, or even fifteen inches; in steppes less than twenty inches; and in *tanezroufts*,[2] it approaches zero. The authors suggest that the term *desert* be restricted to areas that are truly arid.

LOCATION AND CAUSE

These tropical deserts extend roughly from latitude 18° to latitude 31° in each hemisphere. They cover all the surface of the Tropical Zone where the trade winds blow all year round, except windward coasts flanked by mountains. To such coastal areas, the trades bring abundant rain throughout the year; elsewhere in the trade wind

[1] Benjamin E. Thomas, "Limits for American Deserts and Oases," *Yearbook of the Association of Pacific Coast Geographers*, Vol. 17, 1955. This article was written to clarify the subject for students in undergraduate college courses.
[2] Term from the desolate area by that name in southern Algeria.

Figure 9–1 Arid Tropical regions.

zone, such as inland areas and leeward coasts, the climate is very dry. This is true because these winds, in both the Northern and Southern hemispheres, blow toward the equator—from cooler to warmer latitudes.

Another factor contributing to the origin of deserts is cold ocean currents. Examples are on west coasts where cold currents approach the equator: northern Chile and coastal Peru; western South Africa and the coast of Spanish Sahara, and to a much lesser extent, western Australia.

DESERT CHARACTERISTICS

There are many popular misconceptions about the nature of the tropical desert as a type of

human habitat, including the beliefs that it is: (1) a vast unbroken plain, (2) a monotonous expanse of sand, (3) completely dry, (4) constantly hot or torrid, and (5) practically devoid of plant and animal life.

Actually, no one of these statements is generally true. Tropical deserts are not vast plains. Desert plains there are in plenty, but high plateaus, deep valleys and canyons, lofty mountain ranges, rugged hill country and, indeed, all varieties of relief features may also occur. Nor are deserts universally sandy. Locally there are sandy deserts (*ergs*) whose surfaces are covered by dunes and barchans of wind-driven sand, like billowing ocean waves (Fig. 9–3). There are also gravel deserts (*serir* or *gibber*), rocky deserts

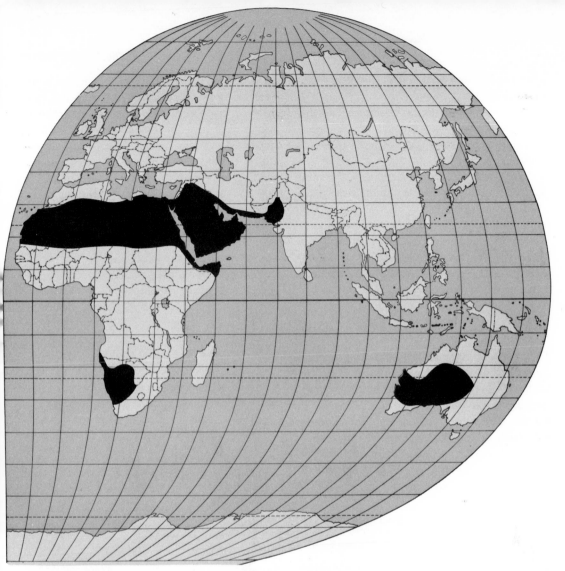

(*hamada*), deserts whose surface is hard sun-baked clay (*bajada*), and salt or alkali encrusted desert flats (*playas*).

Man's interest in climate in such areas centers in rainfall rather than in temperatures. Almost no tropical deserts are completely dry (Fig. 9–4); they invariably receive some rain, as is mutely testified by the dry stream courses (*wadis*[3]) which seam the landscape. But the rainfall of these lands is highly irregular and quite insufficient for agriculture. Moreover, it falls in torrential thundershowers, sudden of occurrence and often destructive in effect.

Tropical desert areas are far from being constantly torrid. To be sure, the noonday elevation of the sun is high, and the clear, dry atmosphere offers little obstruction to insolation from the sun's rays. As a result, daytime temperatures

during the highest-sun period are exceedingly high.

It is in the Sahara that the highest temperatures are believed to have been recorded; a shade recording of 136° F. has been reported and surface temperatures frequently exceed 170° F. Metal objects exposed to the intense heat of the sun may reach a temperature of 180° F. The extremely high temperatures of this type of climate are largely the result of the absence of water for evaporation or transpiration to cool the air. The mean annual cloudiness in the Sahara is normally less than 10 percent. So intense is the sun's glare in Arid Tropical deserts that new-

[3] *Wadis* are of great significance in geography, for in a place like the western Sahara, the vegetation is largely confined to them; thus "wadi" and "pasture" are synonymous in desert parlance.

comers, unless they wear tinted glasses, go temporarily blind.

Unpleasant sandstorms blast many deserts. When the "Shamals" of Arabia blow, it appears as though giant puffs of smoke were ascending thousands of feet into the air.

The clear, dry atmosphere which permits rapid heating during the day, by the same token allows rapid radiation of heat at night. The result is a large diurnal range in temperature (sometimes amounting to 100° F.) in Arid Tropical lands. Dew and light frosts are not unknown in the desert, and films of ice sometimes occur on water surfaces in the Saharan oases.

PLANT GEOGRAPHY

The paucity of moisture where the Arid Tropical climate occurs restricts those lands in their ability to sustain vegetable and animal life. E. F. Gautier,[4] speaking of the Sahara, says "It is impossible to put into words the grandiose and overwhelming impression of absolute emptiness through which one must pass for days and days on the march." This same statement is more or less applicable to all seven Arid Tropical deserts. Yet deserts are

not devoid of life. All told, such regions support a surprising number of plant and animal forms. In many cases, even their human population is greater than most casual observers would believe. However, plants and animals have had to make radical adjustments in physiology and anatomy in order to be at home under the conditions of heat and aridity of this type of climate. As a result, the ecology of tropical desert lands is exceedingly interesting.

Desert vegetation, which is essentially an adjustment to moisture deficiency, results partly from climatic (the average state of the atmosphere) and partly from edaphic (the character of the soil) conditions. The general picture of the desert carried by most people results from climatic conditions, whereas the details in specific locales result from edaphic factors.

Desert plants do not grow close together. The lack of a mat of vegetation is one of the most distinguishing features of desert flora.

Desert plants have many peculiarities which are ecological results of the climate. Many possess

[4] Emile Felin Gautier, *Sahara, the Great Desert*, authorized translation by Dorothy Ford Mayhew (New York, Columbia University Press, 1935).

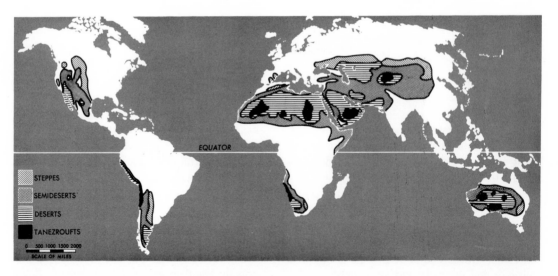

STEPPES
SEMIDESERTS
DESERTS
TANEZROUFTS

0   500 1000 1500 2000
SCALE OF MILES

EQUATOR

Figure 9–2   The dry lands of the world, according to competent estimates, comprise 43 percent of the land area of the earth if based on type of soil (pedocals); 36 percent if based on climate; and 35 percent each if based on natural vegetation and interior drainage. This means that in more than one-third of the land area of the earth, moisture is the dominant limiting factor in the production of plant growth and the dependent animal and human populations. Under the classification presented on this map, the *oasis* is restricted solely to the desert and is never found in the steppe. It is thus understandable why, with the world's population increasing at the startling rate of 70,000 persons every day, mankind is so gravely concerned regarding a more effective use of the dry lands. (Map after B. E. Thomas)

Figure 9–3 An erg or sand desert in Saudi Arabia. This type of desert is probably the most striking and certainly the best known. (Photo courtesy of the Arabian American Oil Company)

widespread root systems which enable them to draw moisture from considerable areas. Often these plants are rooted shallowly to avoid the alkali of the subsoil. Some, on the other hand, have very long roots which enable them to tap ground-water supplies. Many desert plants are equipped with large fleshy or pithy parts for water storage (for example, the barrel cactus). Most xerophytic plants (plants adapted in various ways to dry conditions) are thick and woody in structure so that they require little water; their leaves are reduced to a minimum of size and number in order to reduce the rate of transpiration of moisture. In many instances, the epidermis is superficially covered with wax, resin, or varnish to aid in reducing evaporation or transpiration.

There is also another side to this geographic adjustment of vegetation in the desert. The natural enemies of plants are the herbivorous animals. Plants with disagreeable traits are favored in their fight for survival. Animals may

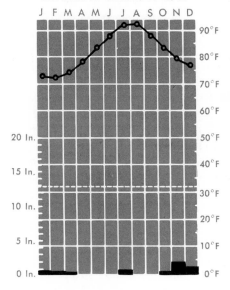

Figure 9–4 Climate graph for Port Sudan, Republic of Sudan.

Figure 9–5 Dromedary camels drinking at a water trough in Saudi Arabia. (Photo courtesy of the Arabian American Oil Company)

avoid them altogether or merely nibble at them. Some of these plants are bitter or malodorous, some are tough or thorny, some are covered with spines and prickles, others have sharp leaves, and a few are poisonous.

SOILS

Most desert soils lack the distinct profile which distinguishes the soils of humid lands (see Chapter 28). Weathering obviously is mainly physical, since there is little water for chemical weathering. Sands predominate, though finer materials may have been carried and deposited by winds from more humid areas.

Most of the soils are gray, though red soils are found in areas where the bedrock consists of red sandstone. Like most desert soils, they are rich in soluble minerals because the light rainfall minimizes leaching. Except where such soils are excessively sandy or excessively saline,

they are likely to be fertile and will produce well if irrigated.

Most of the important oases lying in this type of climate are the floodplains of rivers with extremely fertile soils which (1) have a good texture, (2) contain much topsoil carried from slopes in the upper part of the rivers' drainage basins, and (3) consist of a good mixture, since they are derived from numerous sources.

ANIMAL GEOGRAPHY

The animal ecology of the tropical desert is no less fascinating. It is axiomatic that there can be only a sparse animal life where the vegetation is sparse. Certainly no great number of forms could possibly survive the hard desert environment. Those animals which are present are well adjusted to the dry habitat. The desert, then, "is poor but not dead."

For the most part, small animals are the rule; the desert fox is one of the largest in the Sahara.

Among the true desert animals are the camel, gazelle, hare, horse, and fox. The adax, a species of antelope now quite rare in the Sahara, is meticulously adapted to his environment. In his abdominal viscera is a natural sac which serves to accumulate large reserves of water.

Most desert or desert-edge animals have forms which are peculiarly utilitarian. The camel is perhaps the classical example of desert adjustment (Fig. 9–5). Its long eyelashes afford protection against blowing dust and sand. It can flatten its normally broad nostrils into mere slits and continue to breathe almost effortlessly. Its feet consist of fleshy pads as soft as foam rubber and are therefore perfectly suited to spreading out on contact with the ground, thereby enabling the animal to walk easily on loose sand. Its hump serves as a storage reservoir of fat which grows thin and flabby as the animal draws upon it for sustenance in time of scanty food supply. The lips are tough and hairy, enabling the camel to graze on the toughest grass or browse upon relatively sharp and spiny bushes.

Undoubtedly the most interesting characteristic is its ability to go without water when necessary and then drink unbelievable quantities—as many as twenty to twenty-five gallons in half an hour when it becomes available. It has exceptional tolerance to dehydration.

No other animal of the desert has proved to be of more value and none is probably of as great value to the desert nomad as the camel.

Reptiles, for example, snakes and lizards, are especially abundant; they can dig into the sand quickly and remain there indefinitely; in fact, their ability to spend long periods in torpor is a major factor in their existence in this environment. Underground, they gain protection against the cold of night and against possible enemies.

Where vegetation disappears entirely, as in parts of the Libyan sandy desert, only a few dung-eating insects survive; they feed upon the dung of camels which travel across the region and on that of a few birds and lizards, which in turn feed upon insects. Some varieties of desert sheep have the ability to store surplus fat on the hips or in the tail. The donkey ranks with the camel as a drought resister. Certain varieties of fish in desert streams have the ability to burrow into moist earth and thus survive when the water courses run dry.

DISTRIBUTION OF POPULATION

Tropical deserts are in the main very sparsely populated (see map on inside front cover). This is to be expected because, from the human point of view, the important feature of the desert is its supply of water and the problem of man's adjustment to it. Since, however, in most deserts the one thing of which there is a scarcity is water, the number of people that can be supplied cannot be great. A narrowly limited water supply encourages population to approach the limit. Oasis populations are invariably dense, whereas true desert or nomadic populations are sparse indeed. Egypt as a country typifies this. From the standpoint of human geography, Egypt is not what it appears to be on the political map; it is the wine glass of the Nile (Fig. 9–6). In his *Letters of Travel*, Rudyard Kipling briefly and picturesquely stated the situation: "Going up the Nile is like

running the gantlet before Eternity. Till one has seen it, one does not realize the amazing thinness of that little damp trickle of life that steals along undefeated through the jaws of established death."

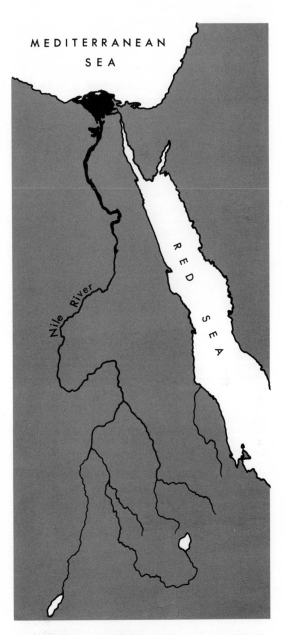

Figure 9–6 The ribbon of irrigated land along the Nile and the broad irrigated Nile Delta. The real Egypt is the Egypt of the Nile. Though preeminently an agricultural country, the density of the population of Egypt's occupied area is one of the highest in the world.

Outside the Nile delta and valley live only some 100,000 of Egypt's 28 million people.

Arid Tropical Australia is a land of empty spaces (Fig. 9–7)—empty because they cannot be otherwise. Low and irregular rainfall and infertile soils are important deterrents but so is maladjustment of settlement. Except for the small areas in the Eyre Peninsula and southwestern Western Australia with their annual rainfall exceeding 10 inches, the whole of Australia west of the 138th degree east longitude is of little or no value for civilized man.

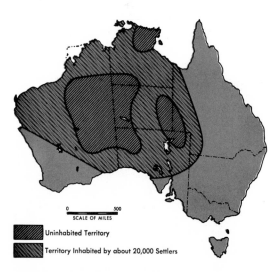

Figure 9–7   Uninhabited Australia includes 54 percent of the area of the continent. Only 13 percent of all Australia receives more than twenty inches of precipitation. *Economic Australia*, the solid gray area, has more than 99 percent of the population. (Map adapted from the American Geographical Society)

Coastal Peru is unoccupied except in the narrow ribbons of green which mark off the courses of some fifty-odd rivers that make their way from the Andes to the Pacific. Chile's Atacama Desert (considered by many to be the driest desert in the world), for centuries, and as late as 1924, had but a handful of people and imposed rigid limitations upon man and his activities. In but a few oases could small groups of Indians eke out a precarious existence. Recently, for the first time in history, conditions have changed. Nitrate and copper mining have been the dominating forces: while population still is largely restricted by the amount of water

available, what is taking place in the Atacama attests to man's capacity to progress and prosper against even the sternest of environments.

Except for the Coachella-Imperial Valley, most of the Colorado-Sonora Desert is sparsely settled, while the Sahara, Arabian and Namib deserts constitute immense blank spaces of the world's population map.[5]

HISTORY

It has been pointed out that for the most part Arid Tropical lands are empty lands. Yet according to archaeologists, historians, and geographers, the Sahara, Mesopotamia, and parts of Arabia were once prosperous and productive. Today in these lands every drop of water and every sign of vegetation are fought for by small numbers of nomads who eke out but a precarious existence. In the Sahara, for instance, are found ruins of cities and towns, temples, aqueducts, arches, monoliths, monuments, implements, and unearthed cut trees.

Why are these areas, which once supported so many people, now barren and largely deserted? It may be suggested that the climate changed and became drier, forcing people to abandon their remarkable cities and works. But Gsell, a renowned geologist who studied the problem for forty years and Gautier, an equally distinguished geographer who spent many years studying the problem, challenge the conclusion that the climate has changed in any important way since Roman times. Lowdermilk believes that the answer, so far as North Africa is concerned, lies in a change in culture and methods of land use introduced by nomads from the desert who overgrazed their animals on lands which in Roman times were carefully and intensively tilled.[6]

[5] In *Sahara, the Great Desert*, E. F. Gautier speaks of an area in the Sahara between Beni-Abbés and Atar of one thousand kilometers without a single human settlement and without any possibility of creating one.

[6] W. C. Lowdermilk, *Conquest of the Land Through Seven Thousand Years*, Agriculture Information Bulletin No. 99 (Washington, D.C., U.S. Department of Agriculture, 1953), p. 20. See other viewpoints on this topic in L. Dudley Stamp, ed., *A History of Land Use in Arid Regions* (New York, UNESCO, 1961).

ECONOMIC ADJUSTMENTS

Economic adjustments to this environment fall into six types: (1) hunting, (2) mining, (3) grazing, (4) farming, (5) manufacturing, and (6) trade.

HUNTING

The aboriginal blackfellow of the Australian desert, though perhaps the world's most primitive human being, is nevertheless a hunter par excellence. According to some authorities, no other native can approach his technique in bushcraft and trailing. He never fails to track an animal; he is even adept at tracking birds and reptiles. For centuries, food in the shape of living things has been his prime target. In the inhospitable and uncultivable desert which is his habitat, he must either be successful in his hunting or perish. His hunting is not only a matter of endurance, speed, and accuracy of spear, it is primarily an amazing capacity to observe in the minutest detail.

Much the same holds for Africa's Kalahari Bushmen. These primitive nomadic peoples rear no domestic animals and grow no crops, but they are skilled hunters. They have developed the stalking of game to an art. Even though they utilize such primitive weapons as the bow and arrow, throwing stick, and the stone-and-bone knife, they are amazingly successful. For a short period during and following the rains, when the vegetation bursts into life, there is considerable game—herbivores, such as the koodoo, zebra, giraffe, and others, and carnivores such as the lion, hyena, and jackal. This is a period of plenty, when the natives gorge themselves. But with the cessation of the rains, the water supply diminishes, the vegetation dries up, and the herbivores migrate to better-watered lands, followed, of course, by their enemies. This is a serious time for the Bushmen—a period when the shortage of food is so acute that they eat anything that is edible.

MINING

Minerals have been found in some parts of the Arid Tropical realm—petroleum in the Middle East and North Africa, salt in the Sahara, gold in Australia, iron ore in Peru, and copper and nitrate in Chile (Fig. 9–8).

For many years Chile had a monopoly in nitrate, but the industry came close to being wrecked subsequent to World War I as a result of the synthetic nitrogen industry of middle-latitude countries. In 1932 and 1933, for example, Chile's share fell to 10 percent of the world output and her economy was shaken to its very foundations. Less than 5 percent of the plants functioning during the industry's peak are operating today, and ghost town sites, cemeteries, and tailing dumps are the frequent reminders of a once-flourishing nitrate monopoly.[7] Now annual sales are slightly over one million metric tons. It is significant that were it not for the pronounced dryness of the Atacama Desert there could be no nitrate, for the mineral would be dissolved by the rain and carried away. On the other hand, so pronounced is the aridity that no other form of adjustment exists. Every item used by the people at the mining camps must be brought from outside the region. This holds also for Chile's copper mine at Chuquicamata, one of the largest and most famous mines in the world.

The African portion of the realm has only limited mining enterprises; in the Sahara are several salt deposits which formerly were assiduously worked. Encountering competition with European salt, they now find only a limited market in the Sudan. In addition, phosphate is produced. Petroleum discoveries in Algeria and Libya have caused much interest both politically and economically. Actually, petroleum has brought a boom to both countries but particularly to Libya, whose economy was less diversified and less developed than was Algeria's. In fact, until petroleum was discovered and developed there, Libya was the "sick man of North Africa," requiring huge infusions of foreign aid annually from the United States and the United Kingdom. Today, the two countries comprise one of the major petroleum regions of the world and are a primary source of crude oil for oil-poor West Europe.

[7] William E. Rudolph, *Vanishing Trails of Atacama*, American Geographical Society Research Series, No. 24 (New York, *American Geographical Society*, 1963), pp. 72–73.

Figure 9–8 El Salvador copper mine in Chile. From the air the geography of the copper industry is visible. One can see the copper diggings, the extraction plant, the complicated network of railroads, road, and trails by which all these are tied together and which connect the mine with the mountains, its source of water supply, and the coastal ports. (Photo courtesy of The Anaconda Company)

Australia has important gold placers at Coolgardie in the very center of the great desert. The climate is so dry and water so scarce, however, that the cradle and sluice box could not be used by the early prospectors. Accordingly, with keen insight, they made use of the strong and constantly blowing wind to aid them in extracting the metal. Since 1903, water has been piped from the Darling Range, 350 miles away.

GRAZING

Outside the oases, man is largely engaged in pastoral pursuits (Fig. 9–9). Few other economic enterprises are possible.

Though the pastoral nomads occupy a considerable proportion of the world's land surface

(Arid Tropical deserts comprise the largest part of the earth's *dry* deserts), they are few in number and their relative importance is small, since their lands are definitely restrictive environments.

Nomadic herders (not individuals only but entire tribes) move their animals frequently, usually from day to day, because the poor pastures (grass and bush vegetation) with their low carrying capacity are soon exhausted. In Saudi Arabia during the hot period, June to October, the nomads encamp as near water supplies as possible. Then they set out on their migrations which last until May, when the tribe once more congregates near sources of water. Throughout this migration, the tents change ground about every ten days because the sparse herbage is grazed clean by the animals.

The principal animals kept are asses, camels, goats, and sheep. Sheep and goats thrive because they can subsist on a restricted water supply and are tolerant of rough browse. The plodding camel, the patient and sturdy donkey, and the strong and beautiful horse all are gradually giving way over large areas, for example, Arabia, to the airplane, railway, and motor vehicle. Yet these animals still are important to life in the desert.

Pastoralism is most common and most important near the edge of the desert, for here is a transition zone where the herbage is better. But pastoralism also characterizes the *true desert*: here, however, nomads are to a certain extent tied to the oases in much the same manner that ships are tied to ports and for the same reason—they are not self-contained. The nomads must come thither from time to time to trade their

Figure 9–9 Camels settle down for a night near Bedouin tents. Sheep- and camel-raising, hunting, and some horse-breeding comprise the principal occupations of the nomads of the desert. The Bedouin tents are black or brown in color, consist of strips of coarse cloth woven from goat's hair or sheep's wool, and can be taken down or put up easily and quickly. During the hot summer months, the tents are placed as near to wells as possible. (Photo courtesy of the Arabian American Oil Company)

wool, meat, leather, and skins for dates, grain (barley and wheat), forage, guns, knives, and other necessaries of life.

The equipment of the nomads—leather water bags, saddles, and woolen garments, tents, and carpets—is simple and made from materials supplied by their own animals. All can be readily packed onto the backs of animals and moved to a new camp with a minimum of trouble.

Ownership of land in the Western sense is unknown. Yet each tribe wanders over an area reasonably well set off and recognized by custom among neighboring tribes. Only a small portion of the territory dominated by a given tribe is actually in use at a given time. Sometimes months pass without specific areas being visited by their owners. Vegetation must have sufficient time in which to grow during their absence. It is easy for animals to overgraze the lean pastures that characterize this climate.

FARMING

Sedentary living is restricted to oases. Yet all the Arid Tropical oases combined comprise but an infinitesimal part of the total dry land area. It is in these oases, however, that most of the human activity is concentrated and hence it is they that are of most geographic interest. There are perhaps five characteristic modes of occurrence of a water supply in the tropical desert: (1) subsurface flow down the axis or *thalweg* of a dry valley or stream course, where water may be procured by shallow dug wells, (2) ground water, which may stand near the surface in low spots between sand dunes, and which occasionally act as perched reservoirs of moisture, (3) springs, which may issue from valley walls or upon the piedmont slopes of mountains, (4) artesian wells, which tap a deep-lying source of water, (5) streams, which may descend from well-watered highlands with sufficient volume to enable them to flow across the desert lowlands despite the high rate of evaporation and absorption.

Any locality in the desert having a permanent supply of water from springs, streams, or ground-water sources is termed an *oasis* (Figs. 9–10, 9–11, and 9–12). Since oases are of infrequent and irregular occurrence in arid lands, they are eagerly sought as loci of agricultural adjustment. Oases vary in size from small one-family "irrigated islands" in the desert to huge areas such as Egypt capable of containing a nation of 28 million people. They also vary greatly in shape and physical characteristics.

The scarcity of oasis land has led men to develop a very intensive system of agricultural land utilization. In many oases of old-world deserts, there has been developed a two- or even three-layer horticulture. The upper tier or layer is formed by the tall date palms, beneath which stand the second and third tiers. The second tier is composed of rows of low apricot, orange, olive, pomegranate, or peach trees, or perhaps grapevines on trellises, while the third or bottom tier consists of a varied assortment of vegetables or crops of wheat or cotton. The existence of the

lower strata of crops under the date palms is possible because of the light feathery foliage of that tree, and because of the almost vertical rays of the sun at all seasons. Even in the Imperial Valley, the great American oasis of the Arizona-Sonora Desert, this same tendency toward intensive land utilization is evident.

SEVERAL ARID TROPICAL OASES

THE NILE VALLEY

The Nile Valley is undoubtedly the most interesting and important of all Arid Tropical oases. The White Nile heads in a lake in equatorial Africa and flows northward to latitude 15° N., where it is joined by the Blue Nile which heads in the high Abyssinian Plateau. Each sum-

Figure 9–10 The Hofuf Oasis in Saudi Arabia. Note the irrigation canal and irrigated plots for tree nurseries, parts of a dunes control project. (Photo courtesy of the Arabian American Oil Company)

Figure 9–11   Inside view of an oasis. Water from the springs in the Al Hasa Oasis in eastern Saudi Arabia flows through a palm-lined canal. It is used to irrigate many acres of date gardens which flourish in the oasis. (Photo courtesy of the Arabian American Oil Company)

mer the southwest monsoon brings a rainy season to Abyssinia, and the Blue Nile swells into flood. From time immemorial until 1902, when the British completed the Aswan Dam, Egyptian agriculture depended upon the overflow of the Nile. Basin irrigation was practiced: the land was divided into embanked basins which were flooded during the annual rise of the river. The crops depended for their water supply on the water left in the subsoil as a result of this inundation. As the water in the basin became still, the rich silt it carried was dropped.

With the fall in the river's level, the dikes were opened, the fields drained, and the crops planted. Water remained on the land from seven to forty days. Only one crop was obtained from a given piece of soil in a year, the fields remaining fallow after the harvest until the next flood. This was the method used in Lower Egypt in the past. It is obsolete today, however, as a result of the dams. Flood waters, which are now held back, are used during the entire year. Perennial irrigation permits more than one crop to be grown on the same land in a year. The irrigated area has thus been considerably increased and the population has quadrupled—6,800,000 in

1882, when the British came, and 28,000,000 now.

Perennial irrigation is not, however, without its weaknesses: soil exhaustion is now a reality and the water table has risen, which complicates the problem of drainage. Egyptian agriculturists now are dependent upon the use of imported commercial fertilizers.

Prior to World War I, Egypt relied largely upon a "single-crop system" of agriculture, exchanging her long-staple cotton for a considerable part of her foodstuffs and for practically all her needs in manufactured goods. The disadvantage of dependence upon this system was emphasized during the war, however, when many sources of foodstuffs were cut off from her by blockade. Since then, and particularly since the world economic depression of the 1930's, Egypt has been growing more of her own food until now she is approaching self-sufficiency.

The High Aswan Dam in the southern part of Egypt, near the border of Sudan, will bring some two million additional acres of land under irrigation. However, there are some estimates which indicate that when the project is completed in about 1970, it will be wholly inadequate

Figure 9–12   In addition to the date crops, sheep are often raised for their wool in the oases of Saudi Arabia. (Photo courtesy of the Arabian American Oil Company)

to take care of the needs of the increased population. In addition, the agreement with the Soviet Union calls for repayment of financial and technical aid in the form of cotton, the production of which also requires irrigated land.

THE ARABIAN DESERT

There are numerous oases, mostly small, in the Arabian Peninsula. The valley of the Shat-el-Arab and its tributaries, the Tigris and Euphrates, create a large oasis. This Mesopotamian (inter-river) oasis supports perhaps two million people. Here the date groves and the fields of wheat, millet, and vegetables duplicate on a less intensive scale those of the Nile Oasis.

Iraq supplies about four-fifths of the world's commercial supply of dates as well as huge quantities for local consumption, since the date is a staple food item. The date palm requires

high temperatures, low humidity, and a copious supply of water.

THE SIND

West Pakistan contains another of these significant oases. The Sind consists largely of the lower valley and delta of the Indus River and lies in an area receiving on the average only 6.1 inches of precipitation. Here the English completed the Lloyd Barrage, which is one of the world's largest irrigation projects. The 6,400 miles of canals permit the cultivation of some 5 to 6 million acres, an area exceeding the cultivable land of Egypt. Vast crops of bajri or pearl millet, cotton, jowar, oilseeds, rice, and wheat are produced in the Sind as well as limited amounts of barley, corn, gram, sugar cane, and tobacco.

THE IMPERIAL VALLEY

Another important oasis is the Imperial Valley in the Arizona-Sonora Desert. The Gulf of California formerly extended between the San Bernardino and the Coast Range far northward into California. The Colorado River then entered the gulf where Yuma now stands. Gradually the river built a huge fan-shaped delta westward into the gulf. Finally the delta reached the western shore and cut off the northern end of the gulf, thereby forming Salton Sea. This inland sea gradually evaporated and left an arid basin plain north of the delta. Much of this plain lies below sea level and its center is occupied by a desert sink. Water is diverted from the river at Yuma and led down the delta by an old distributary of the river toward Salton Sink. Before reaching the sink most of the water is turned onto the land by canals and ditches. This forms the Imperial Valley oasis which lies partly in Mexico and partly in California. Here has developed a miniature "American Egypt," in which are raised dates, olives, citrus fruits, long-staple cotton, melons, and winter vegetables for American markets.

COASTAL PERU

On this narrow plain, rainless for years at a time, averaging about forty miles in width and comprising a mere 10 percent of the nation's total area, is produced virtually all of Peru's two major export crops, cotton and sugar cane, as well as much of its rice and other food and feed crops. This coastal region is the heart of Peruvian commercial agriculture. In fact, agriculture here had reached a high degree of development prior to the Spanish Conquest.

Only a small part of the coastal area is cultivated: the alluvial valleys which cross it from east to west. There are some fifty of these which are irrigated by waters that flow in small rivers from the lofty Andes to the Pacific Ocean (Fig. 9–13).

Only from an airplane can one get the correct picture of coastal Peru. Each irrigated valley is a narrow ribbon of green separated from its nearest neighbor to the north and south by miles of naked terrain.

In the equable climate, crops are grown the year round wherever water is available. Obviously the dates of flow in the various streams are not identical and hence the times of planting and of harvesting vary.

Two types of farming are followed: estate or plantation, which uses scientific methods and produces essentially for export, and subsistence, which employs antiquated implements and produces primarily for the needs of the farmers themselves.

MANUFACTURING

Nowhere are Arid Tropical countries outstanding in manufacturing. Every country is ranked as "underdeveloped." In all, the bases for machine industry, particularly raw materials and fossil fuels, are weak. Yet several of the nations are eager to embrace modern industrialism, even to the extent of making iron and steel. Thus in coastal Peru an iron and steel plant has sprung up in Chimbote. Egypt, too, has a plant near Helway on the east side of the Nile.

Oil refining, obviously, is important throughout the Middle East, North Africa, and in coastal Peru (Talara). One of the world's largest oil refineries is located at Abadan in Iran.

Numerous light industries have sprung up throughout the Middle East and coastal Peru. However, it is in the handicrafts of the Middle East that the Arid Tropics have gained fame

throughout the world. The craftsmanship of the silk spinners, rug makers, silversmiths, and leather workers has been passed down from father to son for centuries. This does not mean, however, that these occupations are hereditary: no youth *must* follow his father's trade.

TRADING

From time immemorial there has been trade in and across some of the Arid Tropical deserts. Antedating the discovery of sea routes, considerable long-distance trade was handled by camel caravan in the deserts of the "World Island."[8] Such trade has declined in recent years. The camel caravan no longer is employed over the long trails, though the animal continues to have no rival for intertribal trade. The motor

[8] A term used first by Sir Halford Mackinder for Eurasia-Africa in 1904.

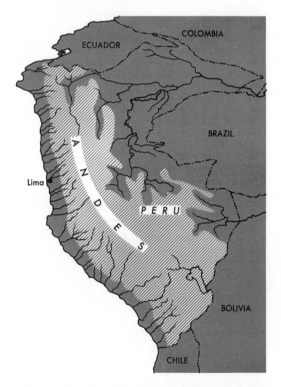

Figure 9–13 Rivers of coastal Peru. The important agriculture of coastal Peru depends upon the life-giving waters of the fifty-two short streams that descend from the Andes. More than half the agricultural capital of the country is believed to be invested in the irrigated farms in these valleys and about 50 percent of the agricultural income is derived from them. Cotton and sugar-cane are the principal commercial crops. (Map adapted from the U.S. Bureau of Agricultural Economics)

vehicle and the airplane are transforming the Sahara—creating new routes and new centers. Buses and trucks, of course, do not operate in the Sahara during the summer months, for the heat is too intense both for man and vehicle. At that time of year only airplanes make the crossing.

Every motor vehicle destined for a trip across the desert must carry several tons of water, fuel, food, and parts. Even sleeping bags or blankets must be carried, since temperatures often drop to below freezing on winter nights.

In South America, trucks, buses, and automobiles make much use of the hard-surfaced Pan American Highway that extends the entire length of the Atacama-Peruvian Coastal Desert.

Although railways are to be found in all countries with this climate, they are of relatively small import. The much-publicized Trans-Saharan Railway has not been completed and probably will not be, both for economic and for political reasons. And there is but one railway in the whole of Saudi Arabia. This railway, which is 357 miles long and was completed in 1951, is owned by the government. It links the Persian Gulf at the port of Dammam with the isolated capital city of Riyadh in the heart of the peninsula and up on the plateau. Surprising as it may seem, this railway is profitable. It resulted in a fall by one-half in the cost of living at Riyadh, which formerly relied on camel caravans or costly airlift.

No part of Chile's Atacama Desert is more than twenty miles from a railroad, the result of nitrate and copper mining. Even coastal Peru is quite fortunate, for a number of railways extend across the desert enroute from Pacific ports into the Andes carrying the products of the contrasted regions.

SOCIAL ADJUSTMENTS

THE PASTORALISTS

The scanty pasturage resulting from the irregular desert rainfall provides only the barest margin of subsistence for pastoral man. The pasture is soon exhausted in any given locality, compelling the herdsman to move frequently. This makes pastoral man nomadic. Under such habits of

life, the flock or herd must be kept small or it becomes unwieldy. By the same token, the social group, which subsists upon the flock, must likewise be kept small.

The clan organization is the basis of nomadic society. Each tent represents a family and an encampment of families comprises a clan. A number of kindred clans grouped together constitutes a tribe. The tent and its contents, along with the animals, are individual property and are jealously guarded; but water, pasturage, and cultivated land are shared by all tribe members.

Often, in years of excessive aridity, the pasture fails locally and the nomad clans are reduced to famine. Under such conditions, pastoral man is faced with the alternatives of robbery or starvation and quite naturally chooses the former. The starving nomad's raids are directed toward the perennially fruitful oasis, the laden caravan, or the more fortunate neighbor tribe whose pastures are not desiccated. Desert man is never far from the margin of subsistence, but in excessively dry years his numbers are seriously reduced by starvation or intertribal warfare. Thus "survival of the fittest" is a natural law operating upon man as well as upon the plants and animals of the tropical desert. Since the defectives and weaklings are periodically eliminated, it is slight wonder that desert man is thin, wiry and enduring, possesses keen powers of sight and direction, and can exist on scant rations of food and water (Fig. 9–14).

The social law of the desert is hospitality and generosity. The richest among nomads exists on a slender margin and even he may find himself destitute at a moment's notice. Any unfortunate person, therefore, is given alms, food, and shelter. Frequently such a person is rehabilitated by collective gifts of animals and gear, because to do so is the best guaranty that the donors will be similarly treated should misfortune overtake them. In times of general calamity, however, each family or clan reverts to self-protection, and is ready to fight, rob, pillage, or kill for survival. Thus desert morality represents a close social adjustment to the nature of the physical environment.

In Arid Tropical Australia, some 47,000

Figure 9–14   A Bedouin drawing water for the camels of a caravan from a well south of Tamenrasset, Algeria. (Photo by P. Keen, courtesy of FAO)

aborigines carry on as did prehistoric men. When the white man first penetrated this forbidding land, these people knew of no economy other than hunting (the work of the men) and food gathering (the work of the women). They still have no agriculture and no domestic animal, save the dog. In fact, their natural milieu provided them with no native plants and no useful do-

mesticable animal. Hence the first touchstones of civilization—agriculture and animal husbandry—were lacking here.

The natives require little clothing most of the year and hence wear none or almost none. They sleep in the open. The men kill with spears (they do not possess the bow and poisoned arrow) kangaroos, lizards, emus, alligators, and fish, and the women gather wild figs, berries, grass seeds, and wild honey. They have developed amazing skills: for one thing, they are able to find water where none apparently exists. Sometimes, however, where a water hole is far distant, the Australian goes out before daylight to brush the dew into a vessel. Unlike the African bushman, the Australian native has little to fear from wild animals and men (Fig. 9–15).

RELIGION

Desert man's religion, too, reveals an ecological stamp: the factors of the physical environment have left their imprint in the forms of many religious concepts. To him who has experienced the high daytime temperatures and the cold night-time temperatures of the desert (the "sun smites him by day and the cold by night") as well as the strong winds, Mohammed's description of Heaven seems appealing indeed: "Paradise is better than anything on earth. It is a garden in which are rivers of water, flowing springs, and branching trees with fruit of every kind."

Monotheism arose in such lands. This does not mean that belief in one universal God of necessity evolves in a desert, but it is true that the evolution of such a belief is more probable there than in the jungle.[9] This is because the things man fears most are big things—wind, sun, cold, heat, drought. They have little of the local, intimate quality of the jungle man's mudholes, snakes, sticks, and malevolent mosquitoes. "Hence it is natural for the primitive desert man to pin his faith to a few powerful gods who rule large areas."[10]

[9] Ellsworth Huntington, *Mainsprings of Civilization* (New York, John Wiley & Sons, Inc., 1945), p. 293.
[10] *Ibid.*

Figure 9–15 Aborigines of a hunting party in the Rawlinson Ranges in central Australia look for game on the plain. They are carrying throwing spears. (Photo courtesy of the Australian News & Information Bureau)

Moslem faith, for example, the religion of most inhabitants of the deserts of the "World Island," is one of fatalism; if something goes wrong, no one is upset—it is "written." This fits admirably into the thinking of peoples whose lives depend on the whims of a barely sufficient and often fickle rainfall. It is interesting to note also that in such regions "there are no more agnostics than on a boisterous sea." It is not surprising to learn that within a millennium Islam was adopted by all the scattered groups of the desert of North Africa and Asia (Fig. 9–16).

Figure 9–16 The Mohammedan world and the ten-inch rainfall line (isohyet). The natural environment imposes an important limitation on most of the Moslem world, for over the greater part of it desert conditions prevail. (Map adapted from Isaiah Bowman)

ARABIA A CENTER OF MIGRATION

Arabia has long served as one of the world's most important population seedbags.

. . . from its burning emptiness the Semitic race has poured out, wave after wave, through recorded time, to become, by conquest and amalgamation, the ancient Egyptians, the Babylonians, the Assyrians, the Chaldeans, the Phoenicians—an unending list.[11]

THE AGRICULTURISTS

The oasis dwellers, on the other hand, are intensely sedentary and are usually densely crowded upon tiny parcels of land. The inhabitants of most oases were probably originally nomads from the surrounding desert who did not at first take kindly to agricultural labor. Hence arose the institution of slavery. On this basis there developed concubinage, polygamy, and the use of luxuries in the oases. The inevitable result was overpopulation. Overpopulation plus the need for social organization in irrigation early taught man the rudiments of complex civilization. The high productivity of irrigated soil has caused not only

[11] Philip K. Hitti, *History of the Arabs* (London, Macmillan & Co., Ltd., 1937).

high valuation of land but extensive systems of tenancy and landed proprietorship in oases. Under such adjustments, real property is highly cherished, boundaries and property lines become important, and exact systems of land survey begin.[12]

Land tillage leaves no time for militarism; accordingly the oasis man is socially pacifistic. His defense has been in many cases the walled city, as typified by the North African village fortified against the Bedouin of the *ergs* and *wadis*.

DESERTS AS CRADLES OF CIVILIZATION

The world's earliest civilizations were cradled in river valleys and mostly in the heart of, or on the fringe of, *tropical deserts*. The floodplains of the Indus, Nile, Tigris, and Euphrates are the best examples. Thus, the determination to make the desert sustain man is old. Conquest of the desert means irrigation and irrigation is a cooperative, not an individual, matter.

Thousands of years ago Egypt had developed a splendid literature, a native art and architecture; Arabia had a philosophy and had laid the foundations of mathematical science; Persia had pioneered in the realm of astronomy; the Mesopotamian countries had developed a commercial life which for those days was far-reaching; and Babylon had created a code of ethics that antedates the Mosaic system by more than two millennia.

Civilization[13] is estimated to be at least eight thousand years old. The oldest center appears to have been in what is now Iraq, four hundred miles north of Ur; here man for the first time began to cultivate the land, herd cattle, build brick houses and make pottery.

THE EXAMPLE OF EGYPT

Egypt, queen of oases (Fig. 9–6), excellently exemplifies the role of the natural environment in the evolution of civilization. Here the land was level, the soil extremely fertile, and much water was available for irrigation. The Nile was navigable and was used for transportation. Important also was the wide distribution of clayey soil that supplied good building material for houses—houses that were cool in summer and

reasonably warm in winter. Clay could also be fashioned into bowls and jars for storing grain and it provided excellent material for written records which could be preserved; thus, the wisdom of generation after generation could be handed down. The dry climate preserved the clay tablets. Since Egyptians could get writing material from a form of papyrus which grew in the swamps, they depended less upon the clay than did the Babylonians.

Yet it is doubtful whether a civilization could have evolved here without natural protection from enemies. Any incipient civilization needs security; from 5000 B.C. to about 1600 B.C. the people of the Nile Valley lived in blissful isolation. In effect the valley was a long narrow island cut off from the rest of the world. On each flank of the valley was an uninhabited and protecting desert. To the south the Nile's six cataracts made river communication with what is now the Sudan difficult; and on the north the Mediterranean Sea and the shallow, confusing Nile mouths (distributaries) below Cairo afforded protection. Possibly no other place on earth had such a degree of natural security, combined with the other *musts* conducive to the cradle stage. Moreover, the Nile Oasis was neither too large nor too small to be governed effectively. Its limited size, which kept it from becoming unwieldy, encouraged national unity.

The seasonal nature of the floods was important too; the annual recurrence of a long period when water for irrigation was unavailable and hence when the land was not producing crops, put a premium on foresight and thus

[12] When man became civilized, it became necessary to measure and map the land he occupied—its extent, its yield, its ownership. In Egypt the need for surveying the lands inundated by the annual Nile floods, during which all surface landmarks were swept away, gave rise to surveying and the geometry basic to it, for the allotted fields had to be remeasured each year. This led also to the erection of the benchmark, an enduring and accepted mark—a monument set in the earth to give the surveyor a starting point. Today a benchmark is regarded as a point of known elevation so marked that it can be found again and used.

[13] By *civilization* is meant the state of social culture—progress in art, science, literature, government, law, religion, morals, and the art of living together.

helped to stimulate the development of civilization.

The Nile Oasis was not invaded until about 1600 B.C., when Arabian desert raiders came by way of Egypt's only gateways—the Sinai Peninsula and the Plains of Goshen.

POLITICAL ASPECTS

This discussion is focused on the Middle East,[14] not because the other Arid Tropical lands are not important, but rather because they are greatly overshadowed by it. The Middle East occupies one of the most strategic positions in the world and it is the center of gravity of the world's petroleum industry.

It is the only land bridge between Asia and Africa and is the crossroads between East and West by air and sea.

This region has been important politically for millennia. In the past, the restless nomadic tribes, which were trailing over the desolate desert with their flocks in their endless search for water and browse, were not easily controlled. Knowing every water hole and pasture spot of their natural environment far better than their would-be conquerors could hope to know them, they could usually resist conquest with complete success. Their enemies' armies were not their superior in armament and equipment and certainly were their inferior in mobility and adaptability to the ways of desert warfare. That day, however, is gone. No desert group could today resist a modern great power waging the type of warfare that was carried on, for example, in North Africa during World War II with airplanes, tanks, and so forth. Against these weapons the nomads would be powerless.

After World War I, Ibn Saud successfully brought all of Arabia, except parts of the periphery, under his control. By 1924 he had introduced the most important reform ever undertaken in the Peninsula—the settling of the nomadic Arabs around the wells of the desert. Thus, he altered even the famous heart of the desert. His aim was to shift his people from nomadism to settled existence by means of irrigation, to improve the economic and cultural situation of the people, and to make possible a stable govern-

ment. Thus, of the 140 existing agricultural colonies in 1934, at least one-half were sustained by water from recently-discovered supplies and more than 100,000 Arabs were occupying lands formerly unoccupied. Of the estimated seven million persons comprising the population of Saudi Arabia, the proportion that is now anchored is placed at one-third. The settled colonies became the backbone of the government. Desert feuds and robberies ceased entirely.

Falling revenues, resulting from the great depression of the 1930's, and serious droughts induced an otherwise reluctant Ibn Saud to grant concessions to foreigners for the exploitation of minerals, particularly petroleum. Royalties from oil are providing and will continue to provide funds for the strengthening of economic and social conditions.

There is always trouble in the Middle East: since World War II, it has been caused by nationalistic ambitions, religious fanaticism, racial hatreds, weak governments, and economic distress. Economically this region is, except for petroleum, one of the poorest in the world.

TWO EXAMPLES OF POLITICAL GEOGRAPHY IN THE ARID TROPICS

A. RISE AND EXPANSION OF THE MOSLEM WORLD

Mohammed, who was born in Mecca, then an important commercial city, was a man whose religious spirit was matched by political acumen. He had a genius for unification. In A.D. 632 (the year of his death), the Arabs set out to conquer the world and within a century had taken over most of that which was known—an empire greater than that of Rome at its zenith. Islam was not checked until 732 when Charles Martel defeated the Moslems at Tours in France. In the past this movement was regarded as one of armed fanaticism. Actually the Islam which con-

[14] The term *Middle East* is variously employed. Actually what we formerly called the "Near East" is today regarded as the "Middle East"—that vast and predominantly Islamic area extending from Morocco on the west to the Afghan frontier.

quered "was not the Islamic religion but the Islamic state." Every so often the desert-dwellers had to spill over the cup—overflow their own boundaries—since the slender resources of their desert habitat were inadequate to sustain the virile and growing population.

Since the Koran was written in Arabic, all the peoples who fell under the sway of Islam have used it and the language has been a political force down to the present.

From time to time we hear ominous rumblings of a movement known as Pan-Islamism—an immense stirring within the desert world aimed at achieving solidarity among the widely scattered units. Could the Moslem world threaten modern civilization? Geography supplies the best answer to this question. Viewed areally, the Mohammedan lands are huge (Fig. 9–16), but at the same time they comprise a comparatively empty world—one with small numbers of people widely scattered, with slender natural resources (particularly minerals), inadequate food, and poorly developed transportation facilities. Much is true *terra incognita*. Add to these deficiencies the seasonal heat, scarcity of water, and the thin and scattered forage, and one is aware of the striking weaknesses. With a low industrial index, the Moslem world could not possibly sustain a long military campaign either at home or abroad. Experience has shown that great zeal and fanaticism are poor substitutes for modern fast-moving machines of war. The Moslem world is today neither a major political threat nor a military power.

B. OIL IN THE MIDDLE EAST

Petroleum in the Middle East rated headlines in the newspapers and priority in radio broadcasts for several years after the termination of World War II. While this example of political geography has nothing to do directly with climate, it is discussed briefly under this topic because we have seen that most Arid Tropical lands are poor lands, passive lands, forgotten lands—lands that would be unimportant in the world of states except for strategic location or mineral resources (both applicable to the Arid Tropical Middle East).

Petroleum is the lifeblood of both peace and war. The Middle East is the earth's richest potential oil area. It is not surprising, therefore, that the great powers did considerable skirmishing politically to get a share. Companies representing nearly all the Free World Powers are interested—the United States, the United Kingdom, France, the Netherlands, Italy, and Japan, though the first two are the most widely and most financially involved throughout the region. Even the U.S.S.R. of the Communist Bloc, from time to time manifests a determination to participate.[15]

This petroleum is dominated by the Free World nations. Yet it is very close to the Soviet Union. If control of this oil should be lost to the West and gained by the U.S.S.R., the whole balance of world power would be changed. Iran particularly stands squarely in the way of Russian expansion.

The geopolitical situation in Iran was particularly dangerous during the early 1950's, when the government (1951) seized the properties of the Anglo-Iranian Oil Company, 52.55 percent of which were owned by the British government. For some three years this poor nation, deprived of its so-called life-blood, seemed to defy the laws of economics. An Iranian official explained it thus: "The great majority of our people not only do not have luxuries, they do not even have necessities. So they can tighten their belts a little more and keep going."

Now an international consortium is handling Iran's oil and the agreement provides for revenues to Iran. This can do much for the country's agriculture, irrigation system, reforestation, grazing, lands, health, sanitation, water supply, transportation, and education.

Saudi Arabia has become one of the highest ranking oil producing countries in the world. In 1960 production reached over 455 million barrels. The Saudi Arabian government has been receiving through royalties and taxation, revenues

---

[15] When King Ibn Saud signed the contract with American companies for concessions in 1939, he revealed that the British, Germans, Japanese, and Italians all had bid for concessions. He preferred the Americans because the United States is so far away and because American negotiations are on behalf of private interests, whereas those of many other nations are carried on through their governments.

amounting to 50 percent of Aramco's net operating income. This torrent of exchange is enabling an otherwise poor country to improve economic and social conditions to an extent that might never have been possible otherwise. Aramco is itself doing many things to win the good will of the people: drilling water wells in areas that had no surface water, teaching the Arabs how to grow crops; building roads, teaching trades, educating workers, and improving health. In 1955 the company entered into a five-year, $500,000 research program in cooperation with the Saudi Arabian government for the study of trachoma. This eye disease, one of the oldest to plague mankind, affects huge segments of the population in the Middle East. In some areas 80 to 100 percent of the inhabitants either have or have had the disease. It is estimated that, for each dollar spent in the Middle East for direct oil installations, the oil companies spend three-quarters as much on projects which are connected with the social and economic growth of the nations involved.

The tiny Sheikdom of Kuwait became one of the world's leading producers of petroleum in the 1950's. Iran, just prior to its nationalization fiasco, ranked as the fourth leading producer of petroleum. When production came to a standstill during the nationalization, Kuwait rose rapidly as an important producer. By 1960, it had replaced Iran as the fourth largest producer after the United States, the U.S.S.R., and Venezuela. Under the consortium, Iran is now producing more than before, but has not been able to regain its former position. What is remarkable about Kuwait is the fact that her reserves are the greatest in the world with estimates of nearly 25 percent of the world's total.[16]

What is important to note is that petroleum and the deserts of the Middle East as a whole are not synonymous. Egypt, for example, is oil poor. This alone goes a long way toward understanding the desires of the United Arab Republic to achieve political unity in the Moslem World.

[16] See chapter on mineral fuels for more detailed account of oil production.

SUGGESTED USEFUL READINGS

Cole, Monica, *South Africa* (New York, E. P. Dutton and Company, 1961), 696 pp.

Cressey, George B., "The Deserts of Asia," *Journal of Asian Studies*, XIX, 1960, pp. 389–402.

Eyre, S. R., *Vegetation and Soils: A World Picture* (Chicago, Aldine Publishing Company, 1963), pp. 226–238.

Hodge, Carle, and Peter C. Duisberg, eds., *Aridity and Man, the Challenge of the Arid Lands in the United States*, American Association for the Advancement of Science, Publication No. 74 (Washington, D.C., American Association for the Advancement of Science, 1963), 584 pp.

Rudolph, William E., *Vanishing Trails of Atacama* (New York, American Geographical Society, 1963), 87 pp.

Russell, Richard Joel, Fred B. Kniffen, and Evelyn Lord Pruitt, *Culture Worlds* (New York, The Macmillan Company, 1961), pp. 191–242.

Shantz, H. L., and C. F. Marbut, *The Vegetation and Soils of Africa* (New York, National Research Council and the American Geographical Society, 1923), pp. 76–84, 179–180.

Stamp, L. Dudley, *Africa: A Study in Tropical Development*, 2d ed. (New York, John Wiley & Sons, Inc., 1964), pp. 253–269, 429–479.

Stamp, L. Dudley, ed., *History of Land Use in Arid Regions*, Arid Zone Research No. 17 (Paris, UNESCO, 1961), 388 pp.

United Nations Educational, Scientific, and Cultural Organization, *The Problems of the Arid Zone*, Arid Zone Research No. 18 (Paris, UNESCO, 1962); and *Changes of Climate*, Arid Zone Research No. 20 (Paris UNESCO, 1963).

White, Gilbert F., ed., *The Future of Arid Lands*, American Association for the Advancement of Science, Publication No. 43 (Washington, D.C., American Association for the Advancement of Science, 1956), 453 pp.

White, Gilbert F., *Science and the Future of Arid Lands* (Paris, UNESCO, 1960), 95 pp.

10

Monsoon Tropical Climate Regions

This type of climate, along with the Semiarid Tropical (discussed in the following chapter) are transitional in character, for they represent a gradation from the always rainy climate (Chapter 8) to the always dry climate (Chapter 9) of the Tropical Zone.

The lands where the Monsoon Tropical climate occurs are also transitional in location. On their equatorward side lie the tropical rain forests (the selvas), while on their poleward margin lies the thorn forest or grassland, which grades into the tropical desert.

MONSOON TROPICAL REGIONS

In general, lands possessing the Monsoon Tropical climate lie in broad belts north and south of the Rainy Tropics. In Africa, where the distribution of climatic belts is most regular, the Monsoon Tropical type extends from the east coast to the west coast roughly between latitudes 8° and 12° N. and also between latitudes 8° and 12° S. Specifically this climate is found in the following areas (Fig. 10–1). In South America it occurs in the Campos of Brazil and the Llanos of Venezuela and Colombia. In North America, it extends over most of the West Indies (including the southern tip of Florida), the west coast of Central America, and most of both the east and west coasts of Mexico. In Africa, the Monsoon Tropical regime holds sway over the southern Sudan, much of Mozambique, the southern slopes of the Congo Basin, and northwestern Malagasy. In Asia it characterizes south China, Thailand, Burma, most of India, Vietnam, Cambodia, Laos, and parts of Indonesia and the Philippine Islands. In Australia it puts its stamp only on the northern coast.

DISTINGUISHING CHARACTERISTICS

The term *monsoon* is an Arab word meaning "season." As one might suspect, the most significant trait of this climate is its possession of a marked semiannual rhythm in rainfall and drought.

TEMPERATURE

Temperatures in the Rainy Tropical and Monsoon Tropical climates are much alike (Figs. 8–2 and 10–2). This means that constantly high temperatures prevail, since the noonday sun is never far from a vertical position and the length of day and night is approximately the same throughout the year. In general, no month averages below 65° F. The annual and the diurnal range of temperature is, however, somewhat greater in the Monsoon Tropical than it is in the Rainy Tropical climate.

As a rule, the highest temperatures arrive just before the period of heaviest rainfall. One significant difference between the two types of climate is that the Monsoon Tropical escapes the monotony—*the everlasting sameness*—of the Rainy Tropics.

PRECIPITATION

Rainfall is the most critical element in the setting apart of the four tropical climates. The total amount of precipitation of the Monsoon Tropics —40 to 60 inches—is considerably less than that of the Rainy Tropics (in excess of 60 inches and in places 150 to 200 inches).

It is the marked seasonal distribution, the strong contrast between a very dry and a very wet season, rather than the amount that is the salient characteristic of the rainfall. The length of the rainy season—five to eight months—is highly variable depending upon the specific area. In most places 90 to 95 percent of the rain falls during the summer monsoon, but 75 percent may fall in three months. During the rainy season much rain falls in a limited period—an inch per hour is not exceptional. The length of the dry season increases with distance from the equator.

One weakness of this type of climate is the *unreliability* of the rainfall: there are wide fluctuations in the totals from year to year. One year may witness so little rain as to bring about crop failure—even famine, while the next may witness a complete reversal—an amount so large as to inundate the low areas, rot the crops, and increase the damage from insects and fungi. Famine may, and actually does, result from both drought and flood.

THE MONSOON REGION OF SOUTHEASTERN ASIA

In southeastern Asia—Burma, Thailand, Vietnam, Cambodia, Laos, and the Republic of Indonesia—the *monsoon winds* are more strongly developed than elsewhere in the world, and hence these regions experience nearly a complete reversal of wind direction within the year. Lands having strong monsoon tendencies usually lie on the eastern sides of continents. The rainy season coincides with the period of onshore winds (summer) the dry season with that of offshore winds (winter).

THE MONSOON AND THE REPUBLIC OF INDONESIA

The trade wind system of the tropical oceans is disturbed by the influence of the two continents of Asia and Australia. Hence, during summer in each hemisphere, air is drawn from the opposite hemisphere across the equator. This relationship renders the Archipelago the most typical monsoon region in the world.

Rainfall is more abundant in the north than in the south, because in the latter the effect of the Australian desert is stronger. Thus the rainy season in eastern Java, Bali, and Lombok arrives when the winter winds are blowing out of Asia— when the *west monsoon* is blowing. The dry season prevails in summer when winds are blowing from Australia, which is then having winter and a prevailing high pressure. Winds blowing toward Indonesia from this region are known as the *east monsoon*. The intensity of the wet season decreases eastwards, that is, toward Australia, and the intensity of the dry season increases. Thus, eastern Java would be expected to receive less rainfall than western Java and such is actually the case.

A YEAR IN A NORTHERN HEMISPHERE MONSOON TROPICAL REGION

A residence of a year in some Monsoon Tropical region in the Northern Hemisphere would reveal the following sequence of events:

In January, the sky is absolutely clear. Day after day follows without cloud or rain. Day after day, too, the hot northeast trade winds blow steadily. The temperatures are high, averaging in many places from 70° to 75° F. The air is dry and often dust laden. Vegetation has ceased to grow; the grass has dried up, and the trees have shed their leaves. The rivers are running low. Week by week the trade winds continue to blow and the vegetation becomes browner, the streams diminish in volume, and the temperature mounts higher and higher.

By May the trade winds become intermittent and finally die down. The land lies parched and brown beneath the vertical noonday sun, and the roads are deep with dust. Gradually, the southwest, south, or southeast winds set in and with them come the rains. At first only light showers fall; then follow heavy showers accompanied by thunder and lightning. Finally the rainy season bursts in all its fury. The air is now hot and humid, recalling conditions in the Rainy Tropical climate. Grasses spring into life, trees put on new

Figure 10–1   Monsoon Tropical regions.

leaves, the rivers become torrents, and the roads turn to abysmal quagmires. Thus the rains continue through the high-sun season until the lowlands become saturated and swamplike and the landscape grows green in a mass of riotous vegetation.

The rains reach a maximum in July or early August and then begin to diminish. Gradually they become intermittent and cease in September or October. The last of October is almost entirely clear and the trade winds once more set in from the northeast. For a few weeks the countryside, with its pools of stagnant water and its masses of rotting vegetation, is extremely unhealthful. But

under the desiccating effect of the trade winds, these soon dry up, the mosquito and reptilian torment diminishes, and conditions once more become fairly healthful. Clear, hot, dry weather ensues for the following four to six months.

WHAT THE MONSOON MEANS TO THE PEOPLE

It is difficult to overestimate the importance of the monsoon in the lives of the inhabitants of southeastern Asia. From mid-October until mid-May the "sun rides unchallenged in the sky." During this period the people are in a state of

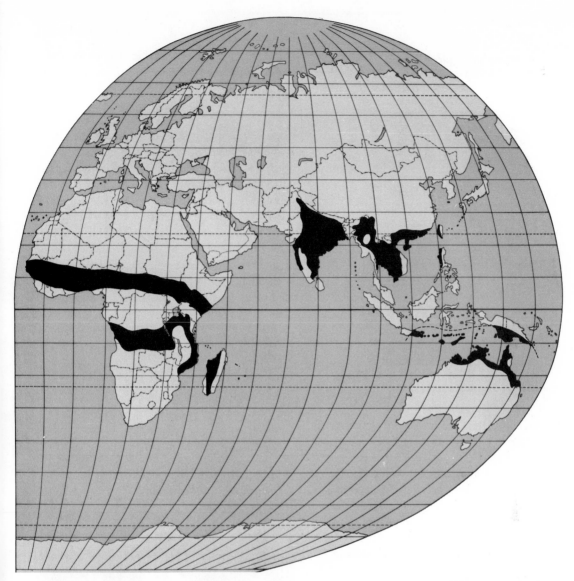

uncertainty. Once the rains come, however, life quickens (both mind and body). This is the monsoon that the people talk about. Plans are now made, for life depends on what is accomplished during the rains. How successful the rainy season will be, however, depends upon the time the rains come and when they cease, how much precipitation actually falls, and how evenly it is distributed throughout the rainy season.

In 1950–1951 and 1951–1952 the monsoon failed and Indian agriculture suffered. Famines were averted only by rationing and importing food. Since then, faster communication and transportation have helped to alleviate major disasters. In 1966 six hundred ships transported about one quarter of the total wheat crop of the United

States to India and in 1967 the United States was feeding sixty million Indians.

But the rains also create numerous problems; communications are disrupted and fevers take a heavy toll of human energy. The summer monsoon drives most of the Europeans and rich Indian princes to the hill stations in the Himalayas.

NATURAL VEGETATION

The natural vegetation of the Monsoon Tropical climate is usually called *savanna*. The equatorial rain forest of the Rainy Tropical climate passes into a deciduous, lower, more open forest. With decreasing rainfall and an increasing length of

167

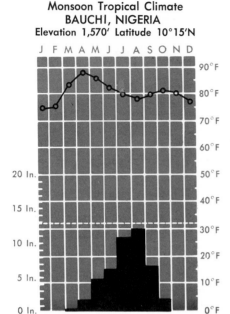

Monsoon Tropical Climate
BAUCHI, NIGERIA
Elevation 1,570' Latitude 10°15'N

Figure 10–2 Climate graph of Bauchi, Nigeria.

Two of the most valuable commercial trees in this forest in southeastern Asia are the *teak* and *pyinkado.*

Teak

Teak is valued for decks and trim of ships and is a fine cabinet wood. The tree attains a girth of about six feet, does not grow in pure stands but normally comprises about 10 percent of the forest. The world's principal teak-growing area is a narrow belt on either side of the Irrawaddy River which widens in the north. The trees are girdled (a ring is cut through the sapwood around the base) three years before felling; this is essential in order for the sap to dry out and permit the logs to be floated out, since there is

dry season, the trees become smaller, more widely spaced and adopt various protective devices such as reduced leaf surface and umbrella-shaped crown. The grasses may be low or tall depending upon local conditions. Actually, the savanna is a mixed plant association of grass and trees. Speaking of Africa, L. Dudley Stamp asserts that in large measure the distinction between forest and grassland is artificial in this type of climate.

MONSOON FOREST

The trees comprising this forest require the same high temperatures as those in the selva, but they can grow in areas having a short but distinct dry season. Possibly southeastern Asia best exemplifies this forest.

The trees are broadleaf deciduous (better *semideciduous*) in character, for not all the trees drop their leaves in the dry season. The trees are more widely spaced than in the selva, they are somewhat smaller in size, there are fewer species, and there is a denser undergrowth, since the crowns of the trees do not form an unbroken canopy that keeps the sun's rays from reaching the ground. Tall bamboo thickets abound.

Figure 10–3 At a logging camp in the Myinbyin Forest Range in Burma, workers, with the aid of a winch, load a truck with heavy logs. Burma is the world's leading producer and exporter of teak. The State Timber Board extracts, processes, and markets all the country's timber. About 100,000 men are employed in this industry and, in addition to trucks, about 1,300 elephants are used for extraction and haulage. (Photo courtesy of the United Nations)

no other effective way of getting the logs from the remote hilly forests and the green wood will not float. About four years are required for the logs to reach the mills; hence much capital is required (Fig. 10–3).

Elephants and buffaloes are used to get the logs to the rivers and also to push logs already in the rivers into deeper water before the floods subside. No machine has yet been invented to displace the elephant for this kind of work.

Pyinkado

The chief use for this wood is for railway ties. The logs are too heavy to float and hence are rafted with bundles of bamboo. Pyinkado is resistant to termites, fungi, heat, and moisture.

TROPICAL SCRUB FOREST

Some areas, where the rainfall effectiveness is not great, support only scrub forest. There are few species, the trees are lower, of smaller diameter, and are separated one from another by more grass-covered space than in the selva or even the monsoon forest. Wherever one sees the scrub forest, whether in South America, Africa, or Australia, it is strikingly similar in appearance.

SAVANNA

The variations in climate, soils, and terrain along with man-induced fires have yielded a wide variety of plant associations over Monsoon Tropical lands. Where grasses predominate they grow in bunches; the grasses are not matted.

Savanna grasses differ widely in height and appearance. A few are soft, curing into a natural hay during the dry season. The majority of them, however, are coarse, harsh, or even saw-edged. In many places, the savanna grasses grow as tall as a man; in extreme cases they may reach even a height of twelve feet (Fig. 10–4). The young grasses may be edible for animals, but in some parts of the world they develop into veritable grass jungles during the dry season. In the dry season the blades become stiff and harsh and

Figure 10–4   Tiger hunting in the grassy jungle of India. Natives, who act as beaters, and elephants are used to corner the game in the high grass. From the ground a person can see only two or three feet in any direction. (Photo from Ewing Galloway)

Figure 10–5   The acacia tall-grass savanna. (Photo courtesy of the American Geographical Society)

the grass sear and brown. Since the vegetation burns readily at this time of year, it is a common practice among natives to burn over such areas in order to make way for the new growth when the rains come. At such times the whole country is blackened and the trees with their scorched trunks stand out prominently in the landscape. These fires are considered by many to be the principal cause of the savanna. L. Dudley Stamp[1] believes that it is becoming increasingly certain that many of Africa's grasslands are primarily due to fires. Fires burn off the dry grass but do not harm the roots; they destroy seedlings and young trees, thereby favoring the extension of grass at the expense of trees. In the South American Llanos the evidence of climatic dominance is not everywhere decisive. The range of climatic conditions under which the savanna occurs in this part of South America, the abrupt boundary between forest and savanna, and the presence of savanna pockets between zones of forest all tend to challenge the idea of climatic theory.[2]

The value of this natural fodder for livestock is not great, it having low nutritional value. The succulent green new growth at the beginning of the wet season and following fires is eaten by the stock, but the large, coarse, mature grasses become hard and unpalatable with progression of the dry season.[3]

There are several varieties of savanna, one of which is shown in Figure 10–5. Bordering the selva of the Congo is the *high-grass–low tree savanna*, which reaches a height of ten to twelve feet mixed with a scattering of trees and even patches of thicket; northward with decreasing rainfall is the *acacia–tall-grass savanna* composed of grasses three to five feet in height with here and there flat-topped acacia trees. Still farther north (now out of the Monsoon Tropical climate) is the *acacia–desert-grass savanna*, where the trees are stunted, stand in lonely isolation, and most of the surface is covered by short desert grasses.

[1] L. Dudley Stamp, *Africa—A Study in Tropical Development,* 2d ed. (New York, John Wiley & Sons, Inc., 1964), p. 113.
[2] C. Langdon White and John Thompson, "The Llanos —A Neglected Grazing Resource," *Journal of Range Management,* Vol. 8 (January, 1955), p. 13.
[3] For excellent discussion of the problems see S. R. Eyre's *Vegetation and Soils* (Chicago, Aldine Publishing Co., 1963), pp. 239–249.

An excellent word picture of the African savanna has been given by H. L. Shantz[4]:

The high grass-low tree savanna is composed of a coarse, rank growth of grasses from five to twelve feet high. The grasses do not form a turf, each plant usually being distinct at the base and somewhat resembling broadcast seeding of the coarser cereals. Growth is rapid, but during the drought period following maturity the grasses dry out and are burned to the ground. . . . At the beginning of the rainy season the fresh young blades shoot up again, forming a dense fresh green cover. Scattered through this grassland are a large number of trees of which the lower branches are in, or barely above, the full-grown grass cover. . . . Except where paths are made, it is difficult to walk through this grass region.

SOILS

It is difficult to generalize on the soils of Monsoon Tropical regions because climate, vegetation, and rock formations vary markedly and because detailed studies have not been made over the greater part of such lands. Most of the soils are classed as red and brown tropical soils, all are leached and have lost their calcium. The minerals of the parent rock have been completely altered and the organic content is generally low.

After the land has been cleared, these soils usually are quite productive for a few years, but if they are to continue so, they must be fertilized.

NATIVE ANIMAL LIFE

The tropical savanna is the home of an abundant and varied native animal life. Part of this is dominantly arboreal in habit as exemplified by apes and birds. Part of it is aquatic, inhabited by the crocodiles, alligators, turtles, hippopotami, and fish. Ground life is especially plentiful. Elephants, giraffes, rhinoceri, and other herbivorous animals are numerous. Several of these are equally well equipped to graze the grasses or to browse the shrubs and trees. In addition, there are peccaries, warthogs, and other wild hogs which live mainly upon roots, nuts, and seeds. Tigers, lions, leopards, and numerous other large carnivores are

also present in the savanna.

The giraffe is probably the most typical animal of the savanna, for it is built both to browse on the leaves of trees and to graze on grasses. When engaged in the former, it avoids stooping (Fig. 10–6). Some of the largest giraffes attain a height of eighteen feet, weigh 4,000 pounds and have legs of six to nine feet from ground to brisket. Such an animal is more than a match for a lion should it get within kicking range.

In many parts of the Old World Monsoon Tropics, human beings have been clearing and utilizing the lands so long that the native fauna is becoming impoverished. Thus, in India the increasing pressure of farming has reduced the

[4] H. L. Shantz and C. F. Marbut, *Vegetation and Soils of Africa,* Research Series No. 13 (New York, American Geographical Society, 1923), p. 50.

Figure 10–6 Two giraffes feeding on leaves about fifteen feet above ground in Kruger National Park, South Africa. These animals, the tallest of all living forms, attain a height of up to eighteen feet. (Photo courtesy of the South African Information Service)

carrying power for wildlife. According to Richard Hesse,[5] the larger animals disappeared from the cultivated areas in the following order: (1) rhinoceros, wild pig, wild buffalo (all breed in swamps), (2) elephant, tiger, and (3) deer and antelope.

There is an interesting story regarding wild antelope in India. In a specific area farmers were being troubled by thousands of these animals. The Hindus would not kill them, however, because their common name was *neilgai* (literally "blue cows") and cows are sacred. Actually these animals are not cows, so the government issued a decree, changing the name from *neilgai* to *neilghora* (literally "blue horses"). The Hindus then felt free to shoot them and today they are much less trouble.[6]

Monsoon Tropical fauna tends to be less arboreal than that of the selva and less fleet-footed than that of the dry grassland but at the same time larger and stronger in body than that in bordering regions.

Insect life is everywhere abundant but especially in the transitional areas between the forests and the grasslands. Many insects are carriers of disease to both man and domestic animals and hence form a serious obstacle to human occupancy. The mosquito, which is responsible for malaria, yellow fever, dengue fever, and elephantiasis is the most common and dangerous, but the tsetse fly of Africa carries the germs of sleeping sickness and *nagana*.

HUMAN ACTIVITIES

Man has adjusted himself in a wide variety of ways to this climate largely because of his differing cultures. The best adjustments are made by the rice growers of southeastern Asia, whereas some of the poorest are made in parts of South America and Africa. When people are backward and poor and hence have few agricultural implements, the savannas do not yield an abundance. Even pastoral peoples in many Monsoon lands experience difficulties in raising their animals. Many such peoples are on a subsistence basis. Even in the Llanos of Colombia-Venezuela, cattle-raising is regarded more as a way of life than as an economic enterprise.

HUNTING AND FISHING

There are two kinds of hunting in Monsoon Tropical lands—that carried on by the natives for food and that carried on by professional hunters (particularly in Africa and Asia) for sport and to make room for human beings when native population increase causes a demand for new territory for crops. If wild animals dispute the course of progress by destroying crops, carrying away livestock, or by killing men, women, and children, they must be killed. In one campaign to rid the Masai reservation of lions that were destroying the natives' cattle, one hunter killed 88 lions in ninety days. This same man in his time killed more than 1,400 elephants, more than 1,000 rhinoceri, and innumerable other animals.

Where people live on or near water, they may carry on some fishing. Especially is this true at the close of the flood season, when the backwaters become well stocked, and at the height of the dry season, when fish are concentrated in pools.

Some Monsoon Tropical regions share with the Semiarid Tropics the distinction of being lands of big game hunting, though actually they are not quite so important (see Chapter 11).

LIVESTOCK

The raising of livestock is important in parts of the Monsoon Tropics. The industry in three areas is presented here.

The Llanos of South America

The vast regions of tropical savanna in South America are, from the standpoint of Occidental cattlemen, among the world's poorest potential cattle lands. Exposed by the march of the seasons to all extremes from flood to drought, clothed with herbage most of which is neither edible nor nourishing, plagued by insects, and remote in location, these regions are misnamed when they are called "natural pastures." Prime beef of the

[5] Richard Hesse, *Ecological Animal Geography* (New York, John Wiley & Sons, Inc., 1937), p. 548.
[6] Bert F. Hoselitz, *The Progress of Underdeveloped Areas* (Chicago, University of Chicago Press), 1952, p. 213.

kind that comes from the great cattle lands of the United States and Argentina is out of the question here; only beef which demands a substantial amount of chewing emanates from the Llanos. Since World War II, however, attempts have been made to improve the economic outlook of the Llanos. Transportation in the form of some all-weather roads and irrigation to carry agricultural settlements over the dry period represent a start in the right direction. With the discovery of iron ore, bauxite, and petroleum some industrialization is taking place. More raw materials still are exported to be manufactured elsewhere. The Llanos, by and large, still remains a relatively poor grazing region for cattle.

Africa

The savannas of Africa are less important for livestock than those of the other continents. This results largely from the presence of the tsetse fly, which must still be regarded as the real ruler of Africa and which is responsible for the disease nagana among domesticated animals. Cattle with this disease usually die.

In some areas, cattle cannot be raised at all because of the tsetse fly; in others only a stunted type of cattle—a type immune to the fly—can exist. In the north, however, the tsetse fly disappears and cattle are kept in large numbers. In the Sudan, some transhumance is carried on during the dry season toward the great marshes to the south. Sheep and goats are far more numerous than cattle in the Sudan.

India

Cattle and buffalo, goats and sheep, all are reared in large numbers. In fact, India has more domesticated animals than any country on earth. Hundreds of thousands of these animals are unproductive. Nearly one-third of the total number of cattle do not bear young or are unfit for work. Nearly all cattle are of low grade. Scant attention is paid to feed crops or to breeding.

Even three-eighths of the manure or some 300 million tons are utilized annually as fuel for cooking and only five-eighths for manuring in a country whose per acre yields of crops are notoriously low. Whole villages make a business of scraping up manure and making it into dung cakes to serve as fuel. Possibly the principal reason for this is the poverty of the masses: they are too poor to purchase the conventional fuels.[7]

India is credited with having one-third to one-half of the world's cattle. Since cattle are venerated by the Hindus, they are not killed. John Fischer[8] tells of being in Calcutta during the serious famine of 1943 and of seeing hundreds of Brahma cattle wandering through the streets, stepping placidly over the bodies of the dead and near dead. But a Hindu would rather he and his entire family die than to eat meat. According to Ellsworth Huntington, the usefulness of cattle for plowing is probably one reason why the Hindu religion prohibits the use of meat. India ranks first in the number of goats and also has large numbers of sheep.

FARMING

When savanna peoples are advanced, they are invariably farmers. The savanna is, in general, the real zone of tropical agriculture. The savanna man does not have to engage in a perpetual struggle with the forest as does Rainy Tropical man; neither must he so laboriously water his fields to win subsistence from the soil as does the Arid Tropical inhabitant.

Among the more primitive savanna people, agriculture is quite simple. At first extreme difficulty is experienced in preparing the land for crops because of the few and inefficient implements. Frequently the soil is stirred with sharp sticks or digging implements and the seed is sown broadcast. As long as agriculture remains in this primitive hoe-and-stick stage, as it does through large parts of the African savannas, it is usually in the hands of women and servants.[9] This leads to polygamy and slavery as established

[7] Marvin Harris, "The Myth of the Sacred Cow" in Anthony Leeds and Andrew P. Vayda, Man, Culture, and Animals, Publication #78 (Washington, D.C., American Association for the Advancement of Science, 1965), p. 221.

[8] John Fischer, "India's Insoluble Hunger," Harper's Magazine, Vol. 190 (April, 1945), pp. 438–445.

[9] One dare not generalize on this topic. There are farmers who use only such crude tools, but there are also many in the same areas who have mattocks and spades. Some even employ steel implements and tools purchased from Europe and America.

Figure 10–7   Farmers preparing a rice paddy with the aid of the carabao or water buffalo. The carabao is the only domesticated animal that can work under a tropical sun in the thick, sticky mud of the rice fields. (Photo courtesy of the Philippine Tourist & Travel Association)

social institutions. However, among more highly developed Monsoon Tropical peoples, plow agriculture has long been practiced (Fig. 10–7). Here farming has ceased to be wholly exploitive and has become intensified and permanent. Under these circumstances, men take charge of agriculture and the entire family labors in the fields.

Among the distinct advantages of farming in this type of climate is a dry season which facilitates clearing and burning the forest and provides a time for harvest. The dry air also renders stored products less liable to attack by insects and fungi.

In most Monsoon Tropical lands, despite the importance of agriculture, methods from our standpoint are backward. For example, in southern Thailand, where much of that country's rice is grown, shallow plowing, imperfect weeding, and lack of manuring are the rule. Harvesting is accomplished by cutting with a knife one rice stalk at a time. A man will then carry home over his shoulders in one or two loads all that he has

harvested in a day. Threshing is done by hand. In India, too, backward methods prevail: the farmers still sow and reap by hand; they do not use good seed or follow a scientific rotation; and despite the huge number of livestock, little manure is put on the land. Insufficient irrigation facilities leave large areas at the complete mercy of the summer monsoon;[10] bad rental conditions result in a low standard of living; and omnipresent illiteracy (estimated at close to 90 percent) constitutes an almost insurmountable obstacle to improvement.

Throughout most of the Monsoon Tropical countries, where any farming is carried on at all, man depends much upon tree crops. Here and there great plantations are to be seen, but over most of the realm, where subsistence farming is dominant, one sees not large continuous orchards but many different trees, often only one or two of each kind—avocado, banana (not a true tree),

[10] Yet no country has so much land under irrigation as India.

mango, papaya, and others. Monsoon Tropical man probably depends even more upon grain crops or cereals. These are really domesticated grasses that are, by their habits, fitted to grow in a climate which produces a variety of wild grasses as a native vegetation. Rice is the key cereal over the Asiatic savanna lands, as is zea maize (corn) over those of tropical America. In a few areas of lighter rainfall, such as northern India, wheat and barley are grown. The African savannas possess as native cereals, milo maize, guinea corn, durrah, sorghum, and numerous varieties of millet. However, white missionaries, traders, and various Oriental, Negro, or white immigrants have so spread these crops that any or all of them may be found growing side by side in even the most remote localities. Yams, beans, peanuts, and manioc are grown almost universally as supply crops, while cotton, sugar cane (Fig. 10–8), and tea are produced in quantity here and there throughout the realm.

RICE GROWING AND PROGRESS

Most of the world's rice is grown in Monsoon Tropical southeastern Asia and the neighboring islands. Not only does rice thrive in the long, hot, rainy summers but it is the most regular in yield of all the cereals, since it must be irrigated. This is not equally true of any other crop. It also yields more than any other.

Rice cannot be grown without at least a fair degree of hard, steady work and painstaking irrigation which involves carefully regulated customs for handling the water. This leads to cooperative effort. As rice becomes more important in a given area, the food supply becomes more abundant and more people can be supported. Thus, the pressure of population on the land tends to mount to the very limits of possibility.

Rice has been a strong factor in promoting the kind of social organization in which people

Figure 10–8 On flat land in Puerto Rico much sugar cane is planted. Note, however, the tree growth and grassy plots on the slopes. Most workers prefer to live on the higher ground to take advantage of winds and lower temperatures. (Photo courtesy of the Department of Agriculture of the Commonwealth of Puerto Rico)

work steadily and peacefully and cooperate in public affairs. By far the best tropical workers occupy the rice-growing regions. This does not mean that they work as hard as farmers in middle latitudes; they are slow in movement as is natural in hot climates.

Rice-growing Java and Madura, with more than 63 million people, about 1,230 to the square mile, support sixteen times as many people as the premier American state of Iowa, which is slightly larger, and this despite the fact that they are mountainous whereas Iowa is mostly flat or undulating. In Java most of the people have but small farms and these they must cultivate intensively. In the better areas the agricultural population exceeds 1,500 persons to the square mile. Thus rice is grown typically on tiny plots by subsistence farmers.

That Java is the most productive part of Indonesia is no accident but the result of a happy combination of natural and human factors. Especially important is the fertility of the soil, rejuvenated by volcanoes which have been active within recent centuries or even decades.

With so great a density of population, the standard of living could not be high. But the desires of rice eaters in the past were not great: food, some simple garments, a dwelling, and a few other necessaries sufficed. Nor were the people unhappy; just the reverse. When the government has offered attractive inducements to get people to migrate to less-densely populated neighboring islands, the Javanese have been reluctant to go.

The situation in all developing nations has been changing in recent years, however. No longer are the people willing to live as their forebears did for centuries; they are not content to be ill, largely illiterate, and poor. One of their main interests is to raise their level of living.

Most of Brazil's productive agricultural land lies in this type of climate. Here is grown a disproportionate share of the world's coffee as well as much cotton, sugar cane, manioc, fruits, and vegetables. The coffee *fazendas* (large plantations) are in the states of São Paulo, Minas Gerais, and Paraná on the rolling upland (1,500 to 2,500 feet) and on the fertile *terra roxa* soils. Many individual fazendas cover thousands of acres and some of these have as many as one, two, or three million coffee trees.

MANUFACTURING

Almost every country in the Monsoon Tropics is classified as "underdeveloped." They and all the others so classified represent two-thirds of the world's inhabitants. Since underdeveloped lands have only about 15 percent of the total world income, since they experience daily endemic hunger, and since they suffer from the ravages of disease, it is not surprising that they wish most ardently to improve their lot. And the principal way of accomplishing this, as they see it, is by industrialization.

An examination of the industrial map of the world, however, shows that the great sweeps of territory comprising Monsoon Tropical lands are relatively unimportant in manufacturing. There are, of course, countless villages having a mild industrial life, with such enterprises as weaving, pottery making, and basketry, but there is little manufacturing as Americans and western Europeans think of it, and there are not many great industrial cities.

While India cannot be considered a major industrial nation, it is a leader as far as Monsoon Tropical and Oriental countries are concerned. With large repositories of iron ore and coal, localized largely in the eastern part of the country, an iron and steel industry, reputed to be the largest in the Commonwealth, has arisen at Jamshedpur Bhilai, Durgapur, and Rourkela. Nevertheless, India's output is small and even to exist at all a high protective tariff is employed. India has an important textile industry, principally in Bombay; she also has rapidly growing aluminum, chemical, fertilizer, machine tool, and newsprint industries. Yet up to the present time manufacturing has not affected economically the great mass of the population.

Monsoon Tropical Brazil is growing industrially, particularly the São Paulo area. In fact this city is now the leading industrial center in all Latin America. Though poor in coal and petroleum, the area near the Serra do Mar is rich in potential water power and many sites have been and are being developed. Factories of many kinds, but especially textile mills, have sprung up in numerous places. Probably São Paulo comes nearer than any other Monsoon Tropical city to being an industrial center.

At Volta Redonda, some ninety miles northwest of Rio de Janeiro, has been constructed the largest iron and steel center in Latin America. Though Brazil is rich in iron ore and manganese, she is poor indeed in coal. Low-grade deposits in the state of Santa Catarina are being utilized. The cost of assembling the three raw materials at the blast furnace is much higher than in most districts in the United States.

TRADING

Monsoon Tropical lands are important for trade. The countries of Asia, Africa, and even Latin America have long been in a colonial or semicolonial relationship with respect to the highly industrialized nations of Europe and North America. The result has been that their economic life has been shaped to serve those nations as markets for manufactured products and sources of raw materials. Britain's most valuable possession for many years was India. For generations British exports to India were greater than to any other country.

Burma, Thailand, Vietnam, and Cambodia are among the world's leading surplus rice producers and hence the sources of much of the world's export rice. Nearly 70 percent of the total rice exports from Monsoon Asia move out of the three ports of Rangoon, Bangkok, and Saigon. Java exports sugar, quinine, tea, kapok, tobacco, and other products. Monsoon Tropical Africa exports cotton, coffee, peanuts, and many other items. Queensland, Australia, exports some sugar, though most of the crop is not grown in the Monsoon Tropical portion. Brazil is the world's principal grower and exporter of coffee and it is of international importance in the export trade in cotton and sugar. Colombia and Venezuela are large exporters of coffee (Colombia leads in growing and exporting *mild coffees*); Colombia, the Pacific side of Central America, and Jamaica are major sources of the world's commercial banana crop; and Cuba, before the Castro regime, had been the world's leading exporter of sugar.

Canton, Hong Kong, Bangkok, Saigon, Habana, Rangoon, and Bombay are among the great ports of the world. In fact all the important Monsoon Tropical cities, with the exception of São Paulo, are seaports.

DISTRIBUTION AND DENSITY OF POPULATION

The population map on the inside front cover, showing the density of population in Monsoon Tropical areas, indicates that this climate is capable of sustaining extensive areas of moderate to dense population. This is in marked contrast to the few areas of density noted in the Rainy Tropics and in the Arid Tropics (except in the oases).

India and Java especially have very dense populations on some of the more fertile plains. Both are important rice-growing lands and dense populations are a necessity for the production of rice as that crop is grown in the Orient. In parts of southeastern Asia a population of nearly two thousand persons to the square mile is supported by agriculture. Nowhere, however, is the population evenly distributed as, for example, in the American state of Iowa. The people live mostly in villages and have almost a communal type of social organization.

Burma, Thailand, Vietnam, Cambodia, and Laos situated in the Orient, are by no means densely populated. Nor are the Monsoon Tropics of Africa, Latin America (except a few islands in the Caribbean), or Australia. In fact, in some of those lands there are vast spaces that are still virtually unoccupied. In South America the Llanos until recently had a steadily declining population and the Gran Chaco is almost uninhabited.

Aside from the small number of port cities just mentioned, Monsoon Tropical lands do not support many great cities. The Monsoon Tropics are not a first-class climate for the white man. Only on the temperate uplands, as, for example, in southern Brazil, does he become more than a supervisor. Hence his numbers are relatively small. But even for supervisory work, he needs fresh vitality which can be got only by making occasional visits to more stimulating climes. Accordingly, private companies and governments give regular and frequent vacations.

The well-watered trade wind coastal area of northeastern Queensland is apparently an exception. There about 300,000 white people do all sorts of work. With a law against the immigration of colored peoples (there is a white Australia policy of "a continent for a nation"), these whites are carrying on one of the most successful white penetrations anywhere in the tropics. The death rate is low for a tropical region. This experiment does not prove, however, that white men can retain full energy in the Monsoon Tropics.

SOCIAL ADJUSTMENTS

Some inhabitants of tropical savannas are in a backward stage of ecology, while others are in a rather advanced stage. Some parts of the realm are occupied by only a few savage tribes, while others are settled by people having a high culture. Some savannas offer opportunities for future economic and social progress, but a greater number offer few, if any.

Some savannas, being dependent upon more or less fickle monsoon winds for their rains, occasionally suffer years of drought. This is especially serious in the more densely peopled areas. In the case of India, there is an immense relief organization to care for the unfortunates during famines. One reason for the large network of railways is to get food to famine areas quickly, because some parts of India are relatively certain of large annual crops.

For the most part, the indigenous civilizations in southeastern Asia, Africa, and Latin America are poor. This is attributable partly to the small and highly variable yield of crops in a climate with great extremes of rain and drought and partly to overpopulation and social conditions.

The economic lot of the peoples of modern India improves slowly despite improvements in public health and primary education, modern irrigation, extended transportation, increased industrialization, and community development projects (Fig. 10–9). This results largely from the pressure of population on the arable land: India has more people, for example, than the United States and the Soviet Union combined— 461 million. Her average population density

Figure 10–9   Native women help unload tins of kerosene from an Indian sailboat in the Sanrashtrian port of Porbandar. (Photo courtesy of Caltex)

is about five times the world average. Facing a future increment of about 125 millions every decade, India is presented with seemingly insuperable problems. Little new agricultural land can be added. One-third of the people are now concentrated on less than 6 percent of the land and each farmer averages not more than four-fifths of an acre. The per capita shortage of food becomes yearly more acute. Industrialization is not the panacea.

In many Monsoon Tropical lands, particularly those in Asia, the efforts and hopes of millions of newly aroused peoples will be frustrated by population expansion unless something can be done to balance births and deaths. In the long run, the only way to have low death rates with all this implies is to have low birth rates also. Without a decline in births, one of the positive checks mentioned by Malthus must function —famine, pestilence, or war.

Most Monsoon Tropical lands suffer from a variety of tropical diseases and while all take their toll, malaria is the most widespread and probably the worst. It is reputed to be the most important contributory cause of the backward economic state of these lands. All malarious countries are poor countries. It causes a sharp loss in working efficiency and cuts down the production of food.

In southeastern Asia and the western Pacific, most of which is Monsoon Tropical in climate, millions of persons live in malarial areas. Fortunately, antimalarial programs are in force in all Monsoon Tropical lands. Residual spraying of houses with DDT gives man a low-cost killer that could enable medical science to reduce this disease to the vanishing point. Venezuela, for example, has all but wiped it out; the moment a case appears anywhere in the country, the machinery for treating it goes into immediate action. However, malariologists are concerned lest the *Anopheles*, which transmits the disease, develop resistance to DDT and to other insecticides.

Another dread disease of the Monsoon Tropics is yaws; it disfigures its victims and for many years was confused with syphilis. In Haiti more than half the rural population was rid of the disease within three years in a campaign to stamp it out. Today there is not a single case of yaws in Haiti. The per person cost was ten or twenty cents (U.S.). Penicillin is the weapon used. Monsoon Asia today has the most extensive program against yaws in the world; however, vast distances, thousands of small islands, temperature variations, high humidity, and danger from floods and wild animals all combine to make the work exceedingly difficult. Through the efforts of the World Health Organization yaws has been greatly reduced in Africa.

SOME POLITICAL ASPECTS

Almost everywhere in Monsoon Tropical lands, but particularly in southeast Asia, political conditions are tense. This results in large measure from the fact that until recently these lands were colonies or dependencies with abysmally low standards of living. They had for centuries been plagued by poverty, hunger, disease, and lack of opportunity for self-development. Now this poverty is a source of active political discontent. The people now desire to enjoy the same amenities as the people of the West. Moreover, they want no more white supremacy in their parts of the world.

Not a single Monsoon Tropical country ranks among the highly or well-developed nations; most are in the backward or under-developed group, that is, they are characterized by mass poverty which is chronic. The latter suffer from obsolete methods of production. Their average per capita annual incomes are less than $150 per annum. They are the true "have-nots," and to make matters worse it is not they that are moving ahead but the developed countries. The discontent of these people gives the countries in which they live a potential influence in world affairs that cannot be ignored. Their great numbers give them an ability to make themselves heard, and it is of the utmost importance to win their willing and effective support.

SUGGESTED USEFUL READINGS

Cressey, George B., *Asia's Lands and Peoples*, 3d ed. (New York, McGraw-Hill Book Company, 1963), pp. 373–475.

Ginsburg, Norton, ed., *The Pattern of Asia* (Englewood Cliffs, N.J., Prentice-Hall, Inc., 1958), pp. 290–697.

Kendrew, W. G., *The Climates of the Continents*, 5th ed. (Oxford, Clarendon Press, 1961), pp. 147–192, 214–229.

Pedelaborde, Pierre, *The Monsoon*, translated by M. J. Clegg (London, Methuen and Company, 1963), 196 pp.

Spate, Oskar, *India and Pakistan*, 2d ed. (New York, E. P. Dutton and Company, 1957), 829 pp.

Stamp, L. Dudley, *Asia: A Regional and Economic Geography* (London, Methuen and Company, 1962), pp. 188–479.

Wickizer, V. D., and M. K. Bennett, *The Rice Economy of Monsoon Asia*, Food Research Institute, Stanford University (California, 1941).

11

Semiarid Tropical Climate Regions

THE CLIMATE

CHARACTERISTICS

The Semiarid Tropical climate is in some respects much like the Monsoon Tropical type described in the preceding chapter. Both are marked by high temperatures throughout the year, and both exhibit a wet season and a dry season annually. There, the similarities cease. The differences are that the wet season in the Semiarid climate is much shorter in duration (varying from two to four months, depending upon the locality), and the rains are lighter and often irregular. The total average rainfall is not large, varying from eight to ten inches on up to twenty or twenty-five inches annually. During the greater part of the year, the weather is hot, dry, and often dusty (Fig. 11–1).

The rains of the wet season occur in the form of sudden heavy thundershowers, interspersed with short spells of fair weather. During the wet season, however, the countryside becomes sodden and the roads are impassable. Traffic ceases except over the few hard-surfaced roads. In semiarid regions north of the equator, the rains usually occur during June, July, and August. In such lands south of the equator, the wet season falls in December, January, and February. In the northern part of Australia, for instance, these three months are referred to as the "lay up" period, a time in which much human activity ceases or is seriously curtailed.

LOCATION

This type of climate occurs in seven fairly large regions scattered about over those continents which lie partially within the Tropical Zone (Fig. 11–2). One of them lies in North America and includes the Mexican west coast states of Sinaloa, Nyarit, and the southern part of Baja California. A second lies in South America—the São Francisco Valley in northeastern Brazil. Africa has two semiarid tropical regions, one of them (the northern Sudan) stretching from Senegal eastward to Somali, and the other stretching across Southwest Africa—the southern part of Angola, Rhodesia, and up onto the plateaus of East Africa. The fifth region is situated in southern India on the leeward or back slope of the Western Ghats. The sixth is a crescent-shaped area in northwest India between the savanna lands and the Thar Desert. The seventh is the interior of northern Australia.

In addition, there are several small semiarid regions: northwest Yucatan, southwest Ecuador, the middle Irrawaddy Valley in central Burma, and southwestern Malagasy. Included, too, are certain so-called desert islands in the tropical parts of the oceans.

CAUSAL FACTORS

A glance at the map (Fig. 11–2) reveals that the Semiarid Tropical regions lie generally between latitudes 12° and 20° in either hemisphere. What is even more important, it reveals also that for the most part these regions lie adjacent to tropical desert areas. Moreover, in all instances, they likewise lie adjacent to Monsoon Tropical regions. With these locational facts in mind, it is not difficult to discover the underlying causes for the occurrence of this climate.

The short rainy season occurs during the

part of the year when the noonday sun is directly overhead, and during that period, this climate is as enervating and trying as the Rainy Tropical type. As the sun reaches an overhead position at each tropic circle, it so heats the atmosphere in that part of the earth lying between 15° and 30° that the trade winds die down and are temporarily replaced by great counter-movements of air (monsoon winds) which flow from the equator into the tropical deserts. During the months when the monsoon winds blow, rains fall on the lands over which these winds pass. It is during this time that the rainy season occurs in both the Semiarid Tropical and the Monsoon Tropical climates. The farther away from the equator a locality is situated, however, the shorter its high-sun period, and hence the shorter the duration of its monsoon winds. Accordingly, the farther a place lies removed from latitude 0°, the less rainfall reaches it—most of the moisture having fallen on lands nearer the equator. Thus, in the Rainy Tropical climate near the equator, there is rain at all seasons; farther away from the equator in Monsoon Tropical regions, there is a long rainy season; still farther away from the equator in the Semiarid Tropical lands, the influence of the monsoon winds is felt but for a short time and then only feebly; and finally, in latitudes 20° to 30°, only a few showers fall each year and the climate is arid in type. What actually occurs is a gradual diminution in both the amount of rainfall and the length of rainy season from the equator outward to the poleward margins of the Tropical Zone. (Compare Figures 8–2, 9–4, 10–2, and 11–1).

PLANT GEOGRAPHY

Since nature has thus drawn no definite and distinct boundaries between types of climate, it follows that there are no sharp divisions between natural vegetation regions. The same gradual transition may be noted in flora as that in rainfall which was described in the preceding paragraph. Going away from the equator, one passes from rain forest to savanna, from savanna to grassland steppe, and from steppe to desert. In general, the Semiarid Tropical lands are regions of grassland steppe. Since the rainfall is scanty, it will support few trees; hence the dominant floral

element is low grass—endless thousands of square miles of it in some areas. In many localities, trees are entirely absent; in others, the landscape is more diversified with bushes and clumps of scrubby trees interspersed through extensive areas of grass (Fig. 11–3). On one margin, these semiarid grasslands grade into tree-dotted savanna; on the other, they shade into the more xerophytic vegetation of the desert.

ANIMAL GEOGRAPHY
BIOLOGICAL SEQUENCE

These great natural grasslands are the home of a very abundant and varied wild animal life. This is particularly true of the grasslands of northern, southern, and eastern Africa.[1] In these areas, the grass-eating (herbivorous) animals are most important. They include zebras, springbok and other gazelles, wild cattle, elands, gnus,

[1] In Australia, the most isolated of the inhabited continents, the native animal life is relatively restricted. The grasslands show only kangaroos, wallabies, coyote-like dingoes, innumerable imported rabbits, bandicoots, wild turkeys, a sort of native ostrich, and a few other faunal forms.

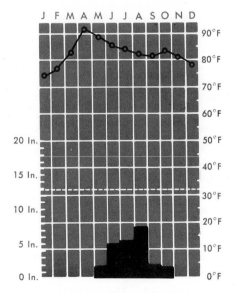

Semiarid Tropical Climate
FORT LAMY, CHAD
Elevation 886' Latitude 12°7'N

Figure 11–1 Climate graph of Fort Lamy, Chad. Compare this graph with that of Bauchi for the length of the rainy season.

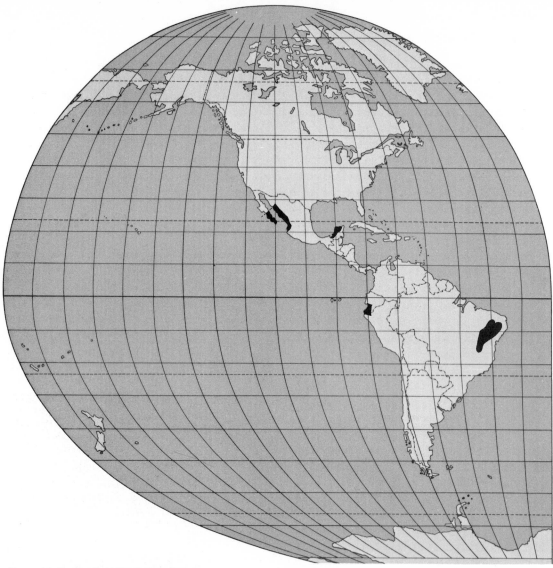

Figure 11–2 Semiarid Tropical regions.

hartebeests and other antelopes, all of which exist in great herds. Because the herbage has comparatively low feeding value, these grazers and browsers must feed off and on all day. This means they must have a wide grazing range. Many of the animals follow the rains and the new grass that springs up afterwards. These herbivores are the first element in the biological cycle which is here better displayed by nature than perhaps anywhere else on earth.

Second in the sequence are the meat eaters (carnivores) which prey upon the herbivores. They include such animals as lions, tigers, leopards, and other cats. Since their food is concentrated high-grade protein, they need to make a kill only at intervals of several days. In short, unlike the herbivores, they need not be feeding all the time. This is reflected in the territory they occupy: it is centered on a den of some sort. Hence they need not go far for their food. These kill their victims and gorge themselves on fresh meat.[2] In the hot tropical sunshine, however, the remainder soon putrefies, whereupon a third group, jackals, vultures, and so forth gather to devour the carrion. Fourth are the bone-eating hyenas, with their powerful teeth and nocturnal

[2] Leopards often cache their kill—a partly grown hartebeest or a reed-buck—in a crotch of a tree to prevent hyenas and other scavengers from getting it.

182

habits, which finish the carrion and crack up most of the bones during the night. Fifth, there are the myriads of ants and other insects which clean up most of the remaining traces of the kill during the following morning.

This cycle of killing and eating, of grass and flesh, of birth, life, and death, is normal routine in the tropical grasslands. These regions have been called the "Land of Big Game," the story of which has fortunately been recorded by the naturalist-cameraman stationed in ambush beside the water hole.[3]

THE WATER HOLE

The water hole may be regarded as the community center of animal life during the long dry season. At some time during the day or night, all animals come to the water hole to quench their thirst (Fig. 11–4).

GAME PRESERVES

The animal life of the grasslands is, however, doomed. The automobile and airplane and the modern high-power rifle with telescopic sights, in the hands of European and American "sportsmen," are far too effective to permit it to survive for long. The remotest grasslands of Africa promise before long to be subdued by man, even as those of India have already been conquered and occupied by comparatively dense populations.

[3] A vivid account of grassland fauna is given in Theodore Roosevelt's book, *African Game Trails* (New York, Charles Scribner's Sons, 1910).

Figure 11–3 Acacia desert-grass savanna. This type of vegetation occupies areas between the acacia tall-grass savanna on the humid side and the desert-shrub desert-grass on the arid side. (Photo courtesy of the American Geographical Society)

However, poachers also kill vast numbers of animals, less for food, unfortunately, than for skins, ivory, and bone, which they sell. In southern and eastern Africa, where big game was originally most numerous, so many animals have been killed by ruthless hunters and poachers that government parks have been reserved. In these, wild animals are being preserved in their natural habitat.

HUMAN GEOGRAPHY— PASTORAL ACTIVITIES

THE AFRICAN GRASSLANDS

The rainy season is too short and the amount of rainfall too light in the Semiarid Tropical climate for most kinds of crops. Therefore, men in these grasslands cannot gain satisfactory subsistence by means of agriculture. The rainfall, however, is sufficient to produce grass; and with grass plus an occasional water hole, man can support himself through the medium of domesticated animals. Fortunately, the aboriginal fauna of the Afro-Asiatic realm contained a number of fairly tract-

able herbivorous animals. Some of these were domesticated by man long before the dawn of history, and so grassland man became a herdsman. The Fulahs, Mandingoes, Tuaregs, and other peoples of the Northern Sudan, the Somalis and Gallas of northeastern Africa, and many of the Bushman and Bantu tribes of south central Africa are pastoral folk. They rear flocks of goats, wire-haired sheep, and humped cattle. In Kenya and Tanganyika dwell the Masai, who are pastoralists and count their wealth and importance by the number of livestock they possess. Their cattle particularly are a temptation to lions which also occupy the region. Hence, in order to protect their livestock, the Masai build *bomas*—walls of thorn brush piled as high as seven feet around their huts. As night falls, the animals are driven within the thorn brush enclosure. Since lions have sensitive feet, they fear the thorny wall and usually remain aloof, though occasionally they take a chance.

North of El Obeid are seminomadic Arab tribes who follow the movement of the sun and of the associated rains with their camels and asses, sheep, and goats. During the driest periods, they remain close to the oases preparing skins and collecting gum arabic which they get by making incisions in the acacia trees. Gum arabic is a major trading item of the Sudan.

THE AUSTRALIAN GRASSLANDS

In the northern part of Australia lie the least utilized of the world's tropical grasslands. They extend over some half million square miles in the northern portions of West Australia, Northern Territory, and northwestern Queensland. This great region, about one-sixth of the Commonwealth, contains only a few thousand people—most of them the descendants of British colonists engaged in cattle ranching. Much of the area is fine range grass with only an occasional brigalow tree or patch of mulga trees. Along the rivers and intermittent creek beds, there are long thin lines of eucalyptus trees.

Inland from the port of Darwin runs for a few hundred miles a single line of railway to Birdum. At a few other points, short railways also lead in from the coast. A few score of small towns and a few hundred ranches are spread thinly over the region. Some of the cattle ranches are enormous; a few contain as much as ten million acres of grassland.

Most of the cattle, when ready for market, or when an occasional severe drought desiccates the range, are not sent out to the nearby northern coast. Instead, they are driven over cross-country trails or "tracks" to markets on the eastern and southern coasts of the Commonwealth. In general, there are four main routes over which the cattle are driven, in "mobs" of 1,000 to 1,500 animals. From the Kimberley District of Western Australia mobs of cattle are driven some 1,500 miles southwestward across the desert to the port of Perth, over what is known as the Canning Track (Fig. 11–5). From the Victoria River Plains in the Northern Territory cattle are driven over the East-West Track for a thousand miles eastward to the railhead at Cloncurry. Thence, the cattle go out by rail to the port of Townsville on the east coast, as do most of the animals of northern Queensland; or they turn southward by way of the Great Georgina Track. This latter runs south from Cloncurry and Camooweal around the eastern edge of the desert to the

Figure 11–4   Zebras and wildebeests at drinking pool at Kruger National Park, South Africa. (Photo courtesy of the South African Tourist Corporation)

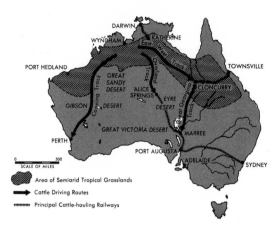

Figure 11-5   Stock trails of the grasslands of northern Australia.

railhead at Marree near Lake Eyre. From Marree, they go by rail to Port Augusta or Sydney. From the Wave Hill and Powells Creek areas, the cattle drovers walk their mobs southward to the railhead at Alice Springs, whence they are hauled across the desert to the port of Adelaide on the Gulf.

THE INDIAN GRASSLANDS

Not all of the grassland has been plowed up for crops. Much of it remains in the hands of the grazier. Sheep, goats, cattle, and buffaloes are exceedingly numerous. India has more cattle than any other country. Most of these, however, that are used as draft animals and as beasts of burden are in the Monsoon Tropical part.

Goats are the most numerous animals. They do well in densely populated regions having poor or limited grazing facilities. In fact, they can survive in areas too arid for most other domesticated animals. The goat is the favorite milk animal.

Sheep are numerous in Semiarid Tropical India but not in relation to the number of people.

The grassland is taxed right up to the carrying limit for livestock. In some years, the monsoon winds are weak and bring little rain to these inland regions. Then drought desiccates the pastures.

THE BRAZILIAN SERTÃO

The semiarid lands of Brazil lie in the hump—back from the coast. Known as the *sertão*, these thinly peopled lands comprise the domain of the

grazier, for they are visited by returning droughts and occasional floods and they are clothed with scrub forest (Fig. 11-6). Only here and there, where water is dependable, do tiny tracts of cropland occur. The sertão is called a land of natural calamity—a name it well deserves, for it is a land of famine and of emigration. Time and again the people of the area have had to flee to other parts of Brazil—to the rubber camps of the Amazon, to the coffee fazendas of São Paulo, to the pioneer zones of Goias, or to the mining camps of Minas Gerais.

HUMAN GEOGRAPHY—AGRICULTURE

THE SUDAN

As we have noted, there is inadequate rainfall for agriculture in most areas having this type of

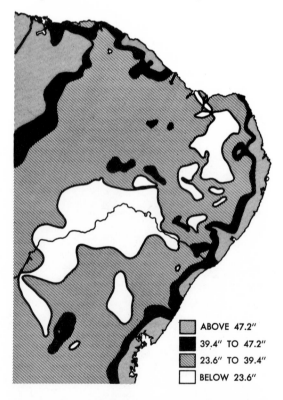

	ABOVE 47.2"
	39.4" TO 47.2"
	23.6" TO 39.4"
	BELOW 23.6"

Figure 11-6   Average annual rainfall in the "hump" of Brazil. Note the variation in the amount of precipitation. The periodic droughts are the dominant geographic circumstances; however, they result more from uneven distribution of precipitation than from a deficiency of annual precipitation. Semiarid Tropical Brazil is a land of natural calamities—drought and flood. It is also a land of frequent crop failure and famine. (Map adapted from Inspetoria Federal de Obras contra as Secas)

climate. Where water is available, however, farming is carried on. One irrigated area—the Gazira in Sudan—is world famous. It is a five-million-acre plain lying between the White and the Blue Nile. The water that supports it and comes from the Blue Nile is made available by the Sennar Dam and its canals. The soils in this nationalized project are deep and fertile.

About half a million acres are cultivated annually with long-staple Egyptian cotton, which is the major cash crop. *Dura*, a grain sorghum, and *lubia*, a leguminous fodder, are also important crops. Lubia is used to feed some 250,000 animals and to attract seminomads from adjacent areas, who are badly needed for labor. Less important crops are wheat, peanuts, and vegetables.

INDIA

Where the southwest monsoon wind first strikes the coast of India, the rainfall is abundant. At Bombay, for instance, the average annual amount is some eighty inches. Seventy-five miles eastward on the back slope of the Ghats, the climate is distinctly semiarid. Far up the valleys of the Ganges and Indus rivers in the lower Punjab and on the eastern plains of Rajputana, similar dry areas occur. In these, the countryside was once covered by poor grassland—treeless except along the stream courses.

So overpopulated are the humid portions of India that the Indians are desperately land hungry. Accordingly, even these semiarid lands have become rather densely peopled. Much of their area has been put to agriculture, but the crops are for the most part not very dependable. Wheat, barley, beans, peanuts, millet, and sorghum are the common crops. Ordinarily they are either not irrigated, or else watered but sparingly from wells or reservoirs. Considerable amounts of cotton and tobacco are raised, but these require almost constant irrigation. Some coffee cultivation is also practiced on the dry hillsides of the southern part of the peninsula.

BRAZIL'S SERTÃO

During good years, variable amounts of land are devoted to such crops as corn, beans, and manioc, which are carefully protected from grazing animals by brush fences. During the drier years, which sometimes follow in succession, these little gardens fail altogether, a scarcity of food ensues, and famine stalks the land. Since the days of Dom Pedro II, the Brazilian government has striven to improve the living conditions in this region. At present there is a plan, modeled on that of the United States' TVA, for the development of the Rio São Francisco area.

LOCUSTS AND GRASSHOPPERS

In this type of climate as well as in many arid, semiarid, and subhumid types, locusts and grasshoppers occasionally contest with man for the land. The problem is old: in fact, it has confronted man since the earliest beginnings of agriculture. Moreover, it is almost a worldwide problem (Fig. 11–7): the only areas free from the scourge are the forests and tundras of the Northern Hemisphere, the equatorial forests, and high mountains.

Locusts do not attack man directly as do some pests but devastate his lands, thereby attacking his food supply—crops and animals. Land so devastated is a land of famine and starvation. The normal cycle of the locust life is closely correlated with the rainfall cycle and the wind systems.[4]

Sometimes locusts travel thousands of miles, particularly in Africa and western Asia. Swarms may blot out the sun for hours at a time. One swarm in East Africa three by sixty miles is believed to have contained a trillion locusts.

In the past man fought the locust on unequal terms; he fought it in many ways. Only recently by employing poison bait, DDT, airplanes, and helicopters has he proved to be really effective.

FAMINE

In this type of climate with its alternating wet and dry seasons, the amount of rainfall is usually not far in excess of what is needed for agriculture. Hence, even a small departure from average rainfall is disastrous to human life. Thus, famine strikes from time to time in India, the Sudan, and the Brazilian sertão.

[4] B. P. Uvarov, *The Locust Plague, Smithsonian Report for 1944* (Washington, Smithsonian Institution), pp. 331–346.

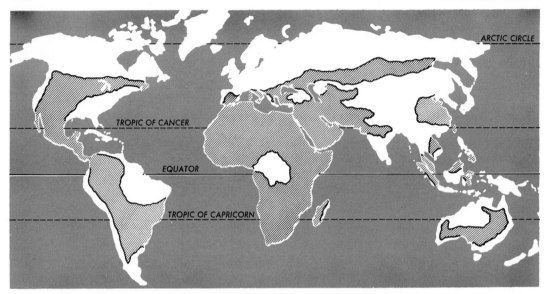

Figure 11-7 Lands subject to invasions by locusts and grasshoppers (seventy-seven countries, indicated by cross-hatching). Not a single continent occupied by man is free from these pests, which are absent only from the forest and tundra belts of the north, the Tropical rain forest, and high mountains. Each spring, as for millennia, migrating locusts gather in huge swarms to plague man and wreak destruction on his crops. Until recently, man has fought this pest on unequal terms. At last, however, he appears to have a chance to vanquish it for all time, by using small airplanes and helicopters for spreading poison. Aldrin has given the best results to date. But to win the battle all lands affected must engage in a coordinated war, which is possible through the United Nations. This war must be based upon a knowledge of breeding places and of the climatic conditions that favor swarming. (Map adapted from Uvarov and the Smithsonian Institution)

INDIA

The great famine zones lie in the Dekkan Plateau on the leeward side of the Western Ghats Mountains and in Rajputana. Famine strikes here with any diminution in the rainfall; and because of the very dense population, loss of life was great until a rail-web was constructed and a famine relief organization set up.

THE SUDAN

Rainfall in the southern Sudan is little above the needs of agriculture; hence even a small departure is disastrous to native farming. Likewise in the northern Sudan a slight deficit in the rainfall greatly reduces the stock-carrying capacity of the pastures and the number of animals.

THE SERTÃO

The limited amount of rainfall in this region along with its variability have again and again forced large numbers of people to migrate. The region has a high birthrate and this, combined with the fickle rainfall, means that there is a real problem of survival at such times. Hence the sertão has long served as a major population seedbag of the nation; actually it is the chief source-region for the migrants to other regions. The sertão promises to remain an area of emigration and famine for a long time.

THE RELATIONSHIP SEQUENCE IN GEOGRAPHY

The student of international relations is interested primarily not in the climates of the earth per se but rather in the contribution which each makes to global economy. The exports from the Semiarid Tropical lands serve to emphasize what the student has already observed in connection with the study of other climates, namely, that each type of climate tends to produce its own distinctive kind of economy and therefore to give rise to a distinctive set of exports into the markets of the world. There is some overlapping in these export commodities, but in general no two types of climate give rise to the same list of exports.

The reason for this, of course, is obvious.

Each climate is characterized by a distinctive human geography, and it is from this latter that the exports arise. The distinctive human geography in question is related to the animal geography, the plant geography, and the climatic conditions of the type in question. The type of climate is, in turn, the product of a specific geomatic position and natural situation on the earth's surface. This chain of relationships might be termed the "geographic relationship sequence."

Viewed in reverse, this relationship sequence can be stated as follows. A certain geomatic position on the earth, coupled with the natural situation of the areas involved, produces a given type of climate. Related to this type of climate is a unique type of natural vegetation. Related to both natural vegetation and climate is a unique type of animal life. Related to all three factors of fauna, flora, and climate is a characteristic type of human geography. Finally, related to this human geography is a specific type of commercial geography giving rise to a specific list of export commodities. There is, of course, nothing rigid about such a chain of relationships, but it is invariably consistent enough to provide a useful instrument of analysis in geographic study.

SUGGESTED USEFUL READINGS

Eyre, S. R., *Vegetation and Soils: A World Picture* (Chicago, Aldine Publishing Company, 1963), pp. 239–249.

Rattray, J. M., *The Grass Cover of Africa* (Rome, Food and Agriculture Organization, 1960).

Robinson, Kathleen W., *Australia, New Zealand, and the Southwest Pacific* (New York, London House and Maxwell, 1962), 340 pp.

Shantz, H. L., and C. F. Marbut, *The Vegetation and Soils of Africa* (New York, National Research Council and the American Geographical Society, 1923).

Stamp, L. Dudley, *Africa: A Study in Tropical Development*, 2d ed. (New York, John Wiley & Sons, Inc., 1964), pp. 331–346.

United Nations Educational, Scientific, and Cultural Organization, *Land Use in Semi-Arid Mediterranean Climates*, Arid Zone Research No. 26 (Paris, UNESCO, 1964), 170 pp.

12

Mediterranean Climate Regions

The Mediterranean Subtropical climate or simply the *mediterranean*[1] climate, as it is most commonly called, is so named because it occurs extensively upon the periphery of the Mediterranean Sea. Lands which possess this climate are usually mere coastal strips lying between the ocean and mountains a short distance inland. This is the case in southern California, central Chile, South Africa, and most other mediterranean areas (Fig. 12–1). The relation between mountains and the occurrence of this climatic type is well shown in north Africa. Here the coastal highlands are discontinuous, and hence in those sections where the coast is not backed by upland, the Mediterranean littoral is interrupted and Arid Tropical climate extends to the sea (Fig. 9–1). Transitional between the hot climates of the tropics and the cooler ones of the Cyclonic Zone, it partakes somewhat of both, resembling the former in summer and the latter in winter. This results from the subtropical locations and from the migration of the vertical sun north and south across the equator, which causes a rhythm in prevailing wind conditions. Hence, mediterranean lands are exposed to hot, dry, land winds during the summer, but to cool, rain-bearing, onshore, westerly winds in winter, a circumstance which makes them climatically one of the most favored regions in the world (Fig. 12–2). Undoubtedly, climate is the outstanding natural resource of mediterranean lands. The sunlit Riviera of southern France and northern Italy, the Crimea of Russia, and southern California are a few examples of renowned playgrounds and winter resorts.

DISTINGUISHING CHARACTERISTICS

The three most strongly marked characteristics of this climate are: (1) most of the rain falls during the mild, cool winter; (2) summer is intensely hot,[2] dry, and sunny, though not completely rainless; and (3) the seasonal range of temperature is considerably less than that in other areas of corresponding latitude (Fig. 12–3).

Mediterranean lands can scarcely be said to possess a winter, for the low-sun period is cool rather than cold. Winter temperatures generally average between 35° and 50° F. for the coldest month. The growing season is usually long—in some places twelve months long. While light frosts are common during the cool season, killing frosts are rare. The remaining nine months are warm to hot.

The precipitation never is great, most areas

---

[1] The word *mediterranean* is universally accepted for designating all the regions having this type of climate. When so written in this book, the word refers either to the group of regions or to one specific area having this climate. When spelled with a capital M, *Mediterranean* refers to the periphery of the Mediterranean Sea.

[2] Summers are hottest in the lands surrounding the Mediterranean Sea, the waters of which modify but slightly the scorching winds from the Sahara. All other regions benefit from cool ocean currents which hug their shores. Summers in San Francisco, for instance, are so chilly as to require furnace heat and warm clothing much of the time. Even in July and August it is not uncommon to see women wearing fur coats.

receiving less than thirty inches annually, the amount varying according to locale. Obviously, the poleward margins receive more than those equatorward. Much of the rain falls at night in hard showers of brief duration, though occasionally continuing as a drizzle for several days in succession. Rain is invariably preceded and succeeded by cloudless, sunlit skies. Thunderstorms are rare because of unfavorable temperature conditions. Winds in summer may be likened to breezes and are variable; in winter, cyclonic storms predominate.

Along several of the coasts, summers are unusually cool because of the oceans themselves, and because of a cool ocean current offshore, which flows equatorward from higher latitudes on west coasts in this latitude.

Fogs too are frequent in summer. As sea breezes induced by the heating of the land cross the cool water near the coast, they are chilled, their vapor being condensed into fog. This means lower temperatures, especially in the morning.

PLANT GEOGRAPHY

Typical mediterranean vegetation (Fig. 12–4) characterizes only the thalassic margins and low slopes, being superseded by steppe and highland vegetation elsewhere. True mediterranean vegetation is a dry evergreen woodland type of small size, the individual species of which are sparse, scrubby, and sclerophyllous. This is a response to drought—the enemy of tree growth. To aid them in gleaning every drop of available moisture from the soil, nature has endowed the plants with water-husbanding devices such as extensive root systems, bulbous and lengthy roots, thickened stems, thick rough bark, thorns, and small narrow leaves sometimes covered with fine silky hairs, sometimes with a waxy coating. Such trees as the eucalyptus are enabled to reduce transpiration by turning their leaves edgeways to the bright sunlight. Throughout this climatic realm, brush resembling California's chaparral is the most typical vegetation.

During the cool rainy winter, the landscape is brilliantly green with grasses and shrubs, but in the hot dry summer, it becomes brown, parched, and unattractive. Never is drought so marked, however, as to cause complete cessation of growth. Some of the thick-leaved trees like the olive, myrtle, laurel, holly, madroñe, and cork oak remain green the year round. Grasses, which must have light showers in spring and early summer, are rare in all mediterranean lands with the sole exception of California. There the hills and low mountain slopes are frequently clothed with grasses. It is believed, however, that these grasses are not native but are of European origin, having come by way of Mexico where the Spaniards had introduced them. In California they spread so rapidly as to have been common by the time the chain of missions was established. The original vegetation was probably chaparral.

SOILS

Since Mediterranean Subtropical regions are characterized by (1) relatively narrow plains along the coasts and in the valleys, and by (2) steep mountain slopes, topography has much to do with soil development. The soils of most slope lands tend to be badly eroded and hence lack a normal profile; those of the lowlands receive so much deposition by wind and water that they too lack a profile.

The humus content of Mediterranean Subtropical soils usually is small because the natural vegetation consists mostly of trees and shrubs rather than of grasses. The lime, phosphorus, potassium, and nitrogen content ranks from moderate to low. Hence to make these soils really productive requires fertilizers and good management.

The immature lowland soils are highly productive. Water is the great need of most summer crops. When it is available, as in California and in parts of the Mediterranean Basin, rich harvests of grain, sugar beets, fruits, and vegetables result. The great cultural systems of Greece and Rome originated on the red soils of the Mediterranean Basin.

The soils of slope lands, being generally thin and infertile, are successfully farmed only at great cost of labor and are, therefore, best suited to grazing.

Figure 12–1   Mediterranean Subtropical regions.

ANIMAL GEOGRAPHY

The fauna of the Mediterranean Subtropical realm lacks the distinctiveness characterizing that of several other climates. This is because mediterranean regions are essentially transition lands between the Tropical and Cyclonic zones. Hence lines separating the different faunal areas are not sharp, and there is more or less mixing or overlapping. Since the distribution of faunas lies outside the pale of the human geographer, it receives only slight treatment here. An idea of the native animal life of the Mediterranean periphery of Eurasia can scarcely be constructed because of man's long residence there and his destruction

of much wildlife. In other mediterranean lands, however, the task is less difficult. In California, for example, among the native mammals are several kinds of bears, weasels, skunks, badgers, foxes, squirrels, gophers, beavers, wood rats, pocket mice, and rabbits. There are also the coyote, the raccoon, the sea otter, the black-tailed deer, and the pronghorn antelope. More than half the species of mammals are rodents of which half are burrowers. Reptiles such as horned toads, lizards, and snakes are present, as well as birds and insects. It is patent that some of the above animals represent woodland species, others steppe migrants, and still others invaders from the desert.

MEDITERRANEAN CLIMATE AND CIVILIZATION

Several localities in the Mediterranean Basin early became seats of outstanding civilizations, reaching the apex of achievement in art, government, literature, philosophy, and religion. "The masters of today write no better literature, think no loftier thoughts, build no nobler buildings than the masters of the ancient world."[3] The Greeks were the first people to speculate freely on such problems as "God, nature, and society." Mediterranean civilization differed from its forerunners in being thalassic rather than riverine.

All these civilizations, whether in Crete, Phoenicia, Carthage, Palestine, Greece, or Rome, were predominantly cultural rather than mate-

rial. Cultural attainment depends upon inherent ability of the mind and hence may reach fruition even in environments of limited natural resources. In the material phases of civilization, such as mining, manufacturing, and transportation, where intricate machinery is necessary, little progress was made.

How came civilization to take root here? The seed was planted, no doubt, during Pleistocene times when the continental ice sheet was bearing down on northern and central Europe, forcing humanity to flee southward before it. The Mediterranean Basin with its relatively hospitable climate, wedged in between the hot dry

[3] R. H. Whitbeck and Olive J. Thomas, *The Geographic Factor* (New York, D. Appleton-Century Company, Inc., 1932), p. 178.

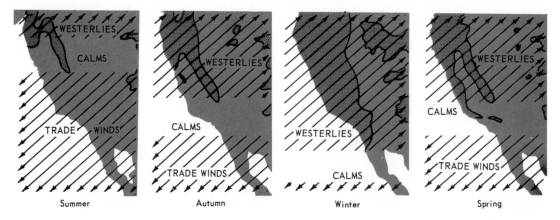

Figure 12–2 Seasonal shifting of the prevailing winds over southern California. Arrows denote general wind directions; dotted areas show the extent of rainfall. The northward and southward movements of the wind belts are a response to the changing altitude of the sun.

desert to the south and the new ice desert to the north, naturally became the magnet that drew this flood of humanity from the north. As the population became more dense, the struggle for existence became more intense. In order to survive, the people were compelled to adjust themselves effectually to their natural milieu. Thus, human ingenuity must have been stimulated to the limit and the sparks of civilization kindled. The earlier Mediterranean cultures were, because of location, undeniably Oriental. But Greece's long and irregular Levantine coastline drew men to the sea and away from their Oriental origins and thence into commerce, one of the most powerful of all civilizing influences.

Man was not restricted to maritime activities, however. The borderlands enabled him to wrest a living from the soil, though an appreciable surplus was a rarity even with the most skilled workers. Seasonal contrasts which stimulated forethought were not so severe as to necessitate grubbing in the soil from dawn to dark. Midday summer temperatures were so intense as almost to prohibit bodily exertion. Hence time was available for leisure, social intercourse, and intellectual development. The problem of providing clothing and shelter, though more serious than anywhere in the tropics, was much less so than anywhere in the so-called "temperate" zone.

Protection and security, indispensable requisites for the development of civilization, were guaranteed to the Mediterranean region by sea and desert on the one hand and by mountains,

frequently clothed with heavy forests, on the other. These barriers militated against the movement of large armies but were not so forbidding as to preclude communication and consequent exchange of ideas. The people could thus direct their energy along constructive lines. Mediterranean peoples, however, were never inventive, a matter attributable, doubtless, to the paucity of certain raw materials and to the abundance of slave labor.

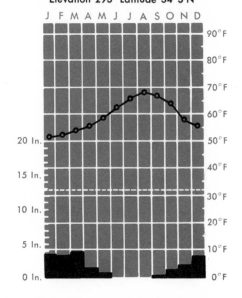

Figure 12–3 Climate graph for Los Angeles.

Ultimately, every one of these civilizations declined or perished, the reasons for which have long perplexed scholars. A favorite theory in the past but one being discounted now by many persons has been that of climatic change. The late Ellsworth Huntington[4] convincingly states that in Rome about 400 B.C., five acres of cultivable land together with space for pasturage were enough to support a family. About 200 B.C., however, when the trees of California were growing very slowly and the lakes of Asia

[4] Ellsworth Huntington and Earl B. Shaw, *Principles of Human Geography* (New York, John Wiley & Sons, Inc., 1951), p. 626.

Figure 12–4   Natural vegetation in two widely separated mediterranean regions. Above, olive trees in Spain. The olive, though originally an example of the natural vegetation of the Mediterranean region, is now a domesticated tree. Below, an open oak forest in the foothills of California. (Photos courtesy of Information Dept., Embassy for Spain, Washington, and of the U.S. Forest Service)

were dwindling (this was the dry part of a climatic cycle), a great change became evident. The careful agriculture of the past was no more. So poor did many of the farmers become that they gave up farming and their land fell into the hands of large owners, who stocked it with cattle and sheep, since ordinary farming was no longer profitable. Farmers who remained and tried to make a go of it fell deeply into debt and many forsook farming for cities, where they sought work. At the time of Christ a return of favorable conditions helped Rome recover, but two centuries later came a most serious drought which was a major cause of her final collapse.

Charles E. Kellogg[5] believes Roman civilization declined because the slaves that were brought to Rome introduced a new kind of farming: the owner no longer worked his land, land became capital, and the fruits of its production were diverted to the city. Hence agriculture declined *not* from a failure of the soil but because of the failure of men. "With this breaking of the ties between men and soil came the weakening of the home race." H. J. Haskell[6] asserts that the fundamental trouble was the failure to work out a fair and equally just economic system, which led to a "tempest of anarchy" in the third century. W. C. Lowdermilk[7] concludes that the decline of a considerable portion of the region resulted from a change in culture and methods of land use that replaced the once highly developed and intensive agriculture. Wasteful erosion followed.

Aside from thalassic Eurasia, no other regions of mediterranean climate developed an early civilization worthy of the name. Each imported its culture from Europe. Today, however, all such areas rank from very high to medium in civilization.

MAN AND HIS WORK

Since the outstanding natural resource of Mediterranean Subtropical regions is climate, the dominance of agriculture is accentuated. Mediterranean agriculture, however, is strikingly different from that found elsewhere in Europe. Climate is also a major location factor in the tourist trade of all mediterranean lands and in the motion

picture industry, shipbuilding, the construction of aircraft, and the making of women's clothing and of men's and women's sportswear in California.

AGRICULTURAL ADJUSTMENTS

Mediterranean civilizations were, are, and probably will continue to be based primarily upon agriculture—the dominant activity. Yet mediterranean climate per se is not one of nature's most favored for tillage. This is because the rain comes during the cool winter, resulting in a waste of heat in the regime of plant growth, and because the long summer drought necessitates making revolutionary changes in the customary methods of farming. In cyclonic regions, summer is universally the season of growth and winter the period of rest. In mediterranean regions, the reverse is true.

Where prosperity characterizes mediterranean agriculture, it depends upon adventitious, rather than upon intrinsic, causes. Man has been the chief factor: through skill and patience and hard work he has triumphed over the stubborn opposition of nature. He has spent fabulous sums of money to take advantage of favorable temperatures by artificially supplying life-giving water. California's transmutation through irrigation of about 15 percent of its area from barrenness to high productivity is an outstanding agricultural achievement (Fig. 12–5).

Three types of crops characterize mediterranean agriculture: (1) those grown in the winter, (2) those able to withstand drought, and (3) those which must be irrigated.

Winter crops

Such winter crops as wheat and barley thrive in this climate. They are planted at the beginning of the rainy season and are harvested in the dry season. It is doubtful whether they find in any

[5] Charles E. Kellogg, "Soil and Society," *Soils and Men,* Yearbook of Agriculture, 1938 (Washington, D.C., U. S. Department of Agriculture, 1938), p. 877.
[6] H. J. Haskell, *This Was Cicero* (New York, Alfred A. Knopf, 1942). See especially Chapter XXII.
[7] W. C. Lowdermilk, *Conquest of the Land Through Seven Thousand Years,* Agriculture Information Bulletin No. 99 (Washington, D.C., U.S. Department of Agriculture, 1953).

Figure 12–5 Irrigation of sugar beets in the Sacramento, California, area, using a robot irrigator, which sucks water from a ditch and sprays it out over the crop; its positive action rotating gun assures even water application. (Photo from Wide World Photos)

other climate conditions which so closely approximate their optimum. Winter wheat thrives when cool, moist weather characterizes its period of vegetative growth and hot dry weather prevails throughout its ripening and harvesting periods. Hence all mediterranean lands are, or have been, important producers of wheat, the Eurasian-African portion ranking as one of the world's twelve major regions. Even the others are of more than local importance, though production varies according to areal extent, location with reference to great consuming markets for such competing crops as fresh fruits and vegetables which are many times more profitable, stage of economic development, transportation facilities, and local needs. One would naturally expect Australia, Chile, and South Africa to devote more of their crop land to wheat than California, and such is actually the case. Barley, especially pearl barley, which is in great demand in northern Europe for malting, finds ideal environmental

conditions in Algeria and southern California where it is harvested at the end of the short rainy season.

Drought resistant crops

The olive is practically confined to lands with mediterranean climate and is one of their most characteristic crops. It requires little water and can withstand a protracted drought. Equipped with a large and widespread root system, the olive tree gets water both from great depths and from the immediate subsurface area even after a light shower. Its tiny silvery, leathery leaves and its thick bark retard evaporation. The tree is very sensitive to cold and hence is distributed most widely in the milder portions of mediterranean regions. Though widely grown throughout Italy, it shuns the level Po Valley with its semicontinental climate and consequent cold winters.

The olive is widely grown throughout the Old World region and has been introduced into most of the other mediterranean lands. It is an ideal crop because it grows on hillsides and even on mountains so steep and stony as to be valueless for most other agricultural enterprises, and because it provides an oil substitute for butter, an important factor where the summers are so hot and dry as to make successful dairying impossible save in irrigated districts.

The vine is one of man's most ancient crops and is believed to be indigenous to Eurasia. It finds in this climate optimum conditions for growth—*a long hot dry season.* It possesses roots that penetrate to great depths in search of water. Accordingly, in the drier sections, it has been crowded onto hillsides by crops that can grow only by means of irrigation. In Italy, only 14 percent of the crop grows on plains. In the "empty agricultural frontiers" of California and Chile, on the other hand, vines are not confined to steep slopes, being mostly irrigated, but this holds only when they are given first choice of the land (Fig. 12–6). When relegated to slopes in the Northern Hemisphere, vines usually occupy southern exposures. When irrigated, they are trailed on trellises; when not irrigated, they trail on the ground, which reduces evaporation by exposing less surface to desiccating summer winds and by protecting the roots with foliage.

In the Mediterranean grapes are used pri-marily for wine, which has been the universal beverage from time immemorial.[8] Wine not only diversifies an otherwise monotonous diet but promotes health when the water supply is impure, as much of it is. The bacillus of typhoid fever is destroyed in twenty minutes in white wine and in two hours in red wine. The vine also supplements the water supply which is significantly reduced in summer at the very time man craves drink most. A logical adjustment was to express juice from the vine. It was the universal custom in the eighth century B.C., in Homer's time, as it is today, to drink diluted wine—one-fourth wine and three-fourths water. For very rich heavy wine, a larger proportion of water was used. The effect, but not the conscious purpose, was to disinfect the water.

Chilean grapes are grown essentially for wine, the white population being of Latin origin with wine-using habits. About a third of Chile's vines are grown under irrigation. Mediterranean Australia and southern California are also important producers of wine grapes.

Raisins and currants are grown almost ex-

[8] The Mohammedan religion prohibits the drinking of alcoholic beverages. Some Mohammedans do, however, drink beer, which they do not consider to be an intoxicant. Beer was not made at the time the Koran was written.

Figure 12–6   Grapes growing on hillsides in California. (Photo courtesy of the Wine Institute)

clusively in mediterranean lands, for the high percentage of sunshine, the rainless summers, the low humidity, and the high temperatures all are conducive to a high sugar content in the grapes and to open-air drying. Not all raisins are sun-dried, however. Some are handled in mechanical dehydrators. Sun-drying, however, is more economical, gives a nonsticky product preferable to the consumer, and hence volume trade has been built on fruit so handled. About the only advantages of dehydration is that raisin variety grapes may be made into raisins in areas not having the long drying period and raisins are apt to be cleaner. The commercial production of raisins is confined principally to the San Joaquin Valley of California, southern Spain, Greece, and Asia Minor. This is partly the result of the availability of water for irrigation and, in the case of California, to the high-pressure advertising campaign of the growers. Currant grapes are restricted mostly to Greece (the name *currants* being a corruption of "Corinths") and to mediterranean Australia.

Irrigated crops

That irrigation was necessary is indicated by the early date at which it became integrated in Mediterranean agriculture. Certain crops never could have succeeded without it. Close to the cultivated lands of mediterranean Eurasia, Chile, and California stand lofty mountains, many snowcapped, whence sparkling streams descend to the thirsty lands below. Without the irrigated crops the monotony of the diet of Mediterranean Eurasian peoples would be almost unbearable. Moreover, the population would be less dense or if not, it would be exposed periodically to famine. Where water is carefully conserved and utilized, and in few places on earth is it more carefully safeguarded than in mediterranean lands, at least twice as many people are supported as before. In southern California, water is so scarce and valuable as to be conveyed frequently in covered conduits. The antiquated earthen-banked open canal with its wasteful evaporation and seepage is a curiosity. In the Central Valley, however, where water is more abundant and hence less valuable, canals are common. Not all irrigation in California, however, is from surface

Figure 12–7   An orange grove in Valencia, Spain. (Photo courtesy of the Spanish National Tourist Office)

waters. A large part, possibly more than half, is from underground sources.

Irrigation encourages intensive rather than extensive farming. Fruits and vegetables[9] of high value needed in distant markets are the leading irrigated crops (Fig. 12–7). Their per acre value in California is twenty to fifty times that of the wheat and barley which formerly predominated and placed their stamp on the state. Mediterranean California has become America's chief source of fruits and vegetables. Thus, it contributes more than 35 percent of the total national pack of all canned fruits and vegetables.

Of real significance is the fact that Roman jurists, living in a region where water had great value, worked out an admirable system of water laws for preventing complications that are certain to arise through the diversion, control, and utilization of water. Not so the fathers of English common law, who dwelt where water was plentiful and of no especial value. Had common law dealt with this problem, much serious trouble would have been avoided in those portions of the United States having dry summers. Wherever irrigation is practiced, laws must be made for preventing waste and for enabling each man to get his just share of water.

[9] California ships out more than 90 percent of its production.

Frost fighting

In California, frost fighting is highly systematized. While killing frosts are rare, they do occur occasionally. In 1922, half the citrus crop was destroyed. So important is this industry to California and to the nation that the United States Weather Bureau created a special fruit frost service. Because frost is so local in its occurrence, special forecasts are made in numerous districts. In addition, thermostats are kept in many orchards and are set to ring a bell in the rancher's house when the temperature falls to 28° or 30° F. In addition many growers have installed automatic signal systems that sound an alarm at the approach of a critical temperature. This is the time to turn on the wind machines or light the smudge pots. The latter are less important today because they contribute to the smog problem.

Severe frost is to be especially feared on calm, clear nights when cold dry air from the north settles over the groves. On such nights the ground loses heat rapidly by radiation.

Orchard blowers or wind machines are gaining in numbers, particularly in the lemon-growing areas. They mix the cool air near the ground with the warmer air some 40 feet above it. At the base of these machines is a button; and when the orchardist presses it, twelve-foot propellers begin to whir. On some blowers are two propellers thirty-two feet above the ground and together they care for about twenty acres of orchard.

Latifundia

In most Mediterranean Subtropical countries, vast acreages are concentrated in the hands of a small number of owners. This system of holding land is very old. In some countries the large holdings were of feudal origin; some resulted from encroachment of great landlords upon large communal holdings or even upon individual ones; still others were the gifts of kings. In the New World, the King of Spain, following an old Spanish custom, granted lands to some of his subjects for services rendered—particularly military services. Thus, Pedro de Miranda, who distinguished himself in the conquest of Chile, received a grant of 8,640 acres. The large estates have tended to continue right down to the pres-

ent. In southern Italy, for example, in 1930, despite repeated Fascist pronouncements to encourage the break-up of large undivided estates, which varied from 125 to 2,500 acres in size (there were only a few of the latter), 2 percent of the farmers still owned 41 percent of the farm land, whereas 79 percent owned less than 20 percent. Since 1950 many thousands of acres of land have been expropriated and it is expected that under the program almost 4 million acres from large private holdings and from public lands will be made available for the creation of small farms. The land-hungry Italians insist on owning their own land. In Spain the situation is equally bad; peasant wages are so low, and poverty so intense, as scarcely to prevent outright starvation.

Wherever latifundia prevails unrest is prevalent among the peasant classes who assert that the best use of the land is not being made and are demanding that the system be abolished. It would appear that something must be done by the several governments.

PASTORAL ADJUSTMENTS

That pastoral pursuits have been conspicuously important in Mediterranean lands is cogently indicated in such literature as portions of the Old Testament, and the histories of Greece, Rome, and Spain. Climate and topography encouraged man to bring this about, for it is not profitable to cultivate dry steep slopes. Nor can they be grazed effectively by cattle, because of scarcity of grass. Sheep and goats, especially the latter, which "represent the survival of the fittest," actually thrive during the heat and drought of summer and on the scantiest forage. For the same reasons, donkeys and mules are numerically more important than horses, except in the better watered portions of Spain and Australia, where feed for horses is produced under irrigation.

Sheep are relatively more important in the lands about the western arms of the Mediterranean, which is more humid, and goats about the drier eastern arm. Mediterranean sheep have always been wool sheep, which thrive on dry, rugged, and sparsely populated lands (Fig. 12–8). Mutton sheep, being hearty eaters, thrive only in better watered lands with more luxuriant pas-

Figure 12–8 Shepherds with their flock in Salamanca, Spain. (Photo courtesy of the Spanish National Tourist Office)

tures; they shun areas having meager forage resources. Yet in Greece, sheep are raised primarily for milk and secondarily for meat and wool. Most of the milk is used for cheese. Small landowners, particularly those in the more mountainous areas, find that sheep enable them to make a better living. Unfortunately, continuous grazing over the centuries and the great pressure of the livestock population have made reseeding difficult; hence the pastures are no better today than they were in the time of Homer.

In California sheep are important, especially in the Central Valley, which is reported to have well over half the total for the state. Changes are occurring in the business, however, for skilled sheep labor is both scarce and costly. So difficult is it to procure experienced and competent Americans that Basque shepherds are being brought from Spain solely for this business.

A major reason for the importance of goats in the Mediterranean region is that the goat is an excellent producer of milk—much better than the sheep. This is significant in a region where cattle are not present in any considerable number. Here the distribution of goats coincides quite well with the distribution of people.

Transhumance, the seasonal vertical migration of flocks from lowland to mountain and return, has been practiced in the Old World region since ancient times and is still important. It is a response to climate, topography, and sparse population. In the past the animals fed on the march, though a recent innovation is the utilization of the railway for transportation of the stock. *Transhumance* is practiced in all the other mediterranean regions. In summer the bleating droves forsake the lowlands where the vegetation is parched and withered and water is scarce, and seek the mountains where lush pasturage exists and where water or snow is present. In winter they avoid the mountains, which then are cloaked with heavy snow and hence are inhospitable, and congregate in the lowlands, green and inviting.

ADJUSTMENTS TO THE FOREST

Lands strictly mediterranean in climate have meager forest resources—considerably less than their climate and terrain might suggest. This is particularly true of the lands about the Mediterranean; it is not so true of mediterranean regions elsewhere, especially those flanked by high mountains. Obviously a new land like California

Figure 12–9 Stripping cork in Portugal. (Photo courtesy of the Armstrong Cork Company)

should be more fortunate than a country on the periphery of the Mediterranean Sea where for thousands of years the forests have waged a losing battle against the ceaseless onslaught of war, fire, reckless cutting, overgrazing,[10] soil erosion, and agriculture.

Cork stripping is the only strictly forest economic adjustment. Spain and Portugal are the outstanding producers of cork, though Algeria, Tunisia, Italy, and southern France are all important. In Spain alone some 35,000 people are employed in this industry. Because cork was classified as a critical raw material by the Amer-

ican Army and Navy Munitions Board during World War II, many thousands of cork oak trees were planted in California and the Southwest in the 1950's, and much botanical and ecological research carried on.

A cork tree varies from twenty to fifty feet in height, may have a diameter of four feet, and has widely spreading branches. The cork of commerce is the outer bark of the tree which is "skinned alive" to get it (Fig. 12–9). Careful stripping, however, does not damage the tree and may continue for 150 years. The first crop is practically worthless, the quality improving with subsequent stripping. The first harvest takes place when the tree is about twenty years old and at nine-year intervals thereafter. The yield per tree at each stripping varies from forty-five to five hundred pounds. The uses of cork are legion because of its buoyancy, lightness, elasticity, and imperviousness to air and water.

Jarrah, a hard heavy timber of mediterranean Australia, is used for street paving and for railway ties.

MANUFACTURING ADJUSTMENTS

In ancient and medieval times, industry was important in the countries rimming the Mediterranean Sea, but it consisted of the simple transformation of local products. Craftsmen converted the juice of the vine into wine and the milk of the sheep and goat into cheese, expressed oil from the ripe olive and dried fruit. Later they learned to fabricate metals and make textiles. With the passing of the centuries, they acquired a skill which they have passed from father to son for generations. Accordingly, many of their articles reach the markets of the world without serious competition. Most of the products are closely associated with definite localities, such as Sherry and Port wine (Fig. 12–10) and Roquefort cheese.

The Industrial Revolution destroyed the old order. Hand power, local markets, and articles of wood, stone, copper, and bronze became in-

[10] The goat, the most characteristic Mediterranean animal, is a ruthless destroyer of trees and forests, because it not only nibbles the lower branches but eats seedlings, thereby preventing natural regeneration.

adequate. The day of iron, and later steel, high-speed machinery operated by steam or hydro-electric power, and world markets had arrived, leaving the Mediterranean borderlands hopelessly behind. Thus Mediterranean subtropical Italy had, until the early 1960's, resisted all efforts of industrialization along modern lines. The North was the industrialized region of the country. However, beginning with the decade of the 1960's, vast sums of capital were injected into industrializing principal centers in the triangle between Naples, the heel of Italy, and the western tip of Sicily. Several very important industries, for example, iron and steel, petrochemical and other chemical industries, have become well established and are transforming Mediterranean subtropical Italy economically. It will, however, probably always be poor when compared with the North.

Manufacturing is not outstanding in most Mediterranean Subtropical lands. Not one ranks alongside northwestern Europe or east-central North America. California, however, threatens to become an exception, for it is not weak to the same extent as are the others. California is one of the world's principal petroleum refining regions, it leads in aircraft production, in the making of motion pictures, in the canning and freezing of fruits and vegetables, and in the manufacture of sport clothes; it ranks high in automobile assembly, in the manufacture of electronics, rubber tires and tubes, and furniture. During World War II it made an enviable record in building ships. The two principal areas are in southern California (Los Angeles-San Diego) and in the San Francisco-Oakland-San Jose or Bay Area. That there is a definite trend toward industrialization in southern California is indicated by the withdrawal during recent years of thousands of acres from use for citrus fruit growing for industrial and urban use.

Mediterranean Chile is also expanding industrially. Manufacturing appears to be the great hope of the future here. To Chileans it means the breaking of the shackles of their semicolonial status whereby for generations they have traded their raw materials for needed manufactures. While to date most of their plants produce con-

sumer goods, nonetheless an iron and steel mill has been erected at Huachipato, near Concepción. The industrialization of Chile is based upon the manufacture of local minerals and agricultural raw materials.

The parts of South Africa and Australia having this type of climate are growing industrially also. Even in the lands around the Mediterranean Sea, which are not rich in the sort of minerals that support large-scale manufacturing, there is considerable light industry.

COMMERCIAL ADJUSTMENTS

From the dawn of history, the Mediterranean Region has been noted for commerce. As early as the second millennium B.C., the Phoenicians, from their base at the eastern end of the Mediterranean, moved from island to island and from peninsula to peninsula until they circumnavigated

Figure 12–10 Wine caves in Oporto, Portugal. (Photo courtesy of Heyward Associates, Inc.)

the entire inland sea. These stepping stones, easily within sight, tempted the early sailor to sea. Thick fogs were absent, as were strong tides and currents and, except for a few months in winter, there were no storms. All this early sailing was along the coast. But the Phoenicians were not the only important international traders —they were only the first; others were the Cretans, Carthaginians, Greeks, Genoese, Neapolitans, Florentines, Spaniards, and Portuguese. These pioneer traders were "the apostles of civilization."

The chief basis of this trade was difference in the stage of economic development; the ancient progressive areas, like Phoenicia and the Hellenic seaboard of Asia Minor, traded actively with the more backward producers of food and raw materials, such as the littorals of the Adriatic, Black, and western Mediterranean seas.

Today, as then, the Mediterranean countries carry on considerable trade. But lean material resources in proportion to population result in unfavorable balances of trade in many. These are corrected by some of the so-called invisible exports—the carrying trade, the tourist trade, and remittances from emigrants.[11]

The other mediterranean regions are not yet of outstanding commercial importance, except California which continues to advance rapidly as its population grows.

SOCIAL ADJUSTMENTS

DISTRIBUTION OF POPULATION

Population in Mediterranean Subtropical regions is dense but much less so than in Humid Subtropical regions, which lie in the same latitude but on the opposite side of continents. This is consequent mainly upon the rainfall—not the amount but the period of occurrence. Eastern marginal lands receive their precipitation in summer when they need it and when it does the most good. Western marginal lands, however, receive theirs in winter when it does the least good.

Throughout Mediterranean Europe, the density of population is not a matter of even gradation; the plains invariably show close settlement, especially where irrigation is practiced.

Blank spaces occur here and there, the result of physical and historical factors. In the final analysis, water determines the distribution of people as well as their numbers.

Over most of the earth, population is not dense in mountainous countries; it is dense, however, in many mountainous sections of the Mediterranean, but always with a resulting low level of living. This pressure of population against the means of subsistence is well illustrated by Italy where 79 percent of the country is hilly and mountainous (39 percent being classed as mountainous) and yet where 41 percent of the country's total area is considered tillable land. Italy is the only nation in the world having a large wheat acreage located on rough terrain; almost one-fourth of the total crop is grown on mountainous land and one-half on hilly land.

Since large farm animals are scarce, there is little machinery. Hence tillage is intensive and population dense. Under such circumstances there is practically no isolated living such as characterizes the American Corn Belt; the typical Mediterranean settlement is the village or town. When physical obstacles prevent intensive farming, the population is sparse and scattered.

The notable increase in population in the mediterranean portions of South America, North America, South Africa, and Australia indicates their attractiveness for human occupancy. California is one of the most rapidly growing areas in the United States. In fact it has far outstripped the nation in rate of population growth in every decade since 1860. Whereas its share of the nation's total population was 1.2 percent in 1860, it had reached 6.9 percent in 1950 and 8.7 percent in 1960. California presently has the largest population of the fifty states.

RELIGION

The Mediterranean Subtropical region has been dubbed "the zone of founders of religion." That a definite relationship exists between climate and the religions born here seems but

---

[11] It is estimated that two-thirds of the money earned in manual toil by the Italian emigrant finds its way to the home country in cash remittances.

natural. In all ages and in all places, every religion has been intermeshed with the natural environment. Peschel[12] insisted that the mediterranean climate favored that *reflection* so indispensable for the birth of religious sentiment.

In the cold of the temperate zone, man has always been obliged to struggle hard for his existence, working more than praying, so that the burden of the day's labor constantly withheld him from deep inward meditation. In warm countries, on the contrary, where Nature facilitates the acquisition of the necessaries of life and the sultry hours of midday prohibit any bodily exertions, opportunities for mental absorption are far more abundant.

To explain precisely how the natural environment has influenced Judaism and Christianity is a highly complex task and will not be attempted. Positive facts are unattainable. That the climate did influence conspicuously these religions is undeniable. The Bible refers to hell as a hot place, one of eternal fire,[13] and to heaven as a place always cool with shade and water and abundant food. Metaphors, applicable only to a dry region where sheep herding and viticulture are dominant occupations, are constantly used: "The Lord is my Shepherd"; "Feed my Sheep"; "I am the vine, ye the branches."

Pork has long been taboo among the Jews and Mohammedans who occupy the eastern and southern rims of the Mediterranean Sea, but not among the Christians of the north. This taboo doubtless came as the result of climate; the drier forests in the south and east do not supply mast for swine, whereas the more humid ones to the north do. Where the rainfall is below ten inches, as it is in Egypt and Tripoli, mediterranean climate is superseded by desert.

POLITICAL ADJUSTMENTS

No other part of the world matches the Mediterranean and its coasts in human interest or has been the focus of so much political attention for so long a time. Here is to be found the eternal tension between land power and sea power where more than elsewhere on earth, they rest upon a natural environment equally favorable to each.

The sea, the mountains, and the deserts together create a notable degree of environmental unity within the basin—a unity reflected in the pattern of economic life. Politically, however, the region has been unified only once in the thousands of years of its history and then by the Romans—a *land people*.[14] Roman genius developed itself on land. Acquisition of the Italian Peninsula was a matter of land conquest, and even conquest of Greece involved military rather than naval strategy, since the distance between the two was short and relatively free from interruptions. It was not until the war against Carthage that the Romans became sea minded. The time came when both Rome and Carthage decided the Mediterranean was too small for the two of them; one had to be vanquished. If Carthage was to be destroyed, only a navy could do the job. Therefore Rome built ships and Rome was victorious.

Ultimately Rome became so large areally that in the face of a declining agriculture, the home resources could not supply the essential food. Hence ships were used to bring grain from Egypt and the Black Sea region.

The peoples around the Mediterranean are so diverse as to offer not even a remote opportunity for political unification. It is difficult to see how Arab and Jew, Greek and Egyptian, Italian and Slav, Spaniard and Turk could have much in common. Pronounced religious differences also foster disunity, for Moslems from the desert occupy the southern periphery, Christians from humid Europe the northern shores, and Jews along with Christians and Moslems maneuver for supremacy along the eastern side.

From the dawn of history to this very day, the Mediterranean has possessed great geopolitical significance. In fact, until the fifteenth century—

[12] Oscar F. Peschel, *The Races of Man*, English translation (New York, D. Appleton-Century Company, Inc., 1892), p. 315.

[13] In Norse mythology, hell was considered a place of cold and heaven a place of warmth.

[14] Of all the states that arose in the Mediterranean Basin, the Italian Peninsula alone possessed the geographical requisites for dominating the numerous widely scattered land units.

the Age of Discovery—world affairs centered here. The new sea routes relegated the Mediterranean with its dead east end to a back eddy in world affairs, but the construction of the Suez Canal several centuries later enabled it to come back into world politics.

Today nations concerned with the Mediterranean are Great Britain, France, the Soviet Union, and the United States along with the weak countries huddled together around the periphery. France, Britain, and the United States have been eager to prevent the Soviet Union from gaining complete domination of the Mediterranean which appeared imminent at the termination of World War II. Both Russia and the Free World, of course, sense the advantages to be obtained by tying the Mediterranean nations into their respective systems.

One of the biggest problems lies in the overlapping of the two so-called "security spheres." For decades Britain wanted no great power encroaching upon her "lifeline" at Suez. Russia's desires for a security zone correspond to the age-old drive toward hegemony in the Balkans, a protectorate over the Slavs, control of the mouth of the Danube and, most important of all, free access to the Mediterranean via the Bosporus and the Dardanelles.

Following World War II only the United States, which appears to have assumed the responsibility of filling the power voids of the earth, was able, willing, and determined to stop the southward spread of Russian Communism. Much needed aid was given to Greece and Turkey, which occupy such strategic positions on the important sea.

A most significant development in this area was Great Britain's withdrawal from the Suez Canal Zone in 1956 due largely to the insistence of Egypt, which felt that the presence of troops on her soil (the canal is wholly in Egyptian territory) was incompatible with that full equality she needed in dealing with other nations. Great Britain, conditioned by global considerations, had not wished to withdraw from this tangled crossroads of the world, leaving a vacuum that might be filled by a hostile power.[15]

There is no denying that the Suez Canal Zone is one of strategic military strength in a vast stretch of defenseless territory. Two world wars proved the Suez Canal Zone to be the keystone in the defense of a vast area. The Middle East is one of the most vulnerable sections politically and strategically, as evidenced in the 1967 Arab-Israeli conflicts.

France's control over North African territory no longer exists. Although she fought long and hard to retain Algeria in the French Community by considering her a part of Metropolitan France, Algerian independence was only a matter of time. While independence has come to much of North Africa it is still an area of political unrest.

Radio Cairo constantly reminds North Africans of the advantages of Arab unity, particularly political unity but, of course, under the leadership of the United Arab Republic. Tunisia, however, has come forth to give some leadership to the Arab opposition. The basic problem remains one of economic growth. The fruitful territory of the Mediterranean lands is more than counterbalanced by large areas of unproductive desert in spite of some mineral discoveries. Add to this the internal and external destructive political forces and these newly independent countries find their long sought freedom a luxury difficult to maintain.

---

[15] With the shrinkage of the British Empire, this water passage to India was possibly not so important to Britain as it once had been, although enormous quantities of Middle East oil move through it to northwestern Europe.

SUGGESTED USEFUL READINGS

Dickinson, Robert E., *The Population Problem of Southern Italy: an Essay in Social Geography* (Syracuse, N.Y., Syracuse University Press, 1955), 116 pp.

Eyre, S. R., *Vegetation and Soils: A World Picture* (Chicago, Aldine Publishing Company, 1963), pp. 125–129.

Houston, James M., *Western Mediterranean World; An Introduction to Its Regional Landscapes* (London, Longmans, Green and Company, 1964), 800 pp.

Lantis, David W., Rodney Steiner, and John Karinen, *California: Land of Contrast* (Belmont, Calif., Wadsworth, 1963), 509 pp.

Newbigin, Marion, *Southern Europe: a Regional and Economic Geography of the Mediterranean Lands*, 3d ed. (London, Methuen and Company, 1949), 404 pp.

Russell, Richard J., Fred B. Kniffen, and Evelyn Pruitt, *Culture Worlds*, brief ed. (New York, The Macmillan Company, 1961), pp. 57–75.

Semple, Ellen C., *The Geography of the Mediterranean Region; Its Relation to Ancient History* (New York, Henry Holt and Company, Inc., 1931), 737 pp.

Sopher, David E., *Geography of Religions* (Englewood Cliffs, N.J., Prentice-Hall, Inc., 1967), 128 pp.

Walker, Donald S., *A Geography of Italy* (London, Methuen and Company, 1958), 256 pp.

Walker, Donald S., *The Mediterranean Lands* (New York, John Wiley & Sons, Inc., 1962), 524 pp.

13

Humid Subtropical Climate Regions

THE CLIMATE

The Humid Subtropical climate offers a striking contrast to the Mediterranean Subtropical discussed in the preceding chapter. It differs from the latter chiefly in the amount and seasonal distribution of its precipitation—having an abundant rather than a scanty rainfall and a summer rather than a winter maximum in occurrence.

LOCATION

In general, the Humid Subtropical climate characterizes the east margins of continents in the Subtropical Zone, that is, between 25° and 35° north latitude and between 25° and 35° south latitude. Specifically there are five regions in the world with this type of climate: southeastern United States, most of the Paraná drainage basin in South America, southeastern Africa, most of eastern coastal Australia, and the middle Orient (including southern Japan, southern Korea, and the great Yangtze Basin of Central China). All of these five areas are similar in their salient climatic characteristics, but each exhibits certain individual peculiarities (Fig. 13–1).

VARIOUS NAMES

This climate is often referred to as the Central China type because its most extensive and representative region of occurrence lies in that area. In the United States it is often popularly called the "Cotton Belt" climate. In Australia, it is frequently designated as the "Eastralian" type. To geographers in all parts of the world, however, it is almost universally known as the Humid Subtropical type of climate.

TEMPERATURE

The temperature regime in this climate is one which can best be characterized as subtropical (Fig. 13–2). Summer is hot, humid, and generally uncomfortable. Nights are often as uncomfortable as the days. The air is muggy, sticky, and oppressive for long periods at a time. The summer season is indeed unpleasant and enervating. The Humid Subtropical regions are certainly not summer resorts.

Winter is characterized by periods of fairly cold weather associated with cold waves which move into the realm from regions farther poleward. On the cooler days in the American South a fire is regarded as necessary in homes and public buildings. On the whole, however, except in China, Korea, and Japan, whose temperatures may be quite severe, winter is to be described as cool rather than cold. Spring and fall are short, changeable, but usually pleasant seasons.

PRECIPITATION

The annual precipitation of these subtropical east-coast areas is heavy and it occurs mostly in the form of rain. A few light snows may fall each winter along the poleward margins of this climate, but in the equatorward portions snow is almost unknown.

The heavy rainfall of east coasts between

latitudes 30° and 40° affords a striking contrast to the light rainfall of west coasts in the same latitude (Mediterranean Subtropical climate). For instance, the annual average precipitation of Charleston is 45 inches; that of San Diego is 10 inches. Similarly, that of Shanghai is 45 inches, while that of Athens is 15 inches.

CAUSES FOR THE ABUNDANT RAINFALL

The maximum rainfall in most areas comes during the hot summer months instead of during the cool winter months as it does in west-coast areas. No part of the year, however, is dry. The causes for the abundant year-round rainfall on the east margins of continents in the subtropics are fairly obvious. During the hot summer, atmospheric pressure over the continents declines markedly and monsoon winds push in from the surrounding oceanic areas. These are actually extratropical extensions of the tropical monsoon winds of the adjacent low latitude regions. Within these inflowing moist currents of air, vigorous thundershower action supplies abundant rainfall during the summer months. In the Gulf states of the United States, single summer thundershowers of four or five inches are fairly common. The monsoon in this climate is not so strong or so apparent as in Monsoon Tropical India.

During the winter months, cyclonic storms from regions in the higher latitudes bring occasional spells of stormy, rainy weather. Consequently, the cooler months are by no means dry, although they are less wet than the summer months. The winds blowing seaward from the great land mass of Asia during winter bring little rain to China.

During spring and autumn, tropical cyclones (known as hurricanes or typhoons) frequently move poleward along the subtropical east coasts and add considerable increments to the total rainfall (Fig. 13–3).

NATURAL VEGETATION

Abundant year-round moisture and a long, hot season produce in the United States a natural vegetation of heavy forest (Fig. 13–4). On poorly drained lowlands and mucky swamplands this approaches the character of a subtropical rain forest—cypress, gum, tupelo, and palms. On the sandy areas of the coastal plain a dense stand of southern resinous pines—long-leaf, loblolly, slash, and scrub—cover the land. On the uplands farther north, there are forests of tulip, magnolia, elm, oak, maple, and chestnut, with an undergrowth of dogwood, wild honeysuckle, and rhododendron. This becomes a veritable jungle on cut-over land.

The forests of central China were formerly even more dense than those of southeastern United States. They have, however, been cut off and culled over for so many centuries that only poor remnants remain. Residual areas indicate that the lowlands of China originally supported dense mixed stands of broadleaf trees with bamboo thickets. The upland areas supported magnificent stands of coniferous trees. Few parts of the world had such a diversity of pines as Humid Subtropical China.

The forests of southern Japan and Korea were somewhat similar to those of China. Black and red pines grow along the coast; on the interior uplands cedar, aspen, poplar, mulberry, upland cypress, lacquer, and camphor trees are found. Bamboo and numerous small shrubs form the undergrowth.

In the Paraná Basin, heavy subtropical forest all but chokes the riverine lowlands. The most important commercial tree is the Paraná pine which grows in the plateau. In fact, it is Brazil's most valuable timber tree and one of the most important softwoods grown in all of South America. However, it is not a true pine, for it has no resin ducts. In the Western Hemisphere pines do not grow south of Nicaragua. Yerba maté also thrives in this region.

On the west side of the Paraná-Paraguay rivers in the Gran Chaco lie important forests of quebracho.

The two smaller regions of southeast Australia and southeast Africa are also lands of heavy forest. In the former, considerable areas are still covered with dense stands of eucalyptus, with here and there open grass. In the latter, there is heavy subtropical forest with shrub undergrowth.

Figure 13-1   Humid Subtropical regions.

NATIVE ANIMAL LIFE

There is nothing very distinctive in the wild animal life of the humid subtropical forests. It shows a sort of transition from that of the tropical forest to the forest of the cool Cyclonic Zone. The forests of China, Korea, and Japan have been inhabited by man for so long that few remnants of the wildlife survive. That of southeastern United States is, or was until a few decades ago, varied and plentiful. Among larger animals, the Virginia deer, the bear, and the fox are most characteristic. The gray timber squirrel, the chickaree or red squirrel, and the rabbit are very numerous. The opossum, raccoon, skunk,

and porcupine are fairly common. At one time, the woods were overrun with turkeys, quail, and grouse, but these are now much less plentiful than formerly. Wherever man finds a hospitable milieu, wildlife declines.

The woods also contain many brightly colored birds such as the American parakeet, cardinal, oriole, bluejay, and woodpecker. The dull-colored mocking bird, noted for its singing, is found here. In the swamps, turtles, muskrats, and in some areas alligators are to be found.

The subtropical forests of the Southern Hemisphere are somewhat poorer in animal life than those of the Northern. Worth mentioning, however, are the woodland kangaroos of eastern

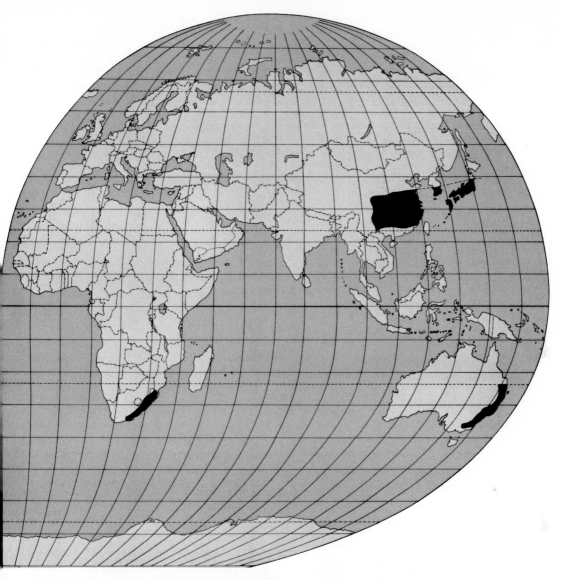

Australia, the rheboks and short-horned buffalo of Natal, and the woodland deer and opossums of the Paraná forests.

SOILS

The soils of Humid Subtropical lands consist mostly of the red and yellow types in the equatorward margins where the rainfall is heaviest and the temperatures are never low. Poleward these grade into the gray-brown podzolic soils, but nearly all of these lie outside this climatic realm. In some regions long cultivation has resulted in the complete removal by erosion of the "A" horizon and the red subsoil is exposed. These soils are low in minerals and need constant fertilization to be productive. In the Orient, the best rice soils consist of alluvium. Here long-continued irrigation has resulted in an impervious layer of fine material in the subsoil which is retentive of moisture and prevents excessive loss of water from seepage.

AGRICULTURE

Although the Humid Subtropical climate is not one of the most pleasant or stimulating types for human beings, it is one of three most productive climates of the world. Its abundant moisture, warmth, and long growing season combine to produce unrivaled conditions for crop growth.

In general, the agriculture of any region is of two kinds, subsistence and commercial. Subsistence agriculture consists of the raising of the

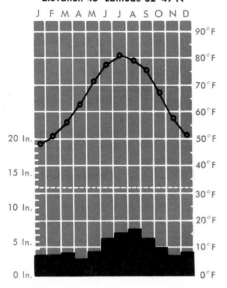

Humid Subtropical Climate
CHARLESTON, SOUTH CAROLINA, U.S.A.
Elevation 48' Latitude 32°49'N

Figure 13–2   Climate graph for Charleston, South Carolina. Compare this with the graph for Los Angeles as to the season of maximum rainfall.

supply crops necessary for the immediate support of a population. Such crops are consumed on the farm or are moved through local market channels to dependent urban populations. They rarely clear

through central markets and are never designed for export. Subsistence agriculture involves primarily the production of food crops and comprises starches, proteins, and various fruits and greenstuffs.

STARCHES

Wheat, which is so characteristic of the mediterranean climate, is of relative unimportance in the humid subtropics because the rainfall is too abundant and because the high humidity fosters certain plant diseases. Barley is of even less importance. Both wheat and barley are customarily found only on the drier margins of the Humid Subtropical climate. Corn, however, is well suited to this type of climate. Accordingly, it becomes an important starch food crop in all five of the Humid Subtropical regions. In southeastern United States, corn is the staple bread cereal. On the wetter lowlands, rice is even more favored by nature than corn. Both corn and rice demand a long growing season with high temperatures and abundant moisture—conditions which are supplied by this climate. Of the two crops, rice produces much the higher yield per acre, but it also requires much more labor in planting and harvesting (Fig. 13–5). Consequently, rice is the favorite starch food of densely-peopled parts of

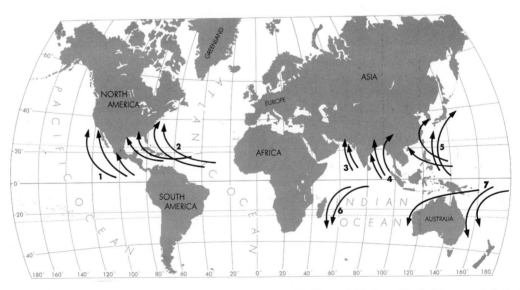

Figure 13–3   Regions and paths of severe tropical cyclones: (1) West of Mexico, (2) Caribbean and Gulf of Mexico (hurricanes), (3) Arabian Sea, (4) Bay of Bengal, (5) Philippines, South China, and Japan region (typhoons), (6) Madagascar, and (7) Australia. (Map from William E. Powers, *Physical Geography*, New York, Appleton-Century-Crofts, 1966)

the humid subtropics.[1] Wet as this climate is, a vast amount of irrigation is done on the rice fields of China, Japan, and Korea in order to obtain the maximum possible yields of grain.

Sweet potatoes, yams, and a few other starch crops grow abundantly in this climate.

PROTEINS

The climate exerts a selective influence on the production of protein as well as starch foods. Mutton, a characteristic protein food in the drier parts of the Subtropical Zone, is for the most part little eaten in these humid lands. The sheep is decidedly not a native of a hot, wet environment. Beef also is not a staple food here. Cattle can be and are reared in the humid subtropics, but unless man gives them much attention (by introducing foreign forage plants better suited to the climate, by crossing his stock with better adjusted breeds, and by eliminating pests), they do not do well. However, new breeds of both dairy and beef cattle have been developed in the American South.

The pig, on the other hand, is very much at home in this climate. Poultry of many varieties also thrives. And, because people ordinarily eat the things they produce, pork and poultry products are favorite foods of China for precisely the reason that the American South is famed for its "Virginia" ham and "Southern" fried chicken. The population in China, Japan, and Korea has reached such a density, however, that land scarcity compels millions of the poorer people in these lands to be virtually vegetarians. Protein-yielding meat substitutes, such as beans, peas, peanuts, and soy beans, therefore, are widely produced. The Japanese, being an insular people, do an immense amount of fishing, but even this fails to furnish an adequate supply of protein.

CORN

The climate is highly suitable for corn and huge amounts are raised in the American South. In fact the principal system of farming has been based on cotton (the cash crop) and corn (the subsistence crop), with nearly every farmer growing both. Since 1938, however, corn acreage has been decreasing, albeit the displacement has oc-

curred mostly in the less humid western margin where the grain sorghums are a more certain and reliable crop. Since 1929 corn acreage has de-

[1] Rice was originally a tropical crop, but has been transferred to the Humid Subtropics, where the growing season is long enough to mature this grain.

Figure 13–4 Virgin loblolly pine in the Kisatchie National Forest, Louisiana. One type of the Humid Subtropical Climate forest, loblolly pine grows mostly, though not exclusively, in draws and bottoms and is extremely aggressive. (Photo courtesy of the U.S. Forest Service)

clined but production has increased. This increase resulted from improved farming practices.

Much corn is grown in central China, but wherever rice does well, corn cannot compete and is, therefore, not impressive. It tends, accordingly, to be raised on hillsides, where the soils are too light and the supply of water too meager for rice. Considerable corn is grown also in Humid Subtropical Africa, where it is a staple food.

RICE

In the Oriental segment of this climatic realm, rice is the dominant crop—China leading the entire world in production. Especially in the lower Yangtze Valley, conditions are highly

Figure 13–5 Japanese farmers weeding rice field after rainy season ends. (Photo courtesy of the Consulate General of Japan, N.Y.)

favorable but poorly suited for most other cereals: there is considerable flat land, the growing season is long, the emphasized monsoon summer rainfall is heavy, the water supply for irrigating the crops is ample (the control of water in the proper amounts at the proper time is the most important factor in growing rice), and the soils consist of heavy clays with nearly impervious subsoils. In the more rugged areas, much rice is grown on terraces.

In Japan, rice, the major crop, occupies more than half the land devoted to agriculture. The population is so dense and the holdings so small that most of the work is done by human muscle though the Japanese use some mechanized equipment (Fig. 13–5). The seedlings are carefully transplanted from the nursery beds, constantly weeded, spaded, and fertilized. The resultant yield is two to three times that in the so-called "rice bowl" countries of Burma, Thailand, Vietnam, and Cambodia. In fact they are the highest in the world for a large producing country. Yet in spite of an annual production two and a half times that of Vietnam and Cambodia, Japan is forced to import much rice.

In Humid Subtropical United States, rice production is confined to the coastal prairies of Louisiana and Texas and to the alluvial soils of the Mississippi Valley in Arkansas. Production differs markedly from that in the Orient: whereas there human labor performs almost every operation, in the American South labor-saving machines are employed. The gang plow, disk harrow, drill, binder, and now the combine perform every significant work operation. Irrigation is easy and cheap because of an abundant supply of artesian water near the surface. Whereas in Japan each laborer averages only one-half to one acre of rice, in the American South each averages at least eighty acres. Total production, however, is not large—around one and a half billion pounds, for Americans eat little rice. Here the crop is grown for sale.

COTTON

This widely grown and much used crop finds almost optimum conditions in the Humid Subtropics. Only Australia, South Africa, Japan, and Uruguay fail to grow cotton.

Southeastern United States was long synon-

Figure 13–6 A mechanical cotton harvester in operation in the American South. Mechanization has reduced the labor needed to grow an acre of cotton from 150 hours with one-row, horse-drawn equipment to about 30 hours with tractor equipment and machine picking. Yet less than 5 percent of the cotton in the Humid Subtropical Southeast is harvested by machine. As long as labor is available and wages are low, handpicking tends to prevail. Also more and more cotton growing is moving to the West, where farms are huge and mechanical pickers can be utilized to greater advantage. (Photo courtesy of USDA)

ymous with cotton; in fact, for generations "cotton was king." The United States continues as the world's leading producing country and cotton still is the first ranking cash crop. Nonetheless, over most of the Cotton Belt, excepting a few counties in Mississippi and Texas, cotton occupies a smaller percentage of the land than formerly. The gospel of crop diversification has not fallen on deaf ears. As far as cotton is concerned, the region has tended to break up into areas of heavy production (the Mississippi Valley and westward) and areas of light production (the old Cotton Belt of the East). Throughout the new "Shattered" Cotton Belt better methods of production and fertilizers mean higher yields (Fig. 13–6).

China is the third-ranking cotton-growing nation. Most of the crop is raised north of the Yangtze River where conditions are favorable—long growing season, ample rainfall, level land, and fertile alluvial soils. There are certain limiting factors too: inadequate, slow, and expensive transportation, destructive floods, too much rain in the autumn, and scarcity of productive land—hardly enough even to meet the food requirements for the teeming millions. Unlike most other large cotton producing countries, China uses nearly all of her crop at home. Her consumption is enormous because of the huge and poor population and because fuel is scarce and costly—too costly to use for heating homes. Thus, as the weather in winter becomes increasingly cold, the people add more clothing; and since they are poor, they wear mostly cotton. Hence the Chinese often speak of two-coat, three-coat, and four-coat weather.

TOBACCO

Humid Subtropical United States and China are the world's leading tobacco growing areas. Tobacco is a major cash crop in the American South, where both climate and soils, particularly the light, sandy soils, contribute to this importance. Tobacco demands almost the complete attention of the farmer (Fig. 13–7). And if an area has grown tobacco successfully, it tends to continue to do so generation after generation. Tobacco is generally grown where cotton does not do well. The several subregions of tobacco production specialize in different kinds of tobacco—Kentucky and Tennessee on burley; Virginia, the Carolinas, and southern Georgia on bright fluecured. It is still too early to tell what effect a possible link between smoking tobacco and lung cancer, brought to light by the Surgeon General's report, will have on production.

China produces tobacco from south to north; but despite this wide distribution, major production is concentrated in a limited number of sharply delimited areas.

TEA AND SILK

The tea bush and the mulberry tree (the leaves of which constitute the feed for silkworms) do not require plow cultivation. Consequently, they may be produced upon hilly or rough, nonarable terrain not utilized for cultivated crops. China, southern Korea, and Japan produce vast amounts of both these crops. The high labor requirements of tea and silk are, of course, easily met by the redundant population of these countries. Both tea and silk are unimportant outside the Orient,

Figure 13–7 Tobacco leaf being harvested on a farm in North Carolina. (Photo courtesy of the Tobacco Institute)

not because of natural environmental deficiencies but because of a dearth of cheap and skilled labor. Their production was attempted in the American South in the colonial period but both were given up. Imported African labor was too unskilled and white labor was too costly. More recently, the development of synthetic fibers, such as nylon and orlon, has had adverse effects upon silk production.

ANIMAL INDUSTRIES

Differences in the attitude of the inhabitants, in the density of population, and in climate cause a concentration of livestock in some sections and a scarcity in others.

The Orient is miserably poor in all except swine and poultry which are kept everywhere. Their distribution coincides with that of people, since they do not compete with man for land or food; they need little room and eat refuse. Nowhere are fowls kept in large numbers, eight being considered a goodly number for any one family. Cattle, horses, and sheep are conspicuously scarce because of population pressure and, in the case of sheep, because the hot, humid summers are disastrous to them. In China and Japan, land is so valuable and the pressure of population so intense that space dare not be used for producing feed for stock, since five times as much land is required to sustain a cow as a man. Farms being tiny, most of the labor is performed by hand. Hence beasts of burden are unnecessary. In the wet rice lands some water buffaloes and cattle are used for plowing. Animals are little used for transportation in Humid Subtropical China; human beings take their place poling or rowing small boats, carrying loads on their backs, and pushing wheelbarrows.

Even hillsides, which in many parts of the world are the birthright of cattle and sheep, are denied them, many being terraced with crops. Moreover, much of the grass is not nutritious. In Japan, where fertile and level land is so scarce, slopes so steep, and rainfall so abundant, the fear of erosion is great among the farmers. Hence grazing on such slopes is restricted.

In southern United States, cattle, mules, swine, and poultry are numerous, but sheep are scarce. In the sandy southeastern section, far more land exists than can be used for fruits and vegetables; hence much of it is used as range for cattle and swine. Real cattle-ranching is carried on, the animals grazing over large tracts of open pine woods. Even the swine have to root and rustle in order to eat and thus differ in appearance from their rotund relatives of the Corn Belt.

In the Cotton Belt proper, livestock is very important because cotton and corn, the two chief crops, require the expenditure of much animal power and because the rural population is comparatively dense. Mules predominate over horses, since they can work hard in a hot, moist climate and can subsist on relatively poor and scanty fare. However, southern farming has become largely mechanized—tractors being common. Dairy cattle are kept by many farmers to supply their own milk and butter.

In the new cattle development the Black Belt of Alabama led the way when backward and ruinous methods of farming, combined with boll-weevil damage, forced abandonment of much cotton acreage. Cattle had not been important before because of the cattle tick, which caused tick fever (no longer present) ; because of poor feeding practices, in large part resulting from the fact that northern hay crops were not well suited either to the climate or to the system of farming in vogue; and because of lack of care in breeding. The whole picture has changed now, however, particularly in the coastal plains of Georgia and Florida, in Louisiana and Texas, in the Black Belt, and in the Mississippi bottomlands. Improvement has resulted from introduction of forage plants—particularly coastal Bermuda grass—better suited to the climatic conditions, from the crossing of European breeds of cattle with the Brahma from India to form new breeds such as the Santa Gertrudis, the Charbray, the Brangus, and the Beefmaster, all of which have been tailored for southern conditions; and from the introduction of oats as a winter grazing crop.[2] The major advantage of this region for cattle is the year-round pasturage provided by coastal Bermuda, and other grasses.

The South American section is probably more important for livestock than for crops. Uruguay, for instance, has more than two-thirds of its area in permanent pasture. The country is said to rank first among all those of the world in number of sheep per inhabitant and per square mile. The sheep receive little care, being free to roam over large fenced pastures (generally 1,200 to 2,500 acres) without herders. Uruguayan sheep are raised primarily for wool. The cost of producing wool is low and the product is of high quality—being fine and free from burrs and seeds. Wool is the principal export of the country and the principal source of foreign exchange. Cattle also are important. Native pastures containing nutritious grasses, mild climate permitting year-long open grazing, traditional preferences of the people for ranching, newness of the country, large estates, sparse population, and profitableness of the industry, all have conspired

to make this country pastoral. Not even Wyoming so typifies ranching as does Uruguay. The situation is thus the reverse of that in the Orient. Humid Subtropical Argentina shares with Uruguay many of the factors just enumerated for the importance of livestock. The southern part of Brazil is the leading livestock section of that country. Humid Subtropical Australia supports the bulk of the continent's cattle but has relatively few of its sheep, the result of warm, moist climate and dense population. In Africa, the portion of Natal lying in this climate has an important cattle industry, but a real problem arises during the dry winter months when the pastures deteriorate.

FOREST INDUSTRIES

Favorable physical conditions for the growth of trees have resulted in Humid Subtropical regions ranking high in forest industries, treeless Uruguay being the sole exception. Of the parts of the world having this type of climate, southern United States is the most important source of forest products. Approximately 25 percent of all the timber cut in the United States, practically all the naval stores, an increasing proportion of paper, cardboard, newsprint, and much of the domestically produced tannin come from these southern forests which contain almost one fourth of the nation's timberland. In fact more than two-fifths of the South still is in forest and 85 percent of this is capable of producing commercial timber. Moreover, trees here grow faster than elsewhere in the United States. The chief trees are the longleaf, shortleaf, and loblolly pines, which grow on the sandy soils. The longleaf pine is the most valuable tree and grows in almost pure stands, though these are usually interrupted along drainage ways by ribbons of hardwood trees and other species of pine. Level terrain and the characteristic openness of the forests facilitate lumbering. Cypress is cut in many swamps.

So ruthlessly was the virgin forest handled in this region that tens of millions of seedlings

[2] Douglas H. K. Lee, *Manual of Field Studies on Heat Tolerance of Domestic Animals,* FAO Development Paper, No. 38 (New York, Columbia University Press, 1953).

are now planted annually in an effort to keep pace with cutting. Its great advantage is in enormous total acreage and in reforestation: yellow pine trees with several years of nursery growth may be planted and they thrive. For pulp, the South's pines reach harvestable age twice as fast as pulp trees elsewhere in the nation. Hence the region has become the country's pulp center.

NAVAL STORES

The production of resin and turpentine was once a great industry, but the harvesting practice of earlier times came close to ruining the forests. Hacking a deep box into live trees yielded only a small amount of resin and caused the trees to die in a few years.

A famous Southern chemist, Charles H. Herty, pointed out that resin was produced not in the wood but in the inner bark, and that merely cutting a strip to the inner bark increased the yield by 25 percent and prolonged the life of the tree many times. Production also was much enhanced when it was learned that old pine stumps could be used to yield naval stores.

NEWSPRINT

The manufacture of newsprint is a relatively new business in the South (Fig. 13–8). It was Herty again who proved that high-grade newsprint could be made from resinous pines by using younger, smaller trees (twenty years old or less) rather than the largest, oldest trees. He pointed out that the older trees contain matter deleterious to newsprint manufacture. Sulfate pulp is also being made from southern hardwoods.

Japan possesses a limited forest industry. The mountainous terrain and the heavy rainfall would result in ruinous soil erosion if cutting were reckless but such is not the case. The upper slopes always are left in forest. More than half the country is still forested and about half the timber is dwarf—best suited for making charcoal, an important fuel for both cooking and heating.

MANUFACTURING

For the most part Humid Subtropical lands do not rank among the world's major industrial regions. Southern Japan and parts of the American South are exceptions. This comparative

Figure 13–8   Started in 1940, the Southland Paper Mill in Lufkin, Texas, was the first newsprint mill in the South. Much of the huge pile of pulpwood in the foreground came from national forest lands in East Texas. (Photo by Daniel O. Todd, courtesy of the U.S. Forest Service)

unimportance derives from four major circumstances: (1) All the countries except those in Asia are historically young and hence have restricted markets. (2) Some areas like Natal (Africa), New South Wales (Australia), southern Brazil, northern Argentina, and Uruguay are dominantly agricultural or pastoral and possess few basic resources for manufacturing. Even the American South has been predominantly agricultural from the very beginning, but this was not the result of slender resources for industry. (3) Nearly all are poor and lack the necessary capital for expensive plants and machinery. (4) In China, industry has been retarded by an ancient social system and poor transportation facilities.

The American South was for decades a land of cotton and corn, of sharecropping and mortgages, and of unpainted shacks and undernourished people. This, however, is no longer true. In the 1940's about half of all southern counties—almost all rural ones—lost population. Beginning with World War II billions of dollars were invested in manufacturing. Everywhere throughout the region one sees new factories that are turning out a wide variety of products among which are textiles, synthetic fibers (this industry is mostly centered in the South), canned foods, synthetic rubber, iron and steel, chemicals (since the Korean War it is believed that one-half of all the new chemical plants have gone up in the South), furniture, tobacco, and newsprint. Whereas before World War II, 32 percent of the South's workers were in agriculture, today only 21 percent are so employed. Thus, if we consider the starting point, the South may be considered to have made the greatest advance industrially of any region in the country during the past quarter century. The region's principal assets are (1) its human resources, (2) its power and energy, (3) its other resources such as bauxite, sulfur, salt, and phosphate rock, (4) its mild climate, and (5) its large commercial forest area.

Until her crushing defeat in World War II, Japan was the only country in the Far East or in all Asia that could be regarded as industrial and that had an iron and steel industry that would have been recognized by the Western world. With the Communist takeover in China, the United States' policy to reduce Japan's in-

dustrial capacity was reversed and Japan is once again in the forefront as one of the important industrial countries of the world with much of its industrial energy directed toward consumer goods. As a result the Japanese enjoy the highest standard of living of any Asian country.

Most of Japan's industrial capacity is to be found in an area extending from Tokyo on the east to Nagasaki on the west. This entire region is close to shipping centers through which many raw materials are imported and huge quantities of fabricated products exported. Cotton textiles, chemicals, ships, fertilizers, machinery, aircraft, and iron and steel are among the more important industrial products.

For millennia China has typified the agricultural economy. The small and rather unimpressive manufacturing, other than the household variety was, prior to the last war, situated along the coast and along the Yangtze and was controlled by foreigners. Thus it could be protected by foreign gunboats and exploited under special privileges.

Today Communist China is determined to become an industrialized state. Despite her five-year industrialization programs and her ability to explode nuclear devices, China still ranks as an underdeveloped nation. Her eventual goal is to have industry account for 70 percent of the combined gross output of agriculture and industry. This goal will not be reached readily, however, for there are major obstacles—85 percent of the people live on farms or in villages with not more than 4 percent living in cities of 100,000 or more; markets are small; purchasing power is low; transportation is poorly developed; and the resources base is not broad.

Industrial development in Australia really dates from 1918. Today manufacturing sustains more people than agriculture and pastoralism. Most of Australia's manufacturing is concentrated in the cities which lie within the Humid Subtropical type of climate. The iron and steel industry is located chiefly near Newcastle and Port Kembla. Australia claims to make the lowest cost steel in the world.

In South Africa, industrialization is moving forward rapidly. Writers invariably refer to the country's industrial revolution. Humid Subtropical Natal, with coal, iron ore, and limestone, has at Newcastle an iron and steel industry. The other principal industries are those concerned with the manufacture of machinery, sugar, woolen goods, wine, and leather. Durban is the principal manufacturing center.

SOCIAL ADJUSTMENTS

Climate has endowed the Humid Subtropics with a high population-supporting capacity. Especially is this true wherever the land is level and the soil fertile. In the plains of China and Japan, the population saturation point would appear to have been reached and both countries stagger under their human burden. Japan's density of population per square mile of arable land is the highest in the world. The Chinese peasant grubs enough from the soil to maintain life, but little more. The standard of living is so low, for example, in China, that the threat of famine is ever present. A combination of political, economic, social, and physical factors has forced Communist China to purchase wheat from the surpluses of the capitalist countries in the last several years. Thus, whenever a physical catastrophe, such as a flood, a prolonged drought, or a delay in the arrival of the summer monsoon occurs, hundreds of thousands and sometimes even millions of peasants die of starvation. Such palliatives as improved farming, emigration, industrialization, or commerce offer but ephemeral relief. The fecundity of China's inhabitants is apparently unlimited.

Japan has a critical population problem but it has made possibly the greatest progress of any nation on earth in solving it. With an area equal to that of California, it has a population of about 100 millions—a population increasing at the rate of about 800,000 per year. Elsewhere throughout the Humid Subtropics the population so far as numbers are concerned is not critical.

In Australia, South Africa, and the American South, color of skin is a major issue. Though Kanaka labor was once introduced to work in Australian cane fields, that was long ago and the native blackfellows are dying out.[3] Hence in time Australia will be white. Probably no other nation faces a domestic problem so acute as South Africa, and Humid Subtropical Natal shares in this. The big problem is racial—the white population (speaking two languages—English and Afrikaans) ; the Negro African; and the Indian.

Almost a century ago Indians were brought to Natal to work on the sugar plantations, and seven-eighths of South Africa's Indians still dwell there. The whites are outnumbered by both the Negroes and the Indians. Fear gnaws at the hearts of white Natalians—fear of the Bantus' numerical preponderance and of the Indians' lower standard of living. Under the apartheid policy racial tensions have remained high and they have had their repercussions far beyond the political boundaries of the Republic of South Africa; among others, was South Africa's withdrawal from the Commonwealth.

In the American South dwell some 15 to 20 million Negroes—descendants of former slaves brought in to perform the hard labor on the cotton and tobacco plantations. Their task also was to clear the forest. The highest densities of rural-living Negroes occur in four areas: the Mississippi River floodplain of northwestern Mississippi; the southern Atlantic coastal plain; northeastern North Carolina and extreme southeastern Virginia; and the Black Belt of central Mississippi and south-central Alabama.

In the areas of highest absolute density, Negroes everywhere make up more than 60 percent of the population and in a few counties the proportion of rural Negroes exceeds 80 percent. In no single state, however, do Negroes comprise as much as 50 percent of the total population; in Mississippi, which has the highest state average, they constitute 45 percent of the total. In 1960, 21 percent of the total population of the South was Negro.

Although the migration of Negroes from the South to the West Coast and to northern cities[4] has been large the South still has 60 percent of the entire Negro population. Despite racial tension in the South, the Negro is making progress socially, economically, and politically. There are still centers of hard core resistance to

[3] "Aborigines Facing Doom in Australia," *New York Times,* May 7, 1950.
[4] For further information on the Negro migration from the South, see Philip M. Houser, "Demographic Factors," *The American Negro,* Fall 1965 issue of *Daedalus, Journal of the Academy of Arts and Sciences,* pp. 851-852.

change in the status of the Negro, but under the pressure of federal legislation and the influence of Southern moderates of both races more progress has been made in the past decade than in the preceding century.

In the American South, the people had to cope with two new problems: the institution of slavery and a subtropical agricultural economy. All the crops were row crops which were worked under conditions of heavy rainfall. Both soil erosion and soil depletion took a heavy toll. The plantation economy in which Negro slaves worked the fields resulted in large numbers of poor whites moving into the hill country where they tended to become poorer.

The Civil War with its resulting emancipation of slaves left the Humid Subtropical South with a landlord class lacking money for paying the newly freed (their former) slaves and with Negroes having nothing to offer except their labor. About all they knew then was the routine of caring for cotton under rigid direction. The inevitable result of such a situation was the sharecropping system, in which these two interdependent groups were brought together. The former slaves were given a share of the crop (usually half) for their part of the labor. This system resulted in some thirty million acres of cropland being seriously threatened by erosion.

THE POLITICAL SITUATION

Nearly all Humid Subtropical regions are struggling with grave political problems. Southern United States and Natal have a racial problem, the seriousness of which can scarcely be exaggerated. In each place the white race, long ago, took advantage of its political supremacy to enact "color bar" legislation. Only since the 1950's has the Negro been able to vote in the Deep South, though he has voted in the Upper South for nearly half a century.

Southern Brazil has a large German element that at times has been a problem of the first magnitude to the Brazilian government. In places the German language and German customs prevail. Australia, fearing Japan prior to the latter's defeat at the end of World War II, legislated against immigration of all colored peoples.

Japan, formerly a small island kingdom, expanded so much that Formosa, Korea, and Manchuria were swallowed and she obtained an economic stranglehold on certain mineral resources, transport lines, and industries in China. This aggression was believed at one time to be largely attributable to poverty of natural resources at home and desire and determination to acquire a place in the sun. Actually there was a cultural lag that had a bad political and social outcome. During World War II, Japan gained control of a huge and rich empire, only to lose it all later. All she salvaged were the four main islands.

Communism has spread from the Soviet Union to China and it is in China that the greatest Communist success since the Russian Revolution has been achieved. Agrarian discontent provided a large part of the fuel for the Communist drive to power and upon it was built the peasant mass support on which the Communist party rose to power. The Communists have consolidated their power over the mainland and it now appears that China has a voracious appetite for land in southeast Asia. Non-Communist China is limited solely to Taiwan and the Pescadores.

In South Africa the social, economic, and political problems are so intertwined that any one can hardly be considered in isolation. South Africa is now dominated by the Nationalist government which came into power because it promised to solve the racial problem of multiracial South Africa. It promised to solve this problem by apartheid—the separation of the races, residentially, socially, and politically. It even involves diverting industry from its present location—an example of a struggle between economic forces and apartheid ideology. The outcome of this struggle is still uncertain.

SUGGESTED USEFUL READINGS

Cole, Monica, *South Africa* (New York, E. P. Dutton and Company, 1961), 696 pp.

Cressey, George G., *Land of the 500 Million; a Geography of China* (New York, McGraw-Hill Book Company, Inc., 1955), 387 pp.

Hamm, Harry, *China, Empire of the 700 Million*, trans. by Victor Anderson (New York, Doubleday and Company, 1966).

James, Preston E., *Latin America*, 3d. (New York, The Odyssey Press, 1959), 942 pp.

Leiserson, Avery, *The American South in the 1960's* (New York, Frederick A. Praeger, Inc., 1964), particularly Chapters 1 to 5 inclusive.

McCune, Shannon, *Korea's Heritage, a Regional and Social Geography* (Rutland, Vermont, C. E. Tuttle, 1956), 250 pp.

Parkins, Almon E., *The South: Its Economic Geographic Development* (New York, John Wiley & Sons, Inc., 1938), 528 pp.

Russell, Richard J., Fred Bowerman Kniffen, and Evelyn Lord Pruitt, *Culture Worlds* (New York, The Macmillan Company, 1961).

Trewartha, Glenn T., *Japan: A Geography* (Madison, Wis., University of Wisconsin Press, 1965), 652 pp.

Vance, Rupert B., *Human Geography of the South: a Study in Regional Resources and Human Adequacy*, 2d ed. (Chapel Hill, N.C., University of North Carolina Press, 1935).

14

Dry Subtropical Climate Regions

This type of climate occurs within interior regions in the Subtropical Zone. It should be remembered that the western margins of continents in this zone possess the Mediterranean Subtropical climate, whereas the eastern margins exhibit the Humid Subtropical climate. Intermediate between these two types lie the lands where the Dry Subtropical climate prevails (Fig. 14–1). Since this type is intermediate in location, it exhibits some characteristics in common with its neighbors but, being entirely an inland or interior development, it possesses certain unique traits.

CONTRAST WITH OTHER SUBTROPICAL TYPES

Like the other subtropical climates (discussed in the two preceding chapters), this type is characterized by very short winters which are cool rather than cold. Like them, too, it possesses long, hot summers. In addition, it experiences only moderate changes in weather conditions. While lands with this climate do experience occasional mild weather changes from time to time during the year, they lack the sharp, stimulating variability of weather characterizing the Cyclonic Zone which borders their poleward margins.

On the other hand, the Dry Subtropical climate displays traits which are in contrast to those of the other subtropical types. It is, in general, much drier, and it exhibits a somewhat greater range in temperature from season to season. Both of these characteristics result from inland location. Since the primary source of precipitation is

the ocean, it follows that interior climates are, other things being equal, usually drier than coastal climates. For example, the annual precipitation at Albuquerque, New Mexico (Dry Subtropical), is less than 8 inches, that of Charleston, South Carolina (Humid Subtropical), is 49 inches, whereas that of Los Angeles (Mediterranean Subtropical) is approximately 16 inches.

The cause of annual range in temperature in any locality is the seasonal rates of heating and cooling of the earth's surface under varying elevations of the sun. Land surfaces heat more rapidly under a high sun and cool more rapidly under a low sun than do ocean surfaces. Hence it follows that interior lands are cooler in winter and hotter in summer than continental margins. The net result of this phenomenon is to give the Dry Subtropical climate a greater annual range of temperature than either of its neighbor types. Although the seasonal contrasts are not large in any part of the Subtropical Zone, nevertheless they are great enough to be appreciable, particularly in this type of climate. For example, Albuquerque exhibits an annual range of temperature of 44° F. as compared with 16° F. for Los Angeles, and 32° F. for Charleston (Fig. 14–2).

REGIONS OF OCCURRENCE

The Dry Subtropical climate is found on every continent except Antarctica; in Africa, two such occurrences may be noted, one near either end of the continent. In general, areas with this cli-

223

Figure 14–1 Dry Subtropical regions.

mate occupy inland positions extending roughly from latitude 25° to 40°. Specifically there are seven such regions, four in the Northern Hemisphere and three in the Southern Hemisphere (Fig. 14–1). They are the following.

1. The Spanish Plateau
2. The Atlas region of northern Africa
3. The Turko-Iranian region of southwestern Asia
4. The Southwestern Plateaus of the United States and the Northern Basins of Mexico
5. The Sub-Andean section of northwestern Argentina
6. The High Veld country of South Africa
7. The Murray-Darling Basin of Australia

Except for the facts that the Dry Subtropical regions of the Southern Hemisphere experience a somewhat milder winter than do those of the Northern Hemisphere, and the southern summer comes at the time when the northern winter occurs (and vice versa), these seven regions are fairly homologous.

CLIMATIC CHARACTERISTICS

In amount, the rainfall of the Dry Subtropical climate varies usually from subhumid to semiarid. Locally, in a few places, it is so scanty as to produce true desert conditions (Fig. 9–2). Examples of such spots are the Mojave Desert of

224

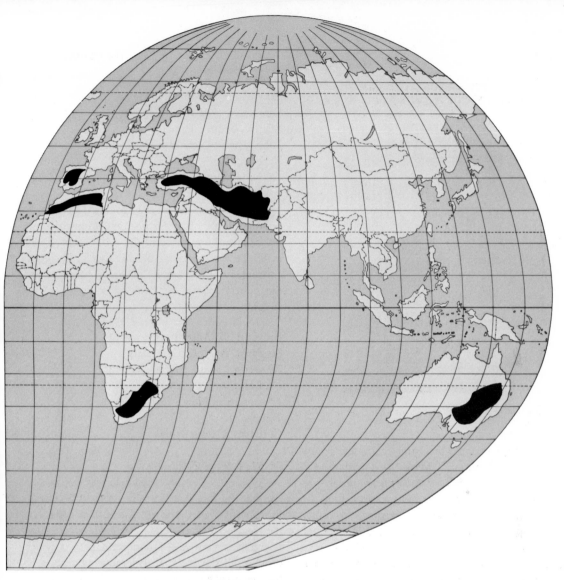

California, the Great Salt Desert of Iran, the Chihuahua Desert of Mexico, the Plateau of the Shotts in Algeria, and the Sub-Andean district of Argentina. The following are typical annual rainfall figures for stations in the drier phase of the Dry Subtropical climate, one in each of the seven regions of occurrence.

Teheran (Iran)	9	inches
Albuquerque (New Mexico)	7½	"
Matjesfontein (South Africa)	6½	"
Broken Hill (Australia)	9	"
San Juan (Argentina)	3	"
Quetta (West Pakistan)	0	"
Biskra (Algeria)	7	"

Large areas of the Dry Subtropical lands, however, are more favorably endowed. The rain- fall is usually less than twenty inches in total annual amount. Stations which illustrate the semi- arid rather than the arid phase of this climate are as follows.

Madrid (Spain)	16	inches
Sivas (Turkey)	17	"
Kimberley (South Africa)	18	"
Flagstaff (Arizona)	22	"
Bourke (Australia)	15	"
Mosul (Iraq)	17	"
Gériville (Algeria)	15	"

The transitional character of this climate is revealed in the seasonal distribution of rainfall. In some instances, there is a winter rainfall maximum; in others a summer one. The former occurs in those portions adjacent to Mediterranean

225

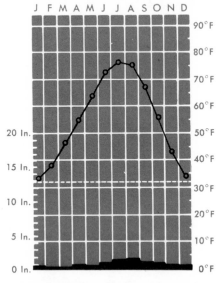

Dry Subtropical Climate
ALBUQUERQUE, NEW MEXICO, U.S.A.
Elevation 5,700' Latitude 35°6'N

Figure 14–2 Climate graph for Albuquerque, New Mexico.

Broken Hill, Australia (July)	49° F.
San Juan, Argentina (June)	47° F.
Kimberley, South Africa (June)	50° F.
Madrid, Spain (January)	39° F.
Albuquerque, New Mexico (January)	34° F.
Teheran, Iran (January)	34° F.
Gériville, Algeria (January)	39° F.

Summer temperatures in this type of climate are quite high, often surprisingly so on the lowlands, resembling those in the Arid Tropical climate. Temperatures on the highlands, however, are cooler and often quite pleasant. Averages for the hottest month, for selected stations, are as follows.

Broken Hill, Australia (January)	79° F.
San Juan, Argentina (January)	78° F.
Kimberley, South Africa (January)	76° F.
Madrid, Spain (July)	76° F.
Albuquerque, New Mexico (July)	77° F.
Teheran, Iran (July)	85° F.
Gériville, Algeria (July)	79° F.

PLANT GEOGRAPHY

Despite the fact that this climate is to be found in many parts of the world and that in each area the vegetation has certain general similarities, nonetheless each has a flora very peculiarly its own. In all the areas, a distinguishing feature is the vegetation's marvelous rapidity to recover from droughts with just a few showers. Within several days all has changed and the country is covered with a green mantle.

In general, areas where the Dry Subtropical climate prevails receive light to scanty rainfall. Obviously the natural vegetation closely reflects this fact along with variations in altitude. In southwestern United States and adjacent Mexico, the vegetation consists of large areas of creosote bush, mesquite, cacti (Fig. 14–3), and desert grass and, where local conditions are favorable as along the New Mexico-Texas border, even considerable prairie grassland. In the adjacent uplands are stands of piñon-juniper (a coniferous woodland) and at the higher elevations forests of yellow pine and fir.

In the Argentine Arid Subtropical region,

Subtropical regions, the latter in those adjacent to Humid Subtropical areas. At Flagstaff, Arizona, there prevails a winter maximum in precipitation, whereas 280 miles eastward at Albuquerque, New Mexico, a summer maximum occurs. A similar contrast appears in New South Wales, Australia, between Broken Hill (winter maximum) and Bourke (summer maximum), although a scant three hundred miles of plains country separate them. There are, of course, midpoints where no seasonal rhythm is discernible.

Winter in the Dry Subtropical climate is rather mild and of short duration, lasting from two to three months. Moderate weather changes occur throughout this season and are caused by marginal effects of high and low barometer storms which pass along the poleward margins of the subtropics. Occasionally, high barometer conditions bring sharp freezes during the winter and even zero weather is not unknown. Low barometer conditions may occasionally cause snowfall, but this is rather rare on the lowlands. During the coldest winter months temperature averages are usually a few degrees above freezing. Averages for the coldest month of the year for representative stations are as follows.

the vegetation consists of xerophytic scrub steppe called *monte*—a vegetation closely resembling the mesquite brush-land of the Texas-Mexican border. On the poorly drained lands where any vegetation grows at all, it consists of useless salt brush.

In Arid Subtropical Spain, the vegetation consists largely of herbaceous plants including grasses. South of the Mediterranean in North Africa the land is clothed with desert scrub, and huge areas covered by chaparral resemble those in southern California. Stretches of steppe characterize the basins of the Atlas Mountains, whereas oak and coniferous forests distinguish the well-watered hill slopes. In South Africa on the elevated plateaus of the Orange Free State, South Transvaal, and neighboring Cape Province is a rolling grassland steppe called the High Veld.

In the Middle East the original vegetation (now gone over much of the region because of man's long occupation and maladjustment to the land and its vegetative cover) has been reduced to open-scrub–shrub-grassland with mixed coniferous and hardwood deciduous forest in the mountains to the north and east.

In the Murray-Darling Basin of Australia, the amount of rainfall exceeds that received by most of the other Dry Subtropical regions and this is reflected in the vegetation. Thus, in the better watered southeast, the countryside is covered with good grass and dotted with eucalyptus trees. Westward from this area, however, with increasing aridity, salt bush and scattered acacia trees take over.

THE NATIVE ANIMALS

Since the dominant natural vegetation in the Dry Subtropical climate is grassland and steppe desert (open country), the animals are largely the swift-footed and the running and jumping types. Moreover, they are predominantly nocturnal in their habits, for in the blistering heat of midday, many would die if they ventured forth. Accordingly, most spend the hot part of the day sleeping—many in cool underground burrows.[1]

Since water is scarce, many animals never have a real chance to drink. Yet, in order to live they must have water! Some of the herbivores get it from the grasses and shrubs they eat, while the carnivores get theirs from the flesh and blood of their prey.[2]

In North America the herbivores include the bison and pronghorn antelope (mostly killed off) and the Arizona white-tail and mule deer. There are some elk in the highlands. Southwestern Asia has the Persian gazelle. The veld

[1] See the excellent article, "The World We Live In: Part IX, The Desert," *Life* (April 5, 1954).
[2] *Ibid.*

Figure 14–3   Natural vegetation in the American Southwest: Saguaro cactus, ocatillo thorn bush, and other desert species. (Photo courtesy of the U.S. Forest Service)

country of South Africa was originally a veritable paradise for steppe animals of this kind. Blesbok, bushbuck, many varieties of duikers, the white-tailed gnu, the hartebeest, klipspringer, kudu, sable antelope, and zebra were extremely numerous. The Australian steppes were, on the contrary, poorly populated by several varieties of marsupials—kangaroos and their immediate allies.

Among this array of large herbivores are several important carnivores that live by preying upon them and other smaller animals. Typical among these are the coyote, desert fox, and puma of North America, the Persian tiger of southwestern Asia, the lion of Africa, and the dingo (wild dog) of Australia.

The grasses of the steppe supply an abundance of seeds, the shrubs and occasional areas of dry forest furnish nesting places, and the mild winter offers a refuge from more rigorous climes. As a result, these lands contain a plentiful bird life—ducks, geese, turkeys, guinea fowl,

pelicans, partridges, pheasants, and numerous others. A few species of large flightless birds are included—the African ostrich, the Argentine rhea, and the Australian emu.

Smaller subtropical steppe animals are rabbits, marsupial rats, lizards, snakes, and others. Insect life, too, is at times abundant despite the aridity. The drier margins of the steppe are the natural breeding grounds of locusts and grasshoppers (Fig. 11–7). Periodically these may become so numerous as to devastate the steppelands. Furthermore, great armies of these insects have been known to migrate into neighboring humid lands carrying destruction with them.

THE RABBIT PEST IN AUSTRALIA

Rabbits are discussed in this type of climate in Australia because they compete with sheep more than with any other domestic animal, and Dry Subtropical Australia is the country's prin-

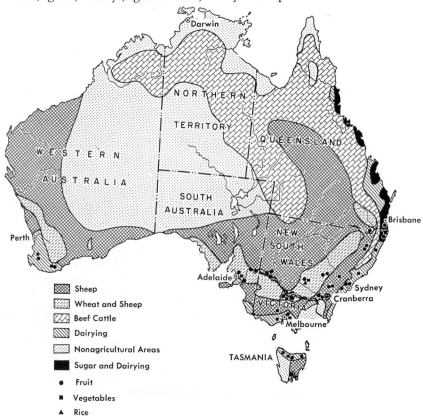

Legend:
- Sheep
- Wheat and Sheep
- Beef Cattle
- Dairying
- Nonagricultural Areas
- Sugar and Dairying
- • Fruit
- ■ Vegetables
- ▲ Rice

Figure 14–4   Principal land-use regions of Australia. Dry Subtropical Australia is the great sheep and wheat region of the continent. (Map adapted from *Atlas—Australian Rural Industries*)

cipal sheep-producing region (Fig. 14–4). Prior to 1859 there were no rabbits in this continent. In that year, however, two dozen were let loose in Hobson's Bay to provide sport for the settlers. With no natural enemies, the ecological balance became upset and within a few decades the animals threatened to overrun the continent. Thus the menace has spread from a tiny area in southern Victoria in 1859 to the greater part of the continent. Even the dead desert heart (Arid Tropical climate) is overrun with them. Hawks, weasels, and snakes have proved ineffective.

Since forty rabbits eat as much grass as one sheep, it is obvious that these animals soon became Australia's greatest curse, for they were destroying pastures that could support forty million sheep. Thousands of miles of wire fences were erected at great cost, but the pests proved highly resistant to confinement. Finally in 1952 a new weapon was employed—*myxomatosis*—a virus disease specific to rabbits.

The rabbits are inoculated artificially, the killing agency being the microscopic virus *myxomatosis* which brings swift fever, paralysis, and death. At first a few rabbits were injected with the virus and set free in the Murray Valley at the border of Victoria and New South Wales. Mosquitoes spread the infection westward to South Australia and northward to New South Wales. Scientists ranged far and wide with their vials of serum and their hypodermic needles. The initial results were disappointing. Later, however, the disease flared up in many spots and whole colonies of rabbits were destroyed. Mosquitoes had spread the disease. It then spread down the Murray to its mouth and up all the major tributaries to their sources and on into Queensland. Rabbits virtually disappeared from some areas. In 1951–1952 *myxomatosis* alone added seventy million pounds of wool to the clip and an increase in sheep and lamb slaughter of $22 million. However, in 1952–1953, the results were largely reversed. More and more rabbits were recovering: the power of the disease was being reduced. This resulted from (1) an alteration of the virus which made it less lethal to rabbits, (2) a temporary immunity on the part of rabbit kits being suckled by recovered rabbits, and (3)

Figure 14–5 Angora goats eating brush in Sonora, Texas. (Photo courtesy of USDA)

the rapid breeding of those rabbits that had hereditary resistance to the virus.

It is not known whether *myxomatosis* ever can completely rid the country of the rabbit. However, with this weapon plus poisoning, trapping, digging-out, and wire-netting fencing, the pest is gradually being brought under control in the principal pastoral areas. The rabbit does supply flesh, fur, and felt, but these add up to an infinitesimal portion of the financial loss sustained by the sheep ranchers.

HUMAN ECOLOGY
ECONOMIC GEOGRAPHY
Pastoral adjustments

Most Dry Subtropical regions vary from semiarid to arid in their rainfall and hence are too dry for agriculture by customary methods. Accordingly, the dominant activity of the inhabitants is the pasturing of animals (Fig. 14–5). Such lands in Europe, North Africa, and Asia have long been the homeland of pastoral peoples —the Spaniards of the Meseta, the Berbers of the Atlas, and the Afghans, Baluchi, Persians, Kurds, and Turks of southwestern Asia. Today these places are important producers and exporters of pastoral products. From the Spanish

Meseta with its 20 million sheep comes an enormous export of fine wool and considerable Merino breeding stock; from Algeria and Iran come goatskins and wool; from the rough, arid pasture lands of southwestern Asia come large exports of coarse wool, and from the Angora (Ankara) District in Turkey comes much goat hair (mohair). Annually too, from the semiarid Meseta of Spain, there is a large export of asses. These little animals go all over the world to be used as breeding stock in the mule-rearing industry.

Since lands with this climate are quite habitable for white people, Europeans have colonized them in South Africa, Australia, and the Americas. The English have settled the Murray-Darling Basin of Australia, the English and the Dutch Boers have spread over interior South Africa, and the Spanish have colonized northwestern Argentina. In North America, the descendants of English and Spanish colonists have occupied the Dry Subtropical lands of the United States and Mexico and made of them a region of large ranches.

In North America before the white man arrived in the Southwest, the Navajos were hunters. They had no domesticated animals other than the dog. However, they acquired the horse, sheep, goat, and cow as the Spaniards penetrated the region. Hence today the Navajos are essentially pastoralists—the only such Indian people in the whole of North America. However, they are not prosperous. They have through excessive trailing of their livestock (that is, keeping them constantly on the move) harmed both the range and the sheep.

In all of these instances man has adjusted himself pastorally to his new environment. Centers of goat raising have developed on the Edwards Plateau of Texas, in the Karroo District of South Africa, and in northwestern Argentina. The Murray-Darling Basin contains approximately 30 million sheep, Transvaal and Orange Free State sustain perhaps 16 million, and the three American states of Texas, New Mexico, and Arizona have about 12 million. Cattle ranching is an almost universal activity in these regions, but cattle are greatly outnumbered by sheep, a consequence of the low carrying capacity of the vegetation and the scarcity of water. Since less land is required for pasturing a given number of sheep than for an equal number of cattle, sheep-rearing is usually a more efficient means of utilizing land where vegetation is scanty. On the other hand, cattle are apparently better able to withstand high temperatures than are sheep. Hence, there is a tendency for cattle to replace sheep, or at least to compete with them, along the tropical margins of the Dry Subtropical steppes. Perhaps goats would replace both sheep and cattle were it not that the goat has always been an animal of comparatively low economic utility.

Most outstanding commercial sheep region in this type of climate is Dry Subtropical Australia (Fig. 14–4). By reason of rainfall insufficiency, the region is essentially sheep country. In fact, wool sheep constitute the backbone of Australian agriculture and wool is the principal export of the nation. The close relationship between the distribution of sheep and precipitation is so marked that the sheep belt is confined to the lands lying between the 10-inch and 30-inch rainfall lines, with the maximum sheep density between the 21- and 23-inch isohyets. Here one sheep can be sustained on about three acres, but westward the number of acres per sheep soars, finally reaching thirty to forty. Dry Subtropical Australia is not well suited to cattle. The country's principal beef cattle areas lie far to the east, northeast, north, and northwest of the sheep lands—outside the Dry Subtropical climate.

Man-made deserts

Close grazing and overgrazing over a relatively short period have resulted in much destruction to the land in the southwest of the United States and in Northern Mexico. And grazing of flocks of sheep and goats from time immemorial on the interior plains and plateaus of the Middle East has resulted in much soil erosion there. These lands have always been in delicate ecological balance and, with man's exploitative and destructive systems of grazing and farming along with military invasions and the devastation that followed in their wake, thousands of square miles of land have been completely ruined. Much of the desert is thus man-induced. In Syria, for example, French archaeologists have found more than one hundred dead cities in the man-made desert.[3] With the soil gone, all is gone. It will take a long time to bring such areas back into productiveness and perhaps they never will be brought back. These lands are poor, and huge financial resources would be required to make many of them even marginal in quality. In addition, technical know-how and a literate populace are imperative.

It is not surprising to learn, therefore, that in the Middle East, in Northern Mexico, and also in the American Southwest (among the Indian population), biting poverty is widespread. These fall into the category of underdeveloped lands. Their lot has been one of neglect, deprivation, and frustration. Among most of the people is the ever-present brutal fact that nothing can be done, for the margin between not enough and starvation is too thin. Here are high rates of illiteracy (70 to 80 percent) and of infant mortality (15 to 20 percent); low levels of living (annual family income is $200 to $300); and numerous vitality-sapping diseases.[4]

Agricultural adjustments

Almost everywhere in this climate, water is a scarce and precious element. A large proportion of the land is too arid for agriculture by the methods customarily employed in humid regions (Fig. 14–6). This means that except in the small number of favored areas that occur here and there, the land is devoted to pastoral activities. If such lands are used for crops, they must be irrigated or dry farmed. A recent map of food production in the United States shows that nearly all the land in the Southwest is range and that most of the rest is classed as nonfarming. The area actually being farmed is but an infinitesimal part of the whole. The only impressive farming areas are those included in projects of the United States Bureau of Reclamation. The Salt River Project in South Central Arizona is one outstanding example. Here the Roosevelt Dam has been constructed in the highlands east of the city of Phoenix by the federal government. This

dam is 280 feet high, 1,080 feet long, and im- here as elsewhere in southwestern United States, yields five or six crops annually, is of immense pounds approximately one million acre-feet of water, which irrigates more than 200,000 acres of land lower down the Salt River Valley in a locality where the annual rainfall is approximately seven inches. Here may be seen typical Mediterranean Subtropical crops (barley, wheat, oranges, grapefruit, apricots, and grapes) growing side by side with Humid Subtropical crops (cotton,

[3] W. C. Lowdermilk, *Conquest of the Land Through Seven Thousand Years,* Agriculture Information Bulletin No. 99 (Washington, D.C., U.S. Department of Agriculture, 1953), p. 10.

[4] Most of these data are specifically applicable to the Dry Subtropical Middle East but would apply in large measure to other parts of the climatic realm.

Figure 14–6 Navajo Indians dry-farming corn in the American Southwest. Coming from what is now British Columbia about A.D. 1000, they settled among Pueblo people and from them learned how to grow crops. Though for the most part pastoralists, their great increase in numbers plus the severe overgrazing over virtually all of their reservation is stimulating the growing of crops wherever possible. (Photo courtesy of the Soil Conservation Service, USDA)

corn, and sugar cane). In addition, alfalfa which, here as elsewhere in southwestern United States, yields five or six crops annually, is of immense importance as feed for livestock.

Near the eastern foot of the Andes Mountains in northwestern Argentina are a number of oases watered by snow-fed mountain streams. Fields of sugar cane, rice, corn, tobacco and pineapples, vineyards of grapes, and orchards of pears, peaches, and plums make the landscape a beautiful and productive one. In favored pockets throughout the American Southwest, Indians grow crops by irrigation, dry-farming, and flood-water methods. Among the best farmers in this region are the Hopis, who occupy lands in the southwestern part of the Navajo Reservation. Long ago they realized that their rainfall was inadequate for agriculture. In order to grow crops, they ferret out all the areas having moist soils and practice floodwater farming—placing their crops in valley bottoms near washes or wherever moisture is available. Such fields often lie far from their pueblos. They plant their corn in hills about six feet apart to conserve water and 6 to 8 and occasionally as many as 14 inches deep to keep it from sprouting until rain falls. They also put fifteen to twenty kernels in a hill. Occasionally they erect small windbreaks about thirty feet apart in parallel rows and at right angles to the prevailing winds. Because of the short growing season (the result of altitude), they have developed quick-maturing strains.

The Hopis, reputed to be the most skillful of all dry-land farmers, cultivate intensively, each farmer handling only two to ten acres. Seldom is their land in one continuous piece. They have developed their agriculture to a degree hardly reached by modern agriculture despite such powerful weapons as soil physics, soil chemistry, plant physiology, and plant genetics.

Perhaps the most important commercial dry-farming area in this type of climate lies in the more humid parts of the "back slopes" of New South Wales, where an extensive lowland plain stretches between the Great Dividing Range on the east, and the Flinders-Gray Ranges on the west, the whole being drained by the Murray-Darling River system. The eastern portion of this basin, which is rolling piedmont, is fairly well watered and in normal years makes fine sheep and wheat country (Fig. 14–4). Australia ranks as one of the world's outstanding wheat regions and the heart of the production is the area under discussion. Next to wool, this cereal is the principal export. Big fields of wheat on huge farms extensively cultivated continue westward down the piedmont slopes and out into the lowland plain for one hundred miles or more (Fig. 14–7). The wheat belt is bounded on the east by the 25-inch rainfall line and on the west by the 10-inch line. When the precipitation falls below 10 inches for the growing period (April to October), wheat production ceases. Thus the rainfall regime helps to determine the position of the Australian wheat belt and is the main physical factor deciding the distribution of the crop. Dry-farming methods involving fallowing and careful tilth became increasingly important as the 10-inch isohyet is approached.

In the Middle East, agriculture is the foundation of the total economy, but by American standards it would seem to be completely outmoded. The threshing board, sickle, wooden plow, and team of oxen still prevail. Yet in some aspects many of these are efficiently adapted to the conditions of the local situation. In some countries the draft animals are physically incapable of drawing heavier plows. If such were to be introduced, the breed of draft animals and the feeding practices would have to be improved. Moreover, the shallow, narrow furrows made by the wooden plow do prevent wind erosion. Thus in Turkey, though 73 percent of the area could be farmed, only 20 percent is under cultivation, the remainder being left in pasture. Even one-third of the cropland is in fallow each year and the fallow period lasts from two to four years. However, since the establishment of the Republic of Turkey, agriculture has improved to the extent that the country now has an exportable surplus of wheat.

In Iran, too, agriculture is the leading economic pursuit, but farming is far more antiquated than in Turkey. Less than 10 percent of the total land area is classed as cropland and even three-fourths of this is normally in fallow. Only 3 percent of the total land area is in crops.

Figure 14–7 Harvesting wheat at Narromine, New South Wales. (Photo courtesy of the Australian News & Information Bureau)

As in all Dry Subtropical lands, scarcity of water is the dominant retarding factor. Few modern methods are practiced and farming is carried on as it has been for millennia. Threshing is primitive and grain is winnowed.

SOCIAL GEOGRAPHY

In general, Dry Subtropical regions are lands of low population supporting capacity. In the best dry-farming sections, such as those in New South Wales and western Texas, the population averages only ten to fifteen persons per square mile. In areas of pastoral adjustment, the population is even more sparse, averaging less than one person per square mile. For the most part, however, the distribution of population is far from uniform, being rendered *patchy* by the presence of mining and irrigation agricultural islands of dense settlement. Far more people could be supported if irrigation were better developed. Throughout all Dry Subtropical lands the urban segment of the population is small indeed.

The primary law of social habit is that man seeks to be sedentary wherever possible. Even pastoral peoples in this climate tend to establish permanent homes, except where locally driven to nomadism by excessive aridity. In some areas, for example, the Northern Basins of Mexico and the Murray-Darling Basin of Australia, the ranches are large. In the Middle East, on the contrary, the holdings are reasonably small (in Turkey 97 percent are 125 acres or less). In the American Southwest, the holdings are huge where the raising of livestock prevails but small where irrigation dominates.

In many countries with this climate, agriculture is an integral part of the whole culture—a way of life rather than an economic activity. Thus agriculture must be understood and analyzed in the light of the whole. Even so simple a matter as the introduction of a new crop rotation becomes a community affair, not one for individual action. This way of life is deeply rooted in centuries of tradition.

In most Dry Subtropical areas the condition of the masses is abject indeed. In the Middle East, there are numerous and complex reasons aside from the niggardly milieu; the most important is the unconscionable indifference of the landowners toward the general misery. Of all the Arab states, only Turkey and Jordan have made commendable progress. Israel has been the brightest spot in the Middle East. In the United States the plight of the Indians is indefensible. This situation applies both to the agriculturists—the Hopis and Zuñis, and to the (nomadic) pastoralists—the Apaches and Navajos. The situation among the Navajos is particularly serious because they are increasing rapidly in numbers and their reservation's boundaries are inelastic. Numbering 10,000 in 1868, there are now in excess of 125,000. Eighty percent are illiterate. Living in *hogans*, they lack all modern conveniences. Since they are constantly following their flocks from one remote spot to another (only one-fourth of 1 percent of the reservation is farmed), it is difficult to see how by their own efforts they can improve their way of life. Several years ago the *New York Times* announced that the conditions under which most of the tribesmen existed make this arid range country little more than an outdoor slum. The health of the Navajos has been neglected: the rate of both tuberculosis and typhoid is high; deaths from pneumonia and dysentery are triple the national average. The life span of the Navajo is fifty years, not the seventy of the white population. Unless the grass that used to wave over this region is brought back and unless adequate water is made available for growing some corn and hay, the future of the Navajos appears dismal.

POLITICAL GEOGRAPHY

Climatic factors bear an interesting relation to many of the politico-geographic problems of Dry Subtropical lands. For example, the paucity of rainfall provides ample incentive for local dispute over water—wells, streams and springs. Accordingly, from Spain to Afghanistan, there are elaborate legal codes governing the control and disposition of water. At times, disputes over water resources have become international, as in the case of the quarrels between the Persians and Afghans over the use of the Helmand River. In another instance, Mexico, Texas, and New Mexico became involved in a serious controversy over the use of the waters of the Rio Grande.

In the Dry Subtropics, irrigation of land, wherever possible, is eagerly attempted by society. In the early stages of adjustment, irrigation works were developed by private initiative. The remaining possibilities for irrigation in these lands of little rain and high evaporation rate entail expensive water storage projects. Private enterprise, apparently, is incapable of providing these on the huge scale necessary for present-day development. As a result, the matter takes on a political significance; the inhabitants look to their government to provide reclamation projects. For this reason, the state and federal governments of the United States, Argentina, Australia, and other countries have come to play a paternalistic part in the development of Dry Subtropical lands (Fig. 14–8).

In regions of less stable and paternalistic government, the dry lands of the Subtropical Zone are apt to be the loci of political restlessness. During cycles of drought, pastoral peoples are invariably thrown into seething unrest. In many instances they raid and despoil the neighboring agricultural and commercial peoples. The pastoral Kurds have long ravaged the Armenians and the inhabitants of Iraq. Of equally long standing is the conflict between Turk and Greek. The dry Northern Basins of Mexico have for decades been the breeding ground for revolution and political discontent in that country. Texas and New Mexico constantly quarrel over the impounding of Rio Grande water at Elephant Butte Dam (Fig. 14–8), Texas claiming that she does not get her share under the interstate compact.

The Rio Grande forms the boundary between Mexico and the United States for nearly half its course. Here indeed are the seeds for possible discord, for the United States has an opportunity to use much of this water before it ever reaches the Mexican border. Moreover, Northern Mexico is a very thirsty land, and mankind's water needs are the same under any flag in the Dry Subtropical climate. To distribute this water equitably calls for the highest type of statesmanship. Accordingly, the two neighbors have set up an international Boundary Water Commission, which has made several important decisions.

The Middle East, which is mostly desert (both Arid Tropical and Dry Subtropical), is one of the most explosive regions in the world. Nearly all of the problems are of long duration

Figure 14–8 Elephant Butte, one of the outstanding dams of the world, forms a huge lake behind it for storing water from the Rio Grande with which a half-million acres of desert in New Mexico and Texas are irrigated. Note the power plant on the left at the base of the dam and New Mexico State Highway 52, which crosses the crest of the dam. (Photo courtesy of the Bureau of Reclamation, U.S. Department of the Interior)

—unstable political establishments, feudalistic social systems, and backward economies that result in large part from aridity and soil erosion. Although the region is rich in petroleum, the masses of the people do not benefit unless their governments are enlightened, which, except in the case of Kuwait, has not been true up to the present. To make matters worse is the constant meddling of Communists. No solution to the region's problems is now in sight.

SUGGESTED USEFUL READINGS

Barbour, Nevill, ed., *A Survey of North-West Africa (the Maghrib)*, 2d ed. (London, Oxford University Press, 1962), 411 pp.

Butland, Gilbert J., *Latin America; a Regional Geography* (New York, Longmans, Green and Company, 1960), pp. 243–251.

Carter, George F., *Plant Geography and Culture History in the American Southwest*, Viking Fund Publications in Anthropology, No. 5 (New York, Viking Fund, 1945), 140 pp.

Cole, Monica, *South Africa* (New York, E. P. Dutton & Company, Inc., 1961), pp. 249–253, 609–622.

Fisher, W. B., *The Middle East: a Physical, Social, and Regional Geography* (New York, E. P. Dutton & Company, Inc., 1961), 557 pp.

Robinson, Kathleen W., *Australia, New Zealand, and the Southwest Pacific* (New York, London House and Maxwell, 1962), 340 pp.

Russell, Richard J., Fred B. Kniffen, and Evelyn Lord Pruitt, *Culture Worlds* (New York, The Macmillan Company, 1961), pp. 193–242.

Wilber, Donald, *Contemporary Iran* (New York, Frederick A. Praeger, Inc., 1963), 224 pp.

Zierer, Clifford M., ed., *California and the Southwest* (New York, John Wiley & Sons, Inc., 1956), 376 pp.

III

The Climatic Factor (cont'd)

The climate regions to be described next have several characteristics which set them apart from those studied so far. The land area covered by and the number of people experiencing Continental and Polar climates are predominantly in the Northern Hemisphere. Note how the continents flare and widen as they extend poleward in the Northern Hemisphere, and how they taper in the Southern Hemisphere. Except for Antarctica and Australia no huge land masses exist in the Southern Hemisphere, especially where these climates could exist.

Continental climates are cold (not cool) in winter, hot (not warm) in summer. The transition from these extremes means a seasonal rhythm of winter, spring, summer, and fall, accompanied by changeableness of the weather. The activities of people who need to recognize and adjust to these changes are described and explained in the ensuing pages.

15

Humid Continental Climate Regions

There are two continental types of climate in the Cyclonic Zone—the dry and the humid. This chapter is concerned with the latter, which occurs in the interiors of North America, Europe, and Asia, and in the eastern portions of North America, South America, and Asia (Fig. 15–1). From the standpoint of human geography, the Humid Continental with Long Summers is one of the most important climates on earth. Cyclonic storms by their pronounced variability from day to day alternately stimulate and relax their occupants.

Winter cold is so pronounced as to check entirely vegetative growth. The crops, therefore, are distinctly summer-grown annuals—those maturing before the advent of killing frost in autumn. Man must accordingly produce enough food in summer to stave off starvation in winter. Except in the *short-summer* type, nature handsomely rewards him for his labor.

The Humid Continental regions comprise so great a sweep of territory and extend over so large a range of latitude that many climatological variations occur within its realm. Three general types may accordingly be recognized in the Northern Hemisphere. First, the *equatorward portions* with *long summers*, which possess narrower seasonal temperature variations, receive more precipitation, and exhibit a greater evaporation rate than the other two. Second, the *intermediate lands* with *medium summers*. Like the short-summer type, its summers are warm to hot and its winters very long and cold. The precipitation is moderate but greater in amount than in the short-summer type and less than in the long-summer type. Toward the east coast, the precipitation increases

and the seasonal range of temperature is less marked. And third, the *poleward portions* with *short summers*, which possess a wide range of seasonal temperatures. Their summers are warm to hot and their winters very cold. In continental interiors, the rainfall is small in amount and the evaporation rate is low.

A. HUMID CONTINENTAL WITH LONG SUMMERS

The *long-summer* type is far and away the most important to man of the three Humid Continental climates. Economically, socially, and politically it is one of the most favored climates in the world.

LOCATION

The long-summer phase, located on the southern margins of the Cyclonic Zone, is the mildest and most equable of the three Humid Continental climates. In the United States it is found from central Kansas and Nebraska to the Atlantic Seaboard, including the states from New England to Maryland; in South America on the Pampa of Argentina; in south central Europe in the Danubian and Balkan states and in the Po Plain of Italy; and in eastern Asia in north China, and parts of Korea and Japan (Fig. 15–1).

CLIMATIC CHARACTERISTICS

This climate is characterized by four well-marked seasons during the year, by marked contrasts in temperature from season to season, by pronounced changes of weather from day to day and

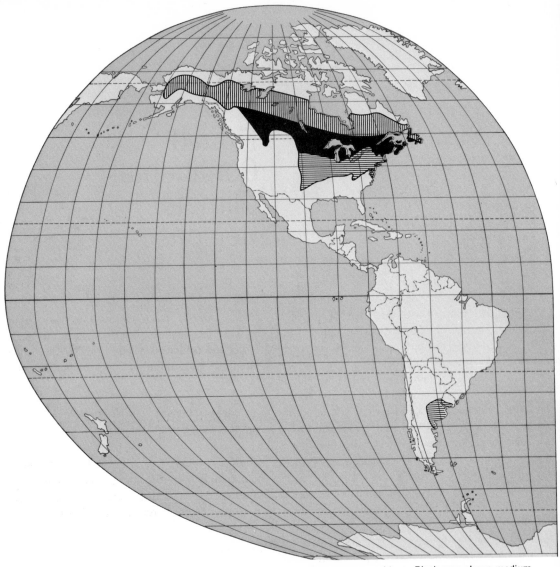

Figure 15–1 Humid Continental regions. Horizontal ruling shows long-summer subtype. Black area shows medium-summer subtype. Vertical ruling shows short-summer subtype.

from season to season, and by absence of a pronounced regular dry season in summer (Fig. 15–2). These characteristics arise from two conditions: (1) the rapidity with which land masses in these latitudes heat up during summer and cool off during winter, as compared with oceans, and (2) the continuous procession of cyclones and anticyclones which move from west to east around the earth between latitudes 40° and 60°. These moving pressure areas (Fig. 15–3) produce within a relatively short time marked changes in wind direction and velocity, temperature, and state of sky. In general, southerly and easterly winds bring warmth, cloud, and moisture, while northerly and westerly winds bring

clear skies and cool temperatures. Thus spells of stormy and of fair weather alternate every two or three days both in summer and winter. Winds produced by cyclones and anticyclones are variable in the extreme. Weather changes often are sudden and decided. A drop of 60° F. and a rise of 48° F. have been recorded at Chicago within twenty-four hours. "Highs" and "lows" tend to follow rather well-defined paths (Fig. 15–4).

Summers are hot; indeed, occasionally spells of summer weather rival and even surpass anything the Rainy Tropics experience. Moreover, the high humidity makes such days oppressive to the inhabitants. Nights as well as days are hot.

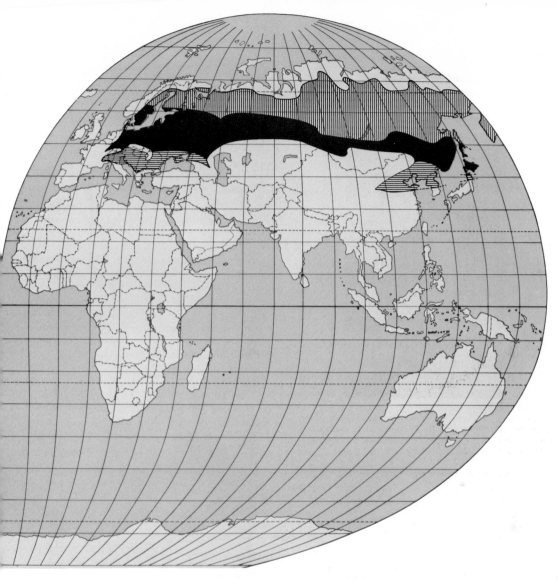

Winters may be quite cold or quite mild, depending upon the year and upon location. At times spells of cold weather may be as intense as temperatures experienced in higher latitudes. But there are usually numerous spells of mild weather interspersed between periods of cold. Regions with this climate experience marked temperature contrasts that result from invasions of polar and tropical air masses across their northern and southern boundaries.

The average frost-free season is five or six months long, the length depending upon latitude, altitude, and distance from the sea or other large bodies of water.

The annual rainfall is moderate, not heavy, in amount and decreases with increasing distance from the ocean. Thus, in eastern United States,

the amount varies from forty to fifty inches near the Atlantic Ocean to twenty inches near the 100th meridian, where the Humid Continental with Long Summers and the Dry Continental climates coalesce. While there is precipitation the year round (Fig. 15–2), the maximum precipitation comes mainly in summer and is predominantly of the thundershower type (Fig. 15–5).

Winter precipitation comes partly in the form of snow, though usually the proportion is less than half.

Although the total amount of precipitation is inadequate in some areas, for example, parts of north China and the Danubian Plain, the distribution tends to be favorable, the maximum nearly everywhere falling in the season when

242

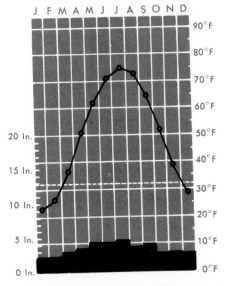

**Humid Continental with
Long Summers Climate
PEORIA, ILLINOIS, U.S.A.
Elevation 609' Latitude 40°43'**

Figure 15–2 Climate graph for Peoria, Illinois. Compare this with the graphs for Winnipeg and Dawson City with respect to the number of months of average temperature there is above freezing line.

crops need it most. Moreover, rain of the thundershower type permits a maximum of sunshine and heat along with the rain.

Winds are variable both in direction and in velocity.

NATURAL VEGETATION

The natural vegetation is not everywhere the same. It varies from tall grass (*prairie*)[1] in the less rainy portions to deciduous forest in the

---

[1] The *prairie* consists of a sea of waving grass. Though small, grass is fierce and determined to win in its struggle for life against the trees. The struggle for water has brought about the development of deeply penetrating and widely branching root systems, which so thoroughly thread the soil at several absorbing levels that trees cannot compete successfully against them. The character of *prairie* flora is a response to climate rather than to soil, topography, or geological formation. Despite the *prairie*'s success in its struggle against the trees, it is disappearing at an alarming rate, for it is no match for man who breaks it for crops and grazes his animals upon it. For a book of rare quality dealing with the American prairie, see J. E. Weaver, *North American Prairie* (Lincoln, Neb., Johnson Publishing Company, 1954).

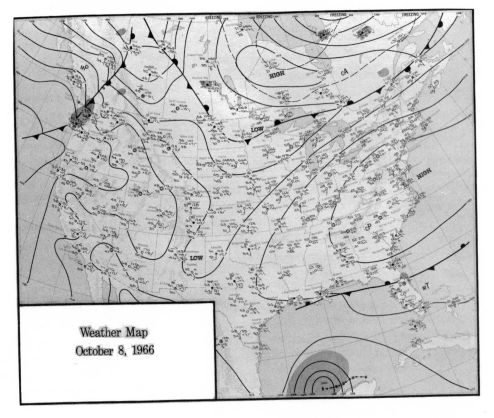

Weather Map
October 8, 1966

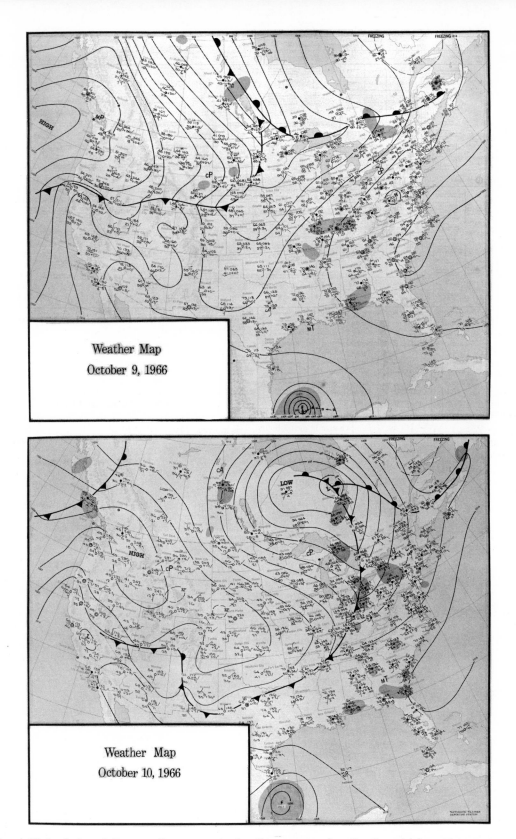

Figure 15–3   Series of three weather maps showing the passage of a "low," containing strong warm and cold fronts, across the continent in three days. Explanation of weather map on next page. (Maps courtesy of the Environmental Science Services Administration)

EXPLANATION OF WEATHER MAP

Heavy lines, called *fronts*, separate air masses of different characteristics. Words "HIGH" and "LOW" indicate centers of high and low barometric pressure. Labels (MTK, MPK, etc.) identify particular types of *air masses*. Fronts and air masses are described below.

Light continuous lines, called *isobars*, are drawn through points of equal sea-level pressure. Dashed lines, labeled "FREEZING," and dot-dash lines, labeled "ZERO," both called *isotherms*, are drawn through points where the current temperature is 32°F. or 0°F., respectively. These isotherms separate areas in which temperatures are above and below 32°F or 0°F.

STATION MODEL

Arrow showing direction of middle cloud.

Feathers showing force of wind in Beaufort Scale.

Arrow shaft showing direction of wind.

Figures showing temperature in degrees Fahrenheit.

Symbol showing amount of sky covered by clouds.

Figures showing visibility in miles and tenths.

Symbol showing present state of weather.

Figures showing dew point in degrees Fahrenheit.

Symbol showing type of low cloud.

Figures showing height of ceiling to hundreds of feet.

Symbol showing type of middle cloud.

Figures showing type of barometric pressure at sea level. Initial 9 or 10 for "hundreds" of millibars, and decimal point, omitted.

Figures showing net amount of barometric change in past 3 hours. *(In tenths of millibars.)*

Symbol showing barometric tendency in past 3 hours.

Plus or minus sign showing whether pressure is higher or lower than 3 hours ago.

Code figure showing time precipitation began or ended.

Past weather during 6 hours preceding observation.

Figures showing amount of precipitation in last 6 hours. *(In hundredths of an inch.)*

Code figure showing amount of lower clouds not including fragments.

The boundary between two different air masses is called a *front*. Important changes in weather often occur with the passage of a front. Half circle and/or triangular symbols are placed on the lines representing fronts to indicate the classification of the front. The side on which the symbols are placed indicates the direction of movement. The boundary of relatively cold air of polar origin advancing into an area occupied by warmer air, usually of tropical origin, is called a *cold front*. The boundary of relatively warm air advancing into an area occupied by colder air is called a *warm front*. The line along which a cold front has overtaken a warm front is called an *occluded front*. A boundary between two air masses, which shows little tendency at the time of observation to advance into either the warm or the cold areas, is called a *stationary front*. Air mass boundaries are known as *surface fronts* when they intersect the ground, and as *upper air fronts* when they do not. Surface fronts are drawn in solid black, fronts aloft are drawn in outline only.

Front symbols, with arrows to show their direction of movement, are given below.

Warm front (surface)
Cold front (surface)
Occluded front (surface)

Warm front (aloft)
Cold front (aloft)
Stationary front (surface)

A front which is disappearing or decreasing in intensity is labeled "FRONTOLYSIS."

A front which is forming or increasing in intensity is labeled "FRONTOGENESIS."

Masses of air are classified to indicate their origin and basic characteristics. For example, the letter P *(Polar)* denotes relatively cold air from northerly regions, and the letter T *(Tropical)* denotes relatively warm air from southerly regions. Letters placed *before* P and T indicate *maritime* (m) or *continental* (c). Maritime air is relatively moist, and continental air is relatively dry. Letters placed *after* P and T show that the air mass is *colder* (k) or *warmer* (w) than the surface over which it is moving. A plus sign (+) between two air-mass symbols indicates mixed air masses, and an arrow (→) between two symbols indicates a transitional air mass changing from one type to another. Two air-mass symbols, one above the other and separated by a line, indicate one air mass aloft and another at lower levels. Air mass symbols are formed from the following letters: m = Maritime; c = Continental; A = Arctic; P = Polar; T = Tropical; E = Equatorial; S = Superior (a warm, dry air mass having its origin aloft); k = colder and w = warmer than the surface over which the air mass is moving.

rainier sections. Trees, such as oak and maple, are deciduous because of a cold season rather than because of a dry season as in the Monsoon Tropical climate.

In the Pampa of Argentina, the only area in the Southern Hemisphere with this climate, grass holds sway. It did also when the Spaniards first arrived. It is possible, however, that the prairie was not always here but replaced an earlier scrub-forest cover as a result of firing by

Indians.[2] The same theory has been advanced for the *prairie* in the western part of the long-summer lands of the United States and Canada.

SOILS

The soils consist of (1) the *gray-brown podzolic soils*—in the more humid parts and those where

[2] O. Schmieder, "The Pampa—A Natural or Culturally Induced Grassland?" *University of California Publications in Geography,* Vol. 2, 1927, pp. 255–270.

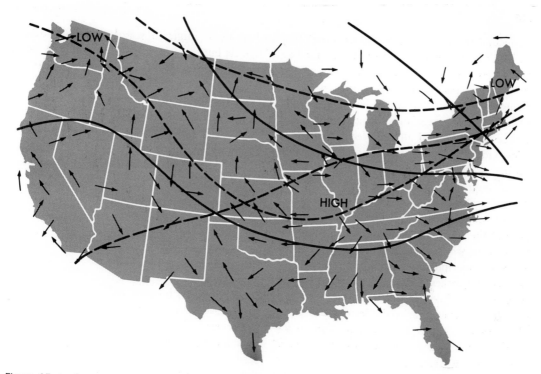

Figure 15–4 Average paths of the centers of "highs" and "lows" across the United States. Solid lines show the paths of "highs"; broken lines show the paths of "lows."

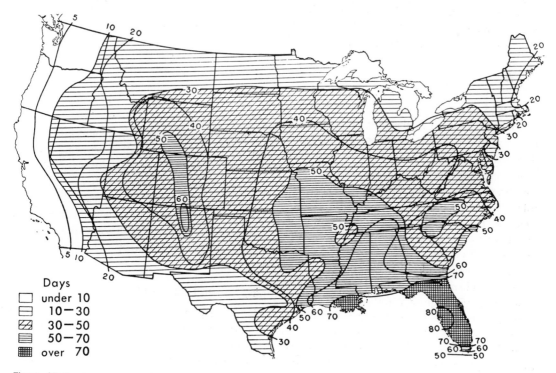

Days
☐ under 10
⊟ 10—30
▨ 30—50
⊟ 50—70
▦ over 70

Figure 15–5 Average annual number of days with thunderstorms in the United States. (Map from William E. Powers, *Physical Geography*, New York, Appleton-Century-Crofts, 1966)

the natural vegetation was deciduous forest; they are fertile and productive and are among the best of all soils developed under a forest cover; they are used for general farming, corn, and small grains; (2) *prairie soils* in the less rainy portion where the natural vegetation was tall grass; these are the most fertile of all *pedalfers*, are black in color, and contain much humus; corn is the principal crop grown upon them, small grains being of but minor importance; when the land is poorly drained, such soils are used for hay and pasture; and (3) *chernozems* occupying the moister portions of the subhumid margins of the long-summer climate, where the vegetation is tall grass and where the precipitation varies from eighteen to twenty-eight inches; because the climatic boundaries fluctuate from year to year, semiarid and even arid climates occasionally invade such areas. Hence these soils frequently contain lime in the lowest or "C" horizon. Chernozems are classed as *pedocals* (see Chapter 28). The surface soils are dark brown or black. Wheat and other small grains thrive in all parts of such areas but corn is grown successfully only in the moister parts. These are the best soils in the world. For all but grain farming, however, they are less desirable than *prairie soils* because of the *uncertainty* of the rainfall.

NATIVE ANIMAL LIFE

The native animal life was abundant and varied. Obviously it differed in the forested and prairie portions. In the forest (Northern Hemisphere) dwelt large herbivores such as the elk and deer, as well as carnivores such as the wolf and fox. The bear, which is omnivorous, was widely distributed. Here also were smaller animals—skunks, squirrels, rabbits, and others. Birds, particularly migratory species, abounded. Insects throve and were of great variety.

In the prairie, besides the smaller rabbits, badgers, gophers, and kindred burrowers, were enormous herds of bison (North America only). It is estimated that there were fifty million of these animals in 1850. Two healthy bison eat as much grass as three steers of similar weight and since green herbage has comparatively low feeding value, the animals had to feed on and off all day and had to have, therefore, a wide grazing range. It was long believed that bison in tremen-

dous herds migrated seasonally from Texas to Canada but this is now regarded as a myth.[3] Random wanderings, however, were common. By 1900 there were fewer than fifty bison left in the United States, so ruthlessly had they been hunted. Many also were destroyed by fire, water, and snow. It is estimated that there are now some 25,000 head in the United States. Carnivores, exemplified by the ubiquitous wolf, trailed and killed large numbers of the herbivores.

ECONOMIC ADJUSTMENTS
Hunting and fishing

These probably were the first adjustments to be made in all areas with this climate. Game usually abounded.

Obviously, hunting and fishing entailed the great disadvantage of uncertainty. Hence life was precarious, poverty extreme, and starvation not uncommon. Numbers were restricted and small scattered tribes the rule. The Iroquois, who combined primitive agriculture with the chase, required from one-half to two square miles for each person. Increasing numbers among all eastern Amerindian tribes had pressed so hard against the natural food supply as to necessitate its being supplemented by the cultivation of corn, beans, pumpkins, and other products of the soil.

Most long-summer lands now have so large a sedentary agricultural and industrial population that hunting is unimportant except as an adjunct of farming. Farm boys who consider trapping a "major epic of the countryside" obtain tens of thousands of small fur-bearing animals each winter and sell the pelts for a considerable sum. St. Louis, Missouri, persists as one of the world's greatest raw fur markets. Commercial fishing formerly was important in the Great Lakes and in certain North American and European rivers unpolluted by sewage and industrial waste.

Logging and lumbering

These enterprises were originally of considerable importance in the forested portions of most areas with this climate but for the most part have given way before the ax, peavy, and plow. Lands with

[3] Frank G. Roe, *The North American Buffalo* (Toronto, University of Toronto Press, 1951).

Figure 15–6   Hay being automatically picked up, tied, and baled in the American Middle West. For five thousand years forage for hay was cut with a sickle or scythe and harvesting remained a hand operation until the middle of the past century. It has progressed from the various hand- and horse-powered methods to several mechanical ones, including, as shown here, the tractor-powered mower and field baler. More than 75 percent of the crop is now put up in bales. Baled hay needs less space and is easier to handle than loose hay. (Photo courtesy of the John Deere Company)

such tremendous agricultural potentialities as these would not be expected to practice logging and lumbering very long; less favored lands can do that. Some farmers retain woodlots and do some cutting. In the southern part of this climatic region in the United States, where this climate merges into the Humid Subtropical climate, a considerable quantity of hard wood is cut on the rough lands where the practice of agriculture is handicapped.

AGRICULTURAL ADJUSTMENTS
Crop production

The Humid Continental with Long Summers is an agricultural climate par excellence. The crops grown are more a response to climate than to any other element of the natural environment. Any humid climate crop not requiring too long a growing season may be raised successfully; hence a wide variety is grown, including barley, clover, corn, fruits, millet, oats, potatoes, sorghum, soy beans, sugar beets (Fig. 15–6), timothy, vegetables, and wheat (Fig. 15–7). Mixed farming is predominant in North America. Where the frostless season is long and the winter not too severe, corn and winter wheat lead in importance, the former in the more humid part,

the latter in the less humid part. The Corn Belt has been called the "heart of American agriculture" (Fig. 15–8) and well does it merit that title, since with less than 1 percent of the

Figure 15–7   Combining wheat in the American Corn Belt. This machine cuts more than thirty-five acres of wheat per day, threshes the grain and delivers it to a tank from which it can be transferred to a truck. (Photo courtesy of the International Harvester Company)

Figure 15–8   Typical agricultural landscape in the American Corn Belt. Note the arrangement of the fields, farmsteads, and roads. (Photo courtesy of the *Daily Pentagraph*, Bloomington, Ill.)

earth's surface, it contributes one-third of the world's corn (Fig. 15–9). It produces more feed for livestock and more meat for human consumption than any other area of equal size in the world.

Figure 15–9   Harvesting corn in the American Corn Belt with a self-propelled grain combine equipped with a picker attachment—a four-row corn head. (Photo courtesy of the International Harvester Company)

To the west of the Corn Belt in the less humid margin of this climate, especially where the precipitation varies from twenty to thirty inches, lies the Hard Winter Wheat Belt, one of the world's outstanding granaries.

The Argentine Pampa raises much the same crops as the long-summer region of North America. Considered commercially, wheat predominates, being most concentrated in a great crescent extending from southern Buenos Aires Province to central Santa Fé Province. Corn flourishes in the more humid section seaward of the wheat crescent. Here flax and alfalfa also thrive.

In Europe, as in North America, much the same response to climate is noted in the arrangement of crops. Corn is important only in Romania and Hungary which, like the American Corn Belt, have long summers. In production, Romania, whose peasants eat corn, ranks next to the United States which feeds it to swine and cattle, and to Argentina which exports it. Hard winter wheat is grown in the Danube Basin for export.

In north China where conditions resemble those of the western edge of the American Corn belt, droughts are frequent and severe and the precipitation quite light—twenty-one inches on the average. Rice, the Oriental staff of life, is grown in only limited amounts, a consequence of sandy soil, dearth of water for irrigation, and custom. Even corn does not thrive. Rice and corn are replaced, therefore, by wheat, both winter and spring, *kaoliang*, a type of sorghum, soy beans, and millet. Millet is important because it is a sure crop in this region of unreliable rainfall. It would not be grown if the summer monsoon were less fickle and if adequate rainfall were assured. *Kaoliang*, which can stand more punishment from both drought and flood than corn, has become the chief large grain crop. In north China, barley, broad beans, peas, and winter wheat are planted in the fall; *kaoliang*, millet, and cotton in the spring; and beans, corn, millet, peanuts, soy beans, and sweet potatoes in the summer. North China ranks among the world leaders in soy bean production. In northeastern China this crop accounts for about one-third of the total productive area and is a principal source of food of the people.

Livestock production

In a climate so productive of grain and hay and so favored with native grass pastures, the livestock industry naturally assumes large proportions. Hogs, cattle, horses, sheep, and poultry are raised in unbelievably large numbers. In the Corn Belt of the United States, more than four-fifths of the corn and practically all the oats are grown for animal consumption; in other words, the Corn Belt produces feed for animals rather than food for man. The income of three-fourths of the Corn Belt farmers is derived from livestock and livestock products. Into this region from much of the West flow annually thousands of stocker and feeder cattle to be fattened (Fig. 15–10). Sheep have persisted numerically in the hilly or the infertile sections such as western Pennsylvania, eastern Ohio, the Panhandle of West Virginia, and central Michigan. Dairy cattle thrive everywhere, a response to favorable physical and economic conditions.

The Pampa of Argentina is the world's outstanding beef cattle region. Here level terrain, fertile soils, favorable climate, and a good supply of ground water favor the growth of alfalfa—a crop as good as corn for fattening cattle. Sparse population and extensive land holdings encourage stock raising and discourage agriculture. Sheep also are numerous but less so than formerly. With

Figure 15–10 Fattening beef cattle in a typical western Corn Belt feed lot. Such cattle are often procured by Corn Belt farmers from the western range as tall, lanky two-year-old "feeders" and are fed during winter and spring and sold usually before June 1. About seven pounds of corn plus other plant products are required to make one pound of edible beef. The animals shown here are ready for market. Contrary to the common notion that the range states provide the breeding ground and the Corn Belt the feeding ground for beef cattle, the fact is that about two-thirds of the animals normally slaughtered in the Corn Belt are bred within it. (Photo by G. W. Ackerman, courtesy of the USDA Extension Service)

the development of the Pampa, sheep are being pushed into the least desirable parts of the country, where inadequate precipitation and rough terrain discourage cultivation. The numbers of both cattle and sheep will continue to diminish with the encroachment of agriculture onto the Pampa.

In Europe, Germany stands out preeminently as a producer of swine and dairy cattle, the latter being largely stall fed. The Danubian countries and the Po Valley, too, are important, but the numbers decrease sharply in southern Russia. Horses show wide distribution, coinciding remarkably well with the distribution of population.

North China has relatively few livestock. It has more horses and mules than central or south China but fewer cattle and no water buffaloes, since it is not a rice country. It shares with the rest of China the general distribution of swine and poultry.

MANUFACTURING

Most countries with this climate are characterized by high industrial development. In fact the only major industrial regions in the world *outside this climatic* realm are Temperate Marine Northwest Europe, Humid Subtropical Japan and the American South, and Mediterranean Subtropical California. Manufacturing, of course, depends upon a large number of factors of which climate is but one. Health, determination, energy, and inventiveness all are inseparably bound up with climate, especially with the temperature factor. A region may have a virile race, sources of mechanical power, good transport facilities, raw materials and markets, but lacking a stimulating climate, it will not throb with industry. On the other hand, one possessing these advantages *and* a stimulating climate is invariably well developed industrially.

All nations with this climate are, of course, not equally industrialized. The Argentine Pampa, poor in minerals and power, appears to be destined to continue as a great agricultural and pastoral region with its cities engaging in manufacturing, to be sure, but *mainly in light industry*. Argentina lacks the basis of heavy industry which has long functioned as the foundation stone for industrialization. North China, with considerable mineral wealth, including exceptionally large and rich deposits of coal, has been retarded by slender capital resources, an antequated social system, and inadequate transportation facilities. China with her five-year plans is trying to change "from an agricultural state into an industrial country." She cannot, however, hope to duplicate quickly the material level of western Europe and North America. In all probability China will continue to be a developing country for some time. The United States, Austria, northern Italy, and the southern part of the Soviet Union typify what can be accomplished when conditions, physical and human, are favorable. Here mass production prevails, the cost of manufacture being minimized by the extensive utilization of machinery.

COMMERCIAL ADJUSTMENTS

Since many regions with the long-summer climate are very progressive, productive, and wealthy, they naturally carry on an appreciable portion of the world's commerce. Situated in the comparatively recently discovered and colonized Western Hemisphere, Argentina and the United States are sparsely populated in comparison with many countries in the Eastern Hemisphere. Hence, with relatively cheap land, rich resources, and modern labor-saving machines, they have long poured a steady stream of foods and industrial raw materials into densely populated Europe in exchange for manufactures and reexports. The primary basis of this trade is difference in stage of economic development. The world's busiest trade route extends across the North Atlantic connecting northeastern United States and southeastern Canada with northwestern Europe.

Unequaled transportation facilities stimulate commerce. Some of the world's principal railway webs have been spun in areas with this climate. The United States has the largest railway mileage in the world, and the most intense development occurs in the part possessing this climate; the Argentine Pampa is without a peer among Latin American nations in rail development and to this the country owes its amazing commercial progress. Humid Continental Europe vies with the United States in rail transportation; central Europe has practically no areas more than ten miles from a railway. Moreover, this region makes greater use of its inland waterways than do most parts of the world.

LONG-SUMMER CLIMATE AND HUMAN ENERGY

Human beings do not do their best and most creative work if they are too hot or too cold. There are some who say that such work is impossible even with stimulating temperatures unless there be violent changes in the weather, but "the sages and artificers of Egypt or India might not concur in this." Nonetheless, sudden changes induce marked alterations in metabolism and functional efficiency of various organs. All inhabitants of long-summer climate are aware of the fact that there is a marked seasonal tide in health and energy. During parts of July and August in eastern United States, when the mercury vacillates for days between 90° and 100° F., factory efficiency, both mental and physical, falls. Discipline becomes demoralized and production falls off sharply. Air-conditioning is doing much to solve this problem. Where whole buildings cannot be air-conditioned or in "hot" industries such as iron and steel-making where men work in temperatures as high as 150° F., it is impractical to air-condition the entire work area. Under these circumstances, however, it is found that by giving the workers short rest periods in air-conditioned recovery rooms, they are more comfortable, their health is better, their morale is improved, and they are more efficient.

SOCIAL ADJUSTMENTS

Intense activity characterizes all Humid Continental regions having long summers. Their inhabitants, along with those from Temperate Marine lands, are the world's principal *doers*. They grow a large part of the world's crops, cut a large part of its timber, catch much of its fish, mine the bulk of its minerals, fabricate a preponderant proportion of its manufactures, and carry on much of its trade. Marion Newbigin asserted that geography's outstanding problem is to find out why man thrives more in some parts of the earth than in others. No doubt climate goes far to explain why man has succeeded so well in lands having the Humid Continental with Long Summer conditions. Certainly people could not accomplish so much in the debilitating heat of the Rainy Tropics or in the numbing cold of the Polar lands, both of which retard man's highest development.

The Cyclonic Zone, of which this climate forms an important part, is the center of the world's present civilization. While civilization developed here belatedly, it rose to supremacy as soon as man learned to clear away the forest, make better clothing, build better houses, supply artificial heat in winter,[4] and utilize coal and iron. The weather "highs" and "lows" which move constantly across such regions stimulate man, goading him toward greater achievements. Significant also is the *seasonal rhythm*. This rhythm in temperature causes a rhythm in productivity; seasons of plenty alternate with seasons of dearth; this causes man to give thought to the future and to hoard—activities which Rainy Tropical man never has had to face. These preparations became the cornerstone of civilization.

A climate so favorable to agriculture and other occupations naturally fosters a dense population. North China and parts of Europe surpass the other regions in number of inhabitants per square mile—a consequence primarily of historical age, the social structure, and a philosophy acquired over the centuries for accepting a low level of living.

Comparing north China and the American Corn Belt we note that, before the Communist takeover, farms in north China were small, probably averaging less than four acres, that the farmers used no chemical fertilizers, were ignorant of modern methods of seed selection, employed medieval methods, and utilized very little machinery. Now, the state owns the farms and they are larger, but all of the other former attributes still hold true. Human labor is plentiful and cheap and hence intensive farming prevails. The American Corn Belt, too, is fully occupied, but the farms are large; they formerly averaged about 160 acres but today the figure surpasses 300 acres and they are continuing to grow. American farmers employ machinery propelled by power (petroleum): they have more than 4.5 million tractors with a combined force of 800 million horses. An average tractor and driver can do the plowing of ten horses, five hand plows, and ten men. Moreover, American farmers use generous amounts of chemical fertilizers, pesticides, and selected seed. Altogether American farmers have more than 14 million pieces of motorized equipment. Obviously not all this machinery is used in the Corn Belt, but no other American region employs so much. Many a Corn Belt farm is in reality a farm factory. Each American farmer feeds himself and forty-one others. In north China most of the people are on the verge of starvation and the region is known the world over as a land of famine.

The Argentine Pampa is a land of gigantic *estancias* and few people—the result of a system of landholding known as *latifundia*. Following expulsion of the Indians from the region, the land was distributed among influential persons, particularly the military, in vast tracts aggregating

---

[4] Civilization in lands having cold winters was not possible until human beings developed a system of heating. Then and only then could people think of "other things than merely how to keep their fingers from freezing."

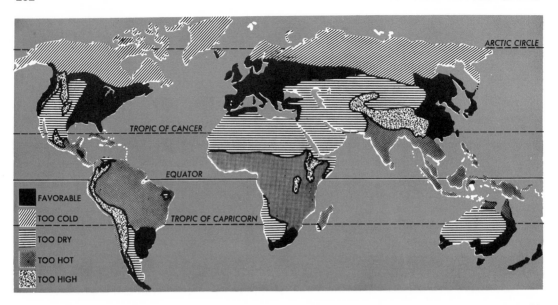

Figure 15–11 Areas that invite and repel man. The greater part of the earth's land surface, somewhere between 50 and 75 percent, is not well situated for human habitation—being too cold, snowy, and icy; too high and rugged; too dry; too hot and moist. This does not mean, of course, that there are no human beings occupying such lands but rather that their numbers in most instances average less than one person to the square mile. Scientists do not as yet know how to make these restrictive environments permanently productive. Everywhere the cost of reclamation is economically excessive. Authorities on land use and population assert that there are only 1 to 1.6 acres of cropland per person in the world and that this is being reduced by the 70,000 additional mouths that must be fed every day.

thousands of acres. This occurred before the period of heavy immigration. In few countries of the world do so few families own so large a proportion of the land as here. Fifty families in the Province of Buenos Aires have holdings of more than 75,000 acres each. Under this system of landholding rural population growth has been slow. Immigrants have experienced extreme difficulty in becoming landowners. The living conditions of the tenants have been far from attractive. Hence large numbers have drifted into the cities or returned to their homelands. The large estates are at last beginning to break up, the result of the inheritance law (which provides that all children must share equally), uneconomic management, and pressure of the national government.

POLITICAL ADJUSTMENTS

A country's political prestige and its prosperity depend upon the richness of its natural endowment and upon the characteristics of its people. While both are important, natural resources are truly indispensable, for the most intelligent hu-

man effort would be of little avail on Antarctica's ice cap.

The political and climatic maps of the world disclose the fact that all the great first-class nations are concentrated in the Cyclonic Zone or the poleward portion of the intermediate latitudes, largely, though not exclusively, in those parts possessing Humid Continental with Medium Summers and Long Summers climates. (To a certain extent Italy and Japan are exceptions to this generalization; though both are partly Humid Continental, they are also Mediterranean Subtropical [Italy] and Humid Subtropical [Japan].) Such distribution discloses the astonishing fact that fully three-fourths of the earth is climatically unfit for man to reach his maximum development, being too hot or too cold, too moist or too dry (Fig. 15–11).

The present strong countries in Humid Continental Europe evolved politically at a snail's pace; the combat between man and the encompassing forest vacillated for generations. Ultimately man conquered, combining the occupied clearings, thereby giving rise to states and countries. Political unification in the New World was achieved more rapidly than in Europe; at the outbreak of the Revolutionary War, thirteen virtually independent commonwealths comprised what is now Atlantic Seaboard United States.

Countries in the Intermediate Zone are the world's richest and most powerful and influential politically. Possibly not a part of the world has failed to be influenced by them. They comprise the developed countries in contrast to the underdeveloped ones which for the most part lie in the tropics and subtropics. Today some signs indicate that the map of developed and undeveloped lands might change appreciably in the foreseeable future, especially on the edges of the Subtropics.

B. HUMID CONTINENTAL WITH MEDIUM SUMMERS

LOCATION

This climate is located between the other two Humid Continental types (Fig. 15–1). In North America it extends eastward (in Canada) from the base of the Rockies in Alberta and (in the United States) from the dry plains of Central North Dakota. In Eurasia it stretches from central Germany and southern Sweden and Finland to the Amur River Basin north of Manchuria and Japanese Hokkaido. The medium-summer subtype of climate is not represented in the Southern Hemisphere.

CHARACTERISTICS

This climate resembles the Humid Continental with Long Summers but there are enough differences to justify separating the two (Figs. 15–2 and 15–12). Especially are the human activities unlike.

Temperatures are lower, particularly in winter, averaging 10° to 30° F. lower. The average monthly temperature dips below freezing (32° F.) more than three months during the year. Winter, as in the short-summer climate, is the dominant season but winters differ from year to year. All, however, are cold! Stefansson, the explorer, asserted he never experienced anything in the Arctic so bad as the prairie blizzards of

North Dakota and Manitoba which he encountered as a boy. The severe winter cold makes well-built houses, artificial heating, warm clothing, and heat-giving food mandatory for human comfort. Sensible temperature in winter is not so low as might be expected because the air is relatively dry.

Summers may be nearly as hot as in the long-summer type but hot spells do not last so long.

The great seasonal extremes derive from distance from the ocean and the marked difference in the length of day in summer and winter. In midsummer there may be fifteen to eighteen hours of sunlight while in midwinter there are only six to nine hours. Length of daylight is extremely important because it makes up for the shortness of the growing season in the case of some crops. The growing season is intermediate (about four months long), being longer than in the short-summer climate but shorter than in the long-summer type. Frost must be expected in late spring and early autumn.

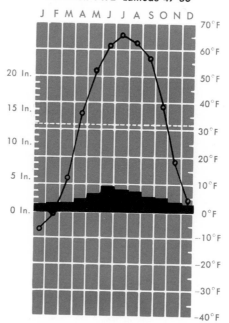

Figure 15–12   Climate graph for Winnipeg, Manitoba, Canada.

Total amount of precipitation is less than in the long-summer but more than in the short-summer climate. Thunderstorms are fewer in number and blizzards more common than in the climate to the south. Interior areas commonly receive less rainfall than those closer to the oceans. The maximum precipitation in the interior areas comes in summer, winter being relatively dry; in regions closer to the oceans approximately as much falls in winter as in summer.

A much larger proportion of the winter precipitation falls as snow than is the case in the long-summer climate. The total snowfall is lightest along the drier interior margins. It is especially heavy in North America north of Lake Superior and in New York State and New England (Fig. 15–13). In Europe, the margins of the Baltic receive heavy snowfall. Almost everywhere, however, the snow does not melt until the end of winter and the total accumulation therefore is great.

Every winter experiences at least several blizzards. At such times many farmers stretch from home to barn ropes to which they may cling to keep from getting lost. Occasionally farmers set out for their barn in a blizzard, lose their way,

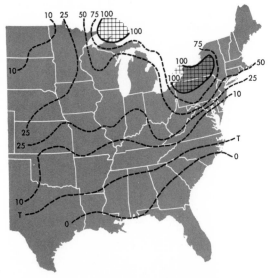

Figure 15–13 Example of annual snowfall in the eastern half of the United States. Note particularly the excessive fall in parts of New York, Pennsylvania, New England, and the northern Great Lakes area. Cross-hatching covers areas receiving more than 100 inches of snowfall. (Map adapted from the Environmental Science Services Administration)

wander into the open prairie and die of fatigue and cold.

AIR MASSES AND FRONTS

Just as the circulation of the air in our homes obeys physical laws, so does the circulation of air over the earth. Some of the most important research in weather forecasting resulted from the fact that during World War I, Norwegians were cut off from outside reports and accordingly had to work more intensively in their limited territory. Studying wind flow and local cloud forms, they deduced what takes place in the upper atmosphere. As a result of their work, present-day weather science is based upon the idea that changes in weather are caused by the ceaseless conflict of great sweeping air streams or masses of warm and cold air along a polar front (Fig. 15–14). They concluded that air moves from place to place over the earth's surface in mass formation. These masses come from two principal regions—polar and tropical—and assume the character of the region of their origin. More recent research gives strong indication that the movement of these air masses is in some degree controlled by the Jet Stream, an upper-air movement following an ever-changing east-west course in the middle latitudes.

There is a more or less continuous conflict between the warm moist currents, usually from the south and southeast, and the cold dry currents from the north (Northern Hemisphere)—a conflict that so resembled the tide of battle along the western European battle front during World War I that the Norwegian school applied the name "front" to the boundary between the different air currents or *air masses*. This led to the polar-front theory and the air-mass method of weather analysis. Thus storms are born in areas where air masses of different types meet—usually along the polar front. Currents of cold northern air and warm southern air of different qualities are like oil and water—they do not mix readily. Accordingly, they seek to underrun or overrun the other according to which is the aggressor, that is, which is exerting the greater dynamic force.

The cold front is the feature of the weather map to watch, for its arrival in an area marks

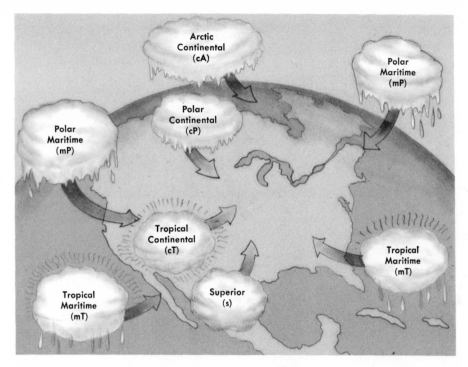

Figure 15–14 Principal sources of the air masses which make weather in the United States. (After *Current Science and Aviation*)

a major event in the weather cycle. It usually brings stormy conditions and forewarns a complete change in the atmosphere—that a new air mass is taking control and a new series of weather events is getting under way. The cold front thus is actually the edge of a cold air mass on the move. No two cold fronts are identical, however, either in structure or in behavior. Some are active, others passive; some move rapidly, others slowly. Seldom are more than three days required for a front to advance from North Dakota to the South Atlantic or Gulf coasts.

A warm front is the leading edge of a forward-moving mass of warm air that is displacing a colder air mass. Since the warm air is lighter than the cold air, the advancing air glides up over the wedge of cool air clinging to the surface (Fig. 15–15). Thus the warm front is the chief rain producer.

CYCLONES AND ANTICYCLONES

Along the plane of contact between these air masses great eddies develop. Where these center about a low-pressure area, often under the domi-

nation of tropical air, they are known as *cyclonic storms*. Where their center is a high-pressure area, commonly related to polar air, it is an *anticyclone*. These storms parade across the United States and across Eurasia from west to east as shown on the daily weather map. They cause the changeable weather of all regions over which they pass within 40° to 60° latitude. Weather is migratory, moving in general with the prevailing westerlies—the wind currents which define the broad course from west to east. Except for their general eastward movement, cyclones obliterate much evidence of the westerlies, particularly on land.

In general, southerly and easterly winds bring warmth, cloud and moisture, whereas northerly and westerly winds bring clear skies and cool temperatures. Thus, spells of stormy and of fair weather alternate every two or three days both in summer and in winter. Winds produced by cyclones and anticyclones are variable in the extreme. Weather changes often are sudden and decided.

In this climate in eastern Asia, the monsoons

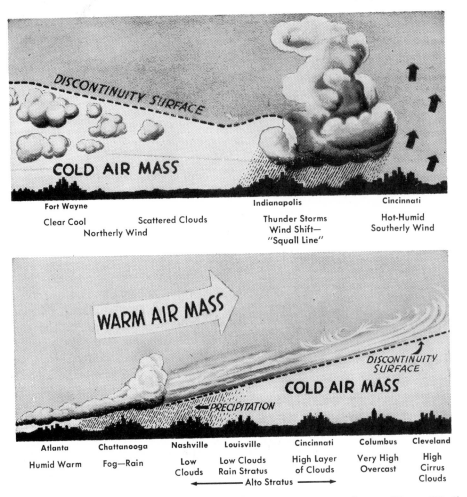

Figure 15-15 Cross sections through cold and warm air masses, showing weather conditions within them and along their advancing fronts. (Courtesy *Current Science and Aviation*)

exert far more influence on the weather than cyclones and anticyclones. Eastern Siberia's high-pressure area results in strong outblowing winds in winter and its low-pressure area gives rise to inblowing winds in summer.

PLANT GEOGRAPHY

The vegetation in this climate is not everywhere the same; in one area it may be prairie, in another coniferous forest, and in still another a mixture of coniferous and deciduous forest.

In the United States and Canada, (1) prairie characterized the less humid sections of the interior; (2) a coniferous forest (a) of spruce and fir covered northern New England, the Adirondacks, and insular concentrations in Min-

nesota, Michigan, and Wisconsin, and (b) of jack, red, and white pines southward from the spruce and fir in the Lake states; (3) a birch, beech, and maple forest grew over much of the same general area as (b) in the Lake states and south of the spruce-fir forest in New England and New York State; and (4) an oak-hickory forest grew over the southern portions of Minnesota, Michigan, and Wisconsin.

SOILS

Three types of soils characterize this climate—the *gray-brown podzolic* soils in the southern warmer, rainier part; *podzols* in the northern part; and the *chernozem*-like soils in the western part (the United States). *Podzols*, soils inseparably associated with this climate, are acid in reaction and are poor in minerals and decayed organic matter. Often they are stony because of glaciation. The gray-brown podzolic soils are among the most fertile and productive of the pedalfers (see Chapter 28), while the *chernozem*-like soils, which are dark brown to black in color, rich in humus with an accumulation of carbonates in the lower part of the solum, are among the most fertile of all soils.

ANIMAL GEOGRAPHY

Since the native animal life resembled to a considerable extent that in the long-summer climate, this topic is not discussed further in this chapter.

HUMAN USE OF MEDIUM-SUMMER LANDS

Hunting

Adjustments to native animal life were the first to be made. Fish and game usually abounded and so long as this was the case, man was a hunter and fisher, feeling slightly, if at all, the urge to progress further. Primitive man, thus dependent upon what nature provided, developed a keen sense of observation and great skill. The American Indian was most likely in this stage when the white man arrived, his existence depending largely upon the kill.

Because large segments possessing this type of climate are characterized by (1) thousands of streams and lakes, (2) large forested areas, (3) much mountain, hill country, and plateau, (4) infertile soils, and (5) long cold winters, considerable hunting and trapping continue to be carried on both in North America and in Eurasia. They make good winter activities and the market for prime peltries is usually good.

Fishing

The waters off the coast of eastern North America are rich in fish. From Newfoundland to Cape Cod lie the Grand Banks—one of the richest fishing regions in the world. Moreover, fishing is facilitated by the coast's being dotted with sheltered harbors, bays, and coves from which fishermen can operate with comparative safety. Both coastal and deep-sea fishing are followed

and tremendous hauls are taken to Boston, Gloucester, Portland, Lunenburg, and Lockeport.

The coastal waters of Asia also support important fisheries; formerly the Japanese, as a result of treaties with the Russians, dominated—their vessels going almost everywhere in the region. This, of course, is no longer true.

Logging and lumbering

Almost from the beginning, man fought the forest. In North America, the Pilgrims had scarcely landed before they began waging unceasing warfare against the stately white pine, a warfare which was carried on by their offspring for three centuries. In the beginning, the use of these forests for lumber was only incidental; the trees were destroyed to make way for agriculture. Logging and lumbering are important in large areas having this climate in Eurasia and North America. Lumbering has long been the very backbone of Sweden's economic life. Productive forest covers 52 percent of Sweden's area and the country supplies more than one-fourth of Europe's total lumber requirements. Probably no country realizes so well the value of its forests and certainly no other has a more enlightened forest policy. Lumbering operations are carried on also in southern Canada, New England, the Lake States, Germany, Poland, the Soviet Union, Manchuria, and Hokkaido. In both Sweden and Canada saw timber is giving way increasingly to pulp. Canada leads all nations in production of newsprint, her output amounting to 60 percent of the world total.

Logging is closely adjusted to climate. Most of the work is done in winter except felling and bucking which are carried on in autumn prior to the heavy falls of snow. A long, cold winter with heavy snow is almost ideal, for the logs are hauled on sleds over swampy or boulder-strewn terrain which in summer would be positively closed to wheeled vehicles. Horses or tractors pull the heavily laden sleds to rivers where the logs are dumped to await the spring freshets which carry them downstream (Fig. 15–16). Fortunately the forested regions are well supplied with streams, and river driving is the most economical method of transporting bulky, clumsy logs. River drivers guide the logs to prevent them from be-

Figure 15–16 A log drive in Quebec, Canada. Millions of logs are stream-driven in regions having this climate in North America and in Eurasia. (Photo courtesy of the National Film Board of Canada)

coming "jammed" or stranded. Hardwoods cannot be so easily handled; hence logging roads are usually built into hardwood forests and lumbering goes on throughout the year. In Russia stream-driving cannot be prosecuted so easily because so many of the rivers flow northward into the Arctic; this means that the ice breaks up in the upper courses long before it does downstream and floods scatter the logs far and wide, which is not conducive to economical operations.

If the logging operations are relatively near agricultural communities, as in Finland, Sweden, and Quebec, many farmers become lumberjacks during winter.

Conservation

In some areas, forests were cleared for agricultural development with amazing rapidity. In many places—almost everywhere—this clearing was done recklessly and unintelligently. It was, however, unavoidable and inevitable. Such countries as Germany and Sweden eventually recognized the folly of this policy and began practicing scientific forestry, including reforestation. The land is continuously bearing timber, since only the large trees are cut. Pests are fought, fire avoided, and waste eliminated. After an orgy of forest raping, America is at last realizing the value of conservation. For decades the United States cut far more timber annually than it grew. The virgin forests were being despoiled by profit-blinded lumber interests and by laws that discouraged rather than encouraged replanting. Many informed persons feared that the nation would be threatened by a timber famine as they watched the logging and lumbering migrate from north to south and then to the Pacific Coast. But in 1955 the federal government announced that the replacement of mature timber was now in balance with its use for the first time in more than sixty years. This has resulted from mass attacks on insects, mechanized fire fighting, new disease-resistant hybrids that produce and guard spreading stands of sturdier timber, tree farming, new methods of handling the forest such as block cutting (Fig. 17–10), and above all an improved philosophy of forest management. *Selective* rather than *clean* cutting now is the rule. The main hope of the future lies with government, both federal and state, and particularly with the Forest Service, which has the best public land policy in the United States. The cooperation of the private companies, however, is imperative. They now realize that treating timber as a crop rather than as a mineral is profitable. Hence they now hold and replant cut-over lands which old-time lumbermen would have let go for taxes.

AGRICULTURE

In the medium-summer climate of North America (unlike the situation in the neighboring long-summer type which adjoints it on the south) corn, except for silage, has not been a major crop. In the past two decades, however, significant increases in corn acreage have occurred on the northern fringes of the Corn Belt. Thus, as a result of development of short-season hybrids, corn for grain has moved as many as one hundred miles northward into medium-summer Michigan, Wisconsin, and Minnesota. By and large the pattern of agriculture became almost identical with that of the climatically similar Baltic countries of Europe. Dairy products, potatoes and other root crops, and certain small grains comprise the list of major crops which are best suited to the short cool summers (Fig. 15–17).

Such lands comprise, however, the world's chief centers of spring wheat and rye production and are important also for barley and oats—cereals that can mature in a short season. Rye ranks with rice and wheat for first place among man's most widely used small grains. Its greatest concentration lies north of the wheat lands in Germany, Poland, and the U.S.S.R. Rye withstands successfully the severe winter temperatures and cloudy skies so characteristic of this part of Europe. The prominence of the crop here, however, is not a response to climate alone, but partly to sandy and acidic soils. The world's most productive potato and rye regions coincide remarkably well. Potatoes thrive under cloudy skies, in the cool temperatures of northern Europe. Flax too is a major crop, being grown for seed in North America and for fiber in Europe. Root crops thrive; accordingly, the medium-summer climate is one of the world's best for growing potatoes and sugar beets. The latter are confined mostly to Europe.

The Soviet Union is one of the world's leading agricultural countries and the greater part of the farm land has the medium-summer climate. But the casual observer is apt to overestimate Russia's agricultural potential, little realizing that more than three-fourths of the Soviet Union is of limited agricultural value, being condemned by cold or dryness often in combination with infertile soil or immature drainage. Less than half the remaining land climatically suited to cultivation is arable and only 10 percent of this enormous country is well suited for agriculture. Accordingly, Russian farmers have to fight severe physical limitations and expend more effort and energy to produce crops than in most of Europe and the United States. This results from the pronounced continentality of the climate and the lack of significant geographical barriers in the north for mitigating the influence of the Arctic.

The best farm lands comprise the small triangular wedge connecting Leningrad, Odessa, and the Ural Mountains. In this "Fertile Triangle" are centered most of the Soviet Union's political, social, and economic activities, all of which are subject to physical hazards not encountered elsewhere in the industrialized world.

Even the greater part of the "Fertile Triangle" occupies a latitude north of that of Duluth, Minnesota, and is to be compared with the North American Spring Wheat Region, where agricultural yields per acre are irregular and relatively low and where the variety of crops capable of being grown is definitely restricted. Russia has no substantial agricultural areas comparable with the American Corn Belt (long-summer climate) and Cotton Belt (Humid Subtropical climate). Thus, despite successive

Figure 15–17 Two methods of farming in medium-summer regions. Top, dairy herd on improved arable pasture land in Massachusetts. Bottom, potatoes being harvested in Minnesota. (Photos courtesy of USDA and the Soil Conservation Service, USDA)

five-year plans, the Soviet Union continues to face the ever-present problem of inadequate farm production. Early in 1955 the situation became so critical that the leaders responsible for agricultural output made plans to increase grain production, particularly corn. But as we have seen in this chapter, the "Fertile Triangle" with

medium-summer climate is poorly suited to corn, that is, corn for grain. Russian agriculture in this medium-summer climate is restricted largely to collective farms which were formed by the forced collectivization of many formerly independent small peasant farmers. Communist officials contend that small farming is just as uneconomic as small-scale steel production. By 1950 collective farms accounted for 60 percent of the total sown area. It is the first obligation of the collective farm to deliver to the state a certain amount of its crops—often as much as a third. Most collectives were serviced by machine tractor stations (MTS) prior to 1958. They have been replaced by Repair and Technical Stations (RTS) which have much less influence and control over agricultural development than the former MTS. Even the RTS is slowly declining with most of the responsibility for machinery and technical advice being assumed by the collective farms.

What of the level of living of the peasants? They are no better off, if as well off, as before collectivization in 1928. The original five-year plans and more recently the seven-year plans have strongly emphasized industrialization over agriculture. This has meant rapid urbanization resulting in increased strain on agricultural production. The peasant, who has always resented and resisted collectivization, has been required to supply an ever-increasing urban population while the incentives for increasing farm production have been few.

In the Manchurian section of north China, agriculture is confined chiefly to spring planted crops—soy beans, *kaoliang*, millet, and wheat for the most part. Manchuria is the land of the soy bean. The crop is used for (1) a type of milk, cheese, curd, meat, oil, and sauce for man, (2) feed for animals, (3) oil, (4) medicine, ink, lacquer, and (5) fertilizer.

This type of climate ranks high among those of the world in dairying. The main dairy region of the United States coincides with that part falling within the Humid Continental with Medium Summers climate. Here the terrain is undulating to rolling (some is even rough) and is well suited to dairying. Large areas, too wet for tillage, are put in pasture or made to yield marsh hay. While the gray-brown podzolic soils are quite well suited to crops, the podzols are not. Thus farmers are tempted to raise cattle rather than specialize on crops. Their income is mainly from the sale of milk. Numerous large industrial and commercial cities are close by and afford ready markets for fresh milk at high prices. Butter and cheese are made throughout the realm. Canada's medium-summer realm—the part comprising lowland—is excellent for dairy farming. Most Canadian milk goes into manufacturing.

Dairying is outstanding in southern Sweden, southern Finland, Germany, and Switzerland. Several of the world's most famous cheeses are produced here. Dairying also is moderately important in the European part of the U.S.S.R. and in western Siberia.

MANUFACTURING

In North America the medium-summer climatic region, while much less important industrially than the long-summer one, is nonetheless growing sensationally in manufacturing. Many people are surprised to learn that Canada has become one of the world's leading industrial nations—pulp and paper, aluminum, electrochemicals, iron and steel, smelted copper and nickel, textiles, and many others. The majority of these mills and factories are located near the international border in the medium-summer climate. New England still ranks as one of the world's most renowned industrial areas and the Niagara Frontier, Mohawk Valley, Lake Erie Plain, southern Michigan, all fall within the American Manufacturing Region.

Medium-summer Eurasia ranks high industrially. Sweden, Germany, and Poland along with the Soviet Union produce a very considerable share of the world's fabricated goods. The U.S.S.R., which today ranks second only to the United States industrially, has the greater part of her manufacturing capacity in this type of climate—extending far into Siberia. The whole gamut of manufactures is contributed, including iron and steel, machine tools, automobiles, aircraft, chemicals, rubber, machinery of all kinds, textiles.

A major concern of Soviet leaders has been the geographical distribution of industry as a whole. Sensing the future importance of the airplane and the vulnerability of the country's location between Germany and Japan, the Bolsheviks initiated in 1928 a bold program of planned industry in the interior—first in the Urals and later in the vast area from the Urals to the Pacific. It is believed that an additional reason for the eastward migration of both population and industry was the maldistribution of energy with respect to population: 90 percent of the coal and water-power resources lie in the Asiatic part, whereas most of the people live in the European part.

TRADE

Lands with medium-summer climate rank high in trade because (1) most are progressive, productive, and reasonably wealthy; and (2) some, as Canada and the United States, are young and sparsely populated in comparison with many countries in the Old World and hence have huge surpluses. With cheap land, rich resources, and modern labor-saving machinery, the American areas have long poured a steady stream of foods and industrial raw materials into densely populated Europe in exchange for manufactures and reexports.

Outstanding transportation facilities stimulate commerce. Medium-summer Canada has an enviable railway system, one of the best in the world, despite its sparse population. The United States portion is well served as are Germany and Poland. Since the Revolution, Russia has built tens of thousands of miles of railway, a considerable proportion of which is in this type of climate (Fig. 15–18). The Trans-Siberian, longest railway in the world, follows the medium-summer climate type all the way to the Pacific and has been double-tracked in recent years. It would be a mistake, however, to assume that rail facilities are as yet adequate. Manchuria has a large and well-coordinated railway system built largely by the Japanese during the period of rapid economic and political expansion on the

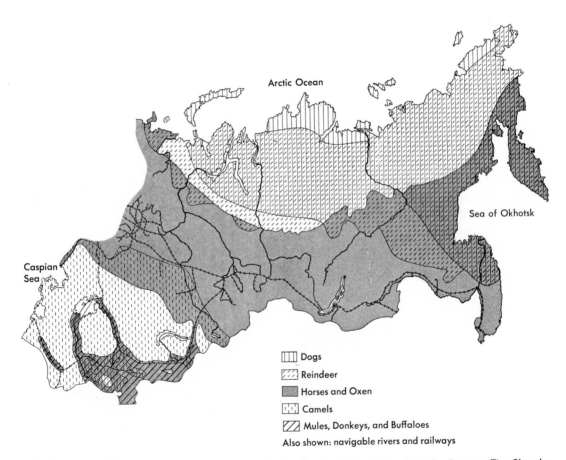

Figure 15–18 Transportation in the Asian part of the Soviet Union. (Map after B. Semenov-Tian-Shansky, American Geographical Society)

mainland. These lines were built both for economic and strategic reasons.

Lands with this climate make much use of inland waterways. North America's Great Lakes are the most used and the most important inland waterways in the world. Without them a large part of the industrial map of the continent would have to be redrawn. The St. Lawrence, too, offers navigable water for large vessels part of the year. With the development of the St. Lawrence Seaway by Canada and the United States, such inland cities as Toronto and Chicago have become ports of entry for international trade. And, of course, few countries utilize rivers and canals to such an extent as Germany and the Soviet Union.

POLITICAL AND SOCIAL ADJUSTMENTS

Possibly nowhere have greater changes transpired than in Russia since the Revolution of 1917. The hard core of Russian revolutionaries was determined to convert the backward, agricultural empire into a balanced agroindustrial nation in the shortest possible time. Within a few decades, Russia telescoped the revolutions that in other countries spread over several centuries. During that brief period monarchy, aristocracy, and feudal estates all disappeared. The greatest national program of deliberate and planned industrialization that the world has ever witnessed was carried out. This change, however, was achieved only in terms of deprivation, heartbreak, and often death. The revolution has involved state ownership, planning, and management of everything—agriculture, mining, manufacturing, trade, and transportation. Heavy industry was favored above all else, for it alone could supply armament—aircraft, artillery, tanks, submarines. The theory was that a nonindustrialized Russia would not be able to withstand military attack by a highly industrialized enemy. It was necessary, therefore, to industrialize with feverish haste.

Poverty, which has plagued Russia for centuries despite natural riches, has not disappeared as a result of Communism. In fact, the leaders have sacrificed everything—food, housing, health, transportation—to gain national strength.

Russia has established along what was once her western border a "safety belt" of territories

as a protection against future attack. Between these puppets and the countries of the West is the Iron Curtain.

Canada, most of whose occupied territory lies in the medium-summer climatic part, is beginning to play a role in international affairs out of all proportion to her small population of nineteen million. The nation is outstanding in the North Atlantic Treaty Organization. The importance of Canada is reflected also in the size of her diplomatic corps. Moreover, Canada now ranks as a major agricultural, industrial, and commercial nation (third largest trade in the world).

The relationship between Canada and the United States is one of the brightest spots in international affairs. Not a single fortification dots the common 4,000-mile boundary between the two neighbors. Since 1940 they have been partners in a Permanent Joint Board of Defense, handling this problem as though the two nations were one.

C. HUMID CONTINENTAL WITH SHORT SUMMERS

LOCATION

This climate is confined to large land masses lying on the equatorward margin of the Polar Zone. It does not occur in the Southern Hemisphere because at the latitude where it would normally be present, there are no large bodies of land. In the Northern Hemisphere, however, this type is extensively developed. Except for breaks made by Bering Strait and the North Atlantic, this climate forms a complete girdle about the inner Arctic lands. In North America it extends from the Yukon Basin in Alaska to Labrador. In Eurasia, it crosses the continent in a broad belt from northern Sweden to the eastern coast of Siberia (Fig. 15–1).

CLIMATIC CHARACTERISTICS

This is an extreme type of continental climate (Fig. 15–19). Such lands receive a moderate to scanty rainfall during the summer, and a moderate snowfall during the winter (a snow layer of three feet is not uncommon in the Siberian taiga). The low rate of evaporation even during

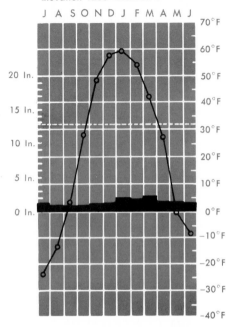

Humid Continental with
Short Summers Climate
DAWSON, YUKON, CANADA
Elevation 1200' Latitude 64° 2' N

Figure 15–19   Climate graph for Dawson, Yukon, Canada.

The water was still; the twilight was chill;
    the sky was a tatter of gray.
Swiftly came the Big Cold, and . . .
    the soft white hush lapped the northland.

Winter temperatures are surprisingly low. The winter "pole" of greatest cold was formerly placed at Verkhoyansk (−90° F.) and at Oimekon, which recorded an even lower temperature.[5] Since the Geophysical Year, however, this distinction has been claimed by Antarctica, where a low of −126.9° was recorded at the Russian meteorological station of Vostok. A similar but lesser "pole" of minimum temperature develops, during the winter, west of Great Bear Lake in northwestern Canada, where the January average is perhaps from −30° to −40° F. At times, the temperature probably falls to −75° F. A minimum of −69° F. has been recorded at Dawson City. Such low temperatures represent continentality carried to the extreme. So, too, do the winter atmospheric conditions; over interior regions, the air during most of the winter is dry, calm, and bracing. The sky is blue and unclouded and the sun shines brightly, even though the temperature be far below zero. Occasionally, however, fierce blizzards occur and icy gales blow from the north. Bald climatic data, however, seldom give one the "feel" of the climate of any region. One of the best ways to get this "feel," unless one can actually experience the climate, is to get it through the adjustments of the people. In one area in the Russian taiga, telephones were used to connect two neighboring wooden huts because of the difficulty, one might say almost the impossibility, of venturing out of doors when the Arctic *purga* was raging for days together.[6]

Summers are short, but quite warm; at times the weather may become uncomfortably hot. Indeed, the average temperature for the whole summer is high. The July average for Fort

[5] Recent investigations show that the central region of the Oimekon River offers monthly January temperatures which are 5° to 11° F. colder than those at Verkhoyansk. The absolute minima are 5° to 16° F. colder.

[6] H. P. Smolka, *Forty Thousand Against the Arctic* (London, Hutchinson & Co. (Publishers), Ltd., 1937).

mid-summer, however, prevents these regions from evidencing any suggestion of aridity, despite their small annual precipitation. The snows which fall do not melt until late spring, and hence mantle the land surface during at least half the year. This creates an undue appearance of snowiness.

This climate possesses the greatest seasonal contrasts in temperature of any on earth. The winters are long and bitterly cold. For example, the Yukon River in northwestern Canada freezes over in September and does not thaw until May. This indicates a winter of approximately nine months' duration. Spring and autumn, the transitional seasons, are necessarily short, and the advent of summer and winter is abrupt. Robert W. Service aptly describes, in his "Ballads of a Cheechako," the sudden onslaught of the Arctic winter:

Then a shuddery breath like the coming of death
    crept down from the peaks far away.

Chippewan, Canada, is 61.9° F., and for Verkhoyansk, Siberia, 59.7° F. An absolute maximum temperature of 93° F. has been recorded for Verkhoyansk, while Fort Yukon on the Arctic Circle reports 100° F. These high summer temperatures result from the rapid heating of a large land mass under the long hours of sunlight which characterize areas lying so far north.

The growing season is very short, varying from fifty to seventy-five days in the Mackenzie Valley of Canada. Freezing temperatures occur in July and August in at least half the years.

The long cold winters cause large areas in Eurasia and North America to be permanently frozen down to great depths. Above the *permafrost* (the name given to permanently frozen ground) is a layer of ground that thaws in summer but freezes in winter. This layer is variable in thickness depending upon the composition of the ground, surface exposure, hydrology, snow cover, and type of vegetation. Permanently frozen soil is absent in southernmost Alaska and nearly all of Sweden and Finland. It does, however, underlie 40 to 50 percent of Canada's total land surface and 40 percent of Russia's.

PLANT GEOGRAPHY

The native flora is dominantly forest. This great northern forest, or taiga as the Russians call it (Fig. 15–20), varies considerably in density of stand from place to place. It consists essentially of coniferous evergreen trees—pines, firs, spruces, and larches with a sprinkling of such leafy trees as aspen, birch, and willow. The taiga is characterized by a small number of species. Broadleaf deciduous trees are scarce because the growing season is so short that such trees can hardly achieve a fully leafed condition before their period of growth is terminated by early autumn frosts. Even the conifers are able to grow, but their growth is slow, and hence they fail to reach an imposing height, except near the southern boundary.

In northern Sweden and Finland, the taiga consists chiefly of Norway spruce, Scots pine, and European larch. Eastward through Russia, Siberian species of spruce, fir, larch, and stone pine become numerous. East of the Ural Mountains, the forest belt widens markedly but the tree growth becomes poorer. Vast swamps and

Figure 15–20 The austere and awe-inspiring Siberian taiga stretches for thousands of miles. It is composed mostly (probably more than two-thirds) of conifers but there is also a considerable number of hardwoods. Tree growth is slow—eighteen-inch logs are often 150 to 170 years old. (Tass photo from Sovfoto)

morasses occupy many low areas. In eastern Siberia, the forest improves in character and is composed mostly of pines, spruces, and larches; pine forest dominates on the sunny, dry slopes; larch forest prevails on the well-aerated soils of both slopes and lowlands; spruce forest reigns in the moister valleys.[7] Of course there are mixed forests too.

The forests of Alaska and Canada are similar in appearance to those of Eurasia. The chief species are black and white spruce, balsam fir, tamarack or larch, and Banksian pine. Fairly continuous stands of these alternate with peat bogs, glacial lakes, and areas of muskeg. In the northern forests of both North America and Eurasia, a few species of broadleaf deciduous trees are present. In North America these are chiefly balsam poplar, paper-birch, and willow. They are hardy, quick-growing, and possess protective devices against severe cold and excessive physiological dryness. In Europe and Asia, the broadleaf trees are represented by white birch, rowan, alder, and elfin willow. The floor of the taiga is carpeted with mosses, lichens, and tough bushes, many of the latter bearing a profusion of berries and small fruits during the summer. The wetter areas support heavy growths of rushes, reeds, and sedges.

SOILS

Infertile acid podzols characterize this climate under the influence mostly of coniferous forest. Some of the land is too stony or too sandy for profitable agriculture (see Chapter 28). Most farms are small and of the subsistence type. Along a few rivers, fertile alluvium provides productive land.

ANIMAL GEOGRAPHY
Insect life

During winter the water surfaces are frozen to a depth of six to eight feet and in some cases even more. Similarly the ground is frozen to a considerable depth. When spring arrives, however, the thawing process is rapid. The ice leaves the streams in a tremendous "break-up" and the soil thaws to a depth of a foot or two. The subsoil remains frozen for several weeks in some areas and permanently in others. Hence underdrainage is poor in many localities. This leaves the lowland surfaces moist or even muddy throughout most of the summer. The combination of warm atmosphere, moist earth, and innumerable lakes and swamps gives rise to an astounding summer crop of insect life. Plagues of black flies, myriads of fleas, and countless billions of mosquitoes fill the air[8] and descend hungrily upon all forms of larger animal life.

Aquatic and arboreal life

The streams and lakes are plentifully stocked with fish. Pike, pickerel, whitefish, inconnu, northern trout, salmon, sturgeon, grayling, and Arctic herring are among the best known species. The northern forests with their streams, lakes and muskegs, together with their abundant supplies of insects, fish, and berries, are the summer home of vast numbers of migratory birds from lower latitudes. Ducks, geese, herons, terns, and many other varieties seek feeding and nesting grounds here.

Ground life

The taiga presents favorable conditions for a large number and variety of herbivorous animals. Some of these, such as the moose, deer, elk, and woodland caribou, are of considerable size. In summer such animals thrive in the forest of spruce, pine, tamarack, birch, and aspen. During winter the forest provides shelter, and since the snow blanket is usually not deep, animals may secure sufficient forage by vigorously pawing off the snow. In addition to these larger herbivores, the forest contains untold thousands of smaller fur-bearing animals. Beaver, mink, marten, otter, skunk, fisher, fox, lynx, bear, wolverine, and wolf are among the better known species. During the summer, most of these are bedraggled and insect-tormented, but with the advent of cold weather they put on beautiful coats of fur and attain a prime physical condition. The porcupine, a true forest animal, is common throughout the year; it does not hibernate, nor does the

---

[7] E. Warming, *Oecology of Plants* (London, Oxford University Press, 1925), p. 315.

[8] According to Vilhjalmur Stefansson, mosquitoes come out in numbers unknown even to the Tropical Zone.

Figure 15–21 Contrasting means of transportation in short-summer lands. Above, reindeer transport and the ropeway in Lapland. Below, the transcontinental passenger train of the Canadian Pacific Railway winding through the Rocky Mountains in Alberta, Canada. (Photos courtesy of the Swedish Information Service and the National Film Board of Canada)

snowshoe rabbit. The latter is brownish gray in summer but pure white, except for black eartips, in winter.

HUMAN USE OF SHORT-SUMMER LANDS

Most of the lands in the short-summer climate are very scantily populated. Indeed, large areas are entirely unoccupied. A few localities on the other hand are fairly well developed, as for example, northern Sweden, Finland, and parts of the northwestern Soviet Union. This exceptional development in northern Europe is perhaps a resultant of the character of the people who inhabit it, but probably in even greater measure it is due to the presence of the Baltic Sea. The waters of the Baltic considerably ameliorate the winter climate and, in addition, provide a degree of geographical accessibility far superior to that enjoyed by most regions having this climate. Also there is no permafrost here. All the remaining lands that have this climate are sparsely populated and little used, despite their tremendous resources of timber, water power, furs, and minerals. One of the principal reasons for this is the paucity of transportation. In all phases of economic life, the greatest curse, especially in those tremendous reaches farthest inland, is their relative inaccessibility (Fig. 15–21). Even the great rivers flow in the wrong direction. Almost without exception they debouch into the icebound Arctic and are so situated on their respective continents that the ice in their lower courses is the last to melt in the spring and the first to form in the autumn. This would render them nearly useless for navigation even if they emptied into an ice-free ocean. In summer the lower parts of the basins become inundated, resulting in extensive tracts of marshland.

Trapping

The taiga is the homeland of several groups of primitive peoples who are still in the hunting or "food-gathering stage." The natural environment apparently has proved so rigorous as to limit native man to the most rudimentary forms of adjustment and to preclude, in most instances, any evolution into higher forms of geographic adaptation. The North American taiga is inhabited by groups of Algonquin and Athabascan Indians, who are scattered from interior Alaska to Newfoundland. These folk live by hunting, fishing, trapping, and gathering berries, roots, and other wild vegetable items. Their food, shelter, and much of their clothing and gear are furnished by materials obtained directly from the fauna-flora of their habitat. In northern Europe most of the inhabitants have evolved beyond this stage, but many of the Karelians and Syrjenians still exist by means of such primitive occupations as gathering and hunting. In the Siberian forests, ecologically similar peoples exist, for example, the Voguls, Ostiaks, Tunguses, and Kamchadales.

Side by side with these rather primitive folk dwell more advanced peoples whose occupancy is based also upon fauna or flora. In 1678, the Cossacks under Yermak began their expansion eastward into Siberia. They were followed by a miscellany of Russian hunters, traders, adventurers, and settlers. By 1706, the conquest of Siberia was complete, and in 1741, the Russians crossed Bering Sea and began to trickle into Alaska. The primary incentive for this migration and conquest was the fur trade. Today there are hundreds of fur posts and trading stations scattered through the Siberian forests. From these collectively is drawn a large proportion of the world's annual supplies of sable, mink, and other fine furs. In North America is a similar northern trapping and fur-trading industry, carried on by several British and American companies. Of these, the most important is the Hudson's Bay Company which has been operating in Canada since 1670 (Fig. 15–22). This has created a highly interesting case of racial symbiosis, wherein some three thousand whites and forty thousand Indians live and work side by side. The former buy the furs, do the governing, and supply the latter with many of the necessaries of life. The Amerindians contribute the furs and some of their own food requirements. The Western Hemisphere crop of peltries (save that of the Hudson's Bay Company which is sold at special auction in London) finds its way to New York, whereas the Eastern Hemisphere crop moves primarily to London.

This trade in furs is, along with mining,

Figure 15-22 A trapper arrives at a northern post of the Hudson's Bay Company with a toboggan load of furs. This famous company, which still gathers about half the furs of Canada, has 221 posts located at strategic points throughout northern North America from Labrador to Herschel Island. It is to the credit of the company that the men representing it have been on the whole men of character. Had they been otherwise, they could not have commanded the respect of the Indians who as the guides, hunters, and trappers were a necessary part of their economy. Hence the welfare of the Indians has long been a matter of primary concern to the company. (Photo courtesy of the Hudson's Bay Company)

some logging, and a small amount of manufacturing, at present about the only reason for the establishment of permanent settlements. This is especially the case in the northern part of the great forest. For this reason scientific studies are made in the fluctuations in the numbers of Canadian animals. Because of the Hudson's Bay Company's long history, reliable data are available extending without a break for a period of more than two centuries. These data show, for example, that the lynx population reaches a maximum on the average of every nine and a half years. It is significant that the numbers of the snow-shoe rabbit, chief prey of the lynx, also vary in cycles of nine and a half years. Research indicates that changes in the numbers of one animal closely follow changes in the numbers of the other. In many areas arctic fox and snowy-owl cycles have been correlated with that of the lemming.

There is not as yet sufficient reliable data to state assuredly the cause of the great wildlife rhythm in the northern forest, but it is probable that climatic fluctuations play an important role.

Logging and lumbering

The timber resources of short-summer lands are still largely unexploited but may be regarded as a notable reserve for the future. Only in Finland and northern Sweden has there been an outstanding lumbering industry for any length of time. In both countries, wood and wood products account for a large share of the exports. The cutting of pulpwood is an even more important forest enterprise than is lumbering in these regions, because the trees of the taiga are in the main small and slow-growing. Hence their ultimate use would seem to be more for pulp and paper than for lumber. Already, a large pulp industry exists along the southern margin of the

Figure 15-23   Truck being loaded with logs for pulp in Ontario, Canada. (Photo courtesy of the Caterpillar Tractor Company)

forest in Finland and Sweden, as well as in northern Newfoundland, Quebec, and Ontario (Fig. 15–23). Canada leads the world in this industry, manufacturing about 60 percent of the total output of newsprint. Although Russia's production is not yet impressive, that nation does nonetheless rank sixth and the trend is definitely upward. In terms of size of the forested area and of pulping species, the Soviet Union appears to be in the most advantageous position of any nation.

Mining

The Canadian Shield, much of which has the Humid Continental with Short Summers climate, is one of the world's leading sources of minerals —cobalt, copper, gold, iron, lead, nickel, platinum, silver, titanium, uranium, zinc, and a host of others. To date only the surface of this region, which covers about a third of the country, has been scratched. High transportation costs make it economically possible to extract only the highest-grade ores. Hence in this region of great distances, scant population, and rich mineral resources, the future must depend largely on what happens in the way of improved surface transport and how soon such improvement will come about is highly problematical.

AGRICULTURAL ADJUSTMENTS

The shortness of the growing season and the prevalence of frosts during the nights of midsummer make this climate a poor one for agriculture. Also the podzol soils are poorly suited for growing crops. Consequently, agriculture is practically lacking over most of the northern interior forest areas. To be sure, the long midsummer days partially compensate for the short summers, so that certain *hardy* crops can be grown. For many years, vegetables, including potatoes, turnips, and cabbages, as well as certain small fruits and berries, have been raised about the fur stations and trading posts of Canada and Siberia. During occasional summers, however, unusually heavy frosts occur, and such ventures are total failures. Locally, however, in the more protected spots and all along the southern margins of the forest, a limited agriculture can be regularly successful. But it must be based necessarily upon potatoes, hardy roots, vegetables, and quick-maturing varieties of cereals. Obviously yields are low, heavy applications of fertilizer are essential, and production costs are high. Even so, it is often less costly to raise food on the spot than to bring it in from great distances at high transport cost.

Considerable areas of the forest in northern Russia were long ago cleared and occupied by a poor rye-and-root crop producing peasantry. But in the past few decades under the Soviet government, phenomenal progress has ensued. Great efforts are being made to develop new and hardier types of fruits, vegetables, and cereals adapted both to the climate and to the soils. It is amazing that arable farming has spread along the Lena, Aldan, and Velyuy as far north as 64° N. These are among the world's northernmost farming areas. To be sure, the absolute limit of agriculture lies much farther north, but the farms there are scattered and consist of "island-oases of poor, unreliable fields." In this part of the world the economic hazards tend to outweigh the scientific.

Finland is a good example of what an energetic people may accomplish agriculturally in this climate, despite the fact that only about

7 percent of the land is under cultivation, the percentage varying from nearly 25 percent along the southern coast to less than 1 percent in Lapland. Moreover, most of the farms are small: more than half have less than twelve acres of cultivated land and another third have only twelve to thirty-seven acres. Meadows cover about half the total cultivated land and the hay crop constitutes two-fifths of all crops measured in feed units. Patches of forest have been cleared, even beyond the Arctic Circle, to make way for crops. Thus barley is being grown up to latitude 68° N., and rye up to 64° and occasionally even to 67°. In addition, many clearings and natural meadows are being utilized for dairying. The dairy cattle must be housed in substantial quarters during much of the year, but the enterprise appears to be quite successful. Though the "Finns have been bred in the school of adversity," they have become one of the most progressive peoples of Europe. In northern Sweden, there is a similar successful combination of summer farming, year-round dairying, and winter lumbering.

In the New World, the French Canadians have for several decades been nibbling away at the southern margins of the forest with the intent of expanding their agricultural occupancy in Quebec. The terrible difficulties of clearing such land, however, coupled with the constant menace of summer frost, would have long since discouraged a less stout-hearted people.

The Yukon and Mackenzie River basins in northwestern Canada and central Alaska seem to offer somewhat better conditions for agricultural adjustment. By means of scientific plant-breeding, government experiment stations there are deriving hardier and more quickly maturing varieties of cereals and vegetables. American settlers in the Yukon-Tanana country already report a considerable degree of success with such crops. But the long, severe winters and the appalling inaccessibility of these vast lands cannot be eliminated, and it is extremely doubtful whether any very large proportion of them can ultimately be won for permanent agricultural settlement. Rather by wise management, the peoples of Canada, the U.S.S.R., the United States, Finland, and Sweden should exploit their northern forests in such a manner as to keep them functioning as future sources of lumber, pulpwood, and furs.

SOCIAL ADJUSTMENTS

A glance at the map of areas having the Humid Continental Climate with Short Summers reveals that most are sparsely populated. Maps of terrain, soils, and climate supply most of the reasons why this is so. Thus, after more than a century following penetration, nearly all of Canada having this climate is still largely empty.

In North America, except in the extreme southwest and east, the greater part remains as it was originally—the home of the Amerindian. To be sure there are in addition scattered white trappers, miners, and woodsmen, and in the several clay belts some farmers. Few railways and roads, however, penetrate this vast north country because there is little opportunity to make profits. The population is small because hunting and trapping are the principal economic activity. In Canada large tracts of land are specifically reserved for the aborigines where they may hunt and trap. The government recognizes that the fur resources must remain adequate, since the Indians' livelihood is almost entirely dependent upon game.

In Europe the white population of the short-summer climate is far more dense than in North America; yet Finland and Sweden are among the least densely populated countries in the continent. Most of the population lives in the seacoast belts. Frequently people wonder why Finland and Sweden support some 12,400,000 persons, whereas Alaska boasts only 226,000. A major reason seems to be that the former have been settled longer.[9] The interesting thing about the occupancy in these northlands of Europe is the high culture the people have attained. Education is on a very high plane and there is practically no illiteracy. Few areas are so highly civilized. And this culture has been achieved in an environment of coniferous forest, general rocky and lake-dotted terrain, and relatively thin soils

[9] Vilhjalmur Stefansson, "The Colonization of Northern Lands," *Climate and Man,* Yearbook of Agriculture (Washington, D.C., U.S. Department of Agriculture, 1941), p. 211.

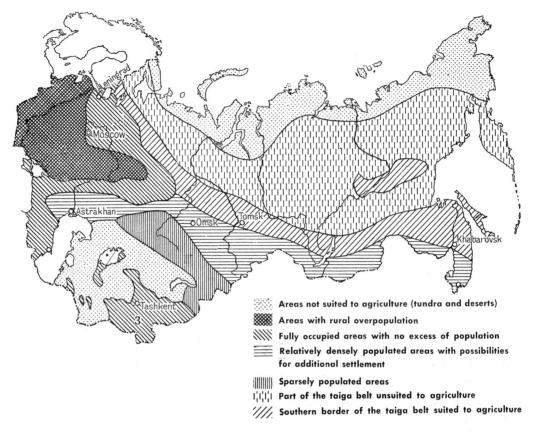

Figure 15–24   Population regions of Russia. (Map adapted from Paul Czechowicz, American Geographical Society)

in addition to the hard climate. One of the best indications of the poverty and limited opportunity of this region is the heavy emigration to North America.

The greatest recent social progress in this climate appears to be developing in the Soviet Union, but the line separating propaganda and truth is so tenuous and unreliable that the subject is not discussed further here.

As far as population is concerned, the Soviet Union is estimated to have in her lands with this type of climate about 30 million people. Most of these live in the southern margins and in the Ural region. In 1950 there were twelve cities of more than 100,000 persons in the taiga. In 1965, Novosibirsk had 1,027,000 people. The authors do not wish to imply that the Russian taiga has more than a sprinkling of people; it is still a land of pioneering where the isolated settlements are separated by hundreds of miles

of wilderness and where man has made but a feeble beginning in his attempt to take over from nature (Fig. 15–24).

POLITICAL ADJUSTMENTS

The short-summer lands of North America were unimportant politically in the past; in fact they were largely ignored by their governments. The long cold winters, the unbelievable isolation, the few neighbors, the myriads of pestiferous insects in summer, and the subsistence type of living forced upon the people held few attractions for the older-stock Americans and Canadians. As long as there are places that seem more attractive to people of "softer" climates, these northlands will be settled slowly. The psychology of the pioneer so necessary for the settlement of such regions appears to be lacking today. Development, too, is retarded by misconceptions—residual beliefs derived from the original Greek postulate that there is a northern limit beyond which life could not exist.[10]

World War II, however, proved that lands characterized by the short-summer climate have high strategic value. The Arctic promises to become the new Mediterranean, since the shortest routes by air connecting the world's principal capitals are over the polar region. Moreover, the only two remaining "heavyweight powers"—the United States and the Soviet Union—now practically face each other across the Arctic. Aircraft and guided missiles have thus destroyed the isolation of the taiga which, till recently, was its best defense.

Because of the Cold War and the vulnerability of Alaska and Canada, the armed forces of both countries are working together, for their problems are identical. They are carrying out jointly much polar research, for troops, planes, and equipment all must be tested for subzero temperatures. Also they have jointly set up radar and "air" lines that reach in triplicate across Canada from the Pacific Ocean to the Atlantic. The new Army principle makes good geographic sense: *"Instead of trying to fight the elements, work with them."*

In Europe, Sweden and Finland are good neighbors. Though Finland fought the Soviet Union and suffered terribly, she is returning to her former rank as an important nation, since the Finns are an able and industrious people. Sweden was one of the few countries able to maintain neutrality during the war. One reason why this was possible, of course, was that she supplied Germany with raw materials, food, and fabricated products almost to the end of hostilities.

Before the 1917 Bolshevik Revolution, the Czarist government attempted unsuccessfully to Russify or weld together by force the diverse peoples under its flag. Education of the peasants was discouraged because the government feared that education would lead to revolution.

The Soviet leaders have used somewhat different tactics. They have been ruthless, however, in enforcing adherence to their program. The U.S.S.R. is a police state; everyone must accept the political and economic doctrines of the Soviet system. The government or state is everything.

[10] *Ibid.,* p. 207.

SUGGESTED USEFUL READINGS

Texts dealing with the regional geography of Canada, the United States, North America (or Anglo-America), Europe, Asia, and the U.S.S.R. are standard references giving more information on this climate region. The literature is quite vast.

16

Dry Continental Climate Regions

The Dry Continental climate[1] characterizes regions lying in the interiors of continents in the Cyclonic Zone just poleward of Dry Subtropical regions (Fig. 7–12). It differs markedly from the Dry Subtropical type only in having a much shorter frostless season and in having a better covering of vegetation—the result of diminished evaporation which comes with cooler temperatures. Places with this climate either lie too far inland to get much rain or repose on the leeward sides of high mountains which shut out the moisture-bearing winds. In either case, aridity or semi-aridity and sharp diurnal and seasonal extremes of temperature prevail, and agriculture by customary methods is not possible. Pastoral pursuits predominate.

This climate is to be found on three continents: in North America on the Great Plains from Alberta to Texas, in the Columbia Plateau, and in the northern Great Basin; in South America in Patagonia; and in Eurasia in the Caspian Plains of southeastern European Russia, the Kirghiz Steppes, the Plains of Turkestan, and the Mongolian Plateau (Fig. 16–1).

DISTINGUISHING CHARACTERISTICS

In temperature, this climate is much like parts of the Humid Continental. The summers are hot. Since the atmosphere is dry and clouds and fog are rare, sunny days prevail and the sun is most effective. Both the relative humidity and the sensible temperature are low. Summers are not equally hot or winters equally cold throughout the realm: thus the plains of Turkestan are hotter in summer and colder in winter than those in Patagonia or even the Great Basin, for Asia's immense size conduces to greater extremes. The winters everywhere are bitterly cold at times. The Great Plains have recorded some of North America's lowest temperatures, many as low as −40° F. Patagonia, of all Dry Continental lands, gets less cold in winter and less hot in summer because South America tapers off in the south, thereby enabling the ocean to modify the climate appreciably.

The wind is changeable all year round—a consequence of cyclonic storms. The diurnal range of temperature may amount to as much as 30° to 60° F. Nights may be cool even in summer—the result of rapid radiation which is consequent upon dry air and clear skies. Evaporation, everywhere great, invariably exceeds precipitation but abates with increasing latitude. West of the Wasatch Mountains in Utah, some forty-five to fifty-five inches of water evaporate in a single year from a free-water surface.

The most striking difference between the two continental climates lies in the rainfall: in the Dry Continental, the amount everywhere is less than twenty inches (Fig. 16–2). Never is rain totally absent, however, although in the driest parts of the realm, such as portions of the Gobi Desert in Mongolia, much of it evaporates before reaching the ground. About 80 percent of the precipitation falls in winter and spring in

---

[1] Very little accurate information is available on the details of this climate in central Asia and Patagonia.

the driest parts of the realm. Much of it in summer occurs in the form of thundershowers and cloudbursts which result from the rapid rise of a heated spot of air.[2] Hence rainfall is highly localized (occurring over but a small area at a time), erratic, and unreliable. Destructive hail storms are not uncommon in this season.

The paucity of rain results from the great distances of such regions from oceans, the principal sources of moisture, or from the interception of rain-bearing winds by mountains, or both. Physical relief becomes highly significant in this climate because of the manner in which it influences rainfall. Increase of precipitation with altitude begins at a considerable distance to windward of a mountain base and progresses at a fairly regular rate on the long gradual uninterrupted slope, decreasing slightly near the summit (Fig. 16–3). Except in the mountains, where it is heavy, winter precipitation is generally restricted to *light* snows.

Two phases of the Dry Continental climate may be recognized—the *semiarid* and the *arid*. The latter is found in certain areas which are practically inaccessible to rain-bearing winds; the former occurs as a transition between the truly arid and the truly humid continental types. By some geographers these are very properly considered as separate types of climate. Since human occupancy is roughly similar in the two, it is not illogical to treat them together under the heading of *Dry Continental*.

Their main difference lies in amount and distribution of precipitation. Whereas the continental deserts receive ten inches or less of rainfall with the maximum in winter and spring, their semiarid margins get as many as twenty, the maximum falling in spring and summer. As in the driest sections, the fall in the semiarid regions is erratic and the quantity inconstant. During some years sufficient rain falls for crops.[3] Cold waves, called *Northers* in North America, sweep over such regions in winter as does the warm, dry *Chinook*. The latter descends the lee side of mountains and within a half-hour's time may cause a rise in temperature of many degrees. A rise of temperature of 40° F. within twenty-four hours is by no means unusual. It frequently melts the snow, exposing the range grasses and

enabling cattle and sheep to survive an otherwise almost unlivable winter. When the *Chinook* descends on a region in summer it spreads disaster, since it burns up the pasturage as well as great stretches of dry-farmed wheat. In order to mellow the annoying and destructive effects of icy blasts in winter and of desiccating breezes in summer, most farmers on the Great Plains have planted windbreaks (Fig. 16–4). Western cattlemen, as well as Patagonian shepherds, find it expedient to erect simple shelters under the lee of a hill or cliff as a protective measure against the relentless winds.

THE "DUST BOWL"

The "Dust Bowl" was an area in the American Great Plains that became a household word in the 1930's (Fig. 16–5). Farming, overgrazing, and low rainfall conspired to produce it.[4] Two systems of farming came into conflict here—that of the north European type, which was introduced by Atlantic Seaboard colonists as they spread westward, and that from Spain via Mexico (cattle raising).

From time immemorial, the soils of this region had been anchored with a thick sod of grasses. Then came World War I and a high price for wheat. Accordingly, millions of acres

[2] In places, an entire year's allotment of precipitation has fallen in a single hour. Cloud bursts cause destructive floods, since (1) the sparse vegetation is unable to hold back the water which finds its way almost immediately into drainage channels as runoff, (2) the surface soil is often so packed as almost to prevent the water from sinking into it, and (3) many stream courses are shallow and hence unable to bear large quantities of water.

[3] Sometimes during several successive years, adequate rain falls for humid farming in this country normally too dry for it. Later, however, follow years when the rainfall is too meager for crops. This irregularity has caused innumerable crop failures and has driven out settlers by tens of thousands.

[4] James C. Malin, historian, University of Kansas, a careful student of the North American grasslands, contends that dust storms were common long before the white man arrived in the Great Plains. Says he: "No more brazen falsehood was ever perpetrated upon a gullible public than the allegation that the dust storms of the 1930's were *caused* by 'The Plow That Broke the Plains.'"

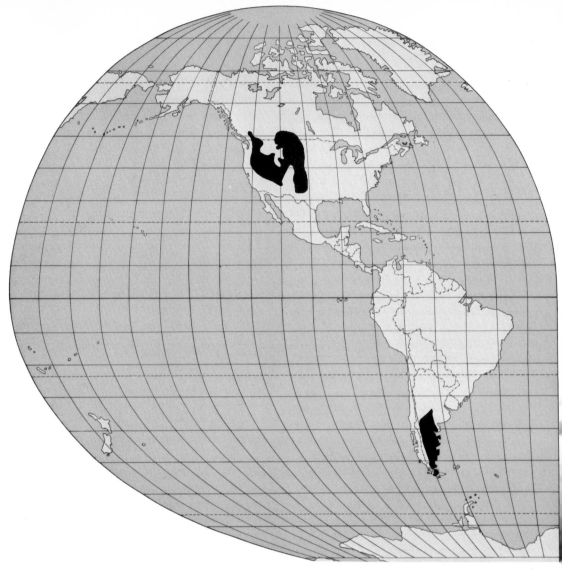

Figure 16–1 Dry Continental regions.

of grass land were plowed up with tractor-drawn plows and planted to wheat. Rains were plentiful and the virgin soils, rich in humus, at first yielded bumper crops. Wheat followed wheat year after year in the same fields, there being no rotation of crops.

Then came the drought. Continuous cropping to wheat had depleted the soil-binding quality of the humus. The resulting poor crops were pastured to livestock and the ground became pulverized by their hoofs. Then strong winds whisked the fine soil particles hundreds of miles distant (often as far as the Atlantic), forming gigantic dust clouds or "black blizzards" (Fig. 16–6), while the heavier materials, such

as sand, were left behind. From May, 1934, wind erosion set in motion by man-made forces transformed five million acres from once productive land into waste areas and stretches of sand dunes and more than sixty million acres more were threatened. As one refugee farmer put it: "Section after section dried up and blowed away."

During the 1930's, thousands of farmers had to migrate, many settling on poor cut-over lands in the Pacific Northwest or the Ozarks or forming part of the pathetic ranks of workers—the "Okies" and "Arkies" in the orchards, the cotton fields, and vegetable fields of California.

Then the "Dust Bowl" began to shrink—the result of greater and better distribution of

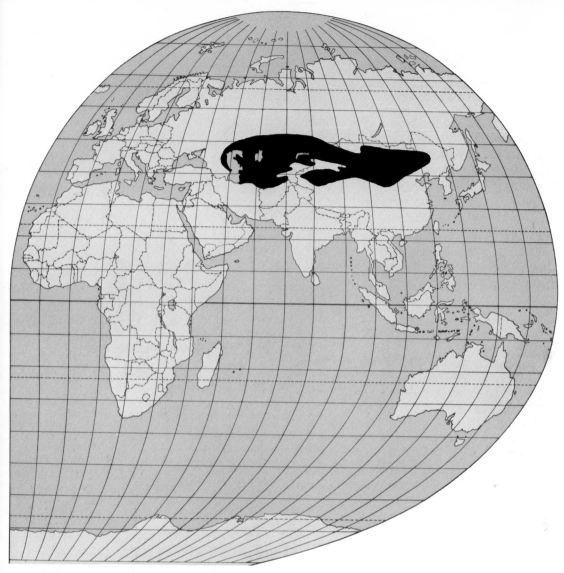

rainfall,[5] of regrassing of extensive areas, of soil-erosion preventive measures, and of new farming techniques. However, in the 1950's, as a result of droughts (in many areas the rainfall was only 50 to 90 percent of normal), dust storms once again plagued the southern and central Great Plains (Fig. 16–5): particularly in the spring months great clouds of dust—the top soil of millions of acres of farmland—darkened the sky, cutting visibility to zero in some sections, halting traffic, smothering out motors, stalling trains, and grounding aircraft. Many farmers "list or chisel" wide strips to minimize the effects of blowing. In these processes the moist subsoil is plowed up and the clods are spread on the surface to hold the loose topsoil. In such fields, the wheat crop is lost but the farmer may plant grain sor-

ghums later in the spring if it rains. Some farmers attempt to control the land by planting alfalfa.

SOILS

In the United States the soils formed west of about 97° W. under short grass are limy and are called *pedocals;* those formed east of 97° W. under tall grass are acid and are called *pedalfers.* The scanty rainfall and the absence of leaching account for the phenomenal fertility of the pedocals. Here evaporation greatly exceeds precip-

[5] Rainfall appears to run in cycles. For several years it may exceed the long-time average; then it will drop below the long-time average for several years as happened over the greater portion of the Great Plains for some years following 1930.

itation, with a consequent upward movement of water bringing nutrient minerals to the surface. The soil is extremely productive when water is available. The soils of the moister Great Plains of North America are black soils, corresponding to the *chernozems* of the steppes of Russia, which occur there under similar climatic conditions (see Chapter 28). Chernozems are the soil aristocrats. The Russian chernozem belt is replaced by brown and chestnut soils in the more arid southern and eastern areas. These soils are shallower and the zone of lime accumulation is nearer the surface —maybe in the "B" horizon. These soils are less fertile than the chernozems.

In the desert, in the Great Basin or in Mongolia, where precipitation is inadequate to support continuous grass cover, the soils belong to a group known as *sierozem* and desert soils. They are gray in color and low in humus. The lime horizon may lie within a few inches of or even be at the surface. Productivity declines progressively in passing from the *chernozems* to the desert soils. This is more an indication of decrease in rainfall than of decline in soil fertility. When such soils are properly drained and irrigated, they frequently prove to be highly productive.

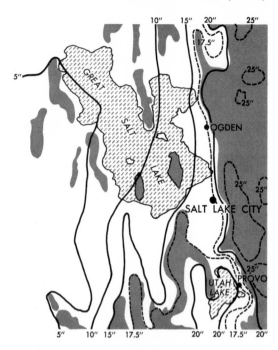

Figure 16–3 Isohyets in the Salt Lake Region, Utah. Note the increase in precipitation with increase in elevation (shaded areas represent mountains). All available information has been entered upon this map, though data are unavailable for the highest levels of the Wasatch Mountains. Since there is no convenient artifice for representing "no data," it has seemed desirable to indicate the probable conditions. These are based upon natural vegetation and altitude and are represented by broken lines. (After J. Cecil Alter, C. F. Brooks, O. E. Baker, and C. Langdon White)

PLANT GEOGRAPHY

High summer temperatures, scanty precipitation, and rapid evaporation conspire to eliminate arborescent vegetation from all but strictly riverine locations where either surface or underground water is available. Accordingly, the pioneers had to construct their first houses of sod. For miles, interstream areas possess not a single tree. In the northern Great Plains, however, cooler temperatures reduce evaporation and trees do grow.

Hardy grasses thrive in parts of the arid regions, their characteristics depending upon both the amount of precipitation and the soil conditions. Thus in the Great Plains, grama grass characterizes the northern section, buffalo grass the central, and mesquite the southern, the last lying without the climatic realm treated in this chapter. Between longitude 97° and 100° W.,

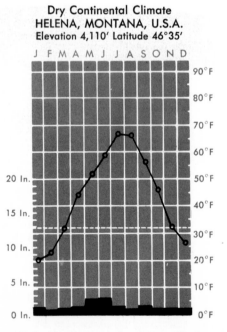

Figure 16–2 Climate graph for Helena, Montana.

Figure 16–4   Feedlot protected by Jack Pine windbreak on a farm in that part of Nebraska where the Dry Continental and the Humid Continental with Long Summers climates merge. Seldom does one see a farm or ranch in this area that is not protected from hot and cold winds by a windbreak. (Photo by A. Taylor, courtesy of the U.S. Forest Service)

the vegetation was conspicuously mixed, representing the merging of species from the tall grass (prairie) and short grass (steppe).

In the truly arid sections, the vegetation consists less of grass and more of shrubs and bushes which grow in bunches and are gray, brown, or pale green in color. These plants have long roots, short strong stems, small thick silvery leaves or thorns, and waxy bark—all of which reduce evaporation to a minimum. It is estimated that as much as 95 percent of the woody vegetation is spiny and prickly.

Areas of bare ground are numerous but not large, except in parts of Asia and in the Great Basin of the United States west of Great Salt Lake.

The Dry Continental vegetation is a reliable indicator of climatic and soil conditions and of the suitability of the land for agriculture. During the pioneer period, and even today in isolated and little known sections where climatic and soil data are wanting, the natural vegetation has been to the farmer what the compass is to the mariner. Thus the sagebrush association (Fig. 16–7) indicates an amount of rainfall and a soil suitable

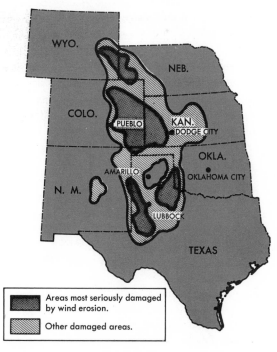

Areas most seriously damaged by wind erosion.

Other damaged areas.

Figure 16–5   The dust bowl of the mid-1950's, like that of the 1930's, presented a serious problem for farmers in the Great Plains. (Map based on data from the Soil Conservation Service)

Figure 16–6 A dust storm approaching Springfield, Colorado. (Photo courtesy of the Soil Conservation Service, USDA)

for the production of wheat and barley by dry-farming methods; white sage, shadscale, and greasewood, on the other hand, reflect such unfavorable conditions as inadequate rainfall or alkaline soil and are shunned.

ANIMAL GEOGRAPHY

The native animal life of Dry Continental regions indicates close adjustment to the natural vegetation and climate. Where precipitation is greatest and vegetation most plentiful, wildlife abounds; but where these are meager, the fauna is impoverished.

In the semiarid lands of Asia, herbivorous animals, such as the saiga antelope, Mongolian gazelle, wild ass, and wild horse, developed to a high degree. All were fleet of foot and had great endurance. Dry Continental Asia is the home also of the two-humped camel which, with

its long, thick fleece and hard feet, its ability to subsist on saline plants and water and to store fat in its humps during times of plenty for use during times of want, is admirably suited to the harsh conditions of the physical milieu. Carnivores, like the wolf, fox, and weasel, are widely distributed.

Among the larger and most important animals in North America were the pronghorn antelope and the bison. These dominated the Great Plains, followed constantly by their cruelest enemy, the wolf. Besides the latter among beasts of prey, the coyote is annoying and so cunning a marauder that sheep herders are obliged to keep constant guard against him. No ungulate evolved in the South American part of the realm. Patagonia's most characteristic larger animals are the guanaco, a kind of camel, and the rhea, or South American ostrich.

Rodents thrive throughout the realm. The

prairie dog, vizcacha, rabbit, gopher, and others take refuge in dark underground chambers during severe storms, temperature extremes, or when pursued by an enemy. Since they eat grasses and some, like the prairie dog, even destroy roots, they compete with livestock and hence are a menace to the human inhabitants, nearly all of whom are graziers. Moreover, where they colonize, they literally honeycomb the ground with their holes, thereby endangering the lives of horses and cattle which graze the general region.

Reptiles, especially snakes and lizards, are numerous. They thrive because they require but modest quantities of food and water and because they avoid hazardous conditions by spending a large portion of their time underground.

Invertebrates, aside from insects, are unimportant but certain insects thrive. During the drier years, clouds of ravenous grasshoppers and locusts, driven by starvation from their breeding places, settle down upon the fat lands of the better-watered agricultural sections near the desert margin or in irrigated oases and consume everything green, bringing ruin to many farmers (Fig. 11–7).

THE AMERICAN INDIAN AND THE GREAT PLAINS

We have seen that before the white man came into the Great Plains, the region was the home of millions of bison (American buffalo). It was also the home of the so-called "Plains Indians" —the Arapaho, Cheyenne, Kiowa, Mandan, Pawnee, Sioux (in part a forest people), and others. Since the region did not have many plants from which the Indians could gather seeds or roots for food, since the climate was too dry for farming (except in favored spots along moist river bottoms), but since the country was alive with game, the Plains Indians were hunters and meat eaters. They were nomads, following the

Figure 16–7   Sagebrush in Utah. This vegetation characterizes much of the semi-desert, the soils of which are not alkaline. Sagebrush indicates to farmers an amount of rainfall and a soil suitable for dry farming. (Photo by Ira Clark, courtesy of the U.S. Forest Service)

herds. Their tepees and clothing were made from hides and skins. Buffalo chips supplied their fuel. Life was hard and the food supply usually uncertain.

Before the white man arrived, the Indians had to do all their hunting on foot. To kill the buffalo they devised a number of schemes. They prowled along the edge of a herd with wolf skins over their heads and backs; they hid in the woods along stream banks and shot the animals as they came down to drink; and they drove buffalo over bluffs and cliffs.

It was the horse more than anything else that changed the way of life of the Plains Indians.[6] It enabled them to hunt the buffalo without working so hard, for horses could travel both farther and faster than men on foot. On horseback the Indians could easily go where the buffalo was, with the horse the Indians were not obliged to change camp so often and, when they did move, travel was much easier. Firearms, too, aided the Indians to hunt more effectively.

Shortly after the Civil War, white hunters began the wholesale extermination of the bison, the animals being shot just for their hides, which brought about $3.50. In 1882 southeastern Montana shipped 180,000 buffalo hides. With its disappearance, the Indians lost their chief support, and the animal which they were taught had been given to them as an inexhaustible food supply was destroyed. Ere long the Indians were rounded up and removed to reservations elsewhere. Possessing the horse, however, enabled them to dispute dispossession longer and more effectively than would have been the case without it.

CONQUEST OF ARID AMERICA

Caravans of covered wagons began to trickle onto the Great Plains in the forties, but they deliberately jumped over them, their goal being the more humid Pacific region. Only the Mormons sought a home in the arid region where they hoped to carry on their religious worship without molestation and persecution. The Amerindian, accordingly, dominated the plains until the arrival of the "iron horse," when he gave way to the cattleman. The grassy plains proved to be as

favorable for cattle as they had been for bison. They became known as the "Cow Country" and remained so until the closing of the open range.

Since the plains were government land and unfenced, many herds of cattle grazed together. In order to establish ownership, branding was resorted to. In the early summer, frequently in May, the cattle over a wide area were rounded up by cowboys and the calves heeling their mothers were branded. Thereupon all the animals were again turned loose and so continued until the fall round-up, when those destined for the eastern market were segregated and taken on the big drive to the nearest railhead.

As barbed wire became cheap, cattle owners found it more satisfactory to fence the range than to employ cowboys to guard their stock and grassland. Hence they enclosed enormous tracts, two companies in Colorado fencing a million acres each. These fences were removed later and no more appeared until the arrival of the homesteaders who were hostile to the roving cattlemen.

During the free-for-all grazing period, the range became overcrowded and hence overgrazed. During the severe winters of 1886–1887, from 50 to 60 percent of the cattle starved.

THE FARMER INVASION

Agricultural settlement vacillated at the eastern margin of the Great Plains as long as friction with the Amerindians persisted. With their expulsion, however, a flood of settlers rushed in. The tall-grass area to the eastward had presented no major obstacle, other than psychological, to the westward extension of traditional forest-man's livestock and crops. The short-grass country proved to be different. Unfortunately, the new settlers knew nothing about the climate. It so happened that the precipitation during this pioneer period was above normal. Ignorant of this fact, they employed humid farming methods successfully for a time. However, when they stubbornly persisted in their effort to grow corn, not realizing that this crop was ill-suited to the climate, they failed. A large part of the excessive

[6] Frank G. Roe, *The Indian and the Horse* (Norman, University of Oklahoma Press, 1955).

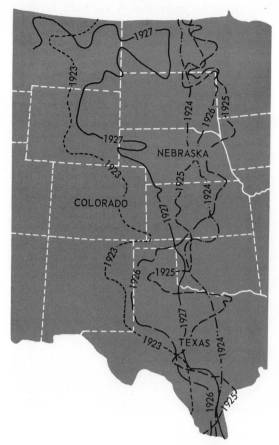

Figure 16–8 The Great Plains of the United States, showing the shifting from year to year of the boundary between the Humid Continental and the Dry Continental climates. (Map after H. M. Kendall)

hardships of the late nineteenth century in the Great Plains was the result of this failure in adjustment. Even the soft wheats did not do well. Belatedly hard wheats—spring in the northern and winter in the central Great Plains—provided a reliable crop as did the grain sorghums for the central and southern Great Plains. These importations from Africa and Asia, resistant to heat and drought, yield well and provide feed for livestock.

The pioneers soon experienced years of normal and subnormal rainfall, and millions of acres of crop land dried up. Grasshoppers added to the disaster and nearly every farmer was overwhelmed. Tens of thousands of courageous souls lost their all and were forced to migrate.

The climatic limitations to farming are now

better understood (Fig. 16–8). However, except during those years when the rainfall is greater in amount, agriculture, except by irrigation, is fraught with uncertainty.

BIRTH OF DRY FARMING

Dry farming or water-conservation farming, which is a direct response to aridity, was inaugurated on this continent by Indians in what is now the American Southwest. It had its beginning by white men in Utah. In 1863, a company of Danes founded Bear River City and utilized the water of the Malade River to irrigate its fields. After repeated experiments, the newcomers became convinced that the water was so brackish as to be injurious instead of beneficial and they ceased to use it. In desperation (the season was now well advanced) they plowed up some sagebrush land above the ditch, planted grain once more, and awaited results. They obtained fair yields which indicated that dry farming with its alternate years of crop and fallow could succeed. It has since been practiced regularly there and elsewhere in the Dry Continental West. Dry farming is often important on benchlands or piedmont plains near oases as for example in the Valley of the Great Salt Lake, and, in many cases, is an adjunct of irrigation farming.

Summer fallowing is generally practiced every other year in the drier sections, but only once in two to four years in the semiarid Great Plains. The fallow land is harrowed once in the early spring, again in summer, and finally just before seeding. The greatest single benefit derived from this practice is the conservation of water through eradicating weeds which consume much of the moisture needed by the crop during the following year, and by maintaining the soil mulch which also helps to reduce evaporation from the soil. A mulch of small clods is superior to one of fine dust, for it will neither blow away nor permit reestablishment of capillarity in the soil.[7]

The chief dry-farmed crops are wheat, barley, and flint corn—all of which have low mois-

[7] The California Agricultural Extension Service, as a result of careful field experiments, claims that cultivation itself does not conserve moisture. See *Circular 50*, September, 1943.

ture requirements. Wheat is the dominant crop and great tracts of it spread for miles over eastern Washington, western Kansas and Nebraska, eastern Colorado, eastern Montana (Fig. 16–9), as well as over vast areas of southern Russia.

In the southern Great Plains, where precipitation is quite light and evaporation is excessive,

corn cannot be grown though it is badly needed. Accordingly, drought-resisting substitute crops such as millet, feterita, Sudan grass, sorghum, Kaffir corn, milo maize, and alfalfa have been successfully introduced from tropical and subtropical semiarid lands (Fig. 16–10). Thus millions of acres which otherwise must have remained in pasture, have become available for

Figure 16–9 Above, dry farming of wheat near Glentana, Montana. Strips of spring wheat and fallow are alternated each year on the land to conserve moisture and to protect the soil, the strips being laid out at right angles to the prevailing wind in order to prevent wind erosion. Below, combining wheat in the American Great Plains. An area of sparse population, huge ranches, and mechanized farming, the trend is toward even greater consolidation of holdings. The large scale in which wheat is grown here is exemplified by this photo with five combines working as a team. (Photos courtesy of the Soil Conservation Service, USDA and the International Harvester Company)

crops. Nevertheless, the Great Plains persist as a land of uncertainty and occasional calamity—one where some such enemy as drought, hail, rust, or insects is ever ready to spread desolation far and wide.

DESERT AND MAN

Figure 9–2 spotlights the dry lands of the world —those in the Tropical, Subtropical, and Cyclonic zones. It is estimated that these cover some 19 million square miles—almost 36 percent of the earth's surface. They are roughly twice as large as the total cultivated area of the world.

Deserts are not uniform: it is difficult to generalize about them. The only thing that can be said about all of them is that the balance between life and death is critical at all times because water is scarce.

With the world's population increasing at an alarming rate in relation to the amount of arable land, scientists are paying more attention to the deserts. Almost annually, scholars from all over the world meet to discuss major problems of the dry lands. For the most part man has not adjusted himself well to the arid and semiarid regions of the world. He has actually been greedy in his misuse of the land. Said Homer L. Shantz at such a meeting,

His herds have removed much of the scanty cover of nutritious grasses and shrubs. . . . His path has been marked by ruins of human settlements. . . . We have seen beautiful areas of desert grassland reduced to bare soil and useless weeds by overgrazing, brushlands reduced to nonpalatable bush by fire . . . and the short grass of our high plains replaced by wheat and summer fallow and followed by the desert bowl.

In these arid and semiarid regions, the value of land hinges on the availability of water. Streams from mountains and lakes can irrigate only a fraction of the areas needing water. Underground sources often prove inadequate after several years' use. Ocean water cannot be freshened economically for purposes of irrigation at present and perhaps never can be. Man is today utilizing only about 2 percent of the dry lands. He will

Figure 16–10 Field of Kaffir corn in the Southern portion of the Dry Continental Great Plains. Farmers grow the grain sorghums, which are the most certain crops in this region of light and unreliable rainfall, instead of corn as a feed for cattle, swine, and work animals. The grain sorghums are well suited to this type of climate because they have a low water requirement. (Photo courtesy of USDA)

utilize more only as he learns more effectually to adjust himself to the dry milieu.

THE DEVELOPMENT OF IRRIGATION

Surface and underground sources of water have transformed millions of acres of sunbaked plain into verdant gardens, from hostile desert to hospitable oasis. Wherever possible in deserts, man irrigates; but owing to light precipitation, limited water supply, rugged topography, or infertile soils, only a small percentage of the total land area is irrigable, probably less than 10 percent in most parts of the realm.

In every Dry Continental region lie oases, insular concentrations of human activity, which, like verdant islands in mid-ocean, are separated from the nearest shores of industry by hundreds of miles of desert, mountain crag, and canyon. Western United States bristles with them.

While man has successfully conquered parts of the semiarid lands through scientific agriculture (Fig. 16–11), he has made little progress in the truly arid sections except where water is

Figure 16–11   Irrigating potatoes planted on the contour in Idaho. Note the gated surface pipe which supplies water to the furrows. (Photo courtesy of USDA)

available for irrigation. Probably 90 to 95 percent of such lands, if they are to be used at all, must remain the domain of the pastoralist.

THE CROPS

The principal irrigated crops of Dry Continental America are sugar beets, fruits, vegetables, potatoes, grain, and hay. Contrary to general opinion, the ordinary field crops predominate.

It should be realized that in many oases, the variety of crops is not limited by the possibility of production but rather by the probability of consumption. With limited local markets and high production costs, crops having high value per unit of weight must be grown, for only they can stand transportation costs to distant markets. Thus the average yield of an acre of sugar beets, 2,500 pounds of refined sugar, can be shipped from our Intermontane West as far east as Chicago.

Alfalfa is the most widely grown crop in irrigated western United States; however, it does not have this high value per unit of weight. But alfalfa is marketed in the concentrated form of beef, mutton, and pork, products which can easily stand the cost of transportation to distant markets.

Potatoes in Idaho are an exception to the concept that this crop cannot be shipped great distances. The potato is perishable and it has low value per unit of weight. Yet Idaho markets its famous superior "baker" into every part of the United States. It also converts huge tonnages into hydrated form capable of standing costly transport.

ADVANTAGES OF IRRIGATION

Irrigation farming is characterized by high per acre yields, a consequence of the following.
1. Fertile soils which have been spared leaching by the light precipitation
2. Water supply which is regulated, so that crops receive the proper amount at the proper time
3. Fine silt, carried by the water, which has value as a soil former
4. High percentage of sunshine
5. Comparative freedom from insect pests and diseases
6. Intensive cultivation
7. Almost ideal weather conditions which do not interfere with field work

DISADVANTAGES OF IRRIGATION

The principal physical geographic disadvantages connected with irrigation are the susceptibility of the soils to becoming water-logged and alkaline. Nearly every irrigated region, even when its agricultural history is brief, has fallen victim to one or both of these misfortunes. Both conditions occur most commonly where bench lands adjoin valleys or plains. Because the soils on the benches are porous, they require heavy applications of water to insure satisfactory yields. This excessive irrigation applied at the higher levels percolates downward until it reaches a layer of fine-grained soil, compact and nearly impervious. Flowing downward along this to a lower level, it comes near the surface and forms a wet spot. This water-logging becomes pronounced in such areas as the Great Basin, where the water obviously moves to the lowest levels. Soils frequently become alkaline after irrigation has been practiced. Saline material dissolved in the underground water reaches the surface through capillarity. The water evaporates but the alkaline salts remain in the surface zone. Land so impregnated cannot be used for crops until tile-drained and flushed with pure water, whereupon it regains productivity. But this procedure is costly.

AGRICULTURE IN DRY CONTINENTAL EURASIA AND SOUTH AMERICA

Most of Dry Continental Eurasia falls politically within the confines of the Union of Soviet Socialist Republics. This is significant, for otherwise in all probability these lands would have remained the domain of the pastoralist, with just a sprinkling of oases dotting the landscape. Under socialism great changes in farming have taken place.

The government has constructed huge irrigation projects in the dry lands of southwestern Asia. There are some large rivers, snow-and-glacier fed, among which are the Syr Darya and the Amu Darya. Until Soviet times most of the waters carried by these and other rivers was lost, for central Asia is primarily a region of interior drainage—of rivers without mouths, of lakes that have no outlets, of seas whose inflow is offset by evaporation and whose salty waters never reach the ocean.

In former uncharted wastes of Kirghizia, Kazakhstan, Turkmenia, and Uzbekistan farmers on state farms or sovkhoses have built hundreds of miles of irrigation canals and are now growing appreciable quantities of cotton, sugar beets, wheat, tobacco, fruits, and vegetables. Thousands of men and women who were nomads only a short time ago now operate complex agricultural machinery.

The state farm is considered the ultimate form of the socialized agricultural unit and is more specialized than the collective farm. On such a farm the worker is paid a regular wage in the same manner as a factory worker.

Most of Russia's cotton is grown in her Dry Continental region and production has soared as a result of the Soviet five-year plans. As early as 1933, the country was supplying almost its entire requirements of raw cotton. Most of the crop is grown in Uzbekistan. Nearly all the cotton is grown under irrigation.

Pioneering is going forward on a huge scale in the Soviet Union. Some 70 million acres of new land were sown in the eastern regions by 1956—half of them in the Dry Continental part, particularly Kazakhstan. Here huge state farms have been created by the Soviet government on the boundless steppe, many of them on lands—the so-called "virgin lands"—never before touched by the plow. Distances are vast, transport is limited, and people are few—six persons to the square mile. The work is being done by armies of young people mobilized from all over the country.

That the parts of the Soviet Union having the Humid Continental with Medium and Long Summers climates (see Chapter 15) are unable to supply the food required seems certain as a result of a major move by the Kremlin of turning to the expansion of grain acreage in this climate of precarious farming. Here the precipitation averages ten to fourteen inches per year, the fall is irregular, strong winter winds blow snow from the fields, late spring and summer droughts are frequent and are aggravated by scorching winds; and the harvest period is often cursed by inclement weather. The conclusion is therefore unavoidable that crop failures must be expected, since this grandiose scheme does not appear to be physically, economically, or technologically feasible.

Very little of Dry Continental Argentina is devoted to agriculture. Patagonia is a land of sheep raising. There are a few oases along the Colorado, Negro, and lower Chubut rivers. Some seventy thousand acres have been settled in a relatively new irrigation project along the Rio Negro where alfalfa, grapes, and pears are the principal crops.

ECONOMIC ADJUSTMENTS OTHER THAN AGRICULTURE

Regions characterized by Dry Continental climate have limited economic potentialities. They can support only relatively small populations and these only where water is available. Grazing, it would seem, must ever be the principal occupation; locally, farming, mining, and even manufacturing assume importance. A few large cities have developed in strategic locations as a result of water and of transportation by railway, highway, and airway.

HUNTING

Originally all sections with this climate were occupied by primitive folk who depended wholly upon the chase and a few untilled vegetative resources. As the population increased, the wild game declined and new adjustments became imperative.

In Asia the domestication of animals followed though hunting continued as an adjunct of grazing. The Kirghiz, for instance, kills the grass-browsing antelope and the seed-eating quail, which add variety to his monotonous diet of sour milk and cheese. He also fights the wolf which constantly preys upon his horses, cattle, and sheep.

The North American Indian, on the other hand, was still in the hunting stage when the white man arrived, and most of the contests between the two were over hunting grounds. Even the first white men were trappers and fur-traders.

In Patagonia, the few remaining Indians are hunters even today, deriving nearly all their food from the wild guanaco and rhea, which they hunt with bolas.

PASTORAL ADJUSTMENTS

Pastoralism must continue to characterize the greater part of all truly Dry Continental regions, because nature has dedicated them for that purpose.

Cattle, which thrive better than sheep on soft grasses and at the same time are more profitable, predominate in the semiarid sections.

Year-long grazing is possible in some of the lowlands, but in the cooler and higher portions of the Intermontane Region and the Great Plains some animals are certain to die during blizzards. In recent years "hay lifts" have been employed for dropping hay from airplanes to the starving cattle.

Only a small proportion of beef cattle now moves to slaughter directly off grass; the Great Plains serve essentially as producing areas of feeder cattle—cattle requiring further conditioning. About half of all western cattle feeding is done on Great Plains ranches and feed lots. The irrigated valleys bordering the South Platte and Arkansas rivers in eastern Colorado are especially important. Feeder cattle are fattened during winter and spring on hay, grain, and sugar beet by-products. Corn, as we have seen, is not a basic part of Dry Continental agriculture (Fig. 16–12). Cattle raised in the Great Basin either are fattened on farms and feed lots in the irrigated areas of the climatic region or in the Imperial Valley of California.

Patagonia differs from other middle latitude semiarid lands in having few cattle; it specializes in sheep. But this is more a response to topography and soil and to poor transport facilities than to climate, though it must not be denied that sheep do better than cattle because of the inclement winters and scant pasturage. Patagonia has become synonymous with sheep, and sheepherding is almost the sole occupation of the people. Gigantic ranches comprising tens and even hundreds of thousands of acres are devoted exclusively to sheep. The large size is a response to the low-carrying capacity of the range, eight to ten acres being required to support one sheep. The ranches are so extensive that neighbors frequently do not see one another for weeks at a time. Hardy merino sheep, famous for their wool, are raised on the poor pastures. Thus, in a land of few railways, wool can be hauled profitably by wagon hundreds of miles to a rail head or to a port. Few products of agriculture can stand such costly transportation.

Sheep properly dominate the desert lands. No other domesticated animal has proved so adaptable to the varying conditions of natural environment; it thrives on the lush green pastures of mountains, which often border arid lands, or on the harsh almost leafless gray shrubs of the desert.

Dry Continental United States is the stronghold of the nation's sheep industry; at least nine-tenths of the land is either too dry, too rugged, or too cold for crops. The entire area, except

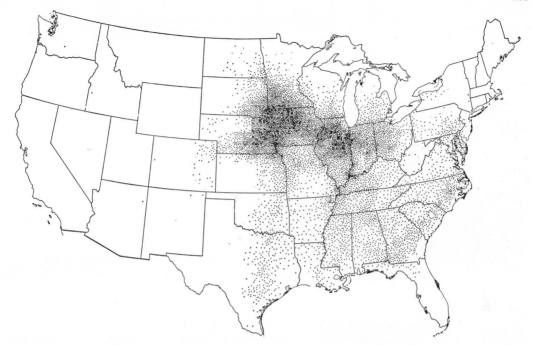

Figure 16–12   Corn harvested for grain in the United States—one dot represents 10,000 acres. Dry Continental United States appears unimpressive on the map of corn acreage. Corn needs hot days and hot nights and eighteen inches or more of rainfall. These conditions are not present in the Dry Continental lands. Hence in Kansas, Oklahoma, Texas, eastern Colorado, and eastern New Mexico, the grain sorghums serve as substitutes for corn. (Map adapted from the Bureau of the Census)

occasional bare spots, can thus be utilized. In Utah, west of Salt Lake City, from seven to twenty-three acres are required to support one sheep for the grazing season of two to five months. Bands varying in size from 1,200 to 5,000 head are cared for by herders who follow them around the calendar, guarding them against predatory animals and directing their grazing. Sheep are admirably suited to the country, since they relish harsh, thorny, and nearly leafless plants.

In winter many of the bleating droves graze over the desert, unless deep snows force them into the irrigated oases where they are fed alfalfa and grain. As soon as the foothills become cloaked with green, which usually is in early April, the sheep are trailed there. By mid-June they move into the lower mountains, grazing higher and higher as the snow-line retreats. By August they may be grazing at elevations of ten thousand to eleven thousand feet. At this period the sheep may go for days or weeks without water (something cattle cannot do), provided

only the dew be heavy or snow be available. By mid-October the animals have descended into the foothills, and by winter they are once more in the desert where they remain till the snow melts and the water supply disappears.[8] Flocks frequently wander as many as 250 miles during a march. This seasonal migration under the care of shepherds is called *transhumance*.

Inner Asia is the original home of the sheep and of the pastoral nomad. (For a discussion of pastoral adjustments in Inner Asia see Chapter 6.)

MINING

Mining attains some prominence in practically all Dry Continental regions. In the greater part of arid America (excluding the semiarid Great Plains), mining became the chief human activity soon after ores were discovered. Prospectors went

[8] Attention should be called to the fact that the pasturage of the desert could support sheep in summer if water were available.

Figure 16–13   Kennecott mine, Bingham, Utah. This mine is one of the world's largest, most interesting, and most profitable copper enterprises. Here a huge mountain of ore is being systematically torn down by blasting and with power shovels. Note the many levels, each completely tracked and completely electrified. So immense are the mining operations that the trains look like toys. (Photo courtesy of the Salt Lake Chamber of Commerce)

everywhere, penetrating even the most remote and hostile districts. Ere long the Rocky Mountain and the Intermontane regions bristled with mines. Only the early Mormon settlements at the foot of the Wasatch Mountains in Utah were based solely upon agriculture. Elsewhere farming was an adjunct of mining. Even today mining is the principal economic basis of life in many parts of the West (Fig. 16–13). This region possesses and supplies a variety of minerals including coal, iron, copper, silver, lead, zinc, tungsten, petroleum, natural gas, various alkaline salts, and a host of others needed in an industrial civilization. Salt is the only one directly linked to the climatic conditions, Utah's Great Salt Lake supporting an important industry. Water is pumped from the lake onto adjoining diked flats and with a series of ponds the density of the water is so

maintained that almost pure salt is precipitated in one pond. After the hot desert sun evaporates the water, the salt is sent to nearby refineries for purifying and packing.

For centuries little was known regarding the mineral possibilities of south central Asia. Under the Soviets, however, geological field parties have been systematically prospecting and surveying the land and today this region constitutes a rich segment of the Russian mineral heritage. Not only are these resources abundant, they also are of great variety.

The government has forced the expansion of mining in accordance with its five-year plans. The risk of depending upon mines near the western frontier was realized. As important deposits were discovered, they were developed. In a number of instances in Dry Continental south-central Asia where the population was sparse and where fixed centers were scarce, mining towns were built by the government.

Patagonia has not yet shown much evidence of potential mineral wealth, and even if rich deposits should be discovered, development will be retarded by isolation and all it implies. Nonetheless, in the Comodoro Rivadavia area on the Patagonian coast are Argentina's largest oil and gas fields. And at Rio Turbio, in the far south of Patagonia near the Chilean border, is the country's largest source of coal, albeit low-grade and noncokable.

MANUFACTURING AND COMMERCIAL ADJUSTMENTS

Manufacturing is nowhere of major importance nor does it promise ever to become so for the small population means restricted markets. The industries that do arise will be those concerned with satisfying local needs and with preparing the limited products of range, ranch, and mine

for transportation to distant markets. Only products having high value per unit of weight can stand the exacting costs of transportation. Hence flour milling, sugar refining, fruit, vegetable, and milk canning, meat packing, salt making, and mineral concentrating and smelting are the characteristic industries. During World War II, the United States government constructed an iron and steel mill at Geneva, Utah, to supply the shipyards of the Pacific Coast. The plant (Fig. 16–14) uses Utah raw materials. It now belongs to the United States Steel Corporation and sends much of its steel to the big mills at Pittsburg, California. Another large iron and steel industry operates in Pueblo, Colorado.

The accepted economic geographic principles of industrial location as they apply to private enterprise in Europe, America, and elsewhere must be abandoned when considering manufacturing in the Dry Continental portion of the Soviet Union, for here all manufacturing is under ownership and control of the government. A

Figure 16–14 A view of the U.S. Steel Corporation's Geneva Works near Provo, Utah. This integrated plant plays a vital role in the industrial economy of the West. (Photo courtesy of Hal Rummel)

major objective of the Soviet Union is industrial self-sufficiency. Accordingly, manufacturing plants have been located with reference to both economic efficiency and strategic safety. Miscellaneous general industries serving local needs have been created and they save much needless transportation. Most Soviet industry, however, is located in the triangular coreland—an area synonymous with the greatest concentration of population.

Hardly anywhere is commerce well developed, a consequence of isolation, poor transportation, and small population. All three of these are magnified in south-central Asia and for generations trade was relatively unimportant. Annual fairs were held in all towns of importance. Transportation was by caravan. Now, however, several railways tap the region and travel by air is common.

SOCIAL ADJUSTMENTS

Dry Continental lands afford an excellent illustration of the manner in which human settlement is limited by an unyielding nature. Save in the occasional oasis, population is very thinly distributed. Everywhere population density depends on the water supply, for water means life to plant, animal, and man. Consequently life and industry are singularly localized—a localization not to be found in humid regions where barriers do not separate the various productive areas.

The land suitable for habitation is always quickly acquired. More land may be reclaimed in nearly all irrigated communities, but only by adopting better methods of utilizing the water supply. There is a limit, however, to the population a desert can support, even when every available drop of water is carefully husbanded and utilized. Such regions undisputedly have a limited future. Since land without water is usually of only meager value and since the supply of water is restricted, the irrigated land almost everywhere (except in the Soviet Union) is held in small parcels and is intensively cultivated.

Since so large a percentage of Dry Continental lands consists of trouble areas, it is obvious that effective solution of the problems has gone beyond the capabilities of individuals and small groups. All the easy things have been done. Small streams of the type that were promptly put to use for irrigation by the pioneer Mormons have long since been tapped. In fact, they had been put to use as early as 1890. Any new irrigation project in the American West must now be on a grand scale and cost tens or even hundreds of millions of dollars—for example, the Grand Coulee.

Many social problems face dry-land man. For example, on the Great Plains ideas and traditions were carried from the East, resulting in the wide and scattered distribution of homes. Hence, the people have to work out some kind of community that enables them to overcome the social isolation that comes from widely scattered farm homes—particularly the high costs of education and health.

As indicated above, not all the inhabitants of dry lands are graziers and farmers; many are miners. Discoveries of ore bodies give birth to camps and even small cities. Because the mining industry expands and contracts continuously, the population fluctuates with it.

POLITICAL ADJUSTMENTS

The oasis farmer, cognizant of the necessity of cooperation, respects law and order and builds a government strong enough to control the distribution of water, the public control of which is essential to its best use. He engages in serious disputes and conflicts only in the early stages of settlement when the water is not properly allocated and farmers upstream use too much while those downstream get too little. At such a time some power beyond the disputants must enter and define their respective rights. Accordingly, water laws have been framed everywhere in arid America as a means of avoiding trouble and they are carefully enforced and obeyed. The Mormons evolved a system of irrigation which is a model of what individuals working in harmony can do, but this was due to the influence of the Mormon Church which, during the pioneer period, served as the source of law in temporal as well as in spiritual matters.

Laws have had to be passed to protect the range from overgrazing also in Dry Continental

United States. In the early days there was free-for-all grazing; anyone was at liberty to use the public domain and there were practically no restrictions. This resulted in a mad scramble to get as much grass as possible, in serious impairment of the range, and in deterioration of herds. The Taylor Grazing Act of 1933 was designed to bring the public range lands under responsible control by withdrawing public domain from homestead entry and by providing for the formation of districts within which public domain is leased to stockmen under regulations leading to conservation of the range.

In a desert and in a humid region, the climate is known and the inhabitants can plan accordingly. But in semiarid regions men are frequently misled because their lands are sometimes humid, sometimes desert, and sometimes a cross between the two. Semiarid lands are lands of calamity. After each serious drought in the American Great Plains there is much land abandonment. Migration from the Great Plains was particularly heavy between 1930 and 1940. At such times, those people who remain find it almost impossible to help themselves; hence they call upon their government for aid. Governments spend huge sums of money trying to improve conditions. This has been true both in the United States and Canada. Such lands appear to be marked by nature as lands of tragedy.

The Asiatic nomad was long hostile toward any centralized government. His idea of government was a tribe or clan consisting of several families and ruled by an aged patriarch whose authority was unquestioned. Such small groups, widely distributed over remote and isolated regions and ever on the move, made possible only feeble political control from the outside. Accordingly, such tent dwellers were generally left to their own devices.

The Soviet government, however, has made serious inroads in the old order. It has convinced the former nomads that they have an important role to play in the development of the Soviet Union. Moreover, it has built railroads, highways, irrigation projects, hydroelectric installations; it is developing minerals and constructing industrial plants. The government has drilled hundreds of wells at strategic points for winter use by livestock and it has built sheds for the protection of domestic animals during particularly severe storms; it has introduced veterinarians to help the people improve the health of their livestock. Consequently, these people who were long considered to be incurable nomads are today working on collective and state farms, many operating complex machinery.

One interesting aspect of the political geography of Dry Continental U.S.S.R. is that the government considered science to be a weapon for transforming nature. A huge afforestation project for changing the natural conditions on the steppe was launched. Forest belts were created for slowing down the dry winds—the *Suxovei*—to mitigate their effect on the cereal lands. The plan, however, proved unsuccessful.

SUGGESTED USEFUL READINGS

Butland, Gilbert J., *Latin America: A Regional Geography* (London, Longmans, Green & Company, Ltd., 1960), pp. 267–271.

Cressey, George B., *Asia's Lands and Peoples*, 3d ed. (New York, McGraw-Hill Book Company, Inc., 1963), 663 pp.

Ginsburg, Norton, ed., *The Pattern of Asia* (Englewood Cliffs, N.J., Prentice-Hall, Inc., 1958), 929 pp.

James, Preston, *Latin America*, 3d ed. (New York, The Odyssey Press, 1959), pp. 318–324.

Kennedy, Michael S., *The Red Man's West* (New York, Hastings House, Publishers, Inc., 1965).

Stamp, L. Dudley, ed., *The History of Land Use in Arid Regions* (Nancy, France, UNESCO, 1961).

Thornthwaite, C. Warren, *Climate and Settlement in the Great Plains*, U.S. Department of Agriculture Yearbook for 1941, 1942, Washington, D.C.

Weil, F. J., *The Argentine Riddle* (New York, The John Day Company, Inc., 1944).

Willis, Bailey, *Northern Patagonia* (New York, Charles Scribner's Sons, 1914).

Zierer, Clifford M., ed., *California and the Southwest* (New York, John Wiley & Sons, Inc., 1956), 376 pp.

17

Temperate Marine Climate Regions

The Temperate Marine is the mildest climate in the world for its latitude and is the only climate in the Cyclonic Zone which truly merits being called *temperate*. Both the diurnal and the annual ranges of temperature fluctuate far less than elsewhere in the zone because of the tempering influence of large bodies of water. According to Kendrew,[1] areas with this climate "are in the most favored part of the westerlies, for owing to their windward exposure they are exempt from extreme cold in winter, and from aridity—the scourges of the temperate belt in the interior and east of continental masses." Thus Ketchikan[2] in southeastern Alaska enjoys considerably milder winters than Washington, D. C., which lies more than a thousand miles farther south. By the same token northwest Europe is about 10° F. warmer, even in the dead of winter, than it would be were it not for the Atlantic Ocean, the waters of which are warmed by the Gulf Stream Drift. This enables civilized human beings to dwell north of the Arctic Circle in Norway.

Temperate Marine regions are situated on the windward side of continents and are, therefore, greatly influenced by the adjacent ocean waters. Hence, in contrast to most portions of the Cyclonic Zone, their summers are warm rather than hot and their winters cool rather than cold. This climate is often called the "mild-winter–mild-summer" type (Fig. 17–1). Pronounced and sudden changes in the weather are rare. Freezing temperatures occur only a few times each winter and snow rarely falls on the lowlands. There are, of course, exceptions, for snow falls each winter in Seattle and Portland. In some years England is blanketed for short periods with heavy snowfall and suffers from the accompanying cold weather.

Glaciers are not uncommon in the Temperate Marine portions of North America, South America, and New Zealand, where but little melting of winter snow occurs on elevated areas (Fig. 17–2).

Landward this climate grades into the continental types, the rapidity of the change depending upon topography. It penetrates farther inland in Europe than elsewhere, because no lofty and continuous mountain barrier intercepts the rain-bearing winds.

One of the most interesting aspects of this climate in the Northern Hemisphere is the failure of the temperature to decrease notably from south to north: instead it decreases considerably in a west-easterly direction—from the coast inland during winter and spring, and from the land seaward during summer. Cyclones and anticyclones pass over Temperate Marine regions but cause smaller changes in weather than in those areas with continental climates.

[1] W. G. Kendrew, *Climate* (London, Oxford University Press, 1930), pp. 317–318.
[2] Many people believe that latitude alone determines climate. Cognizance is not taken of the influence of altitude and of proximity to large bodies of water and ocean currents. Incongruous though it may seem, it is nevertheless a fact that life insurance was once denied a denizen of Ketchikan, southernmost port of Alaska, on the ground that the "severe climate entailed undue risks."

295

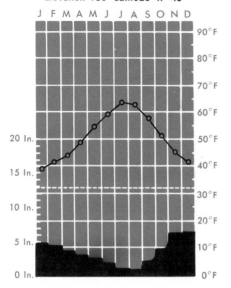

Figure 17–1 Climate graph for Seattle, Washington.

Temperate Marine regions are characterized by heavy to moderate rainfall in the lowlands depending upon proximity to the sea, and excessive rainfall on the uplands, as well as by the absence of a dry period. The coast of Washington

records the heaviest precipitation in the United States, and southern Chile is so wet as to be practically uninhabited (Fig. 17–3). The fall decreases sharply on the lee sides of mountains as in the Willamette Valley of Oregon, the Canterbury Plain of New Zealand, Patagonia, and eastern England.

The maximum precipitation falls in winter when the cool land chills the moisture-bearing oceanic winds. Light showers and gentle drizzles brought by cyclonic storms prevail and sometimes continue for days on end. These drizzly rains result in reduced and slow surface runoff, the net result being a minimum of soil erosion. This situation is in sharp contrast with that, for example, in Humid Subtropical and Humid Continental with Long Summers climates, where thundershowers are a major factor in soil erosion.

Relatively few days are rainless. Cloudy and foggy weather is almost unbroken in winter. Summer is characterized by occasional periods of bright sunshiny weather and by a light haze which frequently obscures distant objects for considerable periods. Thus one may remain in Seattle many days without sighting Mount Rainier fifty-five miles distant. Relative humidity is always high and evaporation correspondingly low. While

Figure 17–2 Aerial view of the head of Chickamin Glacier, Alaska. (Photo by Leland J. Prater, courtesy of the U.S. Forest Service)

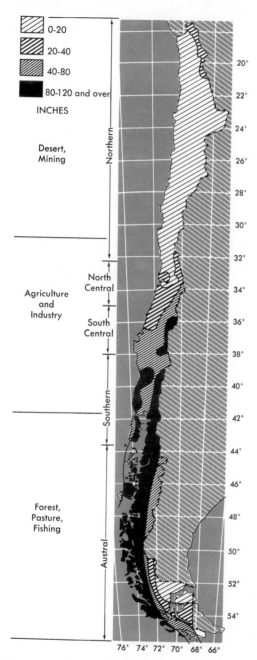

0-20
20-40
40-80
80-120 and over
INCHES

Desert,
Mining

Northern

Agriculture
and
Industry

North
Central

South
Central

Southern

Forest,
Pasture,
Fishing

Austral

20°
22°
24°
26°
28°
30°
32°
34°
36°
38°
40°
42°
44°
46°
48°
50°
52°
54°

76° 74° 72° 70° 68° 66°

Figure 17–3 Rainfall of Chile. The north is one of the driest areas in the world, the south one of the rainiest. The latter, with its high winds and heavy rainfall, is an unpleasant land—the nation's frontier with only about 1 percent of the total population. The economic activities in each region reflect close adjustment to climate. (Map adapted from the Office of Foreign Agricultural Relations, USDA)

winds are prevailingly from the west, they may blow from any point on the compass.

TEMPERATE MARINE REGIONS

This climate is imprinted upon the western sides of continents and extends poleward from regions having the Mediterranean Subtropical type. The boundary between the two is roughly latitude 40°. The only exception to this generalization is the Australia-Tasmania-New Zealand section. This is attributable in the case of Australia to the fact that the continent extends for only a short distance into the belt of westerlies and in the case of the islands to the fact that they are relatively narrow. Except for Australia, east coast Temperate Marine climates do not obtain because of severe temperatures which result from leeward location and because of monsoon wind systems with associated air masses.

Specifically, this climate occurs in North America from northern California to the Aleutian Islands; in the southern third of Chile; throughout much of northwest Europe including the British Isles; on the southern coast of Victoria, Australia; and in Tasmania and New Zealand (Fig. 17–4).

NATURAL VEGETATION

Temperate Marine vegetation is or has been essentially heavy forest, but it is not uniform throughout the realm. In places it exhibits a luxuriance customarily ascribed only to the Rainy Tropics. Conifers predominate in some places, hardwoods in others. Northwestern United States and adjacent Canada possess the world's finest and most magnificent evergreen forest. This consists of Douglas fir, cedar, hemlock, and spruce and, at the southern margin, the redwood. The Douglas fir is probably the most important commercial tree. Nowhere else, not even in the Rainy Tropics, do such forests exist. The stand is often dense, pure, and tall. A giant frequently lifts its head two hundred or more feet into the sky and has a diameter of three to six feet. The great size is a response to the mild rainy climate and physiological resistance to insects and fungus diseases.

The foggy valleys on the western slope of the Coast Range of northern California comprise the Redwood Empire—probably the most majestic forest in the world (Fig. 17–5). The typical

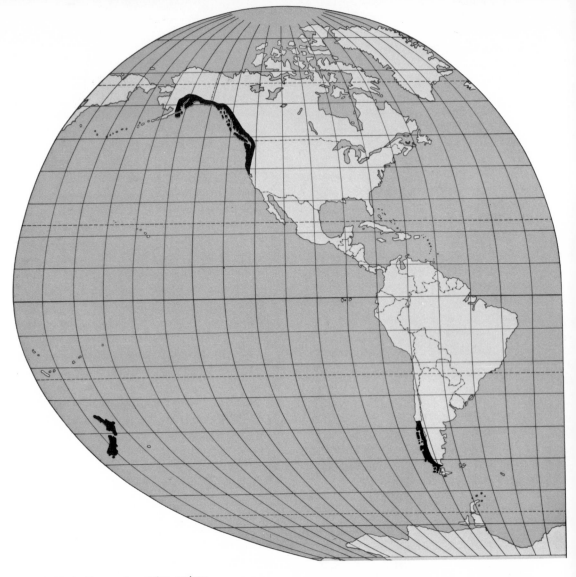

Figure 17–4 Temperate marine regions.

redwood grows higher than any tree known, often three hundred feet. Moreover, the trees make up the heaviest stand of timber on earth. The shade is so dense as practically to exclude undergrowth. There are some broadleaf trees in the Pacific Northwest, but on a numerical basis they amount to but 6 percent of the entire forest and on the basis of timber volume one to one thousand. In other parts of the world having the Temperate Marine climate, broadleaf forests prevail. Actually, the proportion should be greater here on the basis of climatic comparison.[3]

The Temperate Marine forest in northwestern Europe consists essentially of deciduous trees, for example, beech and oak. Some spruce is found in the higher elevations.

The forests of Chile are composed largely of broadleaf evergreens. South of latitude 46° S., the forest is dominated by two deciduous species of beech. Farther north, however, the forest becomes more varied and is essentially evergreen. Conifers, much in the minority, occur throughout but are most abundant in the northern sections.

The New Zealand forest closely resembles that of southern Chile. Mixed forests are the rule, but there are all variations from purely conifer-

[3] Students particularly interested in the composition of Temperate Marine forests will be well rewarded by reading A. W. Kuchler, "The Broadleaf Deciduous Forests of the Pacific Northwest," *Annals of the Association of American Geographers,* Vol. 36 (June, 1946), pp. 122–147.

ous to purely broadleaf forests. The Kauri pine, one of the world's largest trees and New Zealand's best known conifer, is limited to the north.

Where soils are porous, forests of mixed hardwoods generally prevail. In the dripping, poorly drained areas, as well as in those deficient in spring rain, trees give way to grass which grows as thick turf and is always lush and green. Ireland has no forest but much grass, which is so brilliantly green as to earn it the appellation of the "Emerald Isle."

SOILS

Northwestern Europe is the only region having this type of climate where a large percentage of the land is used for growing crops. The mature soils are predominantly gray-brown podzolic soils, with podzols on some of the sandier areas. Alluvial soils are present in the Netherlands and elsewhere in Europe. Glacial soils mantle considerable areas bordering the North Sea—they run the whole gamut from sterile sands to fertile loams. On the whole, the gray-brown podzolic soils of northwestern Europe favor agriculture.

Elsewhere—along the coasts of North America, southern Chile, and Norway—the agricultural soils are limited to valleys and comprise only a small proportion of the total area involved. They are alluvial and though they vary greatly, the gray-brown podzolic types are most common. These soils everywhere are light colored and leached, and were developed under forest cover and humid conditions.

299

Figure 17–5 Old growth redwood stand in California. For 125 miles in a strip 10 to 25 miles wide along the coast of northern California grows this stately and magnificent tree. It thrives in the cool, humid, foggy climate. Many of these trees are more than 2,000 years old, are 350 feet high, and have a diameter of 15 feet. In yield of timber, this forest is unique; single acres contain as many as 1 million feet of lumber, while the average is reported to be about 250,000 feet. (Photo by Douglas F. Roy, courtesy of the U.S. Forest Service)

NATIVE ANIMAL LIFE

The fauna of Temperate Marine lands is not restricted to them but is distributed over several adjacent types of climate. Exceptions to this generalization, of course, do exist. Among the more important animals are the elk, bear, wolf, lynx, fox, rabbit, badger, lemming, otter, beaver, marten, raccoon, squirrel, several varieties of deer, and such reptiles as snakes and lizards.

While animal life is more plentiful in the Northern than in the Southern Hemisphere, it is nowhere abundant in this climate.

THE "IDEAL" CLIMATE

The Temperate Marine has been mentioned by some early geographers as the climate par excellence for maximum human accomplishment, although its low sunshine quotient is productive of deleterious physical effects, particularly in young children. Some say its conditions excel those of all other climates in their stimulating effect on mind and body. They aver that human beings are most alert and can carry on mental activity most efficiently when the out-of-doors temperature is about 40° F. and are at their optimum physically when it is about 60° F. They point out further that people do best in a moist climate and in one that is changeable, particularly where the *variability* of weather spurs man to accomplishment. The Temperate Marine combines many of these favorable conditions, though not uniformly throughout. The North Sea region is said by some to approach the climatic "ideal" most closely, and specifically the climate of southeast England has been held up as approaching closest the ideal for most forms of human activity.

It should be realized, however, that the role of weather and climate in human activities is a much debated issue and promises to be for a long time to come. Bioclimatologists, doctors of medicine, geographers, and others, however, are improving their techniques and acquiring more reliable data year by year. Industries want to know how to make working conditions as favorable as possible for their employees, and the armed forces of several of the stronger nations are carrying on research involving accurate systematic observations by laboratory experimentation and by valid statistical treatment of data.

While climate is significant as a factor affecting the everyday conditions of human life, it should be considered as a limiting factor to be slowly and steadily conquered by science rather than as an absolute determinant.[4]

Some authorities predict that American civilization will reach its peak in Pacific North America (Fig. 17–6). While climate seems to be a salient factor in this forecast, the critical importance of the great potential resources in water power, timber, fisheries, and pastures, and of the strategic location for trade with the Orient and Australia is clearly discernible.

[4] Emily Heine, "Taking the Heat Off Industrial Workers," *Du Pont Magazine*, Vol. 49 (August-September, 1955), pp. 2–4.

ECONOMIC ADJUSTMENTS

The Temperate Marine climate is well suited to nearly all economic activities other than agriculture, for which only the less rainy areas are well adapted.

Temperate Marine Europe is the home and center of the world's greatest industrial development. Climatic factors such as variability, moderate temperatures, and moist air have contributed to this achievement, but the presence of coal and iron ore, along with hydroelectric power, easy access to salt water, strategic and central geographical location, and the genius of the people themselves have contributed as much as or more than the climate. In short, progress has resulted from the intermeshing of physical and human factors.

FISHING

Fishing plays a more vital role in the economic life of Temperate Marine people than in that of civilized folk in any other type of climate. Even in highly civilized northwest Europe, fishing gives employment to large numbers of people— to one-tenth of the Norwegians, for example.[5]

Most northwest European countries send out fleets of ships to catch the fish which constitute so important a part of the food of the poorer people. The fishing grounds of the North Sea and the coastal waters of Norway, which abound in cod, haddock, and herring, are among the most prolific in the world.

More than any other civilized people, the Norwegians depend upon the sea, a result of nature's niggardly endowment in cultivable soil, minerals, and timber (Fig. 17–7). Only 3 percent is arable, the rest consisting of rugged terrain, largely unoccupied. Conditions for fishing, however, are almost ideal, consisting of (1) proximity to prolific feeding and spawning grounds, (2) protection from storms by fiords and skerries, (3) cool temperatures which stimulate the men to perform hard work and at the same time favor a high quality in fish and facilitate drying, and (4) freedom from winter ice.

Great Britain is the undisputed leader of the

[5] Statistically, only 6 percent of Norway's people are directly engaged in the fisheries. This figure, however, does not give the true picture, for many farmers who live along the fiords spend as much or more time fishing as farming, yet they are classed as farmers.

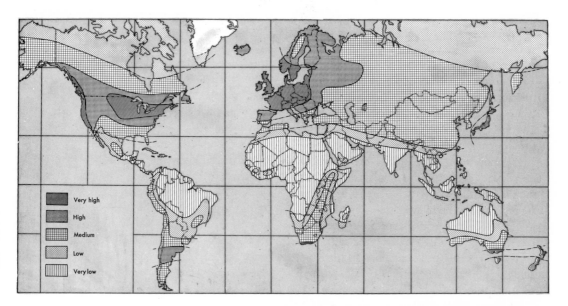

Figure 17–6 World distribution of climatic energy—the combined physical and mental activity which might be expected if people's activity depended upon climate alone. Note that only four areas rank *very high* and that all of these lie almost entirely within the Cyclonic Zone—northwestern Europe, east-central North America, Pacific North America, and Tasmania and southern New Zealand. (Map after Ellsworth Huntingdon and E. B. Shaw, *Principles of Human Geography*, 6th ed., New York, John Wiley & Sons, Inc., 1951)

Figure 17–7   Fishing for herring on Norway's west coast. (Photo courtesy of the Norwegian Embassy Information Service)

famous North Sea fisheries. The business is centered in several large ports, of which the principal one is Grimsby—the largest fish market in the world.

Brittany in France is also a land of fishermen; infertile soil, excessive rainfall and cloudiness, isolation from the heart of France, long coastline and proximity to prolific fishing grounds, all have conspired to entice man seaward.

Temperate Marine North America is one of the world's major fishing regions. Most of the catch is taken from coastal waters or in the lower courses of streams. Some banks fishing also is carried on. Salmon is the principal species caught in the region, although halibut and herring also are important. In fact, Temperate Marine North America possesses the world's leading salmon fisheries.

Salmon have strange habits and fall easy prey to fishermen. They are born in the upper reaches of streams which penetrate inland as far as 2,500 miles. The young spend a short time

in the fresh-water lake or stream where they are born. Then they start seaward, sojourning in the ocean from two to seven years depending upon the species.[6] Although they have enemies in the ocean, particularly seals, large numbers of those reaching the sea attain maturity.

Finally the time arrives during late spring and summer for the female to lay her eggs. Then the salmon, male and female, start up the river —usually the very one where they were born— to spawn. They spawn but once, death overtaking both before they again reach the ocean. So strong is the urge to reach the spawning ground that the salmon are easily caught by man's ingenious devices. The salmon fisheries have long been in jeopardy, largely as a result of overfishing. Hence, today men of the Alaska Fish and Game Depart-

---

[6] The Pacific area fishing industry as a whole exploits five different types of salmon which in order of price per unit of weight are: chinook or king; red or sockeye; silver or coho; pink or humpback; and chum.

ment watch the progress of the commercial fisher-men in given areas and pass the word to them that there shall be no fishing between certain hours to permit large numbers of salmon to escape and make their way upstream to spawn. The word goes out by radio.

Halibut, a choice fish, is caught by both American and Canadian fishermen. The North Pacific fishery supplies about 75 percent of the total world catch. Prince Rupert in British Colum-bia is one of the world's largest shippers of fresh halibut.

Important, also, in Temperate Marine Alas-kan waters are the king crab and the shrimp.

Commercial fishing to date is relatively un-important off the coast of southern Chile despite the fact that the waters teem with some of the finest fish to be found anywhere. This results from the remoteness of the region from the great population centers and hence markets of the world, the paucity of population (less than one inhabitant to the square mile), and the lim-ited facilities for cold storage and for refrigerated transportation. Moreover, Chileans are not large fish eaters.

ADJUSTMENTS TO THE FOREST

Since forests constitute a major resource in most Temperate Marine regions, lumbering and wood-working industries are important, except in those parts of northwest Europe which now have neg-ligible stands of timber and in Chile which lies far from the world's great lumber marts. Southern Chile and the southern part of the Central Valley are growing, however, as producers of lumber, shingles, and plywood. Chile's commercial forest acreage is almost as great on a per capita basis as that of the United States and since the country is badly off financially largely as a result of too great dependence on minerals, every effort is being made to find ways of diversifying the economy. The forest offers one possibility.

In Pacific North America, however, logging and lumbering reach greater development than anywhere else in the world (Fig. 17–8). The forest is that region's greatest natural resource. More than half the remaining saw timber of the United States and nearly three-fourths of that of Canada are restricted to this area.

The Douglas fir is the most abundant and most valuable tree. Attaining a height of 175 to 200 feet and a diameter of three to six feet, and having one-half to two-thirds of the bole devoid of branches, it is relatively free from knots and is a truly remarkable tree. The wood is light, strong, and nonwarping, satisfactory for struc-tural purposes.

The redwood forest of northern California also supports an important lumber industry. Sin-gle acres contain as much as one million board feet of lumber. This resource has passed largely into private ownership and is being logged at a rapid rate. The tree's capacity to reproduce and the heavy expense entailed in clearing discourage the area's transformation into farm land and encourage its utilization for forests.

The Sitka spruce, western hemlock, and red cedar comprise the better species in the Pan-handle of Alaska. The last named supplies Amer-ica with a large part of its shingles. Most of Alaska's timber is best suited to pulp and paper,

Figure 17–8 "Cat" hauling out logs, with log boom in the background, near Coos Bay, Oregon. (Photo from Photo-Art Studios)

Figure 17–9 A cherry picker, which is a portable machine that picks up the logs from alongside logging roads. This operation is at Juskatla, British Columbia. (Photo courtesy of the Canadian National Film Board)

being of the right size and quality, easily logged, and accessible to water power and water transportation.

Many of the trees on the Pacific Coast of the United States and Canada are so massive that logging is essentially a matter of engineering (Fig. 17–9). Railroads are being used more and more because operations are extending farther inland, as most of the timber close to streams and tidewater has now been removed. In high-lead logging, flat cars usually carry the logs to the mills. Often the smaller timber reaching the waterways from the forests comes via flume or chute.

In Norway, lumbering is a major activity but is more closely connected with agriculture than elsewhere. When winter causes cessation of farm work, many farmers become lumbermen. Pulpwood and pulp are the leading forest products.

New Zealand supports a lumbering industry of considerable importance. Clearing of the forest was so rapid, however, that a mere 9 percent of the virgin forest carrying merchantable timber was left after about three-quarters of a century of occupancy. Accordingly, New Zealand developed forestation on a large scale. The timber trees are essentially evergreens. The primary commercial softwood species consist of rimu or red pine, white pine, kauri, matai, and totara, while the commercial hardwoods are beech and tawa. Kauri pine, which grows only in North Island near Auckland, is the most famous and valuable tree. Often the bole will extend as many as eighty feet before the spread of thick branches is reached. It is valuable for both timber and gum.

Waste not—want not

The United States is the world's largest consumer of wood. Because the greater part of its remaining saw timber grows in the Pacific Coast states, this region is going through the same experience that New England, the Lake states, and the South have undergone: its timber resources are being removed at an alarming rate. Since most of the land is not well suited to agriculture, the most effective use can be made of it by putting it into permanent forest.

The forests of the Northwest are under rapidly improving management. Private companies are carrying on commendable programs of conservation and reforestation (Fig. 17–10). Fire detection and suppression systems are improving and there is better control of planting, seeding, and thinning. Trees are now regarded as a crop and tree farms have become common sights throughout the Pacific Northwest. At the same time wastage is being reduced, though it is estimated that only one-third of all the timber felled is put to use. By proper integration of wood-using industries, almost 100 percent could be utilized. The Weyerhaeuser Company, world's largest integrated forest producer, in addition to converting wood into pulp and lumber, processes

bark into insulating board and wood wool and sawdust into cattle feed, fuel briquettes, and other articles.

The excellent work of the Forest Service in this region is so well known that it is not discussed here.

PASTORAL ADJUSTMENTS

The cool, rainy climate, the year-round growing season for grasses, the occasional areas of rough topography suitable only for pasture, and the lowlands with their wet grass-bearing soils would suggest that pastoral adjustments might be of considerable importance in Temperate Marine regions. Formerly, cattle and sheep were pastured on clearings and natural meadows, and swine in large numbers were herded in the beech forests of Europe. Pastoralism, however, is a primitive industry and has generally failed to survive in areas which are the loci of advanced populations. The great areas of pastoralism today lie in arid or cold or rugged or rocky lands where agricul-

Figure 17–10 After harvesting a selected area, the loggers leave a series of blocklike patterns. Trees located near the cut-over blocks will scatter seeds which will spring up quickly in alternating sunlight and rain. When the new crop has been established, the seed trees may be cut. (Photo courtesy of the Wyerhaeuser Company)

ture cannot encroach upon them. Accordingly, in the Temperate Marine climate, pastoralism has given way to agriculture, and the rearing of animals has, except in southern Chile and in parts of far off New Zealand, assumed the form of stock-farming rather than of pastoralism.

Southern Chile is so cold, windy, rainy, and mountainous that farming is unimportant. Sheep, however, do well. In fact, most of Chile's sheep-raising takes place here and large sheep ranches lie on either side of the Strait of Magellan. It is estimated that 60 percent of the country's six million sheep are in the two provinces of Aysen and Magallanes. Here are some of the world's largest sheep ranches. The largest of the companies maintains holdings of a greater size than the Republic of Switzerland. It is said that the cool climate is a factor in producing a heavy fleece of fine quality.[7]

AGRICULTURAL ADJUSTMENTS
Crop farming

Strictly speaking, this climate with its rainy, cloudy, cool weather and its continuously moist soils is not a first-class agricultural climate. It is favorable for growing but not for maturing and harvesting certain crops.

The summers are too cool and cloudy for corn and too wet and cloudy for wheat, although in such leeward positions as eastern England, the Paris Basin,[8] the Willamette Valley of Oregon, and the Canterbury Plain in New Zealand considerable wheat is grown. Rye and oats thrive, as do potatoes, sugar beets, and the hardier fruits.

Yields are high in northwestern Europe, especially compared with those in the great surplus food-producing countries—Argentina, Australia, Canada, and the United States. The Fenland farmer of Britain often gets eighty to one hundred bushels of wheat to the acre.

It is interesting to note that whereas Britain formerly imported most of its food (two-fifths in 1939), it now supplies four-fifths of its own needs. The plowland area has been doubled and contrary to what most Americans believe, British farms today rank as the most highly mechanized in the world.

High yields per acre characterize the agriculture of all the countries comprising Temperate Marine Europe, which indicates that the farmers are adjusting themselves effectively to the physical milieu (Fig. 17–11).

Pacific North America has developed slowly agriculturally, except in the more protected valleys on the lee side of mountains. This is attributable to belated settlement, the difficulty and expense of land-clearing, the profitableness of other occupations, the unfavorable ripening and harvesting weather for most crops, and great distance from large markets. The Matanuska settlements in Temperate Marine Alaska, with their dairy herds, potato fields, and truck gardens, comprise by far the largest and most important farming area in the forty-ninth state.

Southern Chile is the country's frontier; in it dwells only about 1 percent of the total population. It is an unpleasant land, one of high winds and heavy rains. For centuries it was avoided by most Chileans. Now, however, it is being opened up and the colonization laws are for small and medium holdings, to be held by the families that live on the land. Transportation is poorly developed and the people are essentially self-sufficing. The principal crop is potatoes. New

---

[7] Just how potent a factor climate is in causing a heavy fleece is a matter upon which there is no unanimity among biologists, ecologists, and geneticists. It is a fact that sheep produce heavier fleeces under low temperatures than under high ones. There is no evidence, however, that continued existence in a condition of low temperature would result in a hereditary production of heavier fleece, since this would imply the inheritance of an acquired character. The germ cells would not be affected and therefore the characteristic would not be transmitted. The generally heavier coats of animals which dwell in cold climates seem clearly to be due to mutations in this direction which have survived under natural selection. Neither environment nor heredity acts alone; they act together.

[8] France is practically self-supporting in essential foodstuffs including wheat. While the environmental conditions in the Paris Basin are excellent for wheat, those in many other sections are not. In order to get the large crop, all kinds of land must be pressed into service, some of which is too poor for successful wheat production. The only way wheat growing succeeds is through a high protective tariff.

Zealand is relatively unimportant, utilizing seven-eighths of its improved land for pasturage for livestock. It is interesting to note the close relationship in New Zealand between wheat-growing and the warmer, richer, drier land, and between oats-growing and the cooler, rainier, poorer land. Wheat production is declining because it is less profitable than sheep breeding.

Dairying and stock farming

The world's most highly specialized dairy regions fall within this type of climate, because natural environmental conditions are ideal and, in the case of northwest Europe, extensive markets are at hand. Moreover, the finest dairy breeds were developed here—the Alderney, Guernsey, and Jersey on those islands, the Ayrshire in rugged Scotland, the Red Danish on Sjaelland, and the Holstein in the low country of Holland. Pacific North America bids fair to become one of the world's major dairy regions as population increases and markets expand. Physical conditions surpass those elsewhere on this continent, for the milder winters obviate stall feeding, the summers are cooler, and insect pests, especially flies, are less troublesome. Dairy cattle also are numerous in New Zealand in the sections too wet for sheep.

In both New Zealand and southern Chile, however, sheep predominate. That they would be important in New Zealand is to be expected from the fact that the climate, topography, and vegetation in parts of the country are strikingly similar to those in England, the mother country, and that wool, mutton, and tallow all have high value per unit of weight and can readily pay for costly transport to distant markets.[9] While the native pastures were good for sheep, the introduced English grasses trebled and sometimes quadrupled the carrying capacity. Hence large areas of native sod have been replaced. The rearing of sheep has become the dominant industry, and in production New Zealand ranks among the world's leaders. Sheep are confined largely, though by no means exclusively, to the drier eastern sides of both islands.

To many, the importance of sheep in moist, densely populated Britain is an anomaly. It is a

Figure 17–11 New rootstock being planted along the Rhine River in Germany. It takes three years till a grape crop is harvested. (Photo courtesy of the German National Tourist Office)

fact that grazing is a leading phase of agriculture. The sheep industry is highly specialized and a number of breeds are "strictly localized." The Lincoln and Leicester breeds are confined largely to those counties, the Southdown to the chalky downs of the south, and the Romney Marsh to the damp lowlands of southern Kent. Sheep-raising is a dominant occupation because these animals utilize the hilly lands and the porous and well-drained chalk hills to advantage, and because lamb and mutton comprise an important item in the diet. However, as more land has been put into crops (this began soon after the outbreak of World War II and has continued), the numbers of sheep have declined notably.

MANUFACTURING ADJUSTMENTS

Temperate Marine northwestern Europe is the world's most highly industrialized region and

[9] Nearly all the meat and wool are exported. Four-fifths of the wool goes to the United Kingdom—more than ten thousand miles distant.

has more than 20 percent of its working people engaged in manufacturing (Fig. 17–12): the "black district" of England[10] swarms with industrial cities; Belgium is a "hive" of industry, the people pursuing their ends with "the invincible obstinacy of insects"; and Germany's Ruhr[11] is a "forest" of belching factory stacks. Europe's industrialism is consequent upon the interrelation of the following.

1. An inventive energetic population
2. Rich supplies of coal and iron ore
3. An abundance of water power
4. Valuable forest resources
5. A cool, stimulating, healthful climate
6. Well-developed transportation systems, both railways and waterways
7. Easy access to the sea and to markets

Parts of the realm are favored by great resources of water power, the result of strong onshore winds and mountains and hills near the coast. Norway has the largest hydroelectric potential in western Europe and leads all countries in the world in per capita consumption of electricity. This abundant and cheap electric power has fostered industries—electrochemical and electrometallurgical (electrolytically refined copper, nickel, aluminum—3 percent of the world total—zinc, nitrogen fertilizers, and superphos-

phates). The Pacific Northwest of the United States surpasses all other regions in the Cyclonic Zone in potential water power resources. Hence its future along certain industrial lines seems assured and awaits only the increase in population, the decentralization of industry in the United States, and the appreciation on the part of industrialists of scientific plant location. During both world wars, this region, which has the most even all-year temperatures, surprised the nation by building ships faster than any other section of the country. Neither heat nor cold interrupted the work as they did in the East. The region is also a leader in aircraft manufacture and woolen textiles, as well as in the reduction of alumina to ingot aluminum, in copper smelting and refining, in complicated wood-working

[10] For many years much of Britain's industry was concentrated in the coal fields. Now it is developing more rapidly with the help of electrical energy, near the largest markets and where transportation facilities are best. The principal concentration is now in the broad central zone stretching from Lancashire and Yorkshire to London. Greater London has become the leading industrial area in Great Britain.

[11] Actually the Ruhr from the standpoint of climate falls into a transitional area—transitional between the Temperate Marine and the Humid Continental with Medium Summers climates.

Figure 17–12 Volkswagen manufacturing plant at Wolfsburg, Germany. (Photo reproduction authorized by Bundesbildstelle Bonn)

industries and in paper making. Some steel is also manufactured.

Temperate Marine Chile and New Zealand are relatively unimportant industrially because they are sparsely settled and remote from the great markets of the world. New Zealand, however, prepares agricultural and pastoral products for shipment to distant markets, and considerable manufacturing is springing up around Concepción and Valdivia in Chile. In fact, the country's big iron and steel plant is located at Huachipato near Concepción.

COMMERCIAL ADJUSTMENTS

Omitting local trade, Europe carries on more than half the world's commerce, and of this, the Temperate Marine portion gets the lion's share. This is, however, only partly a matter of climate. All the countries are small and densely populated, all are highly civilized and hence have great and varied demands for all kinds of goods, all are strategically situated for world trade in the heart of the land hemisphere, and many of them are highly industrialized. It is only natural, then, that they should engage in world trade. Maps portraying foreign commerce in major products emphasize the fact that northwest Europe is the hub of the trade routes of the world (Fig. 27–15).

During recent years progress toward economic unity in northwest and western Europe has been taking place to overcome the disadvantages of so many national boundaries which can form the basis for tariff walls. While progress has been steady and gains have been made, serious problems still exist. At present, the Common Market countries and those that make up the so-called "Outer Seven" have developed two competing commercial blocs. While some of the problems are economic, others are inevitably tied to the political relations of the countries involved.

The English, Dutch, and Norwegians all are sea-minded and together possess an amazing proportion of the world's merchant tonnage. England's prestige on the sea is well known. On a per capita basis, Norway has the largest merchant marine on earth. Its fleet ranks third among those of the world. About 17 percent of its adult male population earns its livelihood on the sea, and

returns from shipping go far to cover the deficit of the trade balance with other countries.

Pacific North America is gaining commercial momentum: the Panama Canal has had the effect of drawing the two seaboards of the United States together; the region is rich in natural resources, it is growing rapidly in population and in manufacturing, and the cities benefit from strategic location on the Great Circle route to the Orient. British Columbia's trade has developed much too, especially since its port, Vancouver, has become an important outlet for Canadian grain. Wheat from the Prairie Provinces is exported to northwestern Europe from Vancouver. This port also exports lumber and fish.

New Zealand, by way of contrast, does not rank high in commerce, though it exports considerable quantities of wool, frozen meat, hides, skins, and dairy products. Remoteness and the trip through the steamy equatorial belt, which necessitates special preparation and packing, tend to deter commerce.

Least important of all is Temperate Marine Chile. From Punta Arenas (Magallanes), southernmost city of the world, are shipped wool, frozen meat, and skins.

SOCIAL ADJUSTMENTS

When one speaks of civilization today, one invariably refers to *European civilization* and by *European* is meant to a large degree *Temperate Marine*. This civilization is not old. It was just beginning in the Middle Ages. The earliest civilization, it will be recalled, probably began in Arid Tropical Mesopotamia and Egypt; it later spread to Asia Minor and Mediterranean Europe in the Subtropical Belt, and now is localized largely in the Cyclonic Zone. In short, it has migrated to the colder lands, those having a definite winter. The "Northward Course of Empire" sums up human history. In the development of civilization, factors other than climate have been of equal or possibly even greater significance—racial heritage, coal, and iron ore.

The Temperate Marine climate has proved its ability to support dense populations. Thus the Netherlands with 920 persons per square mile,

Belgium with 775, and the United Kingdom with 574 are among the most densely populated whole countries in the world.

Population distribution is not solely a matter of climate, however. Thus Temperate Marine Norway, an old country, has a very small population—barely 30 persons to the square mile. This is the result of rocky land and dearth of soil. The Norwegian population pattern is essentially a response to the sea, the people having been driven thither for the food which their hostile land denies them.

Population distribution in England, on the contrary, is spotty because of coal; lacking coal, its population would doubtless be more uniformly disseminated.

Pacific North America, especially that part in the United States and Canada, has a growing population of healthy, resourceful, ambitious, energetic people who will some day make great contributions to civilization.

New Zealand is only sparsely populated, not because of climate but because it is new historically and lies far away by itself in the heart of the world's largest salt-water desert. If it occupied as strategic a location as Great Britain, its population density would not be a mere 23 persons per square mile.

An apparent denial of what has been said regarding the carrying capacity of Temperate Marine lands occurs in southern Chile, which is all but without human habitation—much of it averaging less than one person per square mile. This, of course, is due to the combined factors of rugged land, excessive rainfall, cold temperature, great amount of cloudy weather, saturated ground, dense forest, and remoteness.

POLITICAL ADJUSTMENTS

At each stage in the northward, coldward, stormward course of human progress, new centers of political and military power and of industry, art, and science developed. Their size and form depended upon such natural environmental factors as seas, rivers, mountains and plains, climatic conditions, natural vegetation, and upon such nonenvironmental factors as race, intellectual activity, including invention, and social institutions. The migration was not one of peoples. The dominant fact seems to be that the people at the center of today's material culture have invariably possessed unusual energy, initiative, and power of leadership compared with the people around them.

This apparently derives from three great factors: (1) innate ability of the people, a situation that would seem to stem from a rigorous selection of migrants from whose midst weaklings—both physical and mental—were eliminated, (2) a favorable, easy to exploit, environment, and (3) inventions, discoveries, and new ideas (particularly political and social institutions)—the result of mutual relations between human beings, their natural environment, and the cultural milieu.

In modern times and until the present, Temperate Marine Europe exerted undue influence on the earth. It actually governed or had a controlling voice in what occurred over the greater part of the habitable globe. It sent its people, languages, religions, and political ideas —its civilization—almost everywhere. There was probably not a single country that was not affected by the foreign policies of such nations as Great Britain, France, the Netherlands, and Germany. Northwest Europe became the barometer of the world's economic, political, and social conditions; and upon that region the world kept its eye continuously focused, for what happened there had global repercussions. The two world wars, European conflicts at first, ultimately engulfed the entire world. The greatest depression of modern times was an aftermath of the first such war and affected every nation and probably every individual. This power of Temperate Marine Europe to dominate resulted from the superior enterprise of its people, strategic location, stimulating climate, availability of many necessary raw materials for industry, particularly iron ore and coal, and political and social ideas and institutions.

This political power of Temperate Marine Europe has now been checked. Many authorities on international relations believe that the British Commonwealth will no longer exert the degree of power in world affairs which it did in the nineteenth century.[12] The Netherlands has lost the former Netherlands East Indies (independent since 1950 and now known as Indonesia) and is far less strong politically since World War II. France is no longer regarded as a *great* power. She has lost most of her far-flung empire although some of the former colonial territories, which have become independent, have remained within the French Community for economic reasons.[13]

[12] See a political map of the world.

[13] Atomic tests in 1966 near French-occupied Pacific Islands seem to indicate that France still needs to be regarded as a "great" power.

SUGGESTED USEFUL READINGS

Bartz, Fritz, "Alaska," *Geographische Handbucher* (Stuttgart, K. F. Koehler, 1950), 384 pp.

Butland, Gilbert, *The Human Geography of Southern Chile*, Institute of British Geographers, Publication No. 24 (London, George Philip & Son, Ltd., the London Geographical Institute, 1958), 132 pp.

Clark, Andrew H., *The Invasion of New Zealand by People, Plants, and Animals: the South Island* (New Brunswick, N.J., Rutgers University Press, 1949), 465 pp.

Cumberland, Kenneth B., and James W. Fox, *New Zealand, a Regional View*, 2d ed. (Christchurch, New Zealand, Whitcombe and Tombs, 1963), 280 pp.

Freeman, Otis W., and Howard H. Martin, eds., *The Pacific Northwest, an Overall Appreciation*, 2d ed. (New York, John Wiley & Sons, Inc., 1954), 540 pp.

Gruening, Ernest H., *The State of Alaska* (New York, Random House, Inc., 1954), 606 pp.

McBride, George M., *Chile: Land and Society*, American Geographical Society, Research Series No. 19 (New York, American Geographical Society, 1936), 408 pp.

Mitchell, Jean B., *Great Britain: Geographical Essays* (Cambridge, Cambridge University Press, 1962), 612 pp.

Monkhouse, Francis J., *A Regional Geography of Western Europe* (London, Longmans, Green & Company, Ltd., 1959), 726 pp.

Watson, J. Wreford and J. B. Sissons, eds., *The British Isles: a Systematic Geography* (Edinburgh, Nelson, 1964), 452 pp.

18

Subpolar Climate Regions

The last of the four general climatic zones to be considered is the *Polar Zone*, that is, the Arctic-Antarctic portions of the earth's surface. In the mind of the average reader there are many misconceptions regarding the Polar Zone, some of which are that

1. It is a cold desert
2. Its lands are barren wastes and will produce nothing of economic value
3. It is almost too cold to inhabit
4. It is perpetually covered with deep snow
5. It lies in darkness most of the time
6. It is populated by a few half-frozen Eskimo
7. These Eskimo live exclusively in snow houses

Actually none of these is true, although locally or temporarily there are situations which may supply the bases for these commonly accepted beliefs.

At the outset, one may ask, What are the characteristics of the polar lands? A satisfactory answer to this question is difficult to give because, like the other zones of the earth, the Polar contains unlike types of climate. In general, however, the polar lands are colder than the rest of the world. The air over the Polar lands is clear and mainly unpolluted. The relatively *high latitude* of these lands means that the sun is never so far above the horizon as in intermediate and low latitudes. Most of the Polar Zone lies within the Arctic and Antarctic circles. On either of these circles the sun disappears entirely for a whole day at the winter solstice. The farther one goes toward the poles, the longer the period of sun disappearance. At the pole itself this amounts to nearly six months. Even outside the polar circles in lands as far equatorward as latitude 60° N., the duration of daylight on December 22 is only five and a half hours. Conversely, as the summer

season approaches, the duration of sunlight lengthens rapidly. Thus on June 21 at latitude 60° N. the duration of daylight is eighteen and a half hours.[1] These alternating periods of continous or near continuous light and dark produce some interesting results as was shown earlier in Chapter 4.

In the *spring* (March 21) and *fall* (September 22), the noonday sun appears 23½° above the horizon at either of the polar circles, and precisely upon the horizon at the poles. Simultaneously, by way of comparison, the sun is halfway up in the sky at Minneapolis in the Cyclonic Zone. In *summer* (June 21), the noonday sun is 47° above the southern horizon at the north polar circle and 23½° above the horizon at the North Pole. In *winter* (December 22), the noonday sun is just upon the southern horizon at the north polar circle but has disappeared completely at the North Pole. At a place in the northern middle latitudes, such as Minneapolis, the noonday sun is then 21½° above the southern horizon. polar circle experiences approximately the same

In other words, during the summer, the sun elevation as does Minneapolis during the spring, and the pole has approximately the same sun elevation as Minneapolis during the winter. This apparently should produce a summer in the lands near the Arctic Circle similar to spring in Minneapolis, and a summer at the North Pole comparable to winter in Minneapolis. But this is not so, because the length of day is not the same in the two instances. To be specific, the duration of sunlight at Minneapolis on December 22 is

[1] For excellent material dealing with the problems included in this chapter, see Lucia C. Harrison, *Sun, Earth, Time, and Man* (Chicago, Rand McNally & Company, 1960).

only eight hours and thirty-four minutes, while in the Polar Zone on June 21 it is eighteen hours and thirty minutes at 60° N., and twenty-four hours at 66½° and all points northward. This longer day more than compensates for the lower sun elevation, with the result that midsummer days in high latitudes become quite warm or even hot. This same set of factors operates in an inverse manner during winter.

In spite of these general characteristics, however, climatic conditions are far from uniform throughout this portion of the earth. Usually, differences in precipitation are of little significance but differences in temperature assume considerable importance. Mainly on the basis of temperature, one may distinguish two types of climate within the Polar Zone: the Subpolar, and the Polar Ice Cap. The first type is treated here; a discussion of the second is reserved for the following chapter.

The Subpolar distinguishes peninsulas, islands, and coasts of the Arctic and Antarctic regions (Fig. 18–1).

SUBPOLAR CLIMATE

All places with this type of climate have a low sun during most of the year. Indeed, during midwinter, daylight disappears altogether for awhile, though nights of dense darkness are rare. Even during the dark period, Eskimos, Samoyeds, and other denizens of the tundra carry on their sledging, hunting, grazing, and fishing, though obviously encountering greater difficulty than in summer. They are aided to a certain extent by the light of celestial bodies. During most of the year the ground is frozen and covered with snow. In midsummer the days become longer and longer until, for a short time, darkness disappears altogether and noon and midnight can scarcely be distinguished one from the other in temperature and intensity of light. At this time, for several weeks the snow and ice melt, the ground thaws near the surface, and the rapid-growing vegetation, consisting of mosses, lichens, buttercups, dandelions, squat cranberry, and hundreds of other types, transforms the landscape. But summer is short-lived and terminates abruptly and quickly. Snow falls again and the country once more takes on the appearance of endless white.

Between the continuous night of winter and the continuous day of summer, twilight prevails. At this time one can read ordinary print at any hour without straining the eyes—a fact not easily comprehended by middle or low latitude peoples. The dearth of real darkness interferes with sleep, resulting in a prevalence of nervousness and irritability among white people. Conversely, the long period of night conduces to idleness with its baneful effects. According to

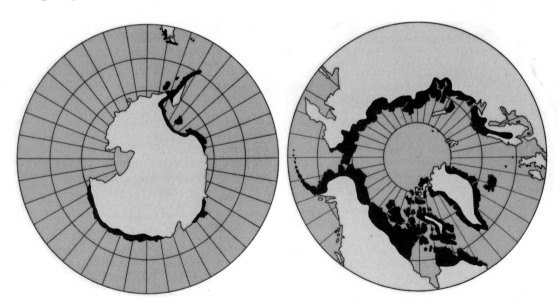

Figure 18–1   Subpolar regions.

Ekblaw, the Eskimo's "psychology of time differs radically from ours. Because of the long day and night, time to the Eskimo is not a succession of defined intervals, but a continuous flow or current. He eats when hungry, drinks when thirsty, and sleeps when sleepy—no schedule for him."[2]

While winter temperatures frequently dip to −50° F., they never tumble to the depths recorded in either the Humid Continental with Short Summers or the Polar Ice Cap types. This indicates the moderating effect of water (Fig. 18–2).

Moreover, because of marine influence and prevalence of ice and snow, the summer temperature seldom exceeds 50° F., considerably below that recorded in the Humid Continental with Short Summers type. Thus the range of temperature is decidedly less than might be expected for a climate situated in so high a latitude.

The precipitation is scanty, seldom exceeding ten inches (except in the southwestern extremity of Greenland), since air at such low temperatures can carry only a limited quantity of water vapor.[3] Practically all precipitation takes

the form of snow, hail, and fog. Snow envelops the land for at least eight months of the year and in some sections falls every month. Winds, always strong, usually dry, and cold as ice, frequently howl day after day during the winter.

PLANT GEOGRAPHY

The Subpolar climate, except the small portion in the Southern Hemisphere, is coextensive with the *tundra* or *barrens*—one of the best defined natural regions.

The *tundra* is a bleak flat or rolling moss sponge-covered landscape, a labyrinth of streams, lakes, convex peat bogs, and swamps, the latter consequent upon poor underdrainage in a land the subsoil of which is permanently frozen. Obviously, it is almost impassable in summer. Its southern limit coincides with the northern limit of the taiga and "roughly with the Arctic Circle" (Fig. 18–3). In the original Russian, the word *tundra* means "barren ground" or "wasteland." Its dominant plants may be mosses, as is so often the case in Eurasia, or lichens, as in North America. A grassy tundra is not uncommon.[4]

Fortunately for the herbivorous animals, this spongy mat of mosses and lichens does not die down during the winter. Moreover, it possesses so much nourishment as to provide a complete ration for reindeer. Strong winds carry much of the snowfall away, thereby enabling the wild musk ox and caribou and the domesticated reindeer to graze even in winter. Tundra occurs in those places where enough snow melts to expose the surface to the sun's rays, at which time (midsummer) the vegetation "bursts" into active life.

Subpolar Climate
POINT BARROW, ALASKA, U.S.A.
Elevation 20′ Latitude 71°23′N

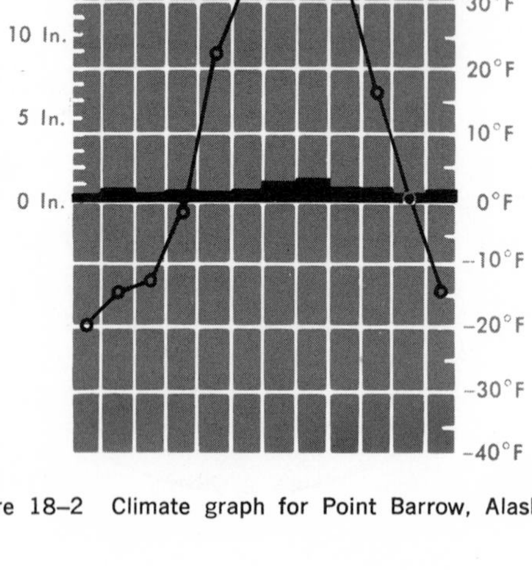

Figure 18–2   Climate graph for Point Barrow, Alaska.

[2] W. Elmer Ekblaw, "The Ecological Relations of the Polar Eskimo," *Ecology,* Vol. II, No. 2 (April, 1921), p. 143. See also Kaj Birket-Smith, *The Eskimos,* translated from the Danish by W. E. Calvert, 2d ed. (London, Methuen & Co., Ltd., 1959).

[3] Precipitation is measured in inches of water and includes both rain and snow. Snow is expressed by its water equivalent obtained by weighing or melting the snow. Ten inches of snow approximates one inch of water.

[4] For an excellent article (both text and illustrations) on the tundra, see "The World We Live In: Part X, Icebound Barrens of the Arctic Tundra," *Life* (June 7, 1954), pp. 90–120.

Figure 18–3   The last stand! Northern edge of the Canadian forest (taiga) south of the Hudson Strait where the forest gives way to tundras. No hard and fast line can be drawn between the taiga and the tundras. (Photo courtesy of the Geographical Review)

This period of activity, lasting only six to eight weeks, terminates as abruptly as it begins.

The dearth of trees[5] and the stunted appearance of the entire vegetative covering are the most distinctive things about the tundra. Contrary to common belief, trees are excluded not so much by low temperatures as by the cold, dry winds which cause great evaporation at a time when water is not available from the frozen ground (Fig. 18–4).

SOILS

Tundra soils comprise a unique class, since soil processes are slowed down as a result of long-continued cold. In fact, there is little evidence as yet indicating that the common soil-forming processes have acted upon the parent material. As a result of the alternate action of freezing and thawing, a certain amount of mixing of mineral and organic materials occurs. Tundra soils consist of dark-brown peaty layers lying above grayish horizons. They are shallow, acid, and obviously poorly drained. They are not included in the two great soil groups—the pedalfers and the pedocals. Only the top layer of the soil thaws during the warm season, the substrata remaining permanently frozen. These soils offer almost no future for agriculture and those now in use are devoted mostly to pasture and to a few short-season crops.

ANIMAL GEOGRAPHY

The tundra everywhere possesses an almost uniform fauna—a consequence, no doubt, of the near joining of the continents along the Arctic Circle. This contrasts sharply with the situation in other types of climate. Thus in the Rainy Tropical, such areas as Brazil, Nicaragua, the Congo, and Ceylon display little similarity in the species of their native animal life. Subpolar fauna is more abundant than might be expected from the harsh

[5] Trees in the true sense are absent, but miniature alders, birches, firs, and willows about a foot high and prostrate are present in places.

Figure 18–4 Frozen muskeg in subpolar northern Alberta, Canada. Muskeg is characterized by undrained basins now filled with peat moss. Around the edges are to be found stands of tamarack and black spruce. The trees get smaller and smaller toward the center of the bog. (Photo courtesy of the Standard Oil Company, New Jersey)

nature of the climate. Marine life, especially, is plentiful.

LAND ANIMALS

The strictly land animals, such as the Arctic hare, Arctic fox, lemming, musk ox, caribou, redpoll, and ptarmigan necessarily adjust themselves in one of two ways: they either manage to find food somehow throughout the year or they live only during the brief summer, as do the mosquitoes and other insects.

The acquisition of food is the paramount issue confronting all life in this climate. Of the land animals, the musk ox and the caribou get sustenance in winter by pawing away the rather light snow cover, the thickness of which is diminished by the strong and frequent winds.[6] The Arctic hare lives essentially upon grass and willow which protrude from the snow or which are

reached from a burrow; the lemming spends the entire winter under the snow. Lemmings are constantly preyed upon by foxes, owls, shrews, and weasels. Moreover, other animals, such as the fox, are so dependent upon the lemming supply that their own abundance fluctuates with that of the lemmings. Upon the several herbivores depend the carnivores which invariably are "intruders from the continents." Thus the Arctic wolf, according to Newbigin, is absent from insular Svalbard, which is far from any continent. It is present, however, in parts of Greenland, as along the northern coast.

Despite the almost universal idea that insects decrease numerically from the hot to the cold parts of the earth, they really find a paradise here. Thus it is estimated that over two-thirds of the tundra there are ten times as many mosquitoes per square mile as over any area of equal size in the Tropics.[7] So obnoxious do they become in summer that even reindeer find it imperative to retreat to the coast. This has given rise to the laconic Lapp saying "mosquitoes make the best herders in summer." The prevalence of mosquitoes is attributable to the immature drainage, the great number of swamps and lakes, and to the long, sunny days with slight variation in heat from night to day, which provides ideal conditions for incubation. Mosquitoes constantly plague both man and beast.

SEA ANIMALS

Marine life is far more abundant than land life. In fact, it seems by no means illogical that the seal, walrus, and whale, which had terrestrial ancestors, took to the sea because of the poverty of the land in these high latitudes. The icy Arctic seas abound with small crustaceans which attract fish and mollusks. These, in turn, entice seals, whales, and walruses.

[6] The average person overestimates the snow cover in this climate. According to Vilhjalmur Stefansson, *The Friendly Arctic, the Story of Five Years in Polar Regions* (New York, The Macmillan Company, 1943), three-fourths to nine-tenths of the surface of Arctic lands is nearly free from snow the year round.

[7] *Arctic Manual,* TM, 1-240 (Washington, D.C., War Department, January 17, 1944), p. 104.

Animals that may be treated as marine, though less so than those just referred to, are the polar bear and the birds. The latter migrate from low latitudes, where they have wintered, to breed in the security of the tundra or on the stone ledges and cliffs near the water. Most of these birds are aquatic—auks, ducks, geese, gulls, terns, and others. The polar bear, as his scientific name *Ursus maritimus* or *Thalarctos maritimus* testifies, shuns the mainland, preferring the margin of the sea where he can fish in the water and hunt seals and walruses on the drift and floe ice.

DISTRIBUTION OF POPULATION

The population of Subpolar lands is remarkably sparse because (1) both vegetation and animals are scarce, (2) hunting and fishing are the chief pursuits, (3) communication is difficult, and (4) violent deaths are common.

While the exact number of these Hyperboreans is unknown, careful estimates place the probable population in round numbers at less than 500,000, or less than 1 per square mile. The total number of Eskimo is placed at some 50,000 of which nearly 23,000 are in Greenland. nearly 16,000 in Alaska, and 11,000 in Canada. While these people extend over a wide expanse of territory, they actually occupy a small area. Their villages are restricted to narrow ribbons of coastland and to offshore islands.

Since the chief source of everything, including food, skins, bone and oil, is the sea, the sea ice, and the coastal periphery of the sea, the natives cling tenaciously to the ocean margins. The hinterland is usually unoccupied. Distribution of population even near the coast is discontinuous, settlements being separated one from another by distances varying from thirty to sixty miles. A settlement seldom consists of over a dozen dwellings and beyond the 75th parallel does not exceed two or three.

THE NATIVES

All aboriginal occupants of Subpolar regions have much in common; all apparently came from Asia, and all possess some Mongoloid characteristics (Fig. 18–5). Those who inhabit northern Scan-

dinavia, northern Finland, and northwestern Russia are called *Lapps* and like their neighbors to the east—the Samoyeds, Tunguses, Ostiaks, and others—are apparently of Mongoloid stock. Those who occupy eastern Siberia, northern and northwestern Alaska, northern Canada, Labrador, and Greenland are called the *Eskimo* and are considered by many a distinct race. Though widespread, they are, nevertheless, quite homogeneous in "character, language, and culture." Thus "An Eskimo from Angmagsalik in East Greenland could probably make himself understood in talking with one from East Cape in Siberia, so essentially similar is their language."[8]

That the physical milieu influences the manner of life among the Eskimo is indicated by the fact that regardless of where they live, they are few in number, hug the thalassic periphery, eat the same kind of food, wear similar clothes, and are alike in ingeniously utilizing the scant materials of their immediate locale.

However, very few Eskimo today cling to

[8] W. Elmer Ekblaw, *op. cit.*, pp. 133–134.

Figure 18–5 Eskimo show strong Mongoloid characteristics. Note their "light" summer clothes, in this photograph taken in northern Canada. (Photo courtesy of John Q. Adams)

the old life; in fact, few live strictly off the land, the sea, and the ice.

Few people anywhere in the world accomplished so much under such severe limitations as did the Eskimo. They have adjusted themselves to their physical milieu in a masterful fashion. Their dwellings, boats, sledges, harpoons, bows and arrows, and clothes were remarkable adaptations to nature. In the past Arctic and Antarctic explorers from the Cyclonic Zone with modern science at their disposal invariably chose Eskimo clothing.[9] Admiral Byrd[10] in his book *Little America*, says of the parka, the Eskimo outer garment:

It is a development of ages of combat with the cold and is the most nearly perfect thing of its kind. Mine was made of reindeer skin, with wolverine rimming the hood. It weighed about six pounds; yet even during walks when the thermometer registered as low as 60° below zero, it offered adequate warmth. It is my opinion that a reindeer skin parka, if properly made and worn, offers double the warmth of the wool parka at half the weight. During the coldest weather, I rarely wore more than twelve pounds of clothing. The cut of my parka I borrowed from the Eskimos at Etah, on the theory that, having lived for centuries in the polar regions, they surely must have developed an efficient cold weather garment.

Denizens of so hard a climate struggle incessantly against a merciless nature for a mere existence. The eternal fight avails them little. Famine is never far away. Life is so hard that the people have little, if any, time to think of the higher things of life. The climate is benumbing rather than stimulating. It is little wonder that the old Czarist regime of Russia exiled some of the most ardent revolutionists to this climate to "cool off" and incidentally to have their energies fully absorbed by the mere routine of living. The Communist regime, too, sends some of its political and other prisoners into the same region.

INFLUENCE OF EUROPEANS ON SUBPOLAR PEOPLES

The European has persisted until he has penetrated every human society, whether it dwells in the Arctic waste, the trade wind desert, the equa-

torial forest, or the lofty mountain. Once the contact is made, does the native benefit or lose? Authorities by no means agree. Vilhjalmur Stefansson believes that "it would be a good thing for the Eskimo if they could be protected from our 'civilization' as a whole." Assuredly the Subpolar Hyperboreans are paying a high price for this contact. So long as they were detached, they were preserved; now they are threatened by an imported civilization. Almost everywhere they are losing their racial character. Interbreeding goes forward. It seems that in the not too distant future the Eskimo's complete dependence upon his native habitat will disappear and his dependence on the white trader from the Intermediate Zone become established.

Even the health of the natives has suffered. Contagious diseases such as smallpox, measles, tuberculosis, gonorrhea, and syphilis were practically unknown during the long period of isolation. Moreover, adoption of the white man's customs has proved unfortunate. Where he substitutes a house of wood for the native igloo, the Eskimo abandons an abode which his ancestors effectually adapted to the climatic conditions and probably only after a considerable period of trial and error; doubtless survival itself hung by a thread during the period of adjustment. Whereas the ancestral home was easy to build and was economical, the modern one is just the reverse. Furthermore, the Eskimo, by our standards, are not clean. When they move from the winter igloo to the summer tupik, they escape the dirt; now with a *permanent* abode, dirt and filth accumulate year after year, making conditions extremely unhealthful. To keep out winter cold the Eskimo fill every chink.[11] Stefansson[12] writes that the

[9] Whereas we in middle latitude countries fundamentally design our clothing for appearance, the Eskimo designs his for warmth, mobility and comfort.

[10] Richard E. Byrd, *Little America* (New York, G. P. Putnam's Sons, 1930), pp. 232–233.

[11] Eskimos are not oblivious to cold: according to Stefansson, they "get their faces frozen as easily, shiver as often, and make all similar responses to chill as readily as whites, Negroes, or South Sea Islanders."

[12] Vilhjalmur Stefansson, "The Colonization of Northern Lands," *Climate and Man,* Yearbook of Agriculture (Washington, D.C., U.S. Department of Agriculture, 1941), p. 209.

door of the Eskimo type is superior to the door of European type.

The sensible door for cold weather is of the Eskimo type. It may be in the same dimensions, 3 feet by 7 (as the typical European door), but it is a horizontal door in the floor. Such a door is typically kept open both day and night, for (apart from a slight "diffusion of gases") gravity prevents the warm air which fills the house from sinking down, while the cold air from below the door cannot press up into the house because it is already full of warm air. Ventilation is assured by a stovepipelike ventilator in the roof, through which the warm air rushes out under terrific pressure from an atmosphere that has been weighted by the outdoor chill, while cold air rises gradually through the comparatively large door and spreads along the floor without any draft or any other effect that discommodes the occupants.

The white man's firearms, while more effective than the native weapons, have caused a notable decline in the wild animal population upon which the people's very lives depend. Thus caribou have practically disappeared from many sections where once they existed by thousands, and nowhere are they so numerous as before the introduction of firearms.

ECONOMIC ECOLOGY

In all parts of the world where nature has been extremely niggardly, the few occupants necessarily live from hand to mouth. They positively cannot contribute much to the outside world. Of the dozen types of climate studied in Part II, which harbor human beings, the Subpolar possibly contributes least to the world.

Since the only important native occupations are hunting and fishing and grazing, brief treatments of the Eskimo, who typify the former, and of the Lapps, who exemplify the latter, are presented. Mining, which is growing in importance as an enterprise but is nowhere a native industry, is presented in a later topic in this chapter.

THE ESKIMO

HUNTING AND FISHING

Where a stern nature prevents the growth of trees and of crops and where the ground is frozen

much of the time, hunting and fishing necessarily become the chief pursuits. Thus the Eskimo, who nearly girdle the earth along the Arctic Circle, are hunters and upon their success depend comfort, health, happiness—even life itself. Almost all they possess and use comes from animals. All animals are utilized, but the land types are less important than the sea types.

Sea hunting

The Eskimo[13] are hunters par excellence; they study the habits of the animals and know exactly how to handle them. Their entire mode of living is based upon hunting: their villages are located with respect to hunting grounds, their clothing is made for life out of doors, their equipment is designed for the chase, and their thoughts pertain to hunting as emphatically as do those of the Norwegian to fishing and the Iowan to farming.

Most of the hunting is done by men in kayaks—narrow, sharp-pointed boats, decked over with skin—in the handling of which the Eskimo is uncannily adept (Fig. 18–6).

In sea hunting, the chief animals sought are seals, whales, and walruses. All serve a necessary purpose. Most valuable is the seal, especially the "ring seal," which is obtained along the coasts throughout the year and furnishes skin for clothing, tents, and boats, meat for food, and blubber for fuel. The bearded seal is valuable as a source of leather for bootsoles, dog traces, sledge lashings, and harpoon lines. The whale supplies meat as well as blubber for fuel and sinew for thread. The walrus furnishes food and ivory, the raw material for harpoon heads and other essential or important artifacts.

When fish and seals desert a particular area, the whole group of Eskimo follow, traveling in the big boat, the umiak, or women's boat, which is clumsy in comparison with the kayak and is held in disdain by the men.

Ice hunting

Ice hunting, a form of sea hunting, takes place only during the time the ice is firm. The animals sought are seals, walruses, and polar bears. While

[13] For a detailed and authoritative account of economic activities and social patterns of the Eskimo, see Kaj Birket-Smith, *op. cit.*

Figure 18–6 An Eskimo in his *kayak* in North Greenland. The kayak is used for hunting and for travel when-ever weather permits. In such a craft the Eskimo is almost a water animal; he can turn over in the water and get right side up again, and he can turn about instantly. (Photo from William E. Powers, *Physical Geography*, New York, Appleton-Century-Crofts, 1966)

there are several methods of catching seals, the most natural and primitive is to await the animals at the breathing holes, harpooning them as they emerge for air. The walrus is hunted from the ice all winter long. The polar bear is sought on moonlight nights in winter and in the dazzling sunlight of spring. Dogs, the only domestic animals, are invariably used when hunting bear, though not for the actual killing. Formerly the Eskimo's weapon was the lance, but it has been superseded by the white man's rifle.

Land hunting

While land hunting is by no means so important as open sea and ice hunting, it is nevertheless necessary. Besides the meat, which adds variety to the diet, material for clothing, which cannot be supplied by sea animals, is obtained. Trapping also involves selling or bartering peltries at trading stations owned by strong companies which are strategically located (Fig. 18–7). From the caribou (Fig. 18–8) which is killed with a rifle, the Eskimo gets his sleeping bag; from the hare which is shot or snared, he gets his stockings; from the fox which is caught in steel traps, he

gets furs for his clothing, and from birds which the women net, he gets his bird-skin underwear.

PASTORAL ADJUSTMENTS

For countless ages, the Alaskan Eskimo had hunted by land and sea and, so long as intruders were absent, he had lived with a fair amount of security. But when the white man arrived, he quickly reduced with his too-efficient rifle the Eskimo's natural heritage—the native animal life. Before long the Eskimo found himself face to face with starvation and possible extinction.

Fortunately a few far-seeing men in the United States government service conceived the idea of making this primitive people of the chase a pastoral people like their neighbors and blood relatives in northern Siberia and northern Europe who, from time immemorial, have depended upon their herds of reindeer. Accordingly, sixteen head of reindeer were introduced and larger importations followed from time to time. Siberian herders were brought over as teachers but, being poorly adapted to the task, they were replaced by Lapps. With these excellent teachers, an apprentice system was established

Figure 18–7   An Eskimo setting a muskrat trap. Inside the "push up" there is a hole through which a muskrat can climb. Beside it is a shelf or bed on which it lies to feed. The trapper places the trap on this shelf. (Photo courtesy of the Standard Oil Company, New Jersey)

experiment in Alaska, contracted for the delivery of several thousand reindeer from Alaska to an area east of the delta of the Mackenzie River. It was believed that with these animals as a nucleus the whole of northern Canada might be stocked in due time. The drive required five years and the distance covered was 2,500 miles. Herders and animals alike suffered untold hardships. It is estimated that not more than 10 percent of the 2,370 animals that started on the big trek actually arrived at the destination; the rest of the number were born en route.[14]

THE LAPPS

As the Eskimo exemplifies the Subpolar hunter and fisher, so the Lapp exemplifies the grazier. Both are poor—a result of venturing into so hard a land. Nevertheless, the Lapp is the better off, for he is always *sure* of something to eat,

[14] Ovid M. McMillion, "Reindeer Trek," *Journal of Geography,* Vol. XXXVIII (April, 1939), p. 140.

and at the end of a four-year apprenticeship, the Eskimo becomes a full-fledged herder and is given some thirty-four animals—the nucleus of a herd. Under favorable conditions, this nucleus should double within three years. This system began only in 1891.

A quarter-century ago the area supported roughly 500,000 head; today, however, there are virtually no reindeer left in Alaska. This diminution resulted from no failure of the pastures, for it is estimated that Alaska could support at least 200,000 reindeer. As long as white men and Eskimo used the same ranges, there was serious overgrazing and much misunderstanding. Accordingly, the United States government purchased all the reindeer owned by nonnatives. There is a small government-owned herd on Nunivak Island in the Bering Sea.

THE BIG TREK

Some years ago the Canadian government, noting that the supply of game for its Eskimo was fluctuating and being impressed by the American

Figure 18–8   The lone wolf (center and far left), which is harrying a herd of caribou as seen from 1,000 feet, appears as a mere dot in a pocket of caribou in Canada's Barren Grounds west and northwest of Hudson Bay. Wolves are unable to outrun caribou; hence they pick off aged stragglers, calves or cripples. In a given year they kill some 25,000 to 30,000 caribou or 5 percent of the herd. (Photo by A.W.F. Banfield, courtesy of the National Museum of Canada)

he has more equipment and more utensils and weapons.

The Lapps occupy northern Norway, Sweden, and Finland, and the northwestern tip of the U.S.S.R. Formerly all Lapps were nomadic graziers, the entire group migrating seasonally with their herds of reindeer. Now, however, there are the *Sea Lapps* who have settled down along the sea in Norway, the *River Lapps* who occupy fluviatile areas in the interior of Norway, the *Forest Lapps* who dwell in the forests of northern Sweden and the *Mountain Lapps,* sole heirs of their forefathers' wandering ways. What the reindeer means to the Lapp may be appreciated by the fact that more than three hundred words in the Lapp language deal with it.

The *Mountain Lapps* are as truly nomadic as

Figure 18–9 Against a summer backdrop in normally snow-covered Lapland the vast reindeer herd is brought to market. Reindeer furnish the Lapps with most of their living. The cows supply milk from May to the latter part of December. Surplus animals are butchered from October to March when the meat keeps fresh and sweet. (Photo courtesy of the Swedish Information Service)

the Kirghiz of the central Asian steppes or the Navajos of plateau Arizona and New Mexico. Seldom does the life of an encampment endure more than a few days because of the low carrying capacity of the tundra.

In winter the Mountain Lapps dwell in the mountains and on the high plateaus, for here the moss is soft and nutritious. During this period, they subsist upon meat, cheese, and frozen milk. Life becomes exceedingly difficult. The temperatures are bitterly cold. Moreover, the reindeer's hereditary enemy, the wolf, hovers about the encampment ever ready to seize an opportunity to devour an animal. Constant guard against this vicious marauder is therefore imperative.

As summer bursts upon the tundra, the reindeer head toward the sea coast followed by their owners (Fig. 18–9). Here they find better pasturage, marine algae that have been cast upon the shore by waves, salt, and greater freedom from the stinging mosquitoes and the biting flies which make the hinterland a hell for both man and beast. Moreover, the pastures inland need this season to recuperate, for in so cold a climate vegetation grows slowly and overgrazing is a constant danger. In summer, the Lapp diet differs slightly from that of winter in that meat is not eaten, and berries, roots, and bark are added to the customary milk and cheese. It is estimated that about fifty reindeer must be slaughtered annually to provide subsistence to the nomadic Lapp family of five. In bad years there are not enough animals to meet this need. Such food as flour, coffee, and potatoes are purchased from the borderline folk whom they meet in their migrations. As winter approaches and the days grow short, the reindeer once more move inland.

OTHER ADJUSTMENTS

Since nearly all natives of the Subpolar regions are hunters, fishers, or graziers, and since all are practically self-sufficing, mining, manufacturing, and commercial adjustments are relatively unimportant.

There are minerals in the land of the Eskimo, Lapp, and Samoyed, but comparatively little mining is carried on, especially commercial mining. The natives possess no knowledge whatsoever of metallurgy. Aside from the little pyrites for kindling fires and soapstone for making lamps, the natives pay no attention to mineral deposits.

The only manufactures are those of the natives for their own use and consist for the most part of clothing and of tools and implements for facilitating hunting and fishing.

The clothing is made mostly from furs and is perfectly adapted to the climate.[15] It is warm irrespective of the outside cold, is windproof, and can be kept dry. It is impenetrable even to the fine, needle-like snow so characteristic of the Arctic. The method of curing skins is unique. Tanning materials obviously are lacking in the timber-starved tundra and would be of no value even if they were present, since leather so tanned would freeze stiff in the subzero temperatures and become brittle and fragile. Hence the women cure skins by chewing them. They begin this practice when children and continue it during the greater part of their lives. By the time they are thirty, their teeth are worn to the pulp and by forty-five, or even before, to the gumline.

Foremost among the Eskimo creations is the graceful, slender kayak, probably the best aboriginal vessel with the possible exception of the finest canoes of the South Sea Islands. It is used in summer for hunting on the sea (Fig. 18–6). Its framework consists of a minimum of driftwood and whalebone held together with tendon and decked-over with raw sealskin. The sledge which carries the Eskimo on land is also a remarkable contrivance. When driftwood is available, wooden runners shod with ivory or whalebone are used. The back is made of deer antlers. Harpoon, spear, bow and arrow—all are ingenious adaptations to the physical environment and to the materials readily available.

Commerce among Subpolar peoples in the past was positively nonexistent, is now of negligible importance, and cannot expand very much in the future. Formerly everything the Eskimo owned had to be made with his own hands from the raw materials at his immediate disposal. Now, however, some exchange takes place as far north from civilization as North Star Bay, Greenland, where at Rassmussen's Thule Station the Eskimo barter furs and ivory for guns, ammunition, matches, oil, and needles. Moreover, small trad-

ing vessels cruise among the islands in the Bering Sea and along the mainland trading modern conveniences for ivory and furs.

The Lapps, who are usually good business men, sell considerable reindeer meat in Stockholm at prices paralleling those for similar cuts of beef. They also sell hides for which there is always a good market.

The Russians keep open their Arctic coast for several weeks during the summer allowing vessels to ascend and descend the great rivers in Siberia (ice-breakers are used at the mouths) that debouch into the Arctic Ocean. Lumber, pulpwood, gold, peltries, and a small number of other items move out and manufactured goods (consumers' items) move in.

CROPS AND LIVESTOCK

Farming and the rearing of livestock other than reindeer are unimportant among Subpolar aborigines. The Arctic is positively no place for the usual kinds of farming. However, in west coastal Greenland root crops, such as broccoli, radishes, turnips, and potatoes, are grown as far north as latitude 66° 15′, and Umanak claims to have the most northerly garden in the world.

Also in the southern, warmer borders of the Arctic, sheep are raised. There are some in the Julianehaab area of southwestern Greenland and in Iceland (only part of these are in the portion having the Subpolar climate).

RECENT WARMING IN THE NORTH ATLANTIC AND ITS EFFECT UPON MAN IN COASTAL GREENLAND[16]

It appears to be a fact that the temperature of the water off the west coast of Greenland has been moderating and has brought about a marked

---

[15] Where caribou have disappeared and their skins are unavailable for clothing, as exemplified by Belcher Island in Hudson Bay, the Eskimo must find a substitute. Here they are using the feathered skins of eider duck and sea pigeon for winter wear. Costumes so made are inferior in wearing quality and are too warm for even the coldest weather. When Eskimos are located near white trading posts, they occasionally wear woolen garments.

[16] M. T. Dunbar, "A Note on Climatic Change in the Sea," *Arctic*, Vol. 7 (June, 1954).

structural change in the economy and lives of the inhabitants. Communities of hunters have become communities of fishermen. Sea mammals have been vanishing from the west coast and are being replaced by cod and other species of fish in the southern waters of Greenland.[17] In fact, cod are now being caught north of the 70th parallel. The history of the west Greenland cod fishery is an excellent indicator of the temperature changes that have been taking place. Although caught as early as 1820, only since 1917 have cod been moving north year by year.

Formerly the economy was not a monetary one; now it is. Cod, halibut, prawn, and shrimp (there are more than one hundred species of fish) from Greenland are now entering world markets and most of the material needs of the people are being met by imports. Formerly the Eskimo and the Greenlanders were hunters, mostly, though not exclusively, of sea mammals; all their needs were met from their own efforts and success. But in a single generation the Greenlander has passed from an extraordinarily self-sufficient economy to one based upon cash and international trade. More than anything else this change has been responsible for Greenland's turning from a closed country with respect to trade to one open to the entire world. It is little wonder, therefore, that the warming of the region is of utmost scientific interest and of great importance to the economy of Greenland.

THE WHITE MAN AND THE SUBPOLAR CLIMATE

Until quite recently it apparently has not appeared worthwhile to the governments of North America or to many of their people to invest heavily in Subpolar lands. The United States and Canada have reasoned that it would be better to leave the tundra wilderness for the benefit of the fur and other wildlife resources.

The Soviet government, on the contrary, is actively developing its Subpolar lands and its accomplishments have been spectacular in its advanced experimental stations and few settlements. The Russians, however, have not moved northward into the tundra over a broad front.

Mining is one economic enterprise that is

opening up many areas in the Arctic. Modern civilization uses unbelievable quantities of minerals, and many of the most accessible and high-grade deposits in middle latitude lands are showing signs of exhaustion. A major factor in the new mining importance of Polar lands is the airplane and helicopter which in a few hours can reach an area that formerly required many weeks by surface transportation. These can be used not only for prospecting, surveying, and mapping but for moving huge pieces of equipment, food, and personnel. Hence the underdeveloped lands, even those in the Arctic, are being both explored and developed. In fact, except for Russia, which has several large cities in its Subpolar region, the only communities of any size (more than a few hundred) are those engaged in mining.

Among the principal Subpolar enterprises are those mining coal in Svalbard; cryolite near Ivigtut, Greenland; iron ore in the Kirkenes district of Norway; apatite and nephelite near Kirovsk in the Soviet Union. And in the huge Russian Subpolar realm (40 percent of the total Arctic land surface) are nickel, copper, iron ore, platinum, radium, tin, coal, fluorspar, and salt mines. Petroleum also is being sought (Fig. 18–10). Despite the region's importance to the Soviet Union, it would be a mistake to consider it a major source of Soviet mineral production, for as late as 1950 only five of thirteen economic regions—the Ukraine, the Urals, the Transcaucasus, Turkistan, and Western Siberia—produced 80 percent of the total, with the others contributing less than 5 percent each.[18]

Commercial fishing is important along the Bering Sea coast of Alaska and in northwestern coastal Russia. In fact, Murmansk today lays claim to being the world's leading fishing port.

There are not many white inhabitants in the Subpolar realm. The total Subpolar population is estimated at only 489,000 (434,000 for Eurasia and 55,000 for North America). In the latter, most of the permanent residents are Eskimo and

---

[17] While climate is undeniably playing a major role, overhunting and the depredations of enemies also have taken their toll.

[18] Demitri B. Shimkin, *Minerals: A Key to Soviet Power* (Cambridge, Harvard University Press, 1953), p. 314.

Figure 18–10   A snowbound oil rig and camp at Bear Creek, Alaska, showing that if the commodity is high enough in value man will go after it to the most inaccessible of areas. (Photo courtesy of the Standard Oil Company, New Jersey)

Greenlanders; in Eurasia, however, natives comprise a smaller proportion of the whole population—probably only one-third in the U.S.S.R.

Life is so hard in the Arctic that most white people prefer to shun it. Almost every aspect of living presents a problem—food, clothing, shelter, fuel, health, transport, even work. A careful study of work performance reveals that human efficiency declines at the average rate of 2 percent per degree of temperature below zero Fahrenheit.[19] Insects also make human habitation unattractive and difficult. In the three summer months they make normal work quite impossible: two thousand insects may take up an area of only a few feet around a person. Gloves and headnets are an absolute necessity but they seriously hamper activities.

SOCIAL ADJUSTMENTS

The denizens of Subpolar lands do not possess an advanced civilization, a consequence in large part of their hostile natural environment. The incessant fight against a benumbing climate and against an environment miserably poor in material resources demands so much time and energy that little of either is left for evolving a higher civilization. Hunters in Greenland, for example, must work so tirelessly that they rest during the period of light only when completely overcome by fatigue.

The social organization of the Eskimo is simple. Small families are the rule, a mother seldom bearing more than two or three children (Fig. 18–11). Several families, possibly two to four, group themselves together in a few houses accessible to the sea. This constitutes a village. Only seldom do the Eskimo occupy a village longer than a year, because the nearby hunting grounds soon become exhausted.

The Eskimo never live in tribes. They have no chiefs. A man becomes a leader after distinguishing himself as a superior hunter or by virtue of personal dignity, force of character, or reputation for magical power. Such prestige is merited, never inherited. There is no such thing as authority over a group; public opinion rules. The only law is custom that is handed down from generation to generation.

The family is based upon economic factors. A man needs a woman to prepare his food, to make his clothing, and to care for his dogs which at times are left behind;[20] a woman must have a man to bring her food, oil, and furs, and to take charge of the frequent migrations. The Eskimo are monogamous. When a girl considers marriage, it is said that she gives most encourage-

[19] George W. Grupp, "Man and Materials in the Polar Regions," U.S. Naval Institute Proceedings (August, 1949), pp. 865–871.

[20] For travel in the Arctic the dog is invaluable. He can live on meat which is more abundant in the far north than vegetable feed and he is intelligent, speedy, docile, loyal, and tolerant of cold, hunger, and hardship. Without his dogs the Eskimo hunter, restricted by foot travel to the territory over which he could travel, would find it almost impossible to kill enough game to support his family. Without the dog, the Polar Eskimo, who inhabit northwest Greenland and are the northernmost people in the world, could not maintain their settlements almost a thousand miles beyond the Arctic Circle.

Figure 18–11 A North Greenland Eskimo family in summer dress. (Photo from William E. Powers, *Physical Geography*, New York, Appleton-Century-Crofts, 1966)

ment to the suitor who is the ablest hunter, re-gardless of whether she actually loves him more than another.

The Eskimo are a friendly, peace-loving folk who seldom fight. Their idea of religion is vague, though they recognize the existence of a hereafter. Heaven quite naturally is a place where work is nonexistent, where warmth and light abound, and where blubber and meat are plentiful. Hell is expectably cold and dark much of the time, and food is scarce.

The social adjustments of the Lapps resem-ble those of the Eskimo. Families, of course, are larger, since the food supply is more certain. Polyg-amy is not uncommon and women are inferior to men as is always the case among pastoral peoples. Lapps are loosely tribal.

POLITICAL ADJUSTMENTS

All inhabitants of Subpolar regions dwell in lands controlled by peoples unlike themselves. Despite

the fact that they were there first, they have all become subject peoples. They are a part of the United States, Canada, Denmark, Norway, Swe-den, Finland, or the Soviet Union.

Most of these countries have tried to help the tundra peoples and prevent them from de-generating or becoming extinct. America's at-tempt to change the Alaskan Eskimo from a hunter to a grazier is commendable. Canada has undertaken a similar task. Grenfell did enviable work among the Eskimo in Labrador. The coun-tries of which Lapland is a part long faced the problem of the Lapps following their reindeer great distances across international boundaries in search of food. Recently, however, border fences have been built between Finland and Norway and between Finland and the Soviet Union to stop these migrations. There has, of course, been almost no movement between Finland and Sweden because of the river boundary separating them.

Denmark formerly had a law prohibiting

vessels from landing in Greenland. The effect of this was twofold: first, it enabled Denmark to exercise a trade monopoly, except in eastern Greenland where Norway had certain concessions; and second, it prevented the Eskimos from contracting tuberculosis, smallpox, and venereal diseases from sailors. In 1950, however, Greenland ceased to be a closed country with respect to trade and free communication was established between it and the rest of the world.

For centuries (ever since 1261) Norway has asserted her claims to Svalbard, claims strengthened by explorations in Svalbard waters. In 1924 she was awarded the islands under certain restrictions: (1) that there be no naval base; and (2) that there be no use made of the islands in time of war. Probably first among Norway's reasons for wanting the area is the presence there of coal, a resource completely lacking at home.

During the Cold War, with its mounting international tensions, Svalbard has received much attention, particularly because of the "mining" activities of the Soviet Union in the archipelago. This is not illegal, since the Treaty of Paris (1920) granted "the subjects of all powers which are parties to it (the treaty) an equal footing with the Norwegians as far as economic activity is concerned." What creates anxiety in the West is whether or not the Soviets, under cover of economic exploitation, may be establishing military installations that could threaten the Great Circle polar air routes. Obviously, such installations would be in violation of the treaty.

The political interest of Canada, the United States, and the Soviet Union in this realm since World War II has been great. This results in large part from the Cold War and the fact that the Polar lands have a new strategic quality; they are no longer considered to be of negligible value. They are no longer remote, since the shortest routes between the United States and the Soviet Union cross the Arctic area and hence would be followed in the event of war (Fig. 18–12).

TRANSPORTATION AND THE AIR AGE

Transportation is possibly the most important problem facing man in the Arctic, for without it no settlements can flourish and no economic enterprises succeed. Poor transport more than anything else has been responsible for our age-long ignorance of this part of the world. To reach it from most middle latitude areas required long and dangerous treks over stormy and ice-ridden seas, through trackless forest and muskeg and over endless tundra. The airplane has revolutionized transport in the Arctic, for it can travel fast and is little influenced by surface condition and surface hazards of pack ice, open sea, frozen tundra, blizzards, muskegs, lakes, and mountains, except where it is necessary to land.[21] On the tundra the lakes provide level airfields for ski-equipped planes in winter and for float planes in summer. At 17,000 or more feet, the meteorological conditions for flying are superior to those prevailing over most of the United States and Europe.

Because of the importance of short Great Circle routes, the Polar region promises to become the world's crossroads of tomorrow. Already regular weekly-scheduled flights are being made from Los Angeles and San Francisco to northwestern Europe via the Arctic.

While aircraft are revolutionizing transport in the Subpolar realm so far as the white inhabitants, military men, and exploiters are concerned, the natives will continue to rely upon the dog, reindeer, and kayak.

SUBPOLAR REALM AND THE FUTURE

Pearl Harbor not only meant the loss of much of the United States battle fleet but it changed Americans from flat-earth to round-earth thinkers. As a people Americans had talked a great deal about living on a round earth, but they have actually lived and acted as though they were living on a flat earth. They now use polar maps as never before, for these tell much of modern history and of the strategy of global war. And the governments of all countries lying in the Subpolar climate are carrying on research to learn

[21] On transatlantic air "runs" today pilots call attention to the Greenland ice cap and the green southern border of this huge island.

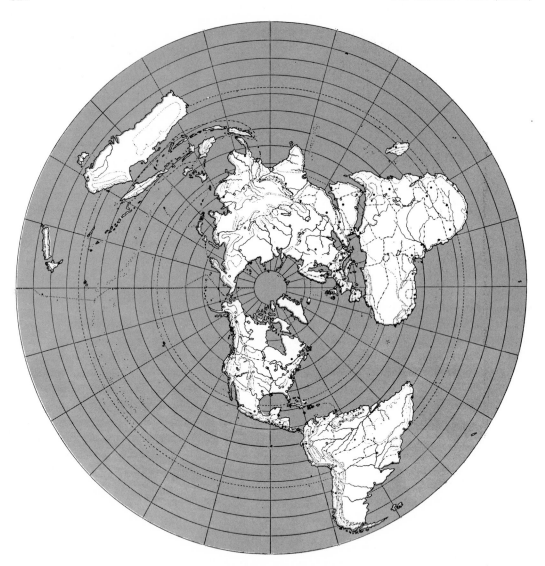

Figure 18–12 This map, possibly more than anything else, has helped Americans to realize that they do not live on a flat earth. It encourages them to look northward. Only this projection enables Americans to clearly comprehend the problems of defense against possible military attacks by air. On this map, America's potential enemies do not appear to be separated from the nation by thousands of miles of ocean. Strategy demands geographic truth and this projection supplies it. Across the Arctic the cities and industrial centers are targets within reach of missiles and bombers of both the Soviet Union and the United States. Politically, the Arctic has been transformed from an unimportant part of the world to one of major significance. (Map after Joseph E. Williams and Pacific Books, copyright, 1950 by Joseph E. Williams)

how large numbers of human beings can live and work in low temperature areas without undue damage to health and property. In short, the Arctic has emerged from a status of economic and political unimportance to one of major strategic significance. It is, however, a hard environment for man, particularly for civilized man— and to fight Nature is futile, for she invariably wins. "She permits man and machines to survive in the Polar Regions if they co-operate with her and do not try to oppose her. To survive in the Polar Regions she requires simplicity in design, construction, and wants, and strict obedience to her laws."[22]

[22] George W. Grupp, *op. cit.*, p. 871.

SUGGESTED USEFUL READINGS

Armstrong, Terrence E., *The Russians in the Arctic* (London, Methuen & Co., Ltd., 1958), 182 pp.

Baird, Patrick D., *The Polar World* (New York, John Wiley & Sons, Inc., 1964), 328 pp.

Birket-Smith, Kaj, *The Eskimos*, trans. from the Danish by W. E. Calvert, 2d ed. (London, Methuen & Co., Ltd., 1959), 262 pp.

Freuchen, Peter, and Finn Salomonsen, *The Arctic Year* (New York, G. P. Putnam's Sons, 1958), 438 pp.

Gould, Laurence M., *The Polar Regions in the Relation to Human Affairs*, Bowman Memorial Lectures, Series 4 (New York, American Geographical Society, 1958), 54 pp.

Jenness, Diamond, *Dawn in Arctic Alaska* (Minneapolis, University of Minnesota Press, 1957), 222 pp.

Kimble, George, and Dorothy Good, eds., *Geography of the Northlands*, American Geographical Society, Publication No. 32 (New York, American Geographical Society and John Wiley & Sons, Inc., 1955), 534 pp.

Stefansson, Vilhjalmur, *The Friendly Arctic, the Story of Five Years in Polar Regions* (New York, The Macmillan Company, 1943), 812 pp.

Suslov, Sergei, *Physical Geography of Asiatic Russia*, trans. from Russian by Noah D. Gershevsky and ed. by Joseph E. Williams (San Francisco, W. H. Freeman and Company, 1961), 594 pp.

19

Polar Ice Cap Climate Regions

THE ICE CAPS

EXTENT

Perennial ice, in the form of a massive continental glacier, blankets all of the land mass of Antarctica except a few coastal strips about the margins. Glacial ice likewise buries the interior of the great island of Greenland, and covers most of nearby Grant Island, Ellesmere Island, and parts of a few other Arctic islands. Pack and floe ice also cover about one-half of the Arctic Ocean. Thus, some 9,500,000 square miles of the earth's surface lie under polar ice, about one-half of which is situated in either hemisphere (Fig. 19–1).

THE CLIMATE

The climate of these regions is usually referred to as the Polar Ice Cap climate, one of the two types found in the Polar Zone and by far the most inclement of the earth's twelve major types. In the first place, areas with this climate are cold all year round. Meteorological statistics are as yet fragmentary, but observations already made reveal that the interiors of Antarctica and Greenland are very cold indeed during midwinter.[1] The presence of enormous accumulations of ice in polar areas means that even midsummer is cold. In some places near the coast, average monthly temperatures rise to 35° or 40° F., but inland it is probable that even the warmest summer month averages near or below freezing (32° F.) in most localities (Fig. 19–2).

The great ice caps, which vary in thickness from 1,000 to 10,000 feet, are not the result of heavy precipitation but rather of the agelong accumulation of snow and prolonged preservation of that little which does fall. Melting, even in midsummer, is very slow and evaporation is small. At the prevailing low temperatures, the air is incapable of holding much water vapor. Hence the total average precipitation is small— probably the equivalent of five to ten inches of rain per year in most areas. Precipitation almost always falls as snow or, to be more accurate, as ice spicules, dry and powdery in form. After the first summer this becomes ice or *nevé* (semi-ice).

Both Greenland and Antarctica are characterized by violent blizzards in winter. During such a period, cold is intense, wind velocities reach one hundred miles per hour or more, and visibility decreases to practically zero. Blizzards may last an hour or persist for several days. Invariably they are followed by short spells of warmer weather. Needless to say, the Polar Ice Cap climate is the only type which does not support permanent human habitation. Blizzards of considerable severity may occur during the summer season.

CAUSES FOR THIS CLIMATE

The inclination of the earth on its axis, plus its revolution about the sun, produce some strange variations in sun elevation and length of daytime all over the earth, but in the Polar Zone, these variations become strangest of all. At the Equinox

[1] During the International Geophysical year (IGY) 1957–1958, scientists of many nations were residents of Antarctica during the winter.

(March 21) the periods of sunlight and darkness are equal (twelve hours of each) everywhere on earth—in the Polar Zone as well as in other zones.[2] At the Polar circles on that date, the sun at noon is about one-fourth of the way up in the sky. At either pole, however, the sun is just visible on the horizon upon which it follows a circular path along the skyline through the entire twenty-four hours, without setting or rising.

The following day the circle followed by the sun around the horizon begins to tilt and to rise higher in the sky. On this day, the sun is visible for the full twenty-four hours, not just at the North Pole as it was on the preceding day, but over a circle a mile or so in radius. Each successive day, the sun's circular path around the sky tips a little more and lifts a little higher. Consequently, the circular patch of constant sunlight increases in diameter day by day. June 21, the circular patch of constant sunlight has expanded until it has covered the entire area within the Arctic Circle. After that date, it begins to shrink day by day until it has dwindled to a single point on September 22.

On the next day the sun fails to appear at the North Pole. Day by day this area without sunshine grows a little larger, until by December 22, darkness[3] covers the entire area within the Arctic Circle. Meanwhile, exactly the opposite

regime is transpiring in the South Polar area season by season through the year.

This is far different from the erroneous concept held by many people, namely, that the Polar Zone has six months of continuous daylight and six months of continuous night. That is true only for the two small points constituting the earth's poles; for all other parts of the Polar Zone there is the complicated geometrical process of shifting from winter to summer and back again, previously described, in which the duration of the periods of *continuous* light and dark is different for each latitude. In general, however, the length of summer is relatively short in all of the Polar Zone, and the winter is correspondingly very long and severe. The seasons of the Polar Ice Caps are *sunlight seasons* rather than seasons of temperature or precipitation as in the other zones. Moreover, the sun's energy during the summer seems quite inadequate to accomplish the melting of the ice and snow which garment the region. There are many climatologists, however, who insist that the summer is adequate to render ice-free all lowland areas and that the existence of

[2] This again becomes true at the Autumnal Equinox—September 22.

[3] Part of this "darkness," however, is twilight. The term as used here means the time during which the sun is below the horizon.

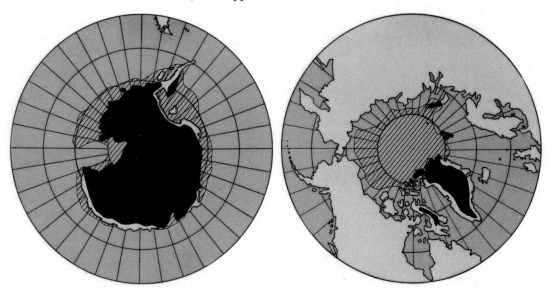

Figure 19–1 Polar Ice Cap regions. Black areas indicate ice caps on land; lined areas indicate portions of the polar seas covered with ice packs.

ice caps is, therefore, owing to the high elevation of interior Antarctica, Greenland, and certain other Arctic islands.

ICE AGES

Great as the areas of polar ice are today, they are much smaller than during certain geological periods in the past. The most recent of the epochs of ice-cap expansion were four periods between 900,000 B.C. and 20,000 B.C. In those times, the ice caps increased in thickness and size until the northern one spread over North America approximately as far south as the Ohio and Missouri rivers, and over large areas of northern Eurasia; while the southern cap spread out as vast fields of ice floes over the southern parts of the ocean. Between these glacial periods were warm interglacial periods, each perhaps 100,000 years in duration. The earth is still relatively cool, the polar regions at present being much colder than during the interglacial periods—indicating that the planet is still recovering from the latest glacial interval.

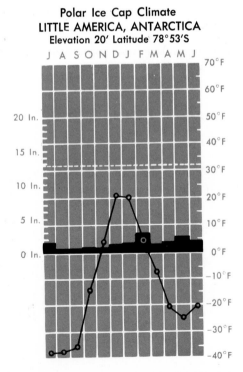

Polar Ice Cap Climate
LITTLE AMERICA, ANTARCTICA
Elevation 20' Latitude 78°53'S

Figure 19–2   Climate graph of Little America, Antarctica.

POLAR REGIONS

ARCTIC ICE FIELDS

The Arctic Ocean covers approximately 5,500,000 square miles of water surface and is nearly land-locked between North America and Eurasia. Most of the Arctic is covered with ice during the winter season to a depth of five to fifty feet. In the spring, this colossal icefield breaks up into packs of ice cakes which move sluggishly in the direction of the prevailing winds and currents. The resulting ice packs cover about one-half of the Arctic Ocean. One of these washes southward along the west coast of Greenland where it picks up many icebergs, sometimes of considerable height (Fig. 19–3). Another ice-laden current moves southward along the east coast of Greenland out of the Arctic Basin. Still another drifts southward past Svalbard into the Norwegian Sea. The floe-and-berg-carrying current creeping past western Greenland often reaches far southward to the waters east of Newfoundland where great masses of fog form and completely obscure the ice. This creates terrible hazards to ocean shipping in the northwest Atlantic. After the S.S. *Titanic* sank upon striking an iceberg in April, 1912, with a loss of 1,517 lives, the International Ice Patrol was established. It is financed by maritime interests of many nations and its object is to prevent any more sinkings by alerting all ships using the North Atlantic Trade Route during the months April to July. The task, performed by the U.S. Coast Guard, consists of charting icebergs and broadcasting their probable course.

In the Arctic itself, the summer gales break the ice into cakes of all sizes. North of the Bering Sea one area of ice cakes is in sluggish motion across the Arctic toward the European shore. A ship getting caught in this ice pack would, if it were not crushed in the process, gradually drift across the Arctic and finally get into the clear somewhere near eastern Greenland or Svalbard. This is precisely what Captain Nansen and his vessel *Fram* did in 1893–1895.

The movements of the ice are erratic, to say the least. In places the floes pull apart, leaving huge stretches of clear water. In other places, they are crushed together with great force, throw-

Figure 19–3 A large tabular iceberg on the west coast of Greenland—it measures approximately ¾ of a mile long, ½ mile wide, and shows 80 feet above the water. Below the surface, it extends 560 feet. Note how small the U.S. Coast Guard icebreaker, *Westwind*, looks by comparison. (Photo courtesy of the U.S. Coast Guard)

ing up huge irregular "pressure ridges," sometimes miles long and many feet high. During the winter, the ice cakes and pressure ridges freeze solid once more and loose snow accumulates on their surfaces (Fig. 19–4).

GREENLAND

Greenland is the nearest large body of land to the North Pole. There are fairly high mountains near both eastern and western coasts, but the interior is a low plateau whose cliffs and talus slopes come to the water's edge in most localities. The island is largely covered with an enormous cap of ice whose surface lies from 4,000 to 10,000 feet above sea level. No one knows how thick this ice cap is, but it probably varies from several hundred feet to more than a mile. If placed upon the United States it would reach from New York to Omaha and from the Great Lakes to the Ohio River. It is the world's largest island.

Ice in small pieces is a brittle solid, but in a chunk as big as the Greenland cap the lower portions become fairly plastic because of the enormous weight of the mass. Because of the resulting pressure, therefore, there is slow movement of the ice toward the edges. Near the coast

the moving ice has gouged out great steep-walled, rounded-bottom valleys called *fiords*. Most of the ice flows to the sea by way of these fiords, in places extending short distances out to sea. In summer, the ice is broken off by waves and tides and floats away to sea as cakes and bergs.

Inland, the higher peaks and ridges project up through the ice as *nunataks*. The interior of the ice cap is covered with ice ridges called *zastrugi*, with great ice undulations and shifting snowdrifts. Near the coast, the bending of the ice downward produces great yawning cracks called *crevasses*.

The supply of ice is replenished by the addition of snow from above, which soon packs and crystallizes into ice. Not much snow per year falls on most of Greenland and the other Arctic islands, for temperatures are so low during the winter that the air can hold little moisture in any form. The snow, however, does not melt during the winter and hence accumulates. In the warm months, there are cold drizzling rains which often turn to sleet and snow even in midsummer.

From over Greenland come the cold air masses with their winds and vertical air currents, producing many of the storm fronts which move eastward across the Atlantic Ocean, the British

Figure 19–4 U.S. Coast Guard icebreaker, *Westwind*, leading a Danish freighter through fifty miles of solid packed ice in Melville Bay, Greenland. The Danish freighter was delivering supplies to a starving Eskimo village in September 1964. (Photo courtesy of the U.S. Coast Guard)

Isles, and the great Eurasian land mass. These passing air masses produce the weather changes of the Cyclonic Zone.

No long-term records of precipitation have been kept in the interior of Greenland, but over most localities less than ten inches of rainfall equivalent per year probably falls, most of this occurring in summer. Nor have temperature records yet been kept over any extended period. Summer temperatures do not rise much above freezing, however, because the energy of the long hours of sunlight is used up in melting the snow and ice rather than raising the temperature of the air. Even though the thermometer may stand at, or only slightly above, freezing, the July sun can cause severe sunburn.

At Eismitte Station, on the ice cap of interior Greenland the average monthly temperatures for 1931 were as follows:

January	−42.2° F
February	−53.0° F
March	−39.6° F
April	−23.8° F

May	−4.5° F
June	4.0° F
July	11.8° F
August	0.9° F
September	−7.8° F
October	−31.9° F
November	−45.7° F
December	−37.3° F

Summer in that locality is obviously not very warm and the winter is bitterly cold. Apparently, temperatures on the Greenland ice cap never reach the extreme minima which sometimes occur in the Humid Continental with Short Summers climate, but winters here are longer in duration than in the latter. When the winter sun is above the horizon, it is, at best, low in the sky and gives out only a pale red glow. At times, the cold air is so still as to seem absolutely motionless, at other times, howling gales roar across the ice: a wind velocity of 174 miles per hour has been recorded.

THE ANTARCTIC

The mass of Antarctica covers more than five million square miles. Whether it is a continent or a swarm of islands is not known because it is deeply buried by ice. The ice cap presents a vast elevated surface whose central portion, in the neighborhood of the South Pole, is 6,000 to 10,000 feet above sea level. Thrust up through the ice are mountain ranges whose peaks attain heights of 13,000 to 15,000 feet, and there is one that reaches 20,000 feet. The Antarctic ice cap would, if transported to our latitudes, cover all the United States, Mexico, Central America, and the Gulf of Mexico. Toward the edges of Antarctica the ice-cap surface descends as it crawls through valleys and gorges to the coast. Thence it extends outward from the coast either as shelf ice or else reaches for scores of miles out to sea in long green glacial tongues. Shelf ice covers portions of the Ross Sea and the Weddell Sea, the two great embayments along the Antarctic coast.

Floating ice, often closely packed, extends outward from the coast for distances of from fifty to five hundred miles. The outer edge of this ice pack is known as the Great Ice Barrier.

Loose floating ice cakes often extend far beyond this, at times reaching to or beyond latitude 60° S.

The bergs that break from the ice are much larger than those off the coast of Greenland. The U.S.S. *Atka* in January, 1955, announced the presence southwest of Little America of an iceberg as large as Long Island.

Antarctica is 2,400 miles from southern Africa, 1,800 miles from Australia, and 850 miles from the tip of South America. Because of these distances and the storminess of the southern oceans, Antarctica was the last continent to be discovered and it is considered the least valuable.

MAN AND THE WHITE DESERT

There are no permanent inhabitants on polar ice caps, since everything they would require would have to be brought in from the outside (Fig. 19–5). Furthermore, there is little likelihood that the area will ever support permanent inhabitants, for the cold and the absence of soil make it impossible to grow crops. One might logically suppose, therefore, that man would willingly and gladly shun these ice caps. He is interested in such areas because of: (1) the fas-

cination of exploration for certain individuals; (2) the desire and necessity to acquire scientific information; many meteorologists, climatologists, and geographers believe that the ice caps exert strong influence on the climates of middle latitude lands; biologists want information on the natural vegetation and animal life and geologists on the structure, terrain, and minerals; (3) the strategic value of these lands, which today is very great; the United States and the Soviet Union are transpolar in relation to each other as far as Greenland is concerned; (4) the possible mineral resources; (5) the important whaling operations (in the Antarctic).

However, if man is interested in going there for any or all of these reasons, he must learn to survive in the severe milieu. A few of the problems are the following. In the coldest periods, one's face when exposed withers in a few seconds as if scorched by a flame; a deep breath will sear the lungs and a wet mitten or shoe may necessitate amputation of a hand or foot; the touch of bare skin to metal pulls off patches of skin; to be without special glasses or goggles when traveling on the ice is almost certain to lead to blindness. In the open, drinking water can freeze the lips and whiskey paralyze the throat

Figure 19–5 The Russian station Mirny in Antarctica. Note the discarded shipping crates everywhere, indicating that all supplies must be obtained from outside. (Photo courtesy of the U.S. Navy)

if consumed in the slushy ice form. Moist cordwood explodes like dynamite and rubber hose breaks like glass. Fuel tanks must be insulated against low temperatures and lubricants pose a real problem: when they freeze in the steering apparatus, gear shift, brakes, and transmission gear, nothing moves until they are thawed out. Even when the lubricant is only stiff, a fully charged battery cannot turn the engine over. Batteries must be carefully insulated with Fiberglas or rock wool. At zero Fahrenheit, batteries produce only 50 percent of their rated capacity; and at −40° F. only 20 percent. In the bitterly low temperatures, leather cracks and tears easily. Steel becomes brittle and because the various metals contract at different rates in the same low temperatures, precision instruments become unreliable when contacting parts are composed of different metals and alloys.

Housing is a problem. The ice cap will not support standard buildings but sucks them down into its depths. Hence the pressure-hull principle used in submarine construction has been adopted by the American armed forces on the Greenland ice cap. The buildings are constructed of heavy-gauge steel formed into curved sections. Men enter and leave through submarine-type hatches which are capable of being lengthened as the building sinks deeper into the snow and ice. A structure sinks several feet per year. These are the first permanent buildings successfully erected on a polar ice cap. The "silent killer" of polar explorers—carbon-monoxide poisoning—is a major problem, for it occurs when the air vents of the shelters are covered by drifting snow.

POLAR EXPLORATION

ARCTIC EXPLORATION

Arctic exploration began shortly after Columbus discovered America (1492–1504) and especially after later explorers found that the Americas blocked the way between Europe and the Orient. Finally, in 1519–1521, Magellan found a way around South America, long and difficult. Consequently, other men began to look for a "Northwest Passage" from the Atlantic to the Pacific. First came John and Sebastian Cabot in 1497, but they got no farther than Labrador. Martin

Frobisher discovered Frobisher Bay in 1576. Between 1585 and 1588, Davis found Davis Strait and explored the coast of Greenland. Henry Hudson came upon Hudson Strait and Hudson Bay in 1610. Five or six years later, Baffin discovered Baffin Bay. By that time, the search was largely abandoned.

Meanwhile, other men began to search for a Northeast Passage from Europe to the Orient via the Siberian Coast. Hugh Willoughby set out along this route in 1533 but got no farther than Novaya Zemlya. In 1607, Henry Hudson got almost to Spitsbergen. Vitus Bering discovered Bering Strait in 1741, while Chelyuskin located Cape Chelyuskin in 1742. Wrangell found Wrangell Island and explored the eastern Siberian coast between 1820 and 1823. But long before this, men had realized that the Northeast Passage was no more practicable than the Northwest Passage.

Arctic exploration was revived in 1818 when the British government sent out Ross and Parry to explore the north coast of Canada. In 1819, Parry discovered Barrow Strait and Melville Sound. In 1826–1827, Franklyn and his men explored the coast from the Coppermine River to the Mackenzie River and then proceeded westward to Point Beechey in Alaska. In 1850, Collinson and M'Clure in an English ship entered the Arctic through Bering Strait whence they drifted in the ice to Barrow Strait. There they were rescued by Edward Belcher in a ship which had come westward into the Arctic from Baffin Bay. They reached home in 1854, the first men to complete the Northwest Passage.

Meanwhile, the Swedish explorer, Baron Nordenskiold, in 1878 and 1879 sailed a ship eastward along the Siberian coast and out to the Pacific through Bering Strait. Thus, in 1854 and 1879, the Northwest Passage and the Northeast Passage were finally found, but they proved to be extremely dangerous and of no immediate value. After the Arctic passages around North America and Eurasia had been found, men began to try to reach the North Pole, and it is then that American explorers entered the picture.

Back in 1607 Henry Hudson had reached latitude 81° 30' N. near Spitsbergen, and in 1765 the Russian Tchitsakoff achieved the same latitude. In 1871, however, the American, Captain Hall, reached 82° 16′ N. After many other men had tried, Robert Peary succeeded in reaching latitude 87° 6′ N. in 1905. Finally in 1909, Peary reached the North Pole by dog-sled over the ice from Ellesmere Island. A man by the name of Cook claimed to have got there first, but careful examination of Cook's records convinced most people that many of them were faked and that Cook had never reached the North Pole.

Between 1908 and 1926, Vilhjalmur Stefansson spent much time in the Arctic studying plant, animal, and human life there. In his writings, he did much to dispel false notions about the northern polar regions. The same may be said of the three expeditions led by Macmillan between 1913 and 1924. In 1925, Commander Byrd of the United States Navy explored parts of the Arctic by plane. That same year, Amundsen and Ellsworth tried to fly to the North Pole. The next year Commander Byrd and Floyd Bennett did fly from Svalbard to the Pole and back in fifteen hours and fifteen minutes. That same year, Amundsen, Nobile, and Ellsworth flew a dirigible across from Svalbard to Alaska in seventy-one hours. Finally in 1928, Hubert Wilkins flew a plane from Alaska to Svalbard. By 1944, the airplane had been developed to the point where a round trip across the Arctic was both safe and relatively easy. Today flights over the North Pole are commonplace.[4]

In 1929, Soviet Russia began to experiment with improved steel ice-breaking ships for Arctic navigation. Its government experts now believe that by using such ice-breakers, it will be possible to keep a sea route open along the Siberian Coast from Archangelsk to the Bering Sea. Certainly in contrast to the Northwest Passage which has been extremely difficult to negotiate and has seldom been navigated, the Northeast Passage has become a rather busy late summer route (it is navigable for two to two and a half months), providing the Soviet Union with supply and communication for the considerable number of budding cities on the Arctic periphery. Because of the growing economic and strategic value of the Soviet Arctic and the lack of an east-west railway or hard surface highway in northern Siberia, the government has given much atten-

tion to the Northern Sea Route. Through passages are rare in number, however; most of the shipments are between Murmansk and Archangelsk and the ports near the mouth of the Yenisei.

EXPLORATION OF GREENLAND

Greenland, the world's largest island, has an area of some 737,000 square miles. Around the southern and western edges, some 37,000 square miles of narrow tundra-covered lowlands have been thinly colonized by Eskimo and a few Danish government officials. The remaining 700,000 square miles are mostly unbroken ice cap, draining slowly outward to the sea by deep fiords.

The great Arctic island was discovered by the Norwegian, Eric the Red, about A.D. 980. In 986, a small Norse settlement was planted along the southwest coast. Later, numerous other settlements were made. For some 450 years these Greenland settlements existed and continued to trade with Iceland and the mother country. Shortly after 1400, the intercommunication ceased and all trace of the Greenland colony was lost.

The first modern European visitor to this region was Baffin, who discovered the great bay now bearing his name. He also found the outlet from Baffin Bay to the Arctic Ocean. The first European to visit Greenland seems to have been the Englishman Captain John Davis in 1585. He found the west coast of the island peopled sparsely by Eskimo.[5] He ascertained that even the Eskimo knew nothing about the vast ice-covered interior. In fact, they avoided it in superstitious terror, believing it to be the abode of spirits. Davis spent three years exploring the waters to the west of Greenland. Following him, many other Arctic navigators sighted the Greenland coast and made landfalls upon it. One of these, a Dane by the name of Hans Egede, visited Greenland in 1702 and from his exploration arose

[4] See Patrick D. Baird, *The Polar World* (New York, John Wiley & Sons, Inc., 1964), pp. 12–47.

[5] These people are not the descendants of the medieval Norsemen nor indeed do they have any legends regarding them. Recent archeological explorations reveal Norse ruins and abundant other evidence of the Viking Age.

the Danish claim to the island. Under Danish colonial control, the southern part of Greenland became fairly well known.

In 1871, Captain C. F. Hall of the U.S. Coast Guard explored the northwestern coast of Greenland. Seventeen years later, Fritjof Nansen crossed the north central portion of the ice cap. In 1890, Lieutenant Robert Peary of the U.S. Navy reached Cape Morris Jessup, the northernmost point of Greenland; and in 1892, he crossed the northern end of the ice cap by sledge.

The Danish explorers, Erichsen and Koch, explored the northeastern coastal areas from 1906 to 1908. Later, Rasmussen, De Quervain, and Koch crossed the ice cap.

In 1925, Macmillan conducted an American scientific expedition to the northwest of Greenland with headquarters at Etah. In his party was Commander Byrd of the U.S. Navy, with nine planes for aerial exploration of the ice cap. Because of adverse weather, however, flying was limited to a few days only. In World War II, the United States took over the control of Greenland during the time when Denmark was occupied by the German army.

EXPLORING THE ANTARCTIC

The Englishman, Captain James Cook, attempted to explore the south polar regions in 1772 but was stopped by the Great Ice Barrier.[6] He made several later attempts to find land with no results. He did, however, cross the Antarctic Circle and succeeded in reaching latitude 72° 10′ S. Because Cook found no land, people came to believe that the south polar area was mostly water and that there was a great Antarctic Ocean. Seal hunters from England, and later from New England, came in considerable numbers, and before long most of the southern islands had been discovered.

Several decades later the whaling industry began in the Antarctic regions. In 1823, a whaler by the name of Weddell discovered Weddell Sea. Three other whalers, Biscoe, Balleny, and Kemp, found Biscoe Island and the Balleny Islands. They also were the first to find parts of the mainland of Antarctica which they named Kemp Land and Enderby Land.

During the next twenty years, other explorers such as Wilkes, Ross, and d'Urville were active.

Ross Sea was found, the coast of eastern Antarctica was explored, and the Graham Islands (at first thought to be a peninsula on western Antarctica) were discovered.

James Ross sailed along the ice barrier and charted its position. He described it as follows: "A low white line extending . . . as far as the eye could discern . . . gradually increasing in height as we got nearer to it . . . a perpendicular cliff of ice between 150 and 200 feet above the level of the sea." Beyond the barrier, which is named Ross Barrier on many maps, he saw clearly a lofty range of mountains extending as far south as latitude 79°. These he named the Parry Mountains. Since it is now known that no land exists where Ross saw these mountains, it is obvious that a "looming" effect in the dry cool atmosphere made some far-distant mountain range visible, seemingly near at hand.

For fifty years after Ross, there was comparatively little interest in south polar exploration. Finally, in the 1890's it was rearoused when the whaling industry was revived—largely by the Norwegians. Bruce, Larsen, Drygalski, Nordenskiold, Scott, Borchgrevink, Charcot, and many other men participated in the exploration.

In 1902, Scott entered Ross Sea, crossed the high coastal mountain range and, sledging over the ice, reached latitude 82° 16′ S. In 1908–1909, Shackleton, using ponies and automobiles, got to latitude 88° 23′ S. In 1911–1912, Scott reached the South Pole only to find that Amundsen, using dog sleds and following a new and different route, had been there a month earlier.

Finally, in 1927–1928, Rear Admiral Byrd of the United States Navy organized an exploring expedition. Leaving Dunedin, New Zealand, he sailed three ships into the Bay of Whales in Ross Sea, carrying with him several airplanes. He established his headquarters during the winter of 1928–1929 at a place near the edge of the ice cap which he named Little America. He built an administration building, dormitories, a mess hall, repair shops, storage warehouses, meat and gasoline caches, and three steel radio towers. Some of the buildings were connected by tunnels

---

[6] An excellent, interesting account of the Antarctic is given by Paul Siple, "90° South: The Story of the American South Pole Conquest" (New York, G. P. Putnam's Sons, 1958).

and lighted by electricity supplied by a small power plant.

Byrd and his party wintered at Little America and kept meteorological and other scientific records. The following is the 1929–1930 record of average monthly temperatures at Little America.[7]

January	19.3° F.
February	3.7° F.
March	−5.0° F.
April	−29.7° F.
May	−22.7° F.
June	−10.6° F.
July	−45.6° F.
August	−28.0° F.
September	−44.2° F.
October	−17.7° F.
November	1.7° F.
December	19.2° F.

The world's lowest temperature, 126.9° F. below zero, has been recorded in Antarctica at the Russian meteorological station, Vostok, elevation 11,440 feet.

The winter blizzards of Antarctica almost defy description. Wind velocities up to one hundred miles an hour have been recorded while the thermometer stood at −20° F. During a blizzard a person cannot see more than a yard distant and soon becomes hopelessly lost. Explorers are accordingly urged to dig in rather than wander off the beaten track.

During the year 1929–1930, the monthly totals in inches of snowfall were as follows.

January	7.2	inches
February	9.4	"
March	24.2	"
April	5.7	"
May	7.7	"
June	17.1	"
July	9.0	"
August	11.4	"
September	2.4	"
October	2.0	"
November	3.0	"
December	2.3	"
Year	101.4	"

In addition to keeping scientific records, Byrd and his men discovered Marie Byrd Land and Rockefeller Range. They explored by plane and took aerial photographs of the Ice Barrier, the South Pole, Discovery Inlet, and large areas of the Antarctic continent. On one flight alone, Byrd covered fifty thousand square miles of previously unknown territory.

Early in 1944, a British party of fourteen scientists under Lieutenant Commander Marr went to the Antarctic to remain until the early part of 1946. They established a camp near Hope Bay in Graham Land, giving as their major purpose "studying the mineral wealth, biological facts, bird movements, and the habits of whales, seals, and fish."

In 1946, the U.S. Navy sent its "Operation Highjump" into the Antarctic under the command of Admiral Richard E. Byrd. Its object was to circumnavigate Antarctica and to establish a camp at Little America from which much of the continent could be photographed by air.

The expedition returned to the United States with an impressive total of achievements. It had photographed nearly 5,500 miles of coastline, flown some 27,500 miles, and investigated a total of 1,700,000 square miles of surface. More than one-third of a million square miles of previously unknown area had been mapped.

During 1949–1952 an international expedition (Norwegian-British-Sweden) explored Queen Maud Land, the Norwegian-claimed Antarctic territory. This was a highly successful expedition and its scientific findings were of a high order. It was an exceptionally well-equipped expedition, with the best of tractors, sledges, aircraft, seismographs, and intricate gear. It also used dog-sledges and skis and small trail tents similar to those employed by Amundsen and Scott a generation earlier.

During the International Geophysical Year more knowledge of the polar region was obtained. Glaciologists found much more ice than they had expected. Evidence of the early weather experienced by the earth was checked back for hundreds of years. Upper atmosphere studies indicate that the south polar winds may have far-reaching effects even to the 0° degree latitude

[7] Data procured from the U.S. Weather Bureau.

line. Ice-free lakes were located. Earth magnetism and aurora relationships were investigated. Whether Antarctica is a continent or a cluster of islands, however, was left unanswered.

NATURAL RESOURCES

PLANT LIFE

The coolness of the summer and the cover of ice and snow mean that land plants are practically absent. A few lichens grow on bare rock surfaces and some minute algae grow on the surface of the snow, sometimes giving the latter a reddish or brownish tint.

In the sea, however, plant life is more abundant. Something like four hundred varieties of algae are found in Antarctica and adjacent waters. Many varieties live in sea water. One form of algae are the minute plants known as *diatoms,* and these are so abundant that in some places they color the sea water brown. When these die, they do not decay in the near-freezing water but either float or settle to the bottom. This accumulation gives a tremendous food supply to such animals as can feed on it. There are also a few mosses and sea weeds.

ANIMAL LIFE

Land animals are almost lacking in the Polar Ice Cap climate, although they are abundant in the nearby tundra coastlands. Mites or acarines, smaller than pinheads, have been found clinging frozen to the under surface of rocks in Antarctica. Rotifers, small fresh-water animals of microscopic size, do occur as do also a few insects whose eggs are not destroyed by freezing. Animal life in the sea, however, is very abundant.

Small shrimp-like crustacea in uncounted trillions feed on the diatoms. Dozens of varieties of fish feed on the crustacea. Penguins, petrels, gulls, seals, walruses, skuas, and other animals feed on the fish. Penguins, which cannot fly, live where no human being can keep alive unless he brings with him special equipment from the civilized world. While the penguin is away from land, its life is shrouded in mystery. The struggle for existence at and below the surface of the sea is a constant and bitter one. Only the fittest survive, and man often hunts these down.

The Ross seal inhabits the pack ice, but after a century and a half of hunting it has become scarce. The sea elephant is sometimes seen but it has been nearly exterminated. The walrus is hunted for its skin, oil, and ivory tusks. Bladder-nose or hooded seals, harp seals, and bearded seals are seen in nearly all polar waters. The hair seal is the most important species of the northern region, occurring not only in the Arctic, but in the Bering and Baltic seas and the northern Atlantic. In the Antarctic, the Weddell seal, the crab-eater seal, and the sea leopard are most common. This last animal is carnivorous and extremely vicious. It attacks penguins in the water and is largely responsible for the scarcity of these birds.

Most important of the animals of the polar seas are the whales. The right, razor-back, humpback, bottle-nose, and white whales, the grampus, the narwhal, and the killer whale are the best-known kinds. The last preys upon seals, other whales, and fish. Many of the other species of whales feed on minute animal life, krill (shrimp-like crustaceans), squid, and fish. Whales are being hunted ruthlessly by Norwegians, British, Dutch, Argentines, Japanese, and Russians, and great numbers are taken each year.

More than 125 species of fish are known in the Arctic and Antarctic waters. At present they are practically unused. If ice-breakers were used to open up the ice packs and seaplanes employed to spy out open lanes of water, very productive fisheries might be developed in the polar seas. Certainly cod, halibut, flatfish, and other valuable forms are abundant.

Thus, while land mammals are absent on the ice-covered lands, marine mammals are abundant in the polar seas—seals and whales especially. Norwegian whalers annually reap a considerable harvest of whale oil from Antarctica. Indeed, whaling is the principal economic activity carried on in this climate, but it affects comparatively few people.

MINERAL RESOURCES

No one knows what minerals are present in the Polar Ice Cap climates. Antarctica may have fabulous resources hidden in its mountains or under its ice cap. Reconnaissance surveys by geologists suggest that Antarctica may have larger coal reserves than any part of the world except the United States. There are verified deposits of copper, molybdenum, and uranium. Exploitation of the minerals of the ice caps would seem to be well-nigh impossible because of the over-burden of ice. Despite this, some authorities believe that the mineral resources of the high latitudes will be exploited in the future.[8] Regardless of the possibilities, a series of national maneuvers is going on in the Antarctic and it is admitted that minerals are a major factor.

VALUE OF TRADE ROUTES

The Antarctic is far from other lands and so may never be very important for its trade routes. The Arctic, however, tells quite a different story. It is a small ocean and is really a kind of Mediterranean sea between America and Eurasia. From Ellesmere Island in northern Canada to the Lena River in Siberia the distance is only a little over 1,500 miles; and from Nome, Alaska, to Murmansk, Russia, is less than 3,100 miles. These distances are much less than a maximum round trip for the latest airplanes. To be sure, the air over the Arctic is often turbulent and foggy during winter and sometimes very hazy during summer, but the placid, clear stratosphere over the Arctic is much closer to the earth's surface than in the middle latitudes. It offers ideal flying conditions; and recent developments in radar make possible landings under conditions of very poor surface visibility. Greenland, in particular, is strategically located on the North America-to-Europe air routes and is close to the North Atlantic steamship lanes. Thus the inauguration of commercial plane service in the 1950's via a polar route between Pacific coast cities and northwestern Europe marked one of the breath-taking advances of the modern age. Hundreds of miles were lopped off the old route, hours were saved, and costs reduced. Moreover, meteorological conditions for flying over polar regions are superior to those prevailing over most of the United States and Europe. The low temperatures are no more severe than those encountered daily in operations at high altitudes anywhere. "In general, with electronic aids to polar navigation, high aircraft and engine efficiency, and proficient flight crews, no special problems are involved in flights across the polar regions."[9]

SCIENTIFIC VALUES

It is probable that the polar ice caps will be the sites of permanent weather stations in the future. Weather data, gathered by whalers in Antarctic waters, show that a colder-than-usual winter in the Weddell Sea generally precedes a drought in the semiarid belt of Argentina some 1,500 miles away in South America.

Similarly, conditions over Greenland presage certain subsequent types of weather in North America and Europe. In 1940, the Germans established a secret weather station in eastern Greenland in order to gather long-range data on the weather for use by their air forces in western Europe during World War II. It is obvious that the need for meteorological study in polar areas, as a basis for understanding and forecasting weather in the Cyclonic Zone, is increasing. The results of the expeditions comprising the 1957–1958 Year of the International Geophysical Union proved to be of inestimable scientific value.

CONCLUSION

In the past, the polar ice cap regions have been largely unknown to man, but during the past century they have been explored—at least in a preliminary manner. Indeed, ever since Cabot's voyage of 1497, they have held great fascination for adventurous and daring individuals. The immediate motives for polar explorations have, however, varied from time to time.

From 1497 to about 1740, explorers were primarily engrossed in a search first for the Northwest Passage and, a little later, for the Northeast Passage. From 1740 to 1820, the primary motivation seems to have been the sealing industry. From approximately 1820 to 1890, the whaling industry was the major incentive. From 1890 to 1912, a romantic race to reach the poles attracted many adventurous spirits to the ice caps. Since 1912, scientific motives have lain uppermost in explorers' minds. Since 1925 particularly, meteor-

[8] "Why the Race to the Antarctic?" *U.S. News and World Report* (November 4, 1955).

[9] Bernt Balchen, "Engineering Problems in the Arctic," *The Military Engineer*, Vol. XLIV (November-December, 1952), p. 426.

ological study has been important. As the Air Age advances, this last-mentioned interest promises to grow, for without adequate weather information, air operation is liable to become extremely hazardous.

The probable importance of the high latitude is suggested by the fact that various nations have staked out claims in the Antarctic.

In the early 1960's, fortunately, a dozen sovereign nations, the United States and the Soviet Union among them, signed a formal treaty, recognizing that it is in the interest of all mankind that Antarctica should continue forever to be used exclusively for peaceful purposes and not become the scene or object of international discord.

SUGGESTED USEFUL READINGS

Baird, Patrick D., *The Polar World* (New York, John Wiley & Sons, Inc., 1964), 328 pp.

Bechervaise, John, *The Far South* (Sydney, Angus and Robertson, 1961), 103 pp.

Debenham, Frank, *Antarctica, the Story of a Continent* (New York, The Macmillan Company, 1961), 264 pp.

Dyson, James L., *The World of Ice* (New York, Alfred A. Knopf, Inc., 1962), 292 pp.

Mieghem, J. Van, and P. Van Oye, eds., *Biogeography and Ecology in Antarctica*, Monographiae Biologicae, XV (The Hague, Dr. W. Junk, 1965), 762 pp.

Mirsky, Jeannette, *To the Arctic, the Story of Northern Exploration from Earliest Times to the Present* (London, A. Wingate, 1949), 334 pp.

Rodahl, Kare, *North: The Nature and Drama of the Polar World* (New York, Harper & Brothers, 1953), 237 pp.

Williamson, Geoffrey, *Changing Greenland* (London, Sidgwick and Jackson, Ltd., 1953), 280 pp.

IV

The Physiographic Factor

It has been said that for man the most important function of the land masses of the earth is to provide a standing place for himself. In the succeeding chapters the variations of the land surface will be treated. When favorable sites of the lithosphere are coupled with favorable regimes of climate and weather, choice spots on the earth's surface may be perceived. The forces from without have been dealt with, now let us proceed to a study of the forces from within the earth's surface, the forces that work together to give us the present day landscape.

20

Land
Relief and
Landforms

THE PLANET EARTH

THREEFOLD COMPOSITION

Our planet, the earth, is not a simple globe of solid matter. Rather, it is part solid, part liquid, and part gaseous material. The solid matter forms the hard part of the earth and is known as the *lithosphere*. Almost covering it is a thin shell of water known as the *hydrosphere*.[1] *Outside* this is a somewhat thicker shell composed of gases and known as the *atmosphere*.[2]

LAND AND WATER BODIES

The solid globe or geosphere is not a perfect sphere, for there are great irregularities on its surface. Some of these irregularities are vast bulges or swells; others are even greater depressions. Salt water fills the deeper depressions, leaving the swells as dry land. All of the larger bodies of salt water, except the Caspian Sea, are connected with one another in such manner as to form a World Ocean. The land areas, on the other hand, are not all connected but occur in large blocks known as *continents* and in small fragments known as *islands*. All of them combined constitute only a little more than one-fourth of the earth's surface.

MAN'S REALM

Mankind exists in the narrow zone where the bottom of the atmosphere comes into contact with the surface of the geosphere and hydrosphere. It is on the continents and islands that the approximately three and a half billion inhabitants of the earth live. It is on or near the surface of the lands and the oceans and in the lower parts

of the atmosphere that all the activities of man are carried on. It is in this narrow zone, rarely exceeding five miles in vertical thickness, that all of human geography occurs. Since it is on the land surface of the globe that all human beings live and carry on most of their activities, the size, arrangement, geographic location, and physical characteristics of the land surfaces are highly important to the student of geography.

THE SCIENCE OF GEOLOGY

To understand the surface forms of the land, the processes by which they were and still are being shaped, and the materials of which they are composed requires a knowledge of geology. The average student of geography may have little contact with geological science, but the possession of a few basic concepts is necessary for him to deal intelligently with the human geography of the earth's surface features. Accordingly, the present chapter presents only the essential facts about landforms and the processes whereby they have been shaped.

SURFACE IRREGULARITIES

The surface irregularities of the earth are of three general orders or magnitudes: *continents, major landforms,* and *minor landforms.*

CONTINENTS

CONTINENTS AND ISLANDS

The world's surface features of the first magnitude consist of the continents and larger islands

[1] See Chapter 27.
[2] See Chapter 7.

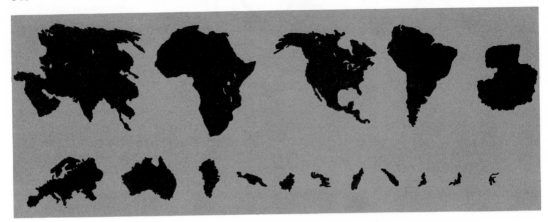

Figure 20–1   The continents and principal islands of the world, arranged according to size.

(Fig. 20–1). There are six[3] continents, varying in size from Asia plus Europe,[4] the largest, down to Australia, the smallest. Their approximate sizes are as follows.[5]

Asia	17,000,000 square miles
Africa	11,700,000 " "
North America	9,400,000 " "
South America	6,900,000 " "
Antarctica	5,100,000 " "
Europe	3,800,000 " "
Australia	3,300,000 " "

In addition to these, there are six large islands, as follows.

Greenland	840,000 square miles
New Guinea	317,000 " "
Borneo	281,000 " "
Madagascar	228,000 " "
Baffin	184,000 " "
Sumatra	183,000 " "

Below these are twelve medium-sized islands with areas between 40,000 and 100,000 square miles. Small islands (1,000 to 40,000 square miles in area) number about 125. Tiny islands (with areas of less than 1,000 square miles) number many thousands. Lines of islands are known as *island chains;* clusters of islands are known as *archipelagoes.*

LAND ARRANGEMENT

When the arrangement of land bodies is studied, it becomes obvious that most islands lie close to the continents; comparatively few of the larger ones are far removed from one continent or another. As for the continents themselves, their arrangement is noteworthy. Three of them are connected to form the great Afro-Eurasian land mass. Two are connected to form the double continent of the Americas lying at some distance from the former. Antarctica and Australia exist singly.

GLOBAL PATTERN

Even more important than these groupings of the continents is their arrangement into a global pattern. The continents of Europe, Asia, and North America form an almost complete ring of land about a small North Polar sea—the Arctic (Fig. 27–1). Southward from this project three continents pointing toward the small south polar land mass of Antarctica. Thus, the northern half of the earth contains a preponderance of land. The southern half conversely contains a preponderance of ocean.

Much of the ecology of human society stems from the arrangements of continents and islands. Much of it is conditioned by the grouping of the land masses and water bodies into land and water hemispheres. This global pattern of land bodies is so important that it has led to much

[3] We shall consider Antarctica a continent in this discussion.

[4] Actually, Asia and Europe form one continent (Eurasia) with an area of over 21,000,000 sq. miles.

[5] Edward B. Espenshade, Jr., *Goode's World Atlas,* 12th ed. (Chicago, Rand, McNally & Company, 1964), p. 169.

speculation about the geologic reasons which might account for it.

CONTINUAL PROCESSES

Nature's acts are so slow that almost no change can be seen during one man's lifetime, and the events which are noticeable do not seem to be parts of any continual process. For instance, man occasionally experiences an earthquake, but he does not connect it with the general process of nature's infinitely slow upheaval of a mountain range. He beholds a volcanic eruption, but he does not see it as part of a continental movement so vast as to liquefy enormous masses of rock below his feet. He sees a mountain stream rolling pebbles along its bottom, but he does not connect this with the water gaps cut by streams through a great mountain ridge as the latter was slowly upraised across the river's path. He sees a stream carrying mud and sand and depositing them as small bars and deltas; but he does not connect this with the carving of wide valleys and deep canyons, nor with the formation of vast layers of sedimentary rocks. He may even look a mile down into the Grand Canyon of the Colorado River and see the thousands of feet of rock strata exposed on its walls and perceive no connection between these and the labors of the small stream on his own ranch.

There is in every case, however, a very direct connection. One is the present slow process; the other is the accumulated results of that process through past ages. And hence, when one looks at the rocks deep in the Grand Canyon, he is seeing sand and mud washed there, grain by grain, at least 700 million years ago. The layers above the bottom were laid in place at later and later times. And finally, the excavating of the canyon itself represents nature's destructive work during the last few million years.

SURFACE FEATURES ARE TRANSITORY

The poets have long sung of the "everlasting hills," but that has been only because the poet, and his whole race of forebears, are very recent arrivals upon the earth. Measured on the geological time scale, the hills are very transitory indeed. They, like every other surface feature of the lands, are marked for destruction in nature's

very long process of building up and wearing down.

THE GEOLOGIC FORCES

TWO GROUPS

The surface of the earth, therefore, is in constant process of change. The forces producing such change are of two kinds: (1) those originating in the earth's interior, and (2) those originating on the surface of the earth.

The former consist of physical forces which uplift, depress, bend, tilt, warp, and break the earth's crust, and of chemical-physical action in the form of liquid rock which upwells from below as molten matter toward the earth's surface.

The latter forces, those originating on the surface of the earth, are the forces of erosion and deposition. The forces of erosion include those resulting from physical and chemical action, the action of gravitation, and biological action of living forms. These erosional agencies operate through rivers, ground water, waves, ice, wind, and plant or animal action.

The forces originating *inside* the earth tend to create irregularities on the surface of the land. The forces originating *outside* the earth tend to tear down all elevations and fill up all depressions, thus reducing the land surface to monotonous uniformity. Neither set of forces seems to be able to outrun the other very far, but instead they balance each other in the long run. No sooner are great mountains uplifted than erosion begins to wear them away, and no sooner has the process of erosion been completed than new mountains are uplifted.

INTERNAL FORCES
Physical

The earth's crust appears to be stable and firm except for occasional tremors and landslides. Actually, however, it is subject to profound but very slow movements. Evidence of the subsidence or upraising of the land is readily seen along coastlines. Along certain of these, the sea has "drowned" former low-lying lands and has entered the lower courses of streams, thereby indicating subsidence. Along others, new strips of former sea bottom have emerged and caused the land to be extended seaward, thereby indicating uplift.

Inland, the evidence for elevation or subsidence is not so obvious, but it exists nonetheless. Countless slight earthquakes are the expression of short, sharp, and rapid movements of the earth's crust. They are most common in the vicinity of young mountain ranges and along rising coasts. Earthquakes often produce cracks or rents in the earth's surface. Recurrent quakes during a long period of geologic time may cause the land on one side of such a crack or rent to rise, while the land on the other side may stand still or even gradually subside. Eventually a long more or less straight fault scarp, sometimes towering up one thousand feet or more, is produced (Fig. 20–2).

Evidence of another kind is also to be seen. In many mountain regions, sedimentary rock layers (strata) whose normal position is horizontal, are seen to be bowed up into great arches or *anticlines* (up folds) or curved downward into *synclines* (down folds). Such folded or bowed structure indicates profound squeezing and folding processes that usually have operated very slowly (Fig. 20–3).

Figure 20–2 The most apparent evidence of the movement of the earth's crust is seen in faults. Above are vertical cross sections of two faults. (From William E. Powers, *Physical Geography*, New York, Appleton-Century-Crofts, 1966)

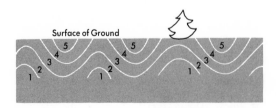

Figure 20–3 Cross section of folded rock strata numbered from 1, oldest, to 5, youngest. Erosion to a flat plain has preserved the youngest strata in synclines and exposed the older strata in anticlines. (From William E. Powers, *Physical Geography*, New York, Appleton-Century-Crofts, 1966)

Chemical

A small flow of molten rock streaming down a mountainside, a shower of small, hot rock fragments, or a cloud of hot dust blown out of a crater is an occasional sight in many parts of the world. These are the visible evidences of a very effective process whereby fused or molten rocks from the depths are moved upward toward the earth's surface. If they congeal before reaching the surface they are called *intrusions*. If they reach the surface they are called eruptions or *extrusions*.

EXTERNAL FORCES
Weathering

Weathering is the result of the action of all the atmospheric agencies upon exposed rock surfaces. Part of this action is chemical; part of it is mechanical; and part is organic. Chemical weathering is most effective in humid lands where moisture, carbon dioxide, and oxygen can work in combination. These processes break down rock structures and render the materials softer and less resistant to removal.

Mechanical weathering is the breaking up of rocks through the expansive effect of water as it freezes in cracks and through the shattering caused by the rapid heating and cooling of rocks in deserts, on mountain peaks, and upon other exposed areas.

Biological weathering includes the work of plants and burrowing animals. Expanding plant roots ferret out crevices in the rocks, pry them apart and split them. Burrowing animals pry and remove materials and in many places are responsible for a very considerable amount of rock breakage.

Solution by underground water

Where underground water is abundant and the rocks are easily soluble limestones or limy shales, a considerable amount of solution may take place below ground. Underground stream channels, caves and grottoes, and even huge caverns may be dissolved by trickling water. When subterranean solution channels are developed, surface depressions known as *sink holes* are formed. Rivers often drain into these sinks or they may disappear into caverns and underground chan-

Figure 20–4 An offshore bar, Atlantic coast of the United States. Two stages in the development of a bar are shown here: (1) the bar flanked by lagoons (on the left); (2) the final stages—the shoreward migration of the bar and the narrowing and filling up of the lagoons (center and right). The lagoons will ultimately disappear. (Photo courtesy of the U.S. Army Corps of Engineers)

nels below their beds. Regions of this kind are said to have *karst* topography.

Erosion

Erosion is the tearing loose, breaking up, and removal of rock material. One of the chief agencies of erosion is *running water*. In some instances, most of the work done by this agency consists of removing the waste materials provided by weathering. In other instances, the mud, sand, and gravel carried by running water act as cutting tools. Running water also has a direct solvent action upon rock. The amount of erosion performed by a stream depends upon its volume (which in turn depends upon the size of the drainage basin and the amount of rainfall upon that basin), and upon its velocity (which depends upon the slope of the land).

Moving ice is a second very active agent of erosion. It may occur either as a valley glacier which, in the form of a slowly flowing tongue of ice, creeps down a mountain side, or as a huge continental ice sheet such as those of Greenland and Antarctica.

Ice, of course, is a solid and it is normally very brittle; but if it exists in a large enough mass, it becomes quite plastic. A glacier starts as an accumulation of snow which, as it becomes a few hundred feet thick, slowly recrystallizes into ice. It then begins to move, either outward in all directions, flattening under its own weight like a pile of bread dough, or in the case of a snowfield upon a mountain, following definite channels down the mountainside. Such moving ice is an erosive agent of great power. It scrapes, plucks, gouges, and scours, using materials frozen into the ice as abrading tools. Locally it melts and then refreezes around objects in its path. Later it plucks and tears away these objects.

The *wind* is a third erosional agent. Armed with grains of sand and dust, it creates a "sand blast" of considerable cutting power. Wind abrasion is especially vigorous in desert regions and along sandy beaches.

Waves, likewise, are erosional agents. Lines of breakers accomplish noteworthy erosion on the shallow ocean bottom offshore. Islands, rocky headlands, and other exposed portions of shores are cut away and removed at a vigorous rate by waves as they break on the shore.

Transportation

All streams carry sediment—mud, sand, gravel, and rubble. *The carrying capacity of a stream increases as the sixth power of its velocity.* A river moving one-sixth of a mile per hour will barely move fine clay; at one-fourth mile per hour, the same stream will transport fine sand; at one-half mile per hour it will carry coarse sand; and at a little less than two miles per hour, it will transport pebbles an inch in diameter. Mountain streams in flood, flowing at high velocities, will move boulders ten feet or more in dimension.

Transportation by glacial ice depends on an entirely different principle. Ice movements are necessarily slow—only a few hundred feet, or at best a mile or so, per year. Materials of all sizes may be frozen into the ice. Sometimes enormous blocks of rock, even larger than a house, may be carried in this manner into an area where no bedrock of this kind exists. Such nomadic rocks are called *erratics.* The exact nature of glacier movement is a disputed question.

Wind cannot carry materials of large size, but it can roll fine and medium-size grains of sand along the surface. It can also pick up and transport for hundreds of miles, enormous quantities of fine dust—*loess.*

Waves and currents are active transporters of sediment removed from the shore or brought down to the coast by streams. *Beaches, bars,* and *spits* are merely accumulations of material in process of slow movement alongshore (Fig. 20–4).

Deposition

Little deposition is done by streams in their upper and swifter portions. As they reach lower and more level land, or as they approach their mouths, their velocity diminishes. Accordingly, their transporting power decreases and the load which they carry is progressively dropped. In this process, the coarser material is deposited first and the medium and fine materials later. Material deposited by running water is, therefore, usually laid down in carefully sorted and more or less

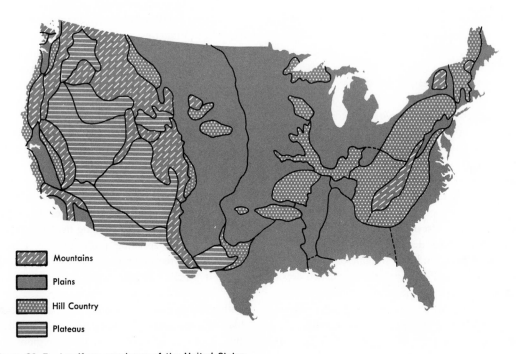

Mountains

Plains

Hill Country

Plateaus

Figure 20–5 Landform provinces of the United States.

horizontal layers. Such deposits are called *alluvium* or alluvial deposits.

Deposition by glaciers shows no such sorting. Ice transports rock materials in a jumbled mixture and drops them, upon melting, in an unsorted and irregular fashion. Such deposits are known as *glacial drift, till,* or *moraine.* If this is spread over an area as a more or less regular sheet it is called *ground moraine;* if it is piled up in an irregular ridge along a line which was once the end position of a glacier, it is called a *terminal moraine.*

Deposition by wind takes two forms. Where the material is sand, it is piled up in heaps or hills from a few inches to several hundred feet in height. Such hills of sand are called *dunes.* Where the material is fine in texture, it is deposited as a mantle of dust over a whole countryside. This may vary from a few inches to several hundred feet thick. Such dust mantles are known as *loess* deposits.

Waves and alongshore currents are also active depositors of rock waste. Coarse sand is piled along the coast as shore deposits. Finer sand is deposited in gently sloping layers on the continental shelf. Very fine silt and soluble limy materials are carried far out and cast down as deep-water deposits.

MAJOR LANDFORMS

BASIS OF CLASSIFICATION

Major landforms may be classified on the basis of two characteristics: land *relief* and surface *configuration.* By relief is meant the vertical difference in elevation, generally between the highest and lowest points in the physical landscape of a given area. By surface configuration is meant the degree of slope in a given area. The surface configurations is visible to the eye of an observer as the cross-section profile of the landscape.

STANDARD TERMS FOR LANDFORMS

Both the geologist and the geographer are concerned with the earth's crust. At every turn the geographer must have recourse to the findings of the geologist. But whereas the geologist is

A. Mountains

B. Hill Country

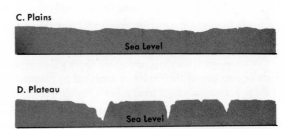
C. Plains

D. Plateau

Figure 20–6 Diagrammatic representation of the horizon lines in four major types of landforms. Vertical scale: ⅓ inch equals one mile. A, mountains: high relief; slope exceeds flat land. B, hill country: low relief; slope exceeds flat land. C, plains: low relief; flat land exceeds slope. D, plateau: high relief; flat land exceeds slope.

concerned with genesis and age of crustal deformation, the human geographer is concerned with landforms only insofar as they are the stage on which man's economic, political, and social activities take place (Fig. 20–5).

MINOR LANDFORMS

The surface of the land, when examined in detail, is seen to exhibit a very great variety of features. This bewildering array results from (1) erosion by running water, glacial ice, wind, and waves, or from (2) deposition by these same four agents.

FORMS CREATED BY RUNNING WATER

It is a truism that valleys are the product of stream erosion (Fig. 20–7). A trickle of water on a slope erodes a rill-mark. The rill-mark is washed deeper and deeper and it grows headward by the process of extending its upper end. Rill-marks thus become gullies. Gullies continue to grow headward, pushing their sources farther and farther back into uneroded land. Branch gullies also develop on either side, creating a small

ELEVATION TERMS (above sea level)

Lowlands	0 to 2,000 feet
Uplands	2,000 to 6,000 feet
Highlands	More than 6,000 feet

SLOPE TERMS (including local relief)

Plains—areas of relatively slight local relief, with gentle slopes (Fig. 20–6C)

Smooth plains (usually depositional areas such as flood plains, old sea floors, or lake beds)	Regional slopes— under 1 degree	Land relief—slight
Rolling plains (usually erosional areas, gently undulating, with occasional low hills)	Regional slopes— 1 to 4 degrees	Land relief— under 100 feet

Plateaus—areas standing noticeably above adjacent areas on at least one of their sides, or areas cut by canyons; in short, plains with high local relief (Fig. 20–6D)

Plateaus (combination of moderate slope and dissection over most of the area, and high relief in limited areas)	Regional slopes— up to 5 degrees	Land relief— hundreds or thousands of feet

Hill country—areas with sloping profiles and only limited relief (Fig. 20–6B)

Hills (gentle to steep slopes, less than 10 percent level land)	Regional slopes— 4 to 10 degrees	Local relief— several tens or a few hundreds of feet

Mountains—areas of slope land culminating in peaks or rounded summits (Fig. 20–6A)

Rounded mountains (usually old and worn down, with soil cover)	Regional slopes— 10 to 20 degrees	Local relief— a few thousand feet
Rugged mountains (usually young, with bare rock)	Regional slopes— over 20 degrees	Local relief— thousands of feet

COMBINATIONS

Lowland rolling plains (as Iowa) or *highland rolling plains* (as Tibet)	According to elevation
Upland hills (as Kentucky) or *upland rounded mountains* (as the Adirondacks)	According to slope, etc.

Table 20–1.   Landform data and terminology.

drainage system. In time, gullies are enlarged to become ravines, drained by creeks or rivulets. Creeks often eventually become rivers. A youthful river deepens its valley rapidly, sometimes excavating a gorge or even a canyon. Later the rate of downcutting diminishes and the valley is widened by slope wash. Eventually several roughly parallel rivers may widen their valleys so greatly as to destroy almost completely the upland divides between them. If this process is left undisturbed long enough, the whole region may be reduced to an almost featureless, gently rolling lowland near sea level. Such erosion lowlands are called *peneplains,* which are considered major, not minor, landforms.

Thus it is evident that valleys, gorges, canyons, stream gaps, bluffs, hilly divides, and peneplains are the products of stream erosion.

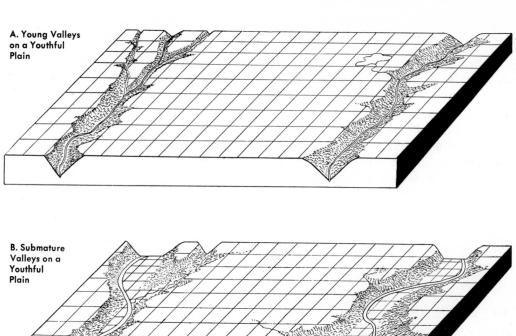

A. Young Valleys on a Youthful Plain

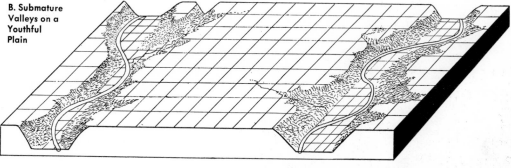

B. Submature Valleys on a Youthful Plain

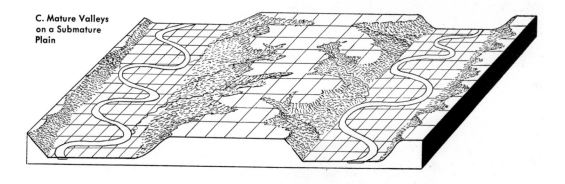

C. Mature Valleys on a Submature Plain

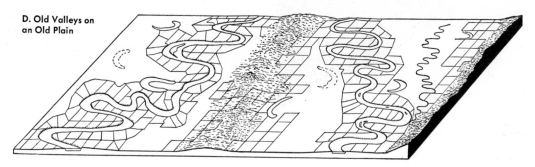

D. Old Valleys on an Old Plain

Figure 20–7 Erosional evolution of a plain and valleys from youth to old age.

In addition to these, a great number of minor landforms are the result of stream deposition.

Many heavily-laden streams deposit *sand bars* in their channels, thus making their courses shallower and rendering them more likely to flood their valleys. Where valley bottoms are wide, continued flooding deposits alluvium over a wide area, and this gradually builds a *flood-*

Figure 20–8 Above, rolling Sand Hills of Nebraska's northern midsection. Below, sand dune encroaching on the Hofuf Oasis in Saudi Arabia. (Photos courtesy of the Nebraska Game Commission and the Arabian American Oil Company)

plain. Along either side of the river itself, an excess of alluvium is cast down in the form of low broad ridges. These are called *natural levees.*

Where a stream laden with rock waste enters the sea or a lake, or where it joins another larger, more slowly flowing river, its velocity is checked rather suddenly and a *delta* is formed.[6]

Where a stream flows down from mountains or rugged hill lands, its velocity is often sharply reduced when it reaches flatter land. Where this occurs, its load is dropped abruptly and accumulates in a fan-shaped apron. To this the name *alluvial fan* is given. Along the bases of some mountain ranges, every stream has built its fan. As these grow wider, they coalesce to form a *piedmont alluvial plain.*

FORMS CREATED BY MOVING ICE

As the ice in a mountain snowfield gradually flows down the mountainside it constantly plucks loose rocks of all sizes.[7] Such continued erosion gradually excavates a glacial amphitheater, called a *cirque.*

As the ice of a mountain glacier leaves its snowfield, it follows a well-defined course, usually an old stream-carved valley. Glacial valleys, however, differ from river valleys: they are relatively steep walled and flat bottomed, and hence possess a U-shaped cross section. They are called *glacial troughs,* even though today they may no longer contain glaciers.

At the lower ends of some glacial troughs in high latitudes, ice erosion continued for a short distance out to sea. In such cases, the valley bottoms were sometimes deepened far below sea level. When the glacial episode ended and the ice melted away, the sea filled the lower ends of such troughs. The long, deep, steep-walled arms of the sea formed in this manner are called *fiords,* excellent examples of which exist along the coasts of Norway, Greenland, southern Chile, and elsewhere.

Continental glaciers (such as the ice cap now covering Antarctica, or such as those which

---

[6] The term is derived from the Greek letter *delta,* which is roughly shaped like a triangle, similar to the shape of the river alluvium at the mouth of the Nile.

[7] It is, of course, constantly replenished by snowfall as long as glacial conditions continue.

once covered northern North America and northern Europe) create surface features on a larger scale than do mountain glaciers. Beneath the area of glacial accumulation, the ice mass acts as a "bulldozer" or giant grader. It scrapes off ridges, hills and low mountain ranges. Its end product is an *ice-scoured plain*. Farther away from this central area, the ice mass acts as a steam-roller, filling in the depressions with debris, and producing a rolling *moraine plain*. Such a plain is often surmounted by hills and ridges of moraine or dotted by small "kettle" depressions. Such plains exhibit great contrasts in surface appearance with adjacent unglaciated regions, or even with small local "islands" or driftless areas which for some reason or another were bypassed by the glacier.

FORMS CREATED BY THE WIND

In certain areas, winds produce *dunes* and *loessial plains*. Dunes, most common near large sources of dry sand, are hills of wind-deposited sand and vary greatly in form and height, occasionally attaining elevations of several hundred feet. Dunes abound over thousands of square miles in the semiarid parts of the American Great Plains, though they reach their greatest development in the Sahara and Arabian deserts (Fig. 20–8). Loess is a buff or gray colored silt, coarser than clay but finer than sand. The most extensive deposits are to be found in northwestern China, though loess is found also in the United States, parts of Europe, and in South America. Loessial soils are extremely productive of crops when well watered. Whereas sand is rolled along the ground to build up dunes, loessial silt is carried in suspension and may be carried many miles from its source.

FORMS CREATED BY WAVES AND CURRENTS

Wave-cut cliffs, marine benches or terraces, truncated headlands, and stacks are products of wave erosion. Beaches, offshore barrier islands, bars, spits, and hooks are depositional forms of waves and currents (Fig. 20–4).

CONCLUSION

We have noted some of the salient factors in land relief and landforms. In the next four chapters we will see how these factors enter into the human geography of plains, mountains, hills, and plateaus. There are three and a half billion people on the earth and supplying them with food is no doubt man's greatest single problem. We have studied the several types of climate and noted their relation to agriculture. Later we shall do likewise with soils. Now we are concerned with the role of landforms in food production. If landforms were to be considered alone, about two-thirds of the earth's surface could yield crops: 95 percent of the plains could do so, 75 percent of the plateaus, 25 percent of the hills, and 5 percent of the mountains. However, when climate and soils enter the picture, only one-fourth of the land can be used for agriculture. In the following four chapters we shall also be concerned with the relation of the major types of landforms to the distribution and density of population.

SUGGESTED USEFUL READINGS

This list of readings is meant for Chapters 20 through 24.

GENERAL WORKS

Lobeck, Armin Kohl, *Geomorphology: An Introduction to the Study of Landscapes* (New York, McGraw-Hill Book Company, Inc., 1939).

Penck, Walther, *Morphological Analysis of Land Forms: A Contribution to Physical Geography*, trans. by H. Czech and K. C. Boswell (New York, St. Martin's Press, Inc., 1953), 429 pp.

Powers, William E., *Physical Geography* (New York, Appleton-Century-Crofts, Inc., 1966), pp. 1–216.

Strahler, Arthur Newell, *Introduction to Physical Geography* (New York, John Wiley & Sons, Inc., 1965), 455 pp.

Thornbury, William David, *Principles of Geomorphology* (New York, John Wiley & Sons, Inc., 1954), 618 pp.

Trewartha, Glenn T., Arthur H. Robinson, and Edwin H. Hammond, *Fundamentals of Physical Geography* (New York, McGraw-Hill Book Company, Inc., 1961), 409 pp.

Trewartha ,Glenn T., Arthur H. Robinson, and Edwin H. Hammond, *Physical Elements of Geography*, 5th ed. (New York, McGraw-Hill Book Company, Inc., 1967), 527 pp.

Van Riper, Joseph Edwards, *Man's Physical World* (New York, McGraw-Hill Book Company, Inc., 1962), 637 pp.

Wooldridge, Sidney W. and Ralph S. Morgan, *An Outline of Geomorphology: The Physical Basis of Geography* (New York, Longmans, Green & Co., Inc., 1959), 409 pp.

SPECIAL WORKS

Caudill, Harry M., *Night Comes to the Cumberlands: A Biography of a Depressed Area* (Boston, Little, Brown and Company, 1963), 394 pp.

Davis, William Morris, *Geographical Essays* (New York, Dover Publications, Inc., 1954), 777 pp.

Fenneman, Nevin M., *Physiography of Eastern United States* (New York, McGraw-Hill Book Company, Inc., 1938), 714 pp.

Fenneman, Nevin M., *Physiography of Western United States* (New York, McGraw-Hill Book Company, Inc., 1931), 534 pp.

Flint, Richard Foster, *Glacial and Pleistocene Geology* (New York, John Wiley & Sons, Inc., 1957), 553 pp.

Hunt, Charles B., *Physiography of the United States* (San Francisco, W. H. Freeman and Company, 1967), 480 pp.

Leopold, Luna, Gordon M. Wolman, and John P. Miller, *Fluvial Processes in Geomorphology* (San Francisco, W. H. Freeman and Company, 1964), 552 pp.

Lobeck, Armin Kohl, *Things Maps Don't Tell Us: An Adventure into Map Interpretation* (New York, The Macmillan Company, 1956), 159 pp.

Thornbury, William D., *Regional Geomorphology of the United States* (New York, John Wiley & Sons, Inc., 1965), 609 pp.

21
Plains
Habitat

We have noted that types of terrain are differentiated primarily on the basis of two factors: (1) *relief* or distance from the lowest to the highest element in the landscape; and (2) *configuration* or ratio of flat land to slope land. Since any two factors may be so associated as to yield four possible combinations, it is apparent that there are four major types of landforms which demand recognition in a study of human geography. These are mountain, hill country, plain, and plateau. The first two are alike in showing a predominance of slope over flat land but they differ in relief. The last two are similar in possessing more flat land than slope but they also differ in relief. The first and fourth are alike in exhibiting great relief but unlike in ratio of flat to slope land. The second and third are similar in possessing small relief but dissimilar in configuration.

The natural environment of a region influences to an amazing degree the pursuits its denizens will follow and indirectly their economic, social, and political status. By superimposing a world map of the distribution of population upon a physical map of the world, one notes that, with the possible exception of certain areas in the tropics, where the people prefer mountains and high plateaus as a means of escape from the debilitating heat of the lowlands, the great bulk of the world's habitants dwells on plains. Here are the productive farms, the busy industries, the maze of transportation lines, the clusters of cities, large and small, and the centers of art, literature, science, and government. In short, plains are synonymous with progress and civilization!

What is a plain? To the average person there is a great difference between a plain and a plateau. Yet, as a matter of fact they differ only slightly; the chief distinction is the fact that the valleys in plains are shallow, whereas those in plateaus are deep.

The word *plain* ordinarily brings to mind such concepts as *level, low,* or *near sea level.* Yet this is not necessarily true, for the Great Plains occupy large areas lying nearly a mile above sea level. Nor are plateaus always high above sea level; the Columbia Plateau of Washington, for instance, is only half as high as the Great Plains of Colorado. Furthermore, plains need not be flat, though as a general rule they contain more flat than sloping land.

ORIGIN AND KINDS OF PLAINS

Plains differ one from another in origin, relief, soils, drainage, climate, natural vegetation, native animal life, and hence in the nature of their occupation by human beings. Some lie at high elevations, others at low; some embrace the sea, others cling to the interiors of continents; some are small, others large; and some are tropical, while others are subtropical, cyclonic, or polar (Fig. 21–1). In general, plains are *erosional* or *depositional*. In short, they result from the wearing down of an area as a result of erosion or from the building up, layer by layer, by deposition.

EROSIONAL PLAINS

In most parts of the world, the erosional action of running water is constantly wearing down the physical features of the land. Given sufficient time, running water is capable of reducing mountains, plateaus, and hill country to areas of almost featureless flatness. On every continent are found erosional plains which are the results of stream work and weathering. A good example of this type of plain is the Amazon Basin—a relatively

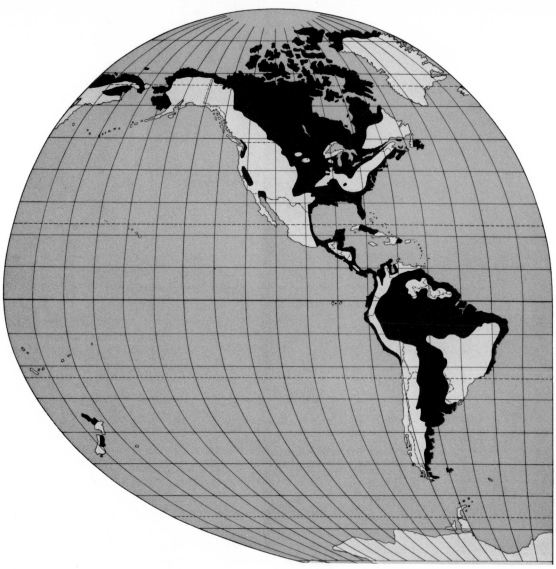

Figure 21–1   Plains areas of the earth.

smooth land which definitely owes its form to erosion. Here large streams eat their way into the land and carry away enormous quantities of materials (Fig. 21–2). Rain wash has eaten at the sides of the ridges which the streams created when they dug their valleys and have thus lowered the interstream areas. Here and there, standing conspicuously above the stream-eroded plain, are monadnocks—erosion residuals, which in this instance appear to consist of more resistant rock than the surrounding material. By noting the tops of the various monadnocks, the observer can deduce the general level of the former surface and appreciate the gigantic scale of the erosional task already completed.

DEPOSITIONAL PLAINS

Probably no better example of a plain resulting from deposition could be found than the North China Plain—that created by the Hwang Ho (Yellow River). This river, flowing from uplands to the west, has been dumping its loads of silt (two and a half billion tons annually) over the centuries into the Yellow Sea and the Gulf of Po Hai. These materials have built up from sea bottom a low featureless plain.

All plains obviously fall into one of the two classes—*erosional* or *depositional*. Geographers, however, also concern themselves with other types of plains. These are considered either from the standpoint of *location* or of *origin*.

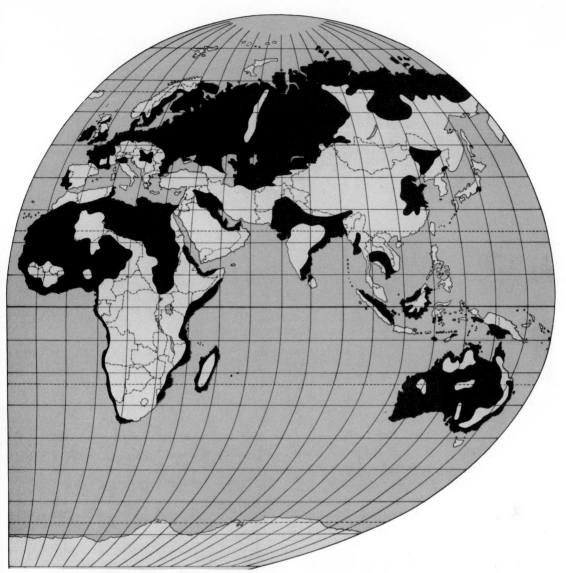

PLAINS CLASSIFIED ACCORDING TO LOCATION

COASTAL PLAINS

Coastal plains, which characterize most of the continents to a greater or less degree, represent elevated sea bottom. Their slopes are low, their surfaces flat to undulating, and their valleys shallow. The Atlantic and Gulf coastal plains of the United States are excellent examples. No parts stand more than a few hundred feet above sea level. The valleys seldom exceed fifty feet in depth and are separated by broad areas of gently undulating land. Unmistakable evidence indicating that coastal plains once were under water is the presence in the unconsolidated material of shells and other animal remains which closely

resemble those to be found on the shallow parts of the continental shelf at the present time. Most coastal plains are covered with a thin mantle of clay, gravel, lime, marl, and sand—materials washed from the land by streams and deposited on the floor of the ocean. Much of this material has not yet been consolidated into rock.

In some places there are extensive swamp lands where the sluggish, winding streams are unable to carry off the rainfall. Agriculture is important on most coastal plains, despite the two crop enemies—sandy soil and poor drainage.

The fall zone

The inner or landward edge of the coastal plain of eastern United States lies against the hard, crystalline rocks of the Piedmont Upland.

Figure 21–2   Erosional plain in the Amazon Basin, Brazil. (Photo from DeWys, Inc.)

This line of contact is known as the fall zone because the streams from the upland must traverse a zone of falls and rapids as they descend to the soft, unconsolidated sediments of the coastal plain en route to the ocean. Coastal plains in other parts of the world make somewhat similar contact with the old land of their respective continents.

Above the fall zone in the United States, the streams are unsuited to navigation, while below it they are navigable. For this reason the zone is marked by important cities on nearly every large river crossing it. Most important of these are Newark, Trenton, Philadelphia, Wilmington, Baltimore, Washington, Raleigh, Columbia, Augusta, Macon, and Columbus.

The geographic importance of the fall zone has been great; cities here became important commercially because they were necessarily bulk-breaking points, and important industrially because they possessed water power.

INTERIOR PLAINS

Many parts of the interior plains were formerly coastal plains bordering upon an interior sea. Uplift of the land in the geological past caused the sea to recede and the emerged area was added to the expanding interior plains of the growing continent.

The relief of interior plains is greater than that of coastal plains, since they have been fairly high above sea level for a long time. Hence their streams are more powerful and their valleys deeper than those in coastal plains. An excellent example of this type of plain is the Interior Lowland in central North America.

PIEDMONT PLAINS

Piedmont plains, which are formed by the coalescing of alluvial fans at the foot of a mountain range, are especially well developed in arid and semiarid regions where the vegetative covering is meager and where the precipitation is dominantly torrential in character. During a cloud burst, the rain water, heavily charged with debris, rushes immediately into drainage channels. The streams, often puny and insignificant during dry weather, become raging torrents during a storm, and just before emerging from a canyon mouth may be a wall of water twenty to fifty feet high. As the velocity is restrained and the load is dropped, the deposition takes the shape of a fan which ultimately may extend over several miles.

Such plains are important for agriculture, providing there is water for irrigation, though the amount is never adequate to fill all needs.

On the sloping piedmont plains of southern California there is a definite zonation of crops— three types of farming in three different zones (Fig. 21–3). Fruit preempts the sections near the mountains because it is sensitive to frost and needs much water. When so placed, orchard trees benefit from air drainage[1] afforded by slope on the one hand, and from a larger supply of water on the other. Such crops as alfalfa, wheat, and barley are capable of withstanding considerable punishment from both frost and drought and hence are allocated to the lower sections of the piedmont.

PLAINS CLASSIFIED ACCORDING TO ORIGIN

ALLUVIAL OR FLOODPLAINS

The greatest amount of deposition occurs along the river banks, since the largest checking of the current takes place here. Over a period of time the margins of the channel are thus built up, and these higher parts of the floodplain are

called *natural levees.* In order to prevent floods or at least mitigate their devastation if they do occur, the people who live on the floodplain construct *artificial levees* along the crests of those made by nature. Away from the channel in the lowest places are the back marshes which tend to remain wet even during low water.

Rivers on such plains meander (Fig. 21–4). They flow in straight lines only when man is determined to control them. During a flood, whole meanders may be cut off and the river channel shifted to another position. Hence the typical floodplain is characterized by abandoned channels or oxbow lakes—all arranged in crescentic plan.

Deltas

Where a stream carrying sediment debouches into a body of water characterized by inactive currents, its velocity is suddenly checked and it is rendered powerless to carry sediment held in suspension. This deposition of material, as time goes on, causes new land to be built up, over

[1] At night the air, which is cold and therefore heavy, drains down the slopes settling in the lower elevations. Hence danger of frost is least at the head of the piedmont plain and greatest at its foot. This phenomenon is known as *air drainage.*

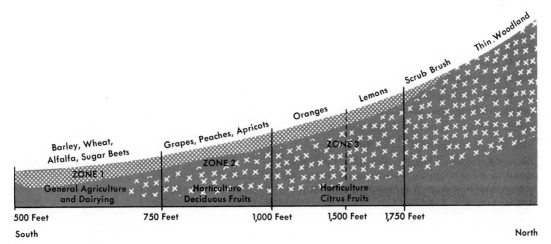

Figure 21–3 Generalized cross section, about fifteen miles long, of typical piedmont agriculture in southern California. The crops grow in three zones or bands as a response primarily to air drainage but also to water supply and soil texture. Since at night cool air, which is heavy, flows down the slopes and settles upon the valley floor, the upper piedmont is a zone of moving air and relative warmth, and hence not very susceptible to killing frost. Upon it, therefore, are grown the sensitive fruit crops, while in the valley bottoms are grown those crops able to withstand considerable punishment from frost, such as alfalfa, sugar beets, beans, wheat, and barley. Most of the crops are irrigated, the small grains being the exception. Grapes may or may not be irrigated, depending upon the amount of water available. Grapes can subsist upon surprisingly little water.

Figure 21–4 Meandering Mississippi River between New Orleans and Baton Rouge. Floodplain materials are easily eroded and this accelerates the development of meanders. Also the current's force on the outside of a bend causes it to "eat" into the bank, thereby increasing the stream's curvature. Hence the course of a river on a floodplain becomes a series of loops lying across the trend of the valley. Meanders greatly increase the airline distance for river craft, which may be obliged to go ten to fifteen miles in order to cover a distance of three or four miles up or down the valley. (Photo courtesy of the U.S. Army Engineer District, New Orleans, La.)

which the river laboriously makes its way after first breaking up into distributaries. These distributaries, which may be likened to the ribs of a fan, build out the deposit laterally, giving rise to a delta, so-called because of its resemblance to the Greek letter Δ.

Most deltas are flat and poorly drained. Their soils are exceedingly fertile because of the mixture of rock material from the entire drainage basin. Hence delta plains in regions of suitable climate, such as the Ganges-Brahmaputra, Yangtze-Kiang, Nile, and others, are densely populated. In parts of the Ganges-Brahmaputra delta including areas inundated for months each year, the agricultural population averages 1,030 persons to the square mile.

Delta occupants live often in fear of floods. Millions of Chinese in the delta of the Hwang-Ho, China's "river of sorrow," have perished from flood. For an account of the human geography of floods on the north China plain see Chapter 26.

LACUSTRINE PLAINS

Another type of plain is the lake or lacustrine plain, one of the flattest landforms extant. The low relief is consequent upon the fact that many streams debouched into ancient (now extinct) lakes, carrying sediment which they deposited on the lake bottoms and which was redistributed smoothly by waves and currents. A change of climate or cutting down of the outlet caused such lakes to disappear or shrink, exposing the level plains of their bottoms. The former is precisely what happened in the case of Lake Bonneville in Utah, which, during the Glacial Period, was about ten times the size of its puny, salty remnant, Great Salt Lake. It was fresh, having an outlet into the Pacific Ocean via Cache Valley, Red Rock Pass, and the Portneuf, Snake, and Columbia rivers. Many of the present Basin Ranges were then islands. The story of Lake Bonneville's death struggle is graphically indicated on the mountainsides by old shorelines, the highest of which, the Bonneville, lies about one thousand feet above the present level of Great Salt Lake (Fig. 21–5).

Lacustrine plains in arid regions are apt to be productive agriculturally if water for irrigation is available, for their soils are quite fertile. The floorlike levelness, however, may mean poor drainage and hence alkaline soils.

In humid regions, such plains are famous agriculturally; the Lake Agassiz Plain is one of the outstanding wheat regions of the world.

GLACIAL PLAINS

Some of the world's most important plains from the standpoint of land utilization were formerly occupied by vast sheets of glacial ice. When the continental ice cap receded (as the climate again became warm), there was left upon the surface over which it passed the earthy material which it was transporting. Some of this material was piled into ridges, now called *terminal* or *reces-*

sional moraines, and some of it was scattered evenly as *ground moraine.* Both consist of a heterogeneous mixture of earthy material varying from the finest clay to large boulders (Fig. 21–6). Because it is more level, ground moraine constitutes the productive agricultural lands in those parts of the world once covered by the ice sheets. The Corn Belt of the United States, probably the most important agricultural region in the world for its size, consists largely of ground moraine with a sprinkling of terminal moraine. That part overridden by the ice cap was left smoother than before; the topography was mellowed by having the tops of the hills planed off and the transverse valleys filled.

Another good example is to be found in the wide arc around Hudson Bay and extending to the Arctic. Here is a plain that has resulted from the processes of erosion—from the lowering and smoothing of a formerly higher and more

Figure 21–5 A bit of lacustrine plain in Salt Lake Valley, Utah, with shorelines of old Lake Bonneville, of which Great Salt Lake is but a shrunken remnant. Lake Bonneville was a body of fresh water as large as Lake Huron. The highest shoreline lies 1,000 feet above Great Salt Lake. (Photo by Droft, courtesy of the U.S. Forest Service)

Figure 21–6   Ground moraine in northeastern Illinois. Usually ground moraine constitutes very rich agricultural land in those sections once covered by continental glaciers. (Photo from William E. Powers, *Physical Geography*, New York, Appleton-Century-Crofts, 1966)

rugged area. Stream action first wore the surface down to a plain; later this was mellowed by the great ice sheets. Farming here is unimportant, and the small scattered population ekes out a somewhat precarious living by mining or trapping or logging. The region, however, is proving to be one of the world's richest in metallic minerals and a number of large and important mining towns are developing.

Glacial versus Nonglacial Plains

Glacial ice *made* some areas, like the Corn Belt, and *broke* others, like the Canadian Shield. But what of glaciated and nonglaciated lands that adjoin, as in Ohio and Wisconsin—are they of equal value for farming? Several field studies in Ohio and Wisconsin indicate that the per acre yields of crops are invariably higher in the glaciated than in the unglaciated counties.

RESOURCES OF PLAINS

With favorable climate, soils and location, plains become the productive, progressive lands of the earth, for their levelness facilitates farming, the "basis of all permanent advance in civilization."

Nearly all outstanding agricultural nations lie on plains.

Timber is another important resource of plains in humid regions. Those plains (save the prairies) east of the twenty-inch isohyet in the United States were richly endowed. To the colonists and explorers America was a vast, unbroken forest. Even after Americans had extended the frontier to the Pacific Ocean, crossing the prairie, the steppe, and the deserts, they learned that nearly half the nation's land area had been originally forested. Little of this plains country produces timber today, however, for the dense population requires that crops have preference over trees which do well in rugged areas where farming is impossible.

Plains stand uniquely in regard to navigable waterways. Mountains and plateaus do not have gentle gradients, and as a result their streams lack the depth and slow current essential for navigation. Too much emphasis cannot be placed upon the significance of cheap water transportation in the lives of the plainsmen of Belgium, Brazil, China, France, Germany, the Netherlands, and the Soviet Union.

Though rich in many resources, plains are

comparatively poor in minerals, especially the metallics, which are less accessible than in mountains. Plains do, however, contain much of the world's coal and lignite which were formed in ancient flat-lying swamps, petroleum and natural gas, which were trapped in dried-up estuaries, and deposits of salt and potash, which were and still are formed in desert lakes and seas.

CLIMATES OF PLAINS

Plains are so widely distributed throughout the world that they run the whole gamut of climatic types—the hot and cold, the wet and dry, as well as all gradations of these. The climate in each case depends upon latitude and position with respect to mountain barriers, oceans and other large bodies of water, ocean currents, or continental interiors. Climate thus becomes the compelling force affecting the life of plains: on it depends whether the plain will be occupied by sparse populations of backward natives, such as the Chukchis of Siberia who herd reindeer, the Eskimos near the Coppermine River east of Great Bear Lake who hunt and fish, the Mura Indians of the lower Amazon who catch fish and turtles, the nomads of the Sahara who graze sheep and goats, or by dense populations of advanced peoples such as the Corn Belt farmers of Iowa, the gardeners of the Netherlands polders, or the closely packed manufacturers of Chicago, St. Louis, Cleveland, and Detroit.

PLAINS AND HUMAN MOVEMENT

Man is most mobile on plains, especially the grass-covered ones. American pioneers pushed the frontier westward at an unbelievably rapid rate once the prairies were reached, filling up and subduing hundreds of millions of acres with unparalleled speed. Level terrain, too, in combination with a great system of branching waterways with only slight portages between, enabled intrepid Russian pioneer trappers to traverse a boundless wilderness, reach the Pacific with comparative facility, and extend the empire of the Czars over thousands of miles. Russia formerly was laconically called the "all-on-land empire."

Because the Germans believed they could more speedily reach Paris via the level Belgian plain than across the lines of limestone cliffs between Germany and France (Fig. 21–7), they invaded Belgium, thereby violating the little country's neutrality and bringing Great Britain into the fray. The 1940 invasion varied only slightly from that of 1914.[2] Bowman says: "The reason for Belgium's melancholy history is clear: she stands upon a great world highway that joins central and western Europe."[3] And Brunhes remarks that "Belgium, since the time of Caesar, has been the road for armies."[4]

Railways and highways may be built easily and without exorbitant cost on plains, since the country often extends for miles without any appreciable changes in elevation and grades are insignificant. A railway in North Carolina has a stretch of one hundred miles where there is neither curve, excavation, nor embankment. A somewhat similar situation prevails throughout parts of the Pampa of Argentina. Moreover, railways may go in any direction and the network may be as dense as the country's economy demands.

On many plains, railways tend to follow streams; on the Great Plains, nearly all of them do so because of the more uniform grade, the relative straightness of the courses, and the location of the resources there.[5] On the coastal plain of Virginia, on the other hand, lines of communication follow divides rather than valleys, since the former are level and continuous.

UTILIZATION OF PLAINS

It is well known that the human race has progressed most in agriculture, manufacturing, transportation, commerce, and urban development on plains. It is equally well known that approximately 90 percent of the world's population dwells thereon, though only about 41 percent of the earth's land surface may be classed as plain.

[2] Samuel Van Valkenburg, *America at War: A Geographical Analysis* (Englewood Cliffs, N.J., Prentice-Hall, Inc., 1942), pp. 74–78.

[3] Isaiah Bowman, *The New World* (Yonkers-on-Hudson, N.Y., World Book Company, 1928), p. 194.

[4] Jean Brunhes, *Human Geography* (Chicago, Rand McNally & Company, 1952).

[5] Nevin M. Fenneman, *Physiography of Western United States* (New York, McGraw-Hill Book Company, Inc., 1931), p. 91.

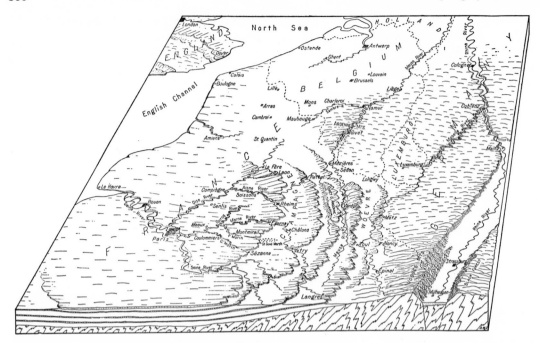

Figure 21–7   Diagrammatic view of the western theater during World War I. The underground rock structure is shown on the front edge of the block. Note that Paris lies in the center of a basin made by a series of hard-rock layers, and that each layer makes, where it outcrops along the eastern side of the basin, an east-facing cliff toward Germany. The German leaders realized that these cliffs constituted natural fortifications of the first order and that they could never reach Paris that way. Accordingly, they attempted to go around them by way of the level Flanders Plain, although they knew it meant violation of Belgium's neutrality and the probable entry of Britain into the war. (After Douglas W. Johnson)

It would be incorrect, however, to suppose that all plains are equally hospitable for human occupancy. A plain may be level, have fertile soils, and excellent commercial location, all factors conducive to utilization by man, but an adverse climate may make it a veritable no-man's land. Some plains are too dry, others too hot and moist, while still others are too cold for efficient human occupation. Accordingly such places, along with mountains, constitute the great blank spaces in the world's population map and are permanently doomed. Climate then, rather than physical relief, is actually the dominant factor affecting habitability.

Where plains have suitable climates for crops, livestock, and human beings, and where their location permits access to markets, they usually have distinct advantages over plateaus and mountains and become outstanding agricultural areas (Chapter 15). Moreover, the low relief insures that the soil will be relatively permanent, for erosion is comparatively ineffective. This permanency of agriculture is especially significant because, as stated heretofore, agriculture is the foundation of all enduring advance in civilization.

If plains possess a covering of fertile soil, they are obviously more livable, but even fertility is not always essential for agricultural progress. Witness Denmark on the great plain of northern Europe which in the eighties of the last century was a country of despair. The growing of grain, the leading agricultural enterprise, was destroyed by cheap cereals from the Midlands of the United States. In less than two decades, however, the Danes staged a recovery which was the most complete in history. They turned to dairying, concentrating their attention, ability, and energy on butter. Swine and poultry were added later. Some feed was grown but more was imported, payment being made with money received from the sale of dairy products, bacon, and eggs. Today the Danes supply many countries, particularly Great Britain, with these articles, the quality of which is unrivaled. The Danish standard of living is high. Cooperation is the keystone of progress and prosperity. There is no illiteracy. It is said that the Danes read more newspapers per capita than any other people in the world. Denmark is, of course, only one of many plains countries which have achieved much in agriculture, but it has accomplished this in a plain that is poorly endowed with natural resources. Mountain, hill country, and plateau habitats record nowhere similar agricultural triumphs.

Plains also contain most of the great industrial centers, for here are unexcelled transport facilities, markets, labor, level land and plenty of it, water, and frequently raw materials and power. If these last be absent, they usually are located not far away and are easily procurable at relatively low cost. The development of manufacturing and of cities as well as of commerce during the past 160 years was accompanied and partly caused by the revolution in agricultural technique. Surplus sons and daughters as well as crops and livestock move regularly to the cities. If urban centers are to grow or even hold their own in population, they must draw on the fertile farm families from their hinterlands.

Plains are, if endowed with stimulating and productive climates, the lands of opportunity for man. They are "born great" and hence it is little wonder that they are utilized by and provide homes for the majority of mankind.

PLAINS AND THE DISTRIBUTION OF POPULATION

Plains are, generally speaking, densely populated. Nine-tenths of the earth's habitants dwell at elevations of less than two thousand feet, though not all terrain below this altitude may be classed as plain.

The only lowlands which man shuns are those blighted by hostile climates, poor drainage, unproductive soils, death-dealing diseases, remoteness, or inaccessibility.

Because plains are so well suited to farming, manufacturing, trading, and transporting, man, except in hostile climates, selects them for his habitat. On them he has located nearly all his

great cities. Rare indeed is a strictly montane city of 100,000 persons. Only when the more level land becomes preempted does mankind take to the rugged areas on a large scale, except in the tropics.

In mountains, the agricultural population is always distributed unevenly, being concentrated in the broader valleys; in plains, it is distributed evenly, save where marked differences occur in the soils[6] or poor drainage is present. The state of Iowa is characterized by topography relatively so gentle and soils so fertile that probably more than 80 percent of its area is arable. People, therefore, can and do live almost anywhere. It is on plains, also, that the close-packed industrial populations are situated.

PLAINS AND CIVILIZATION

Civilization was cradled in plains and modern civilization is the child of a plains environment. This results in large measure from ease of mobility, which facilitates the circulation and exchange of both goods and ideas. Plains in progressive countries are literally spider-webbed with transportation lines—railways and highways.

Interchange of ideas is invaluable. "There is a constant exchange, conflict, comparison, and accumulation of the ideas of many—a continual competition which spurs to progress." Plainsmen are, hence, more cosmopolitan and less provincial than mountain men.

A boundless plain, like that of the Soviet Union or interior United States, fosters economic, political, and social uniformity and solidarity, whereas a small hilly area, like the Balkans, has evolved into a crazy quilt of races and nationalities which have lived side by side for centuries without acquiring much from one another.

Plains inhabitants, regardless of vocation, have unique opportunities to benefit from civilization. If they are farmers, they can complete tasks in less time than their contemporaries in the

---

[6] Though the topography on the Great Plain of north China is uniform, the soils are so varied that the distribution of population is spotty; certain portions swarm with humanity while others are moderately and even sparsely populated.

mountains, which results in more time for neigh-borly contacts. The level topography invites, even stimulates, contact through the ease of movement. A larger income permits the enjoyment of amen-ities permanently denied mountain farmers. Pro-gressive schools assure an education and cultural centers in nearby cities beckon all. If the people are industrial workers, they have access to such civilizing influences as art, historical, scientific and commercial museums, libraries, music halls, theaters, and institutions for the education of adults.

SUGGESTED USEFUL READINGS

See especially the texts by William E. Powers (pp. 67–125), Arthur Newell Strahler (pp. 363–381), and Glenn Trewartha, et al. (Chapter 14) listed on p. 356.

22

Mountain Habitat

Of the several types of landforms, mountains are the least hospitable to human cultures. Hard lands, they force a hard life upon those who would inhabit them. Possibly every traveler who penetrates a mountain region and witnesses the one-sided struggle progressing between nature and man asks himself time and again why people ever settled there and why they remain.

Almost nowhere are mountains densely populated, for the rugged surface, the shallow and stony soils, and the often inhospitable climate greatly restrict the area suitable for human occupation.

WHAT ARE MOUNTAINS?

It is easy to identify a mountain, but difficult to give a definition that will truly represent *all mountains*. There are high ones and low ones, steep ones and gentle ones, rounded ones and flat ones. Geographically speaking, mountains may be considered prominent elevations with restricted summit areas, as indicated by such strictly montane words as *peak* and *crest*. More strictly defined, a mountainous area is one which exhibits great relief wherein slope exceeds flat land (Fig. 22–1).

DISTRIBUTION OF MOUNTAINS

Mountains are distributed on every continent, to a greater extent on some than on others. They tend to cling to the peripheries rather than concentrate in the interiors of the continents (Fig. 22–2). The loftiest mountains, constituting almost continuous chains, practically circumscribe the Pacific Ocean and in addition extend westward to the Atlantic by way of southern Eurasia and northern Africa.

In contrast to the distribution of the higher mountains, the lower ones are detached and isolated. They occur in central and northern Europe, eastern and southeastern Asia, eastern Africa and Australia, and eastern North and South America, where they often take on the characteristics of plateaus or hill country.

Figure 22–1 Mt. Rainier, Washington, nearly three miles above sea level, has radiating from its peaks one of the largest glacier systems in the country. In winter the ascending moisture-laden winds from the Pacific Ocean are suddenly chilled and therefore deposit heavy snow, much of which forms ice under pressure. (Photo by the National Park Service, courtesy of the U.S. Department of the Interior)

369

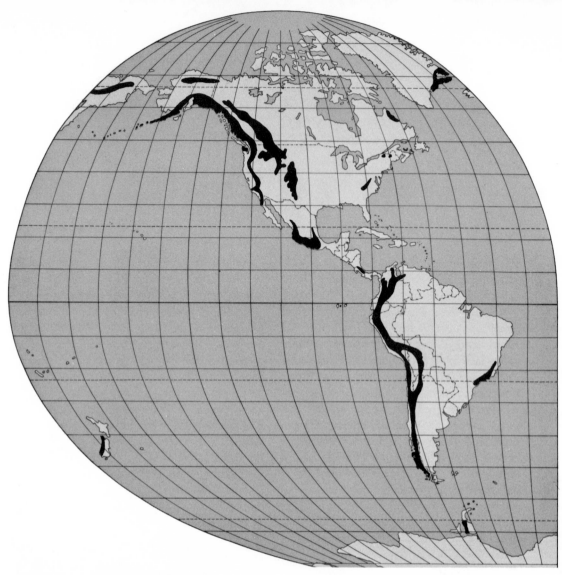

Figure 22–2 Mountain areas of the earth.

TYPES OF MOUNTAINS

The geologist classifies mountains in various types on the basis of their origin. Thus he would recognize the following.

1. *Volcanic* mountains, resulting from the construction of conical or irregular piles of lava and ejecta poured out or exploded from volcanic vents

2. *Laccolithic* mountains, resulting from the arching of the earth's surface above a lens-shaped intrusion of molten magma into the outer portion of the earth's crust

3. *Folded* mountains, resulting from the lateral compression of a segment of the earth's outer shell, which wrinkles the strata into corrugations consisting of parallel arches or anticlines and troughs or synclines, as though the rocks had been squeezed between the closing jaws of a gigantic vise

4. *Overthrust* mountains, resulting from the shoving of an uplifted portion of the earth's shell over an adjacent less-elevated portion, as though the lateral compression which causes the folded type had been continued beyond the point at which the stresses could be accommodated by wrinkling alone, or because the rocks responded to the compressional forces by breaking and sliding, rather than by bending

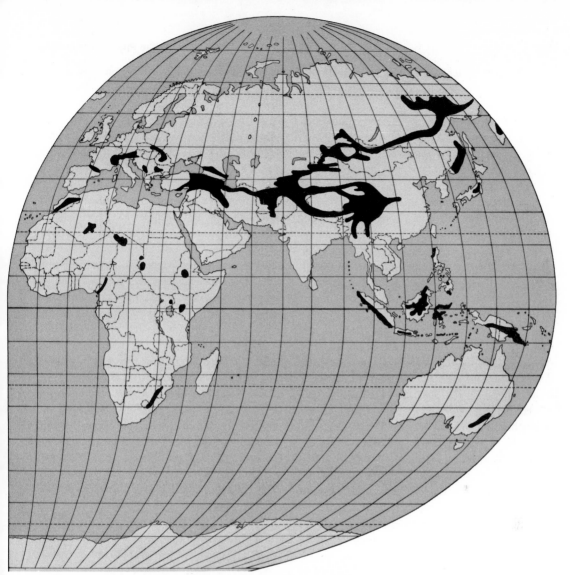

5. *Block* mountains, resulting from the shattering of a portion of the earth shell into a mosaic of angular fragments, each bounded by a more or less vertical plane of fracturing or faulting, and many of which are twisted or turned so that the edge of one block may stand thousands of feet above the edge of an adjacent block

6. *Domal* mountains, resulting from the vertical uplift and doming of a circular or oval area in the midst of a larger undisturbed region

7. *Residual* mountains, resulting from the superior resistance to erosion of certain portions of a broadly elevated region during an episode of long-continued erosion which reduces the less-resistant rocks to a level much lower than that of the stronger residuals

8. *Complex* mountains, embodying a combination of two or more of the factors noted above

The geomorphologist classifies mountains on the basis of their more recent geologic history. Thus he would distinguish old, worn-down mountains from young, rugged mountains. In the last few geologic epochs the former have suffered no major crustal movement nor volcanic activity, and in consequence the forces of erosion have been able to reduce the summits to subdued and rounded forms. In contrast, crustal movements on a large scale and volcanic activity have been conspicuous during comparatively recent time in the young, rugged mountains and, in consequence, erosion has thus far been able merely to sculpture the summit regions into jagged peaks and serrate ridges.

The geographer, on the other hand, should classify mountains on the basis of his relation to them and should give consideration to their origin and recent history only insofar as they bear directly upon his relationships to them. Thus, the geographer might recognize such types as (1) *linear* mountains, (2) *domal* mountains, and (3) *irregular* mountains.

As the name implies, linear mountains are long, relatively narrow uplands standing conspicuously above their surroundings. Such mountains may belong to any of the geologist's types except laccolithic or domal and may represent either of the two major types recognized by the geomorphologist. Thus the geographer might classify them in such subdivisions as (1a) *young, rugged, folded* mountains like the Alps and Carpathians, (1b) *old, worn-down, folded* mountains like the Appalachians of West Virginia, Maryland, and Pennsylvania, (1c) *overthrust* mountains like the front ranges of the Rockies in Montana and western Canada, (1d) *block* mountains like the Wasatch Range in Utah and the Sierra Nevada in California, (1e) *residual* mountains like the Great Smokies in the Southern Appalachian System, and (1f) *complex linear* mountains like the Southern Rockies in Colorado and adjacent states or the Andes in South America. Such distinctions are far from being merely academic. Young folded mountains are commonly continuous barriers, stretching for long distances across a con-

tinent, which may be crossed only by arduous ascents to high and difficult passes. Old, worndown, folded mountains are commonly characterized by water gaps through which the master streams make their way as they cross the residual ridges of resistant rock from the linear valley on one side to that on the other. Such gateways provide a "water-level" route into or across the mountain range and have had a profound influence upon the history of human occupation of such regions. Long, relatively narrow block mountains commonly present very different aspects on either side; generally the faulted edge of the tilted block is steep, whereas the other slope is comparatively gentle. Thus the faulted west face of the Wasatch Mountains rises precipitously and impressively above the eastern edge of the Great Basin to the west, with its foot concealed by material eroded from the upper part of the fault rock (Fig. 22–3). In contrast the eastern slope of the Wasatch is nearly as gentle as the western slope of the Sierra Nevada.

The domal mountains of the geographer's classification likewise embrace more than one geological type. Some of the domal mountains are (2a) *laccolithic* like the Henry Mountains of Utah; others are (2b) predominantly *sedimentary* like the Black Hills of South Dakota, or (2c) predominantly *igneous* in their rock composition like the Adirondacks of New York. Still others are (2d) *volcanic* like Mauna Loa in the

Figure 22–3   The Wasatch Mountains, an excellent example of the block mountain type, looking from a point about forty-five miles south of Salt Lake City. (Photo courtesy of Hal Rummel)

Hawaiian Islands or Vesuvius in Italy, or (2e) *residual* like the Monteregian Hills in the St. Lawrence Valley. Again, the distinctions are more significant to the geographer than might appear at first glance. If the domal mountains are composed largely of sedimentary rocks and have been exposed to erosion for a long time since the movements occurred to produce the dome, there will probably be a fairly regular system of peripheral valleys and ridges, the latter broken occasionally by water gaps. If it is predominantly igneous rock that forms the domal mountain, there is likely to be a notable irregularity of valley and ridge in spite of the tendency toward development of a radial drainage pattern. Volcanic domes may consist largely of lava flows or may be constructed of fragments exploded from the volcanic vents with only a small percentage of flow material. The latter type ordinarily display much steeper slopes than the former.

Irregular mountains, as designated by the geographer, are likely to belong to the class of residual mountains of the geologist and hence are generally of the old, worn-down type, or they may be notably complex in their origin and structure. The White Mountains of New Hampshire and the San Juan Mountains of southwestern Colorado are good examples. Their influence upon the life of man is as diverse as their topography and mineral resources.

MOUNTAINS AND THEIR INFLUENCE ON CLIMATE

Everyone who has climbed among mountains knows they are a potent influence upon climate; it is always rainier and cooler there than in the surrounding lowlands. When a wind is forced to rise up the slopes of a mountain, it expands, cools, and loses part of its ability to retain moisture. Hence clouds form and rain or snow falls. Thus, in California, the precipitation is only 22.7 inches where the winds strike the low hills at San Francisco, but it is 50 inches on the upper slopes of the Sierra Nevada. On the lee side the air descends, compresses, warms, and consequently increases its capacity for holding moisture. Hence this area is dry; Reno receives only 8.7 inches of rain per year.

The influence of mountains on temperature

is equally marked. On some mountains, one may climb vertically from tropical jungle to snow field in a single day (Fig. 22–4). The temperature drops about 1° F. for each 330 feet increase in elevation in summer and for each 400 feet in winter. It is interesting to note that climatically one mile of altitude is roughly equivalent to 800 to 1,000 miles of latitude. In the Polar Zone, a mountain has snow and ice at sea level.

The most interesting example of the effect of mountains on climate is to be found in the high mountains of tropical lands where several zones of climate occur in vertical arrangement in close proximity. Because they are best developed in the mountains of Latin America, these zones are usually accorded Spanish names: *Tierra caliente, Tierra templada, Tierra fria,* and others. Thus are to be seen the effects of increasing altitude on temperature.

Figure 22–4 portrays the vertical zones on the slopes of Mexico's Mount Orizaba, latitude 19° N. At the base of the mountains is the zone of the rainy tropics, with its rain forest and such crops as bananas, cacao, manioc, and rice; at the top is the zone of permanent snow. The upper limit of agriculture on Mount Orizaba lies at approximately 10,100 feet above sea level, which corresponds to the upper limit of wheat.

The *Tierra templada,* or temperate land, which towers above the *Tierra caliente* to approximately 6,000 feet is the climatic zone that supports the mountain resorts or hill stations in the Orient and the one sought by the Europeans who came to live in the New World tropics; it is here that the Spaniards established many of their cities.

ACCLIMATIZATION TO ALTITUDE

Atmospheric pressure, which is low at great heights, reduces the amount of oxygen which the blood carries to the tissues, makes breathing difficult and causes newcomers to suffer from mountain sickness[1] if they exert themselves. The body attempts to adjust itself to the change in altitude, therefore, by increasing the number of red corpuscles, whereby the blood is enabled to absorb oxygen with greater facility.

[1] Symptoms of mountain sickness are nausea, vomiting, headache, muscular weakness, depression, dizziness, and fainting spells.

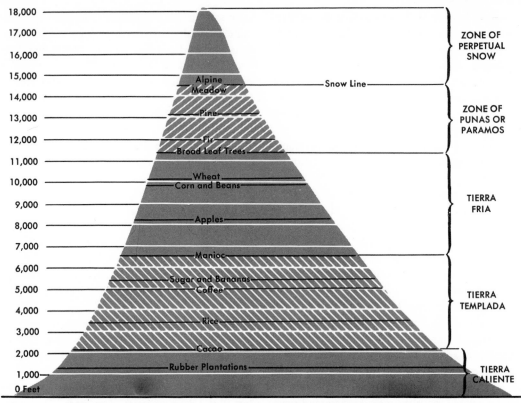

Figure 22–4   Diagram showing the influence of altitude on climate and crops. Horizontal lines indicate average upper limits for various crops and vegetation types.

In Peru the Indians, who are the product of centuries of adaptation to scarcity of oxygen, are immune to mountain sickness or *soroche*, as they call it.[2] They have long thick hearts that can do 20 percent more work than the hearts of lowlanders. They also have greater lung capacity and huge barrellike chests. It is they who perform most of the physical work at elevations exceeding 10,000 feet.

Most foreigners eventually become more or less accustomed to life at high altitudes. Travelers, however, are advised to stop for awhile at some point en route from coastal plain to mountains; otherwise the change puts too sudden a strain upon the body.

MAN'S USE OF THE MOUNTAINS

Fewer economic opportunities present themselves to the habitants of mountains than to those of plains. Moreover, in mountains, man's adjustments to nature are generally direct and simple rather than complex and subtle as on plains.

HUNTING AND TRAPPING

Since mountains are so difficult of access, they are a natural reservoir of wildlife, for it is axiomatic that beasts grow increasingly numerous as their human antagonists grow scarce. Accordingly, mountains are sought out by trappers who seek fur-bearing animals. It was these "wild sons of the trail" who made known western United States; they were the real pathfinders. In the Rocky Mountain region, the fur trade flourished from the beginning to about the middle of the nineteenth century. Since furs have high value for their bulk and weight and are not perishable, they can stand long, difficult, and costly transportation even by primitive means.

GRAZING

This is a distinctive mountain enterprise; it was one of the first to invade the solitude of moun-

[2] C. Langdon White, "Altitude: Its Role in the Life of Man in the High Peruvian Sierra," *Journal of Geography*, Vol. LII (December, 1953), pp. 361–374.

tains and has remained the most enduring, provided, of course, intelligent methods have been employed to prevent overgrazing and ultimate deterioration of natural pastures. Since crops are largely ruled out because of the limited level area, steep grades, thin rocky soil, cold climate, and restricted frostless season, grazing is possibly the best use that can be made of the land.

Mountain pastures consist of grasses, mosses, and flowers above timber line, like those of the Alps of Switzerland, or of grasses and other herbaceous plants in parks or open places such as those which dot the forests of western United States.

In either event they are strictly summer pastures. As the mountains become inhospitable in autumn, the animals must be driven down into the valleys. This regular seasonal migration from mountain to lowlands and return is called *transhumance*.

In the high central Andes, Indians herd llamas and sheep which graze the *ichu* grass. The llama has been an essential feature of Andean economy for centuries and has the following advantages over any other beast of burden in high mountains: (1) it is not subject to mountain sickness; (2) it is sure-footed; (3) it needs only the roughest fodder and little water; and (4) its flesh, wool, and dung all are utilized. But it carries only a moderate burden—usually fifty to one hundred pounds.

MINING

Modern civilization is based largely on minerals which for reasons discussed in Chapters 33, 35, and 36 are more easily found and mined in mountains than in lowlands. The quest for the golden fleece has gone forward since the dawn of civilization, enticing the adventurous. In the past prospectors went everywhere—into the snow-clad waste of the Klondike, the thirsty desert of Arizona, the fever-infested jungle of Colombia, or the dizzy heights of the Andes. They are now largely replaced by geologists and engineers who represent powerful mining corporations with far-flung interests (Fig. 22–5).

Many mining communities lie far beyond the last outpost of civilization. They persist, despite their absolute dependence for existence on the outside world, because the great hives of industry, the cities, cannot get along without their flow of mineral wealth. Regardless of remoteness or inaccessibility, such camps are connected with the lowlands and civilization by means of railway, pack train, cable, boat, airplane, or porter. The less valuable the ore, the more modern must be the transport facilities and the lower the rates. Thus gold may be carried by porter, canoe, airplane, or sledge, but the ores of iron, lead, and zinc do not warrant the cost of such expensive transportation.

Mining, of course, is a robber industry and therefore a relatively transitory enterprise. In a generation or two and often in much less time, the high-grade ore is extracted; then if techniques have been perfected for handling low-grade ores and if the deposits are sizable, as for example, those at Bingham, Utah, and Chuquicamata, Chile, the mines may be worked for many additional years. However, when a profit can no longer be made, the mines, mills, and railways all are abandoned.

LOGGING

Trees of economic value grow from the tropics to the Arctic (but not including the tundra), wherever moisture conditions are favorable. They hold their own even on infertile and shallow soils. Mountains are regarded as the natural forest preserves of the world.

As populations increase, the mountains will be pressed into greater production of lumber and pulpwood, since those plains capable of growing crops will be employed for that purpose. In some places, Germany, for example, the words *mountain* and *forest* are almost synonymous—Black Mountains and Black Forest.

Trees grow upon the mountains of both humid and arid regions, for mountains always intercept the rain-bearing winds. Thus, the Rocky Mountain slopes are clothed with excellent stands of timber at elevations of 6,000 to 10,000 feet. Even in the middle of the Sahara, the high mountains which rise 6,000 to 10,000 feet support a growth of trees—mostly pistachio and cypress.

More than trees, however, are needed to justify logging and lumbering operations. Favorable conditions of transportation are essential and the forests either should be reasonably near

Figure 22–5 An aerial view of the Eagle Mountain iron mine, source of Kaiser Steel Corporation's ore for their nearby Fontana, California, plant. (Photo courtesy of the Kaiser Aluminum & Chemical Sales, Inc.)

markets or should be connected with them by ocean transport. Where mountain forests are remote or economically inaccessible, their exploitation is delayed, though the high prices now being paid for forest products are bringing about changes in this respect.

In addition to supplying lumber and wood pulp, mountain forests check erosion, retard floods, preserve the water supply for irrigation, city use, or power development, afford facilities for recreation, and supply pasturage for large numbers of livestock. Most of the government forest preserves of the United States have been established in mountain country.

AGRICULTURE

Mountains are poorly adapted to agriculture and are accordingly shunned by farmers, save in the Orient and parts of the American tropics.

Problems connected with mountain farming

Farming everywhere is hard work and is beset by many obstacles. But farming in mountains is especially difficult and is faced by three almost insuperable problems. First is the dearth of level land which frequently necessitates the cultivation of slopes so steep they ought not to be tilled. Second is the erosion of soil which inevitably follows where steep slopes are used for intertilled or clean tilled crops (Fig. 22–6). Every rain takes its toll of soil. The prevention or at least the retardation of erosion is one of the gravest problems facing civilization today. Third is the difficulty of using large-scale machinery. While this is not so serious in the Orient where labor is cheap, it is extremely serious in the United States where the whole economic fabric is based on machinery.

In some places, especially where the winters

are long and cold, the farmers supplement their income by engaging in household industries. These are naturally based upon the resources of the immediate area, such as wood-working in the Alps of Switzerland.

TRANSPORTATION AND COMMUNICATION

Whereas the topography of plains enables roads and railroads to go almost anywhere, the topography of mountains imposes a tremendous handicap on them; they must go where nature directs —through the passes and along the valleys (Fig. 22–7). Occasionally, where productive mines, or sometimes even plants lie in high, rugged, almost inaccessible mountains, the building of company railroads or roads down to a main line may not be economically justifiable. Accordingly, aerial ropeways are utilized. These traverse only one-half to one-fourth of the distance required by a mule track or a rough road and therefore their cost is considerably less. Nevertheless, some

of man's outstanding triumphs in engineering are the railways that have been laboriously built to the dizzy heights of great mountains. The Central Railway of Peru, for instance, which is believed to have the world's hardest operating conditions, climbs to an elevation of 15,665 feet in a distance of only 106 miles from Callao on the Pacific Coast. In constructing this railway, great chasms of the Rimac River had to be spanned by bridges that appear to hang in mid-air. Sometimes in order to get surveyors and construction crews across the canyon, aerial tramways had to be rigged up. And some of the tunnels entered rock faces so steep that drillers had to be let down on ropes in order to begin operations. The toll of human lives has been estimated at fifteen thousand.[3]

Nearly all mountains have passes; some, like the Blue Ridge, have many, while others, like the Rockies, have comparatively few. Geographically

[3] Brian Fawcett, "Switchbacks to the Sky," *Trains* (January, 1955).

Figure 22–6   Corn is grown on a steep Andean slope in Venezuela. Erosion, the price for growing corn on such slopes, is evident in the background. (Photo courtesy of Consejo de Bienestar Rural, Venezuela)

Figure 22–7 Canadian National rail route through the Rockies. In many mountainous regions, river valleys furnish comparatively easy routes through the barrier. Railroad builders recognize this fact and wherever possible place their tracks along the graded routes which rivers have prepared. (Photo courtesy of the Canadian Government Travel Bureau, Ottawa, Canada)

speaking, passes are nature-made grooves cut across the grain of mountains which enable life to surmount the barrier. A pass usually has a valley leading to it from each side making it a route of moderate gradient. Many passes have become great roads of history (Fig. 22–8).

KHYBER—A WORLD FAMOUS PASS

Khyber Pass, one of a series of breaches through the mighty buttresses of the Hindu Kush[4] between Pakistan and Afghanistan, though only about forty miles long, is probably the most famous pass in the world (Fig. 22–9). It lies directly athwart the main route from Kabul to Pakistan. Though about 6,825 feet above sea level, it has permitted some of the greatest military expeditions in history to make their way into the Indian subcontinent of Asia. India's hodge-podge of population is attributable in no small measure to the fact that from immemorial antiquity wave after wave of invasion swept into the country from the northwest via the Khyber Pass.

The prize of these pillagers never was the mountain country itself: this was so very poor as to have no lure, hence invaders never tarried long; instead they advanced southward into the fat riverine lands. Thus the mountain tribes were left alone. In time they came to dominate the trade through the Pass, which compensated them for the niggardly resources and the unproductivity of the country. The route through the Pass has always been a dangerous one; human life means little or nothing to the tribesmen, who have for years successfully imposed tolls upon passing caravans and plundered them as well.

The highway through the Khyber consists of an upper road for motors and a lower one for caravans of camels and bullocks. Both are rather steep of grade and sharp of curve. Only since 1925 has it been possible to make the trip by rail.

The natives in the Khyber country recog-

[4] The Himalayas terminate in northwest Pakistan in a huge jumble of lofty mountains known as the Hindu Kush.

Figure 22–8 The Rolle Pass in Trentino, Italy. (Photo courtesy of Istituto Italiano di Cultura)

Figure 22–9 A portion of the historic Khyber Pass between Pakistan and Afghanistan. The Khyber follows closely the course of the Kabul River, a few miles away. Through it passes India's and Pakistan's landward trade. (Photo courtesy of the Pakistan Mission to the United Nations)

nize no authority except their own tribal customs and they resent restraints imposed from without. They are a hardy people to whom independence is the breath of life. Their hereditary professions are raiding, plundering, and killing—all of which they have developed to a remarkable degree. Here apparently is a people that will change little more than the mountains in which it dwells.

THE AIRPLANE AND MOUNTAINS

In rugged lands of few resources and small population, where railroads and roads can be built in relatively few places because of lack of funds, the airplane is invaluable, especially for passengers, mail, and freight having high value. Railroads require grades usually of less than 3 percent and long-radius curves; highways can be built to grades of 7 percent or more and sharper curves, while the airway can follow a nearly straight line. It is little wonder that the airplane is so indis-

pensable, for example, in the Andes. Mining machinery is frequently carried in by plane.

The case of the Tipuani Gold Mine

Buried deep in the heart of the towering, snow-capped Andes of Bolivia, sixty miles across the crest of the range from La Paz, lies the narrow, jungle-choked valley of the Tipuani River. For centuries the gold mined here found its way to the treasure rooms of the Inca kings. Then came the *Conquistadores*, who enslaved the Indians, making them work in the mine and forcing them to carry the gold over the formidable mountain pass to the shore of Lake Titicaca. Eventually the jungle overwhelmed the mine, the treasure trail grew dim, and for two hundred years the mine was lost.

Today the descendants of these slaves living in the valley will not work in the mine. Without human laborers, mining is possible only by utilizing modern machinery. But how could a million pounds of machinery, some pieces weighing as much as 1,800 pounds, be transported over the steep, narrow, difficult jungle trail? Neither the donkey nor the llama could haul the heaviest pieces. The round trip from La Paz to the mine required twenty days by pack animal. To deliver the machinery this way would require *eight years!*

Blocked at every turn on the ground, the executives finally turned to the air. But to fly the equipment in would be a hazardous task. The airport at La Paz lies at 13,000 feet above sea level and the crest of the Andes between La Paz and the mine reaches up to 18,000 feet. A meteorological station was set up and winds and weather were recorded. Air currents and fog were studied. Finally a huge trimotor plane was loaded and soared into the air. In twenty-eight minutes it covered the route that could be made in not less than seven to ten days by pack animal. Ten thousand pounds of machinery were delivered to the mine site every day and actual production of gold was under way within a week after the last load of machinery was delivered. Thus, here and elsewhere in the Andes where only a few regions have fully entered the twentieth century so far as cheap and regular transport are concerned, the airplane has proved to be of supreme importance.

MOUNTAINS AND CULTURE

Because they live in landlocked areas where travel is difficult, isolation great, and intercourse with the outside world negligible, mountaineers have not always been progressive; in fact the word *mountaineer* has long been associated with both economic and social backwardness. Antiquated customs are preserved in the mountains long after they have been forgotten in the lowlands. Local dialects persist. Education is backward, the percentage of illiteracy is abnormally high, and inbreeding is common. Professional and artisan classes are almost completely absent.

People in landlocked mountainous regions must be practically self-sustaining; they must make or produce almost everything they use— implements, furniture, clothing, and food. Thus they are unbelievably removed from and independent of modern civilization with its highly developed division of labor.

One of the best examples of such people are the Indians who live concentrated in pockets in the high Andes of Peru and Bolivia (see latter part of this chapter).

The small amount of level land forces families to scatter, which in turn precludes community life and the civic consciousness that accompanies it. Used to grappling with every problem single-handed, mountaineers are invariably hostile to all matters demanding cooperative action.

In many mountainous regions, economic development is penetrating and going far to wreck the old order. Railroads and highways are wedging their way in to get coal, metallic minerals, and lumber; and hydroelectric companies are locating at appropriate sites. Moreover, the airplane now can and does go anywhere. The progressive newcomers who accompany these industries are bringing about a social metamorphosis. Even in Indian communities of the Andes, life is changing slowly.

MOUNTAINS AS BARRIERS

Mountains are barriers in many ways: they cause a marked difference in the amount of precipitation on their windward and leeward slopes, which is reflected in the diverse conditions of life, and they hamper movements of people. The American colonists were largely confined to the Atlantic Seaboard till the close of the Revolution, for the "Blue Ridge rose like a frowning brow" before them.

The Cascade Mountains of Oregon and Washington intercept the winds from the Pacific Ocean forcing them to rise, expand, cool, and lose moisture on the windward side. On the lee or eastern slope, however, the winds are dry and evaporating, since they descend, are compressed, and are thereby warmed. Hence a journey in summer along the Columbia River Highway, which in a single day enables a person to see both sides of the Cascades, opens up two entirely different natural and cultural landscapes. On the west side is a green country with a heavy covering of gigantic trees, principally Douglas firs, while on the east is a brown country with only a little timber high up the slopes; on the west, the population is relatively dense; on the east, it is extremely sparse.

As barriers to human movement, mountains impede communication, the spread of culture, and political expansion. Thus the Himalayas have no railway over them to connect two of the world's oldest civilizations in China and India; when a traveler wishes to go from one country to the other, he goes generally by sea or air.

Boundaries are the most discussed geographical features of modern states and most people believe that a mountain chain forms one of the best kinds of frontier where defense is necessary. No doubt this was true in the past when land fighting meant essentially fighting by foot soldiers—infantry. Today, however, the airplane and the rocket are free from the barrier influence of mountains.

THE ORIENTAL HILL STATION

Mountains in the tropics attract large numbers of lowlanders during the hottest months (Fig. 22–10). In India and the Netherlands East Indies during the nineteenth century, British and Dutch colonial masters, as a means of making their sojourns less uncomfortable, began the institution known as the hill station (Americans in the Philippines use the term *mountain resort*). Going to the hills to avoid the hot months is now a regular part of the routine of nearly all Occidentals and also of many Orientals in southern and eastern Asia.

Every country in the Orient has some part of its territory in the mountains—outside the oppressive heat of that climatic zone. The altitude at which cooler temperatures and more bearable humidities are reached varies with the rainfall regime.

The lowlands from western India to southern Japan and north China are so hot, humid, and uncomfortable during some part of the year that white people suffer acutely if they attempt to reside there continuously. Medical science still has much to learn regarding the relationship of

Figure 22–10 Darjeeling, one of India's famous hill stations (elevation 6,900 feet). In order to escape the hot season, many Europeans and rich Indians come here to rest on the cool mountain slopes. (Photo from Ewing Galloway)

climate and man in the tropics. It is a fact, however, that the white man in the Orient is much better off if he gets occasional relief from the continued heat and this he can get in the mountains.

INDIANS OF THE PERUVIAN SIERRA—AN EXAMPLE OF HUMAN ADJUSTMENT

In Peru's majestic upper Andes, in a world apart, dwell several million descendants of the once great Inca civilization. Nowhere else in the world do so many people live at such high elevations —9,000 to 12,000 feet. Thousands live even above 12,000 feet; in places they are growing potatoes up to 14,000 feet. Concentrated largely in one region—the sierra, in the center and the south, where dwell only small numbers of whites and mestizos—Peru's large Indian population is here overwhelmingly in the majority (Fig. 22–

Figure 22–11 Peruvian Indians with their llamas on the square in Cuzco, navel of the Inca Empire. (Photo courtesy of Braniff International)

11). Spanish is little spoken in the Andes; Quechua and Aymara, the latter near the Bolivian border, prevail.

These Indians, miserably poor and neglected, are believed to be now worse off than at any time since the Conquest. For the most part Peruvian economy ignores them. Their white masters, by and large, scorn them.

Centuries of repression have left their mark on the aborigines and have affected their whole outlook. They are suspicious of most, if not all, white people and their pent-up antagonisms smolder ominously. These millions of people have been kept by their conquerors and by geography in the mental molds of the sixteenth century.

Despite the plethora of archaeological material in Peru, no one knows very much about the ancient civilization of the Andes. Reconstruction is still speculative. Authorities disagree passionately on innumerable issues. Possibly the two

principal reasons for this dilemma are, first, that the Incas had no written language and, second, that the Spaniards in their Conquest held a "Roman Holiday"—destroying fanatically and killing the Inca leader, Atahualpa, and his close associates. This last deed was especially significant because the Inca was supreme—all-powerful —and with his destruction the whole system collapsed like a deck of cards. The subservient masses, unused to making independent decisions, did not know what to do; without their leader they were doomed.

Some things fortunately are known. We know that about A.D. 1100 a superior people under the first Inca, Manco Capac, began to build in lofty, cold southwestern Peru a solidly organized empire that was to grow and flourish until its overthrow four hundred years later by the Spaniards under Pizarro. As the Incas began their ascent up the ladder of dynastic grandeur, they emigrated from their bleak home base down into the hospitable valley of Cuzco—a valley rimmed with superb mountains and supplied with water by the Huatanay River.

Within this difficult terrain the Inca dynasty welded a host of tribes, having diverse languages and customs, into a political and cultural unit of 8 to 10 million people occupying an area that, if superimposed along the Pacific seaboard, would equal in length the distance from Seward, Alaska, to the Gulf of California and would exceed in width the State of California.

The magnitude of this task almost staggers the imagination of one who knows the region. Theoretically, the environment would appear fit only for producing and maintaining a backward, poverty-stricken people. The Incas, however, succeeded in making use of their natural surroundings by employing exceptional ability and through possessing an inborn genius for growth and organization.

The milieu of the Incas was a severe one. In addition to the difficult terrain, there was the matter of piercing cold in their practically fuelless world. Also the air was thin, oxygen-deficient. Fortunately, the rulers were altitude-wise; they knew that their mountain people possessed biological characteristics distinct from those of sea-level men, that they were the product of centuries of painful adaptation to scarcity of oxygen. Thus when they colonized newly conquered territory, they always sent people who were accustomed to its altitude. When they warred against coastal peoples, they divided their large army into sections, each of which served only a short time on the coast and afterward returned to the sierra to recuperate.

The Incas became truly great agriculturists. Not only are they credited with having domesticated from seventy to eighty different species of agricultural plants—root and seed crops, fruits and vegetables, pot herbs, condiments, medicinal plants, intoxicants, poisons, dyes, and fibers—but from scratch, with only crude hoes and planting sticks as their farm tools, they developed a "scientific" agriculture which included the preparation of the soil, destruction of weeds, use of fertilizer (guano), the terracing of steep mountainsides, irrigation of dry lands, and the devel-

opment of special varieties and strains of plants through selective breeding. The making of these contributions took intelligence and time.

They developed their great agriculture, moreover, without the aid of the ox, horse, or any other power than that of their own muscles; the only work animal they succeeded in domesticating—the haughty llama—never has to this day condescended to permit man to harness him to a plow or a cart. Hence the foot plow was employed, a pointed stick with footrests and handles and guided by hand. It penetrated only to a depth of about four inches. Women and boys knelt down in front of the "plowmen," turning over the sod as rapidly as it was pried loose.

The foot plow was well adapted to steep mountainsides and tiny fields. Inca terraces are among the man-made wonders of the world. Steep, even precipitous, slopes were terraced to form staircase farms. Constructed of stone, the terraces were so well built that even today, after centuries of neglect, many are still in use.

The Incas, however, were not agriculturalists only. They were skilled road builders and great workers in stone. Cuzco and its environs fairly bristle with masterpieces of their art. In making, designing, and dyeing textiles, they have probably never been equaled, certainly never surpassed. They developed and used vegetable dyes with an almost incredible range of colors. They discovered and made use of every technique of weaving. The finest of their weaving was made from the wool of the vicuña, softest of all animal fibers—270 threads to the inch as compared with 140, otherwise considered to be the world's finest. Because the vicuña was hunted almost to extinction, the Peruvian government now protects it. Fortunately, the animal is being bred successfully in captivity.

The Spaniards were surprised and delighted to find so large a population of sedentary Indians, for they could put them to work in the mines and on the land, and the Church could convert them to Christianity. It was only where the Indians had been living in an environment where irrigation and cooperative living had been practiced for several centuries that the Spaniards were able to take over easily. The Conquest meant at first only a change in rulers.

During the colonial period the Indian population declined notably, the causes being epidemics brought by the Spaniards (the Indian had no immunity to smallpox, measles, and tuberculosis); forced labor in the mines; servitude; destruction of the elite of the population with a political purpose of subjugation; and obligatory migration to zones of different climate.

Can anything at all be said *for* the conquistadors? They were indisputably vigorous and fearless men; they were energetic explorers and great conquerors. They also brought cattle, horses, asses, goats, and sheep, and they introduced such crops as barley, wheat, and sugar cane. They inaugurated many new farm practices and they built cities, universities, and monasteries.

What, then, of the Andean Indian today? What type of person he was prior to the Conquest has been presented. What is he like now? The descendants of the highly civilized Incas are like most of their buildings, terraces, and roads—they are in ruins. Exploited for four hundred years, they have become merely degraded peons. Where the Indian still has land, he guards it with unbelievable affection. He fences it with a wall of stones! He guards faithfully the boulders which mark its bounds. He suspects every stranger—white and mestizo. Though he can wring from it only the meagerest subsistence, the land is his dearest possession. He leaves it only when forced to do so: centuries of occupation have fixed him to the soil. Even if the land be absorbed by an adjoining hacienda and passed from one owner to another, the Indian stays on, being transferred with the soil.

The mountain Indians suffer from poverty. Their homes, food, clothing all reflect this. A house is built for protection against wind, rain, and snow. It is a small, one-story, thick-walled adobe or stone hut, frequently of one room with a thatch roof. There frequently is no window or door; there is, of course, no chimney. The family spends most of its time outside the house, for warmth is found there in the sun rather than inside. There was good reason why the Incas became sun worshipers!

It is bitterly cold in the sierra. Hence clothing is worn for warmth, wool being the textile material. Sheep, introduced by the Spaniards, now supply most of the wool for clothing, though some llama wool is also employed. Alpaca wool is reserved only for finer garments and for export.

Despite modest wants and unbelievable thrift, the mountain Indians are continuously on the verge of starvation. The failure of a crop means famine. Their diet consists mostly of potatoes, *oca,* dried beans, and quinoa.[5] Beans supply most of their protein. Meat is eaten only occasionally and sweets rarely. This problem of food is important because it is tied up with the matter of health. Malnutrition is common, since the sierra is one of the worst-fed regions in the world, sickness is widespread and a shocking death rate is prevalent among children.

The agriculture in the sierra is largely of the subsistence type, that is, the crops are grown for the consumption of the farm family. Only an infinitesimal part of the yield of the soil ever reaches even a local market; almost all is consumed on the spot of its growth. Thus Andean agriculture hardly affects the outside world at all.

No discussion of mountain agriculture should fail to mention the terraces. At elevations of five thousand to eleven thousand feet, the terraces or retaining walls were built of huge rocks, unsquared but fitted together with precision. Hundreds of thousands of these terraces transform even precipitous slopes into small level fields. Some are six to seven hundred years old and some possibly two thousand years old. Though many have fallen into disuse, many still are yielding abundantly. Terraces enable tens of thousands of people to live in a milieu that in its natural condition could not have supported man agriculturally at all.

In the higher areas far above the possibilities of cultivation, as well as on the *puna,* Indian shepherds pasture their sheep, llamas, and alpacas. In fact, the highest permanent habitation in the world is to be found here at an elevation of 17,100 feet.

Most of the minerals, especially the metallic

---

[5] Quinoa is an ancient crop of the Andes and was regarded as sacred by the Incas. It can stand more cold than any other cereal.

ones, are located high up in the Andes where the air is thin and only the "mountain men" are at home and can perform physical labor. It is estimated that about twenty to twenty-five thousand Indians are employed in the mining industry at large.

Probably one hundred thousand men are involved in the seasonal labor migrations of the sierra to mines in the Andes and to haciendas in the coastal region.

Only the Indians are well adjusted physically to the severe mountain conditions.[6] Only they are able to perform hard physical work at such high elevations.

It has been pointed out that the amount of arable land in the sierra is definitely restricted and that the methods of farming are centuries behind the times. It has been pointed out also that, in spite of ill-health, the population is increasing at an amazing rate and that the standard of living is dangerously low. Tyrannies have been heaped upon the Indian population ever since the days of Pizarro. When the dam breaks

—as it most certainly will unless the small influential class, the oligarchy, does something constructive—a terrific storm may be expected to break forth. This favored group soon must realize that the Indians are not merely statistics, they are human beings. Nor are they inferior. What they need is a chance—something they have not yet had.

The difficulties and bewilderments in the Andes are many but at the root of almost all the trouble is land. There can be no real political and economic stability in Peru until an honest attempt is made to bridge the tremendous chasm that separates the classes and the masses.

[6] Students wishing to pursue this interesting topic further should read Carlos Monge, *Acclimatization in the Andes* (Baltimore, Johns Hopkins University Press, 1948); or C. Langdon White, "Altitude: Its Role in the Life of Man in the High Peruvian Sierra," *Journal of Geography*, Vol. LII (December, 1953), pp. 361–374; or George W. Gray, "Life at High Altitudes," *Scientific American*, Vol. 193 (December, 1955), pp. 58–68.

SUGGESTED USEFUL READINGS

See especially the texts by William E. Powers, Joseph Edwards Van Riper, and Nevin M. Fenneman listed on p. 356.

23

Hill Country Habitat

Hill country is often regarded as miniature mountain environment. This, however, is a somewhat erroneous concept, for hill country is intermediate in character between mountains and plains and in many respects unlike either.

A hill country is wholly unlike a plateau, but shows certain similarities to a plain on the one hand and to mountains on the other. Hill country resembles mountain country in that slope land predominates over flat land in surface configuration, but nowhere manifests the profound relief which characterizes mountains. In relief, it resembles plains country in that it shows topographic contrasts of from a few feet to a few hundred feet, but the broad expanses of flat or rolling surface possessed by plains are lacking. Thus hill country may be described as land too rough and broken to be classed as plains but possessing far too small a relief to be classed as mountains (Fig. 23–1).

VARIETIES OF HILL COUNTRY

A variety of geologic structures and physiographic processes may yield the type of landscape known as hill country. The simplest of these is *dune* topography. An originally flat or rolling terrain may be rendered exceedingly hilly by the slow accumulation of sand dunes. These are hillocks and ridges of wind-blown sand which sometimes reach a height of several hundred feet and may collectively cover an immense area.

A second variety is *foothill* topography. Many mountain regions are bordered by extensive areas of this type of hill country. In certain instances where the mountains are of simple

folded structure, approach to them is had through a series of low ridges that gradually increase in size and relief until the mountains themselves are reached. In instances where the mountains are more complex in structure and history, the foothill zone may consist of a marginal belt of hogback ridges and of rough, broken topography developed upon inclined strata of rock.

A third variety of hill country consists of *maturely dissected plains and low plateaus*. So long as streams are few in number and their tributaries short and rudimentary, a plain or plateau preserves its flattish appearance. Such a region may be said to be in the youthful stage of erosion. As the streams cut their valleys deeper and as their tributaries become more numerous, this flattish aspect of the landscape gradually disappears. Finally the streams and their tributaries develop into a completely ramified drainage pattern and little or none of the original flat or rolling surface remains. Rather, most of the terrain then consists of valley slopes and the divides which separate them. This condition is said to mark the stage of maturity in the erosion of a plain or plateau. By the time submaturity is reached, such a region no longer bears a resemblance to the original plain or plateau and must be described geographically as hill country.

Old, worn-down mountains constitute a fourth variety of hill country. Mountains, like all other types of landforms, are subjected to the destructional processes of the erosion cycle. In this cycle, weathering and the work of streams proceed with inconceivable slowness but immutable sureness toward their goal—the reduction of the landscape to a featureless plain approximating sea level. Hence, in its final stages, a stupendous mountain range may be reduced to what is geographically a low plain. Thus, a mountain region in its old age period passes through the hill-country stage. Many areas of hill country are of this type, wherein the former mountain landscape with its concave profiles has been reduced by erosion to the softened convex outlines and low mild relief of old age. Whether hill country be of the dune or mountain foothill type, whether it be due to the mature dissection of a plain or to the wearing down of a mountainous area to the softened and subdued contours of old age, its result upon the ecology of man is roughly the same. Hill country, of whatever variety, is one of the four major types of habitat to which man must adjust himself—a habitat type in which the handicaps in general outweigh the assets.

RESOURCES OF HILL COUNTRY

The natural resources of hill country vary rather widely in kind and amount. Generally, the climate of such an area does not differ greatly from that of the adjacent plains. This together with the moderate relief usually tempts man to encroach upon an area of hill country with a plains type of adjustment. Since there is a dearth of flat, easily cultivable land and since manifold obstacles to intraregional communication and transportation exist, such transfer of plains ecology usually meets with slight success.

The rugged, broken configuration of the landscape defeats attempts to establish anything like a regular road pattern in the hill country.

The interlacing net of railway lines which characterizes many plains is lacking in areas of hill country. The railway pattern of the latter consists usually of a few spurs or stub lines which run into the region by way of the valleys. Through-lines, never numerous, are achieved at great expense of money and labor and then only by following up some large valley, carrying the roadbed through tunnels or over steep grades into the upper end of an opposed valley and thence down to its debouchment upon the plains.

Although this type of habitat is usually poor in such resources as soil, arable land, and facili-

ties for transportation, it is richer than plains in others. Owing to poorer accessibility and a lesser demand for the clearing of land for agriculture, many hill regions contain large residual areas of timber, wild game, and fur-bearing animals. In minerals, too, hill country is apt to be richer than plains. Where the hill topography is derived from the mature dissection of flat-lying strata of rock, coal seams may appear recurrently in valley after valley in such a manner as to render mining simple and the removal of the coal easy. In hill country derived from the age-long wearing down of mountains, minerals, both metallic and nonmetallic, are sometimes abundant. In such cases, the comparatively barren upper rocks have long since been removed leaving only the old, worn-down highly mineralized stumps or roots of the mountain structure. Certain mineral deposits, usually the products of prolonged weathering, such as bauxite and kaolin, are especially apt to occur in such an environment.

THE SAND HILLS OF NEBRASKA[1]

Nebraska's Sand Hills occupy an area of over thirty thousand square miles of the central part of the state. The north boundary is along the Niobrara River and the south along the Platte River. The western boundary is sharply marked by the High Plains and the eastern, less well marked, is the Glaciated Central Lowland. During a drier climate cycle of the geologic past, drifting sand dunes developed, mainly from the sandy surface formations and in a small part from the floodplains of the streams. The dunes obliterated the original drainage of the area, and the sand piled up until the relief varied from scores to hundreds of feet among the dunes. Basins were formed which were eroded by wind below the water table which was to develop later under a humid climatic cycle. Today the Sand Hill region is dotted with many lakes and ponds which vary in size from a few acres to more than a square mile. Most of these are kept fresh

[1] Written by V. Calvon McKim, formerly of the Department of Geography, Fresno State College, who at one time taught in the Sand Hill Region.

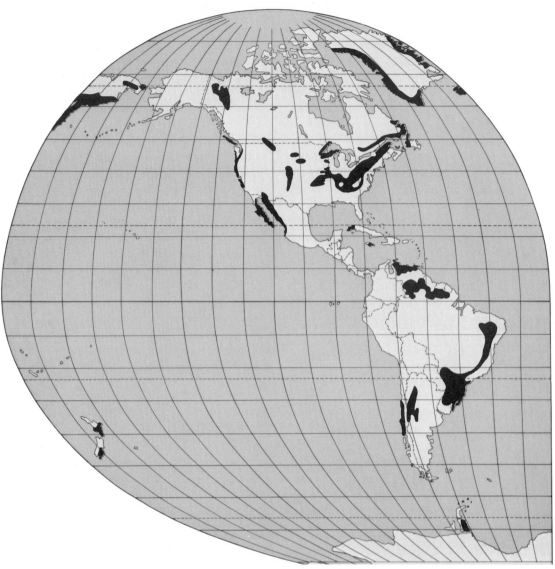

Figure 23–1 Hill country areas of the earth.

by underground drainage but a few are salty or brackish. During World War I when the imports of potash from Germany were cut off, a few of the latter lakes became a limited source of this mineral. Many of what were formerly lakes between the dunes have been filled with wind-carried sediments to form rich meadows of tall prairie grass. It is these basins which furnish winter forage for livestock. The dunes are now anchored by bunch grass, yucca, sage, and several other varieties of semixerophytic vegetation.

Most of Sand Hill land was homesteaded during the opening years of the twentieth century. Sod houses were built, crops planted, and cattle pastured on the hills. If the next year was wet, the homesteader prospered. If it was dry, his farmland became a blowout. Generally, the small farmer did not prosper. Gradually there has been a tendency toward consolidation of the small land holdings into large ranches (Fig. 23–2) containing thousands of acres (ten sections per unit). The average size of holdings for Cherry County is six thousand acres. Cattle are pastured on the land in the summer and fed forage during the winter. With the increasing commercialization of modern agriculture, the small farmer has either sold out and removed to the more favorable plains or is slowly sinking

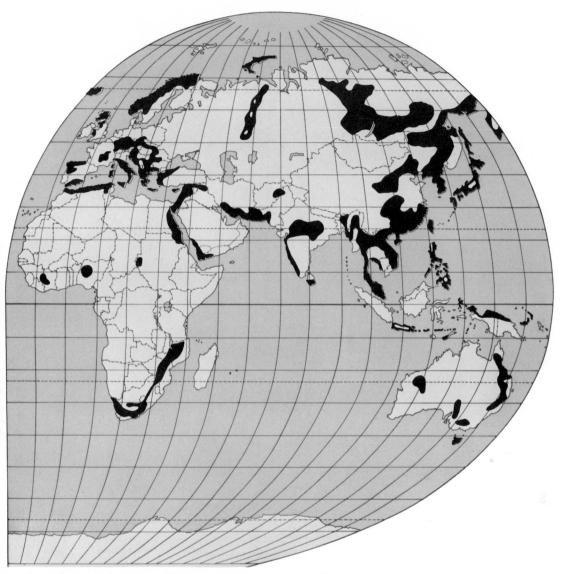

in socioeconomic status. (During the heyday of the Resettlement Administration it was found that the size of land holdings in the Sand Hills was better adjusted than was true of any of the surrounding area. The per capita ratio of those seeking relief was not over 25 percent of the number on the plains.)

There are no cities, few towns, and the railroads are marginal to the Sand Hills. The population of the central portion is less than one per square mile, rising to five or six in the periphery. Roads are poor, markets are hard to reach, and the isolation is frequently appalling. A large proportion of the Sand Hills is included in one political unit—Cherry County. This is by far the largest county in Nebraska and, indeed, one of

the largest counties in the United States, a fact which eloquently reflects its marginal value as compared with the surrounding plains land where county units are small.

The Sand Hills of Nebraska are a comparatively young region from the standpoint of human ecology. As a result, their influence in the evolution of a social type has scarcely begun, but if one observes the people from the Sand Hills on their visits to the nearest market town on Saturday night, he notes that they afford certain contrasts with the farmers and ranchers of the Great Plains. A few families make their weekly or fortnightly trips to town in wagons, some in buggies, and many in ancient automobiles. The size of families exceeds that of the national aver-

Figure 23–2   A typical ranch in the Sand Hills; cattle graze most of the land, though sheep dominate in the drier districts. (Photo courtesy of the Nebraska Game Commission)

age. There is a friendly hospitality about the people of the area that is in marked contrast to the cold sophistication of those from the surrounding plains. It can truly be said that the border of the Sand Hills marks the boundary between the West and East in the United States.

THE CUMBERLAND HILL COUNTRY[2]

In nearly all of the eastern one-fourth of Kentucky, in parts of east-central Tennessee (between the Highland Rim of central Tennessee and the Folded Appalachians of eastern Tennessee), and in northwestern Alabama, there is an extensive area of hill country called the Cumberland "Mountains" or the Cumberland "Plateau." Locally the inhabitants give certain sections definite regional names, such as Walden Ridge and Daisy Mountain in parts of Tennessee, and the Cumberlands (or just the "mountains") in Kentucky. Geologically, the Cumberland Hill Region is a dissected plateau. It possesses local relief of

from five hundred to two thousand feet between valley bottoms and hill tops. Parts of the area rise to as much as 3,600 feet above sea level. Only in a few localities, particularly near the southern portion, does any true flat-plateau surface remain; elsewhere the region is a rugged hill country, exceedingly rough and heavily forested, and is today a source of a considerable portion of the nation's hardwood timber. Highways, the great majority of which are secondary rather than main roads, thread the valley bottoms. The bottoms contain what little level land there is in the region, except for the few flat-topped plateau remnants on the divides (Fig. 23–3).

From the north and west the Cumberlands are accessible only by tortuous roads leading up the river valleys from the Blue Grass Basin of Kentucky and the Nashville Basin and Highland

[2] Much of the material in this section was contributed by Loyal Durand, University of Tennessee. He also read critically the entire section.

Rim of Tennessee. These main highways, all of which are hard surfaced, are relatively far apart as compared with main highways in a plains region; their chief function is to connect the cities west of the hill country (cities such as Lexington and Nashville) with cities east of the Cumberland Hill Region (such as Knoxville). However, in addition, these highways provide good communications to the parts of the hill country in their environs; numerous portions of the hill regions, however, are still distant from the main highways. On the east, the hill country is cut off from the Folded Appalachians by the "mountain wall" (really a plateau escarpment) which is known as Walden Ridge in some places and Cumberland Mountain in others. This escarpment has but few gaps in it; the best known is Cumberland Gap at the common meeting point of Kentucky, Tennessee, and Virginia. The highways descend this escarpment in great loops and curves. Only in one locality is there a water-level route through the Cumberlands; this is where the Tennessee River flows through the region in a deep, winding valley. The city of Chattanooga

is located at the eastern entrance to this route; accordingly roads westward from the city do not climb over the hill region but go through it by following the Tennessee Valley. Elsewhere in the area, transport is extremely difficult.

Between 1775 and 1820 the Cumberland Hill Country was settled by American frontiersmen of English and Scottish-Irish stock. At the outset, it offered superior inducements to the pioneer settler; the valleys could be planted to corn and the forests abounded in wild game. Shortly after the opening of the Erie Canal, however, and after the development of the railways, the region was relegated to the position of a back eddy in American life. The region became overpopulated with respect to its limited amount of arable land. As late as the beginning of the twentieth century, the "mountains" had changed so little that the inhabitants were aptly referred to as "our contemporary ancestors," "pocketed Americans," or "American survivals of Elizabethan England." Recently, however, much of the region has lost some of its isolation. This came about through: (1) the development of

Figure 23–3 Farm site in Cumberland Hill country. Level land is scarce and what little exists is restricted to the bottoms of stream valleys. Agriculture is the chief occupation and rural living is almost universal. Farming is of the subsistence type and there is much poverty. (Photo by Forsythe, courtesy of USDA)

coal mining in the Kentucky-Tennessee portion with resultant railway and highway construction; (2) the development of commercial lumbering also resulting in road construction; (3) state and federal highway projects (unrelated to resources); and (4) contact with the outside world through the medium of radio and television. Scholars now find it increasingly difficult to locate areas where old ballads and songs, as well as archaic forms of English speech, have persisted so well as here.

Agriculture is the chief occupation and rural living is almost universal. Wherever possible, all river-bottom land is farmed and clearings for fields and pastures are constantly climbing higher and higher on the hillsides.

Corn is the staple crop by reason of its multiplicity of functions: human food, animal feed, and the general domestic uses for its by-products. In addition, corn lends itself to thin stony soil, steep slopes, and hoe agriculture. Although corn is perhaps the most easily grown crop in the Cumberlands, it contributes indirectly to the poverty of many of the hill people. Not only does it exhaust the fertility of bottom and slope land alike, but the clean cultivation demanded by corn keeps the soil loose and facilitates its utter ruin through hillside washing.

Today the area, where farmed, consists (in Tennessee) of small general farms (52 percent) and part-time farms (23 percent). In addition to corn, vegetables, sorghum, poultry, and hogs, which the people themselves produce, the "mountaineers" in the more accessible areas now purchase much of their food.

The degree of isolation was formerly so intense that extra-regional trade scarcely existed. Sheep were occasionally driven out to market or wool was carried out by wagon or on horseback. Corn, the mainstay of agriculture, was too low in value in proportion to its bulk to be marketed as corn; hence some of its was converted into a concentrated form—whisky; since whisky is only one-thirtieth as bulky, it could stand the high cost of transportation over the poor roads and trails, for it moved out in jugs. Hence, a certain amount of illicit distillation of spirits was long important and still is locally.

The limited trade with the outside world in the past made for the continuance of household industry and local economy. The soap kettle, the spinning wheel, and the loom were operated by the women and in the more remote areas (as well as along some of the tourist highways) still are. At the present time there is much instruction in the handicrafts, and goods are sold in regional "crafts" centers such as Berea, Kentucky, and at numerous roadside markets and stands. Among the men a knowledge of smithing, carpentering, tanning, shoemaking, and coopering is almost universal.

Many of the homes of the Cumberland Hill Region are simple board shacks of one or two rooms; some few log cabins remain but these have or are in process of being replaced. Seldom are the older houses painted, although the more newly-constructed ones are painted, tar-papered, or are covered with imitation brick siding.

The Cumberland hill folk are intensely religious. They tend to be mostly fundamentalists. Highly emotional revival meetings are still held locally. Much distrust of outsiders exists and they are commonly spoken of as "furriners"; however, in those few parts of the hill country which support a summer tourist industry (some of the areas of southern Tennessee near Chattanooga and Sewanee, and many of the cooler upland areas in Alabama) the outsider is welcomed.

Early marriages and large families are the rule; a household of eight to ten children still is relatively common. Many of the valleys actually support a denser population than the most productive parts of the Corn Belt. Considering the type of region, some of the valleys in the hill area are as densely peopled as any rural area in the United States. The Cumberland Hill Region, however, since the 1920's has furnished thousands of laborers for the industrial cities of the Middle West and East; today there is hardly a family in the Kentucky and Tennessee portion of the region which does not have a close relative working in Detroit, Youngstown, Dayton, Indianapolis, Chicago, or other "northern" (particularly Middle Western) industrial center. The region has also, from its "surplus" population, furnished all of the coal miners for the coal fields, such as those of eastern Kentucky and northern Tennessee, and has supplied hundreds of workers to the nearby cities of Knoxville and Chattanooga and to the growing industries in the cities to the west—Nashville, Shelbyville, and Murfreesboro.

The limited contact of valley with valley has resulted in local inbreeding to such an extent that family kinship may extend over the greater part of a hydrographic unit. Under such conditions, society has assumed broad family relationships and a very democratic aspect.

The difficulty of access of the Cumberland Hills Region has long weakened the effectiveness of federal and state governments, and hence social control is partly a matter of local custom. Crimes against property are rare but against person have been common. In the past, the usual method of dealing with the latter was through direct retribution, a matter which often embroiled whole clans in bitter feuds. But feuds have disappeared with better educational facilities and improved transportation.

Agencies of the federal and state governments have brought many changes to the region since the advent of improved transportation. The TVA has exerted tremendous influence in those parts of the Tennessee River watershed included in the Cumberland Hills Region—the portions in southern Tennessee and northern Alabama (actually, however, most of the hill region is not in TVA territory). The Soil Conservation Service, the state farm agents (County Agents) and Home Demonstration agents, county nurses, and "4-H Clubs" are bringing better living conditions. Some of the churches and their missions have accomplished much; certain colleges for "mountain" youths have been established. Home demonstrations in canning, sewing, and household management have improved the living conditions; and with better roads, centralized schools whose pupils are gathered by school buses are aiding in the promotion of the regional welfare.

It is apparent that the region as a whole has been moving rapidly into the twentieth century and that over the greater part of it much social and economic progress has been made. It would be a mistake, however, to fail to realize that locally there still remain backward areas; some of these have stood still for decades and some have even retrogressed.

THE WESTERN CASCADE FOOTHILLS

The Cascade Mountains run in north-south direction through the state of Washington, separating the Columbia Plateau on the east from the Puget Sound Lowland on the west. The western edge of the mountains is skirted by a narrow belt of foothill country which affords a transition from the high, almost uninhabited Cascades to the populous lowland. This belt is exceedingly rugged and youthful in configuration and exhibits a relief of three hundred to two thousand feet. Flat land is restricted to the valleys of the westward flowing rivers and to the old glacial outlet valleys which trend north-south along what are probably major fault lines.

The Puget Lowland was settled in the main by a rather select emigration from the North Central states, most of it biologically and socially equipped for success in various economic activities. Along with this predominant class of immigrant, however, were the usual number of socially less fitted types. Considering the recency of settlement in western Washington, there has been an interesting ecological segregation of types in the area. The socially superior peoples have settled in the cities and towns or on the alluvial farm lands of the Basin, while the socially inferior have gravitated to the foothill lands of marginal value.

Nowhere is the ecology of the Cascade foothills better shown than in the valleys of the upper Cowlitz River and its tributaries in the eastern part of Lewis County. This is a wide broken stretch of country just south of Mount Rainier. It contains a few very small towns or hamlets, each of which consists of a general store or two, a few houses and perhaps a recently added schoolhouse. The majority of the inhabitants, however, live on farms, and except for a few remaining Indian families, consist almost entirely of native Anglo-Saxon stock. The farms in the Cowlitz Valley itself are fairly large and prosperous and from them a small amount of produce is trucked to city markets. But farther back in the hills this comparative affluence is lacking and the cultivated plots become smaller, the trails poorer, and the houses mere shacks or cabins of hewn logs. The small "scratch farms" of the back hills usually cannot support a family and hence existence is eked out by hunting, fishing, and trapping. Occasionally the men folk find employment in the logging camps or migrate to the towns of Kelso, Chehalis, Centralia, Grays Harbor, or Tacoma, returning with the savings of a few months in their pockets. Some of the men do a little prospecting at "off" times and a few small gold mines are said to be in operation.

Many of the Cowlitz hill people are of Cumberland Hills stock. Others came from the Ozarks and the Ouachitas. Still others have sprung from the early fur trappers of the Northwest. Some are descendants of Middle Westerners who prefer the easy life of a "scratch farmer" to the competitive commercial agriculture of the lowlands.

There are still many "old timers" who get together each year for their annual "turkey shoot" at which time the youngsters are regaled with tall tales of "back home in the Kentucky or Missouri hills." Fishing and game laws are commonly disregarded, and it is reported that the making of moonshine liquor for sale in the cities is all too common. The hillsmen are rather clannish, and outsiders are usually not welcomed.

THE NEW ENGLAND UPLAND

The New England Upland includes most of Vermont, New Hampshire, Maine, and a portion of Massachusetts. At one time, in remote geological antiquity, this region was extremely mountainous and was traversed by ranges of considerable height. Prolonged erosion has, however, reduced the topography to one of subdued, rolling hill country, above the general level of which rise small residual mountain groups such as the Green and White mountains, or isolated remnants such as Greylock, Katahdin, and Monadnock. Among the rugged forest-clad hills and low mountains nestle thousands of ponds and small lakes. Many of the hills were scraped bare of soil by conti-

nental glaciation during the Pleistocene Ice Age. Nearly everywhere the soil is poor, thin, and stony.

Approximately three hundred years ago, this region began to be settled from the overcrowded lowlands of southern New England. For many years it supported a moderate population. Families were large, isolation (particularly during the severe, snowy winter) was intense, and a system of local pioneer economy prevailed. The nearly self-sufficing farm units were divided so as to have a meadowland for hay, fields for grain, a wood lot, and an upland pasture. Each part fitted into the economic scheme.

After 1830, a period of land abandonment began. This was in part occasioned by the opening of fertile, level lands in the Middle West and the development of commercialized agriculture thereon. In part it was owing to the growth of factory cities in southern New England with their insatiable demand for workers.

Obviously the Upland farms with their rough terrain, infertile soils, and stoniness could not compete with the farms of the Middle West. The Upland's stone walls which run everywhere —along county roads, around upland pastures and small fields and over the brows of low mountains—attest the great labor involved in clearing. A century and a half ago, wall-making was a regular part of the farmer's operations. Whenever he could spare a day from customary seasonal tasks, he hitched the yoke of oxen to his stone sledge and worked on his wall. To build a good one demanded skill: the foundation had to be dug below frost-line; big rocks were placed at the bottom, small ones at the top. A rod a day for two men and a yoke was a standard measurement. So abundant are stones that it took about a month on the average for a man to remove them from one acre, getting the latter ready for farming.

Modern farm machinery can be used to only a limited extent on the New England Upland and the amount of man labor required to produce even moderate yields is extraordinarily high. Accordingly, supplementary sources of income were long sought.

Among the more conservative there is still considerable uneconomic farming on the hillier, more remote or otherwise less productive parts. Nevertheless, farm abandonment has taken a heavy toll.

At the present time, the remoter parts of the New England Hill Region are marked by stagnation wherein a relict population consisting of the less enterprising elements of the original stock barely holds its own in village and country. The population because of prolonged outmigration contains a surprising proportion of unmarried women and old people. This population is provincial and conservative, and the tempo of life is almost as slow as it was in the closing years of the nineteenth century.

Recently the region has entered a period of revival; it has been "discovered" as a playground both by summer tourists and lovers of winter sports (Fig. 23–4). Summer boarders, meals for tourists, and dairy products for distant cities are pouring money and new life into the New England Upland. A few industries such as the quarrying and working of marble, slate, and granite, the manufacture of maple syrup, scales, pipe organs, textiles, and wood pulp are maintained

Figure 23–4   The T-bar lift at Spruce Peak, Mt. Mansfield, Vermont. (Photo courtesy of the Vermont Development Department)

by a combination of raw materials and native Yankee skill and shrewdness.

ECONOMIC STATUS OF HILL COUNTRY

Many hill regions today are characterized by poverty and ecological maladjustment. In the main, this results from the failure to capitalize the intrinsic resources of this type of habitat. In America particularly has man tried to use hill country as though it were plain. The Cumberland and Ozarkian highlander with his corn agriculture has ruined hundreds of square miles of hill land and compelled its abandonment. This in turn has augmented the poverty of these people. Similar results in soil destruction and impoverishment have been occasioned by grain agriculture in the hill country of north China.

What is perhaps the first step toward efficient utilization of hill country is the realization that such a habitat is fitted primarily for grass and tree crops rather than for cereals. Where population density compels hill cultivation, the laborious construction of permanent terraces is perhaps justifiable. The terraced vineyards of the Rhineland, the wheat terraces of the Apennines, and the rice terraces of the Philippines are costly in human labor but not destructive of land if properly maintained (Fig. 23–5).

As one travels along the prosperous and well-kept countryside in Corsica and other Mediterranean hill lands, it becomes strikingly evident that the proper agriculture for such terrain is one preeminently of tree crops. Many Mediterranean lands, too rugged for agricultural use as measured by the plainsman's standards, support in comparative prosperity dense populations by growing such trees as the olive, chestnut, pistachio, and others. Similarly, the apple orchards of southeastern Ohio, the northern Ozarks, and a few other districts stand out as oases of prosperity in the midst of comparative agricultural unproductivity (Fig. 23–6). Tea culture on the wet hill lands of the Orient (Fig. 23–7), coffee raising in Brazil, and silk-worm raising in the densely populated lands of Japan and China are also profitable uses of hill country.

Dairying and livestock rearing are construc-

Figure 23–5 Ifugao rice terraces range for miles across the hill country of Luzon, Philippine Islands. These stone-wall terraces, which cover about 250 square miles of land, are the highest, best-built, and most extensive in the world. Archaeologists believe the native builders spent more than two thousand years in their construction. They are admirable engineering feats even in modern engineering terms. Since flat land for rice is scarce, terracing is the one way of providing it. Stones usually form the walls. Water from mountain springs irrigates the tiny fields and is carried by dikes from one rice patch to another. (Photo courtesy of the Philippine Tourist and Travel Association, Inc.)

tive instruments in rough land adjustment. The sheep farms of the Ohio hills and the dairy farms of Vermont and southwestern Wisconsin exemplify profitable utilization of such land. Grass is the basis of such industries, and grass retards rather than promotes soil erosion.

In many hill districts of eastern United States it is customary to burn over the scrub forest in order to insure an abundant crop of wild berries. This is an appalling price to pay for paltry results. Such cut-over hill country (much of it unfitted for agricultural occupance) might, under state control and scientific management, yield an annual timber crop sufficient to meet an appreciable part of the demand of the nation.

Much hill-country forest in the world's more

backward lands has been and is being destroyed by those who gather wood for fuel. The charcoal makers, for example, have taken a terrible toll.

SOCIAL STATUS OF HILL COUNTRY

Hill country areas frequently harbor fragments of so-called primitive peoples. Under race migration and race conflict, the stronger races usually occupy the fertile lowlands, pushing the earlier and weaker occupants into the hill lands. Here, because their habitat is of marginal productivity, they do manage to maintain themselves. The Gaels in Scotland, the Welsh in Cornwall and Wales, and the Bretons in France are classical examples. Sometimes these relict hill folk are

Figure 23–6 Apple orchard on a hillside in southeastern Ohio. Orchards situated on hillsides benefit from air drainage as well as good soil drainage. Very little erosion takes place in a hill country orchard because the roots hold the soil. Note the sheep running through the orchard, indicating that this land is also used for grazing. (Photo courtesy of the Soil Conservation Service, USDA)

almost unbelievably primitive as are the Ghonds, Bhils, and other hill tribes of India, the Veddahs of central Ceylon, the Aetas of the Philippines, and the Semangs of Malaya. Apparently their hill-country habitat furnishes them with sufficient isolation to maintain islands of neolithic culture in the very midst of an advanced civilization.

Where the hill folk are of the same race and basic culture as the inhabitants of the adjacent plains, their environment apparently leaves its differentiating mark upon them. Hill country everywhere is inhabited by unique social types. The Appalachian and Ozark "hillbilly" or poor white, the Scottish "highlander," the "Schwarzwalder" of southwestern Germany, the "sandhillers" of South Carolina, the hill "cracker" of Georgia, and the "Slovak" of the Czechoslovakian hill country are a few characteristic examples. Such peoples may be backward, conservative, and provincial. Isolation tends to foster clan organization in society.

POLITICAL STATUS OF HILL COUNTRY

Hillsmen are often individualistic and liberty loving. Almost invariably they are governed from the more populous communities of the plains,

Figure 23–7 Tea pickers on a plantation in Assam, India. Tea is generally grown on slopes because it must have good soil drainage. Moreover, tea serves advantageously as a means of utilizing slopes without wasting soil. In the wild state, the tea plant is more like a tree, attaining a height of ten to fifteen feet; but under cultivation it is more like a shrub, being limited by frequent pruning to a height varying from three to five feet. (Photo courtesy of Tea Council of the U.S.A., Inc.)

but the arm of the law is usually weak if not indeed merely nominal. Hill folk may be law abiding enough according to their own local standards but they may at the same time evade the plainsman's taxes and laws, just as formerly they may have raided his richer farms and villages.

Hill lands have been the locus of secessionist movements. The Appalachian hill country has been involved in the planning of at least four such separatist states, Transylvania, Westsylvania, Franklin, and West Virginia, the last being successful. Even where not actively separatist in intent, hill people are sometimes reactionary in their political notions. The Cumberland people in Kentucky are traditional Republicans, although the state at large is Democratic. The hillsmen of Illinois and Ohio are usually Democratic, although either state as a whole is normally Republican. The Scottish highlanders, in similar manner, supported the Stuart Dynasty long after it was discredited in England.

24

Plateau Habitat

A plateau is a generally flattish or tabular surface exhibiting pronounced topographic relief. It may or may not lie at a high altitude. As a physical habitat for man, plateaus are usually less favorable than plains but distinctly more advantageous than mountains or hill country. Several interesting examples of human adjustment to this type of habitat are afforded by the Altiplano of Bolivia, the Plateau of Tibet, and the Trans-Canyon Plateau of Arizona.

CHARACTERISTICS OF PLATEAUS

The surface of a plateau is predominantly flat or rolling. Locally, however, it may vary from apparent levelness to considerable roughness. Occasional groups of hills, low ranges of mountains, or solitary buttes may interrupt the general flatness. In spite of this, land of low inclination or gentle slope predominates over steeply inclined land. In such a region, the vista is wide and the horizon line is far distant from the eye. Although plateaus resemble plains in general surface configuration, they differ from them in exhibiting great relief. Streams on a plain flow in shallow valleys or wide flat trenches, but those of a plateau are incised far below its surface and flow in canyons and gorges. It is to this stream dissection that the high relief of plateaus is usually owing, although in a few instances it is occasioned by faulting or the tectonic breaking of the structure into blocks. In either case, however, a plateau's high relief, whether due to stream dissection or faulting or both, is its most important single characteristic.

Plateaus vary considerably in elevation or altitude. The Columbia Plateau possesses an altitude of from 500 to 2,500 feet; most of the Spanish Plateau lies between 1,500 and 3,500 feet, while the plateaus of Bolivia and Tibet average above 12,000 feet. Many plateaus are lower in altitude than some high plains. For example, the western portion of the American Great Plains is considerably higher above sea level than either the Columbia or the Spanish Plateau. The point of distinction between plains and plateaus is not, therefore, elevation but relief. The mere factor of elevation or altitude is, save in its extremes, of slight importance in the culture patterns and distribution of mankind. Instead, the significant factors in this, as in other types of physical habitat, are relief and surface configuration. The low relief and the absence of topographic barriers on a plain permit ready communication, transportation, and migration, because the approach to and egress from such an area are easy. Internal social flux is, therefore, facilitated and isolation is minimized.

The relief of plateaus, on the other hand, is frequently as great as in mountain regions. The Colorado Plateau exhibits a relief of profound magnitude where it is trenched by the Colorado River and its tributaries. For many miles, the Colorado flows at the bottom of a gigantic canyon, in places more than a mile deep and approximating ten miles in width (Fig. 24–1). Such a feature is a negative rather than a positive barrier, but it is as disruptive ecologically as a mountain range. In addition to the canyons of the Colorado Plateau, barriers are afforded by a series of bold escarpments leading from the lower plateau levels up to still higher surfaces. From many directions access is impeded by steep marginal escarpments which rise boldly from the

399

Figure 24–1 The Colorado River cutting through the Grand Canyon. The river is incised far below the surface (1 mile) and flows in a canyon. This is typical of plateau streams. Since the change in temperature in 1 mile of altitude is equivalent to that of 800 to 1,000 miles latitude, the bottom of the canyon has a climate entirely different from that of the rims. (Photo by the National Park Service, courtesy of the U.S. Department of the Interior)

surrounding lands. Such barriers, whether they be marginal escarpments or transecting gorges and canyons, are characteristic of plateaus and play an even larger part than does the generally flat surface in determining the utility of such a habitat for man.

VARIETIES OF PLATEAUS

Geologically the term *plateau* is restricted to landforms of horizontal structure. But geographically, any area characterized by a fairly level landscape and exhibiting great relief may be regarded as a plateau. Judged from this standpoint, there are a variety of geologic structures

which may yield this type of feature—horizontal series of sedimentary rocks or of lava sheets, basins filled with detritus, and *massives* or planed-off areas of complex structure. From the standpoint of general topographic relations, plateaus fall into two general categories: (1) *intermontane basins* or elevated nonmountainous areas located between ranges or entirely walled about by a mountain rim and (2) *tablelands* or extensive tabular areas overlooking lowlands and separated from them by a marginal escarpment.

MAJOR PLATEAUS OF THE WORLD

Plateaus occur on every continent (Fig. 24–2). Nearly half of Africa consists of a tableland known as the Great African Plateau, the higher northern end of which is called the Abyssinian Highland. Outliers of this are the Ahaggar in the Sahara and the island of Madagascar (Malagasy).

Europe possesses only one plateau—the Meseta of Spain and Portugal. Asia, on the other hand, contains no less than seven—the Anatolian, Arabian, and Iranian plateaus in the southwest, the Tarim Basin and the Mongolian and Tibetan plateaus in the central part, and the Deccan Plateau in India.

South America contains two—the Brazilian Highland and the Bolivian Altiplano, together with several small ones. North America is particularly rich in plateaus. One of these, Greenland, is located in the eastern part of the continent, while no less than ten lie in the western Cordilleran area. Of these, two, the Yukon-Tanana and the Fraser, lie in Alaska and western Canada, whereas three, the Columbia, Great Basin, and Colorado lie within mid-continental United States. The Northern Basins (Bolsons del Norte) and the Anahuac (Mesa Central) are in Mexico. Farther south are the Chiapas Highlands of southern Mexico and Guatemala, the Central American Plateau of Honduras and Nicaragua, and the Mesa Central of Costa Rica.

HUMAN USE OF PLATEAUS

As a general rule, plateaus are arid or semiarid in climate. There are exceptions to this, as for instance the Abyssinian Highland which is so located as to receive rain-bearing winds (the Zanzibar Monsoon and the Congo Monsoon) from two directions. In most cases, however, the interior portions of plateaus are areas of deficient rainfall and the seats of pastoral populations.

The dissected edges of plateaus usually receive somewhat heavier precipitation than the interior portions and hence are often put to agricultural use. Winds forced to rise up the marginal escarpment are cooled adiabatically and may yield a heavy precipitation. Above, on the plateau surface, these same winds are comparatively dry and produce rain only locally in thundershowers. An interesting example of this is the Deccan Plateau of India. On the western edge, the rainfall of more than eighty inches annually supports a dense agricultural population averaging between 250 and 525 persons per square mile. The outstanding products from this section are coconuts, rice, sugar, and teak. Eastward on the plateau, the annual rainfall ranges from twenty to forty inches, and the population varies from 25 to 250 persons per square mile. The animal industry becomes relatively more important—cattle, goats, and sheep being very numerous.

Despite certain broad facts which may be observed, it is difficult to generalize very far upon the human ecology of this type of habitat. In addition to the specific set of environmental conditions possessed by an individual plateau area, there are certain larger conditions imposed by the general climatic zone in which the area may be located.

Plateaus in the Tropical Zone are usually characterized by a temperate or subtemperate climate. For this reason, living conditions are, in the main, superior to those in the hotter lowlands. In many instances tropical plateaus are, therefore, rather densely populated despite their obvious disadvantages for human occupancy. Thus in Bolivia and Mexico, nearly three-fourths of the total population live on the tablelands. A similar situation is approximated in Guatemala and Costa Rica. In both Brazil and Colombia a large proportion of the people are highland dwellers.

Tropical America was colonized by Europeans more than four centuries ago. Settlements were planted on both highland and lowland, but those in the former were markedly more successful than those in the latter. So great was the advantage of plateaus as loci for European colonization that today they are, with few exceptions, the seats of white and *mestizo* settlement. This contrasts strikingly with the pure Indian population of the mountains and with the Indian and mixed Indian and Negro (*zambo*) stock of the plains. In like manner, the East African Plateau is providing a locus for white settlement on that continent.

In the Subtropical Zone, plateaus, as exemplified by Anatolia, Iran, the Meseta of Spain, and South Africa, are usually thinly peopled and the inhabitants largely pastoral. Where water is available, however, irrigation agriculture is carried on.

In the Cyclonic Zone, plateaus are far less favorable for settlement than plains. Not only are they apt to be arid or semiarid, but if their elevation is at all considerable, they are too cool for optimum living conditions during a large part of the year. This latter is illustrated by the Tibetan Plateau which lies between latitudes 30° and 40° N. and stands at an altitude of from two and a half to three miles above sea level. This mighty highland, often called the "Roof of the World," is sparsely inhabited, chiefly by nomadic shepherds and yakherders who in the main eke out an unenviable existence.

Cyclonic Zone plateaus, even where much lower in elevation than Tibet, are sparsely settled and their inhabitants are engaged largely in the raising of livestock. The Great Basin and the Colorado Plateau are for the most part regions of large and widely scattered ranches. However, where either surface or underground water is available, intensive farming is prosecuted, for example, in the Salt River Project of central Arizona, where cotton, alfalfa, citrus fruits, etc. are grown and in the Reno, Nevada, area, where alfalfa, wheat, vegetables, etc. are grown. The Columbia Plateau also shows pastoral adjustments in its drier portions; in the better watered sections, however, it is used for subhumid wheat farming. Seaming the plateau here and there are irrigated valleys which, with their green patches of deciduous fruits, alfalfa, and vegetables, stand

Figure 24-2 Plateau areas of the earth.

out as gems in an otherwise monotonous land-scape.

Plateaus in high latitudes or in the Polar Zone, present practically no utility to man. The surface configuration of Greenland and Antarctica is not fully known, but both of these regions possess extensive plateaus which are buried beneath coverings of ice several thousands of feet thick.

ECONOMIC ASPECTS

Plateaus are usually less favorable than plains for economic activities. Since in most instances they are decidedly dry in climate, they are poor

in timber and water resources. Pastoral pursuits tend to predominate, although dry farming and irrigation are usually practiced where possible. Wheat, by reason of its adaptation to cool and subhumid conditions, is commonly grown and is to be found on plateaus in the Tropical, Subtropical, and Cyclonic zones. Coffee is grown almost exclusively on tropical plateaus, three-fourths of the world's annual production emanating from Brazil, Colombia, Mexico, Central America, and East Africa (Fig. 24-3).

Economic isolation is the curse of most plateau regions. Navigable rivers are generally absent, owing to falls and rapids which so frequently interrupt the stream gradients. The steep

marginal escarpments and deep valleys also discourage the construction of facilities for land
travel and trade (Fig. 24–4). A capital example
of this may be seen in Colombia, where the
principal production and population areas lie not
in the tropical valley floor of the Magdalena
River but in the temperate plateau which flanks
the valley. Bogotá, often described as the world's
most isolated national capital, is completely shut
off by distance and by natural barriers from the
other settled districts and by hundreds of miles
from both the Caribbean and the Pacific. This
district is the seat of a large Spanish population
and the city prides itself upon its urbanity and
intellectual activity. But such a remote center of
civilization has been achieved only at cost of
tremendous effort (Fig. 24–5). Transportation

everywhere is poor. The Magdalena River is the
principal thoroughfare and the chief means of
penetrating the interior. Goods moving from the
Caribbean to Bogotá, a distance of only some
eight hundred miles, are doubled in price because of the necessary five unloadings. Moreover,
goods are often delayed in transit, especially on
the Magdalena during the dry season, because
of low water, countless sand bars, and snags.
Most of the country's railways connect with the
river. But building railroads down from the
plateau to the river ports is difficult and costly,
because the mountainsides which flank the main
valleys are very steep and because the plateaus
are mostly shut off by spurs and ridges from the
main cordillera. Where railroads are nonexistent,
and this includes most of the highland region,

Figure 24–3 Picking coffee on the Brazilian plateau. Tropical plateaus are the coffee regions of the world and the one in Brazil is the greatest. Forty-one percent of the cultivated land of this region is in coffee. The rolling terrain provides air drainage and soil aeration; the soils are rich in iron and potash; the area is large; the region lies relatively near the sea; and the climate with its distinct rainy and dry seasons (the latter favoring harvesting, washing, and drying) is excellent for the crop. (Photo courtesy of the Pan-American Coffee Bureau)

transport is by mule and pack steer and occasionally even by human porter as in colonial days. Exports have, in the main, been restricted to gold, platinum, emeralds, Panama hats, hides, and sacks of coffee. These commodities are nonperishable and valuable in proportion to their bulk, and hence are able to return a profit in spite of the slow and expensive mode of transportation. Under such conditions it is but natural that Colombia should have developed the first commercial air transport service in South America.

SOCIAL ASPECTS

Plateaus, by reason of their poor accessibility, encourage neither immigration nor regional contact. The cultural and racial flux of peoples is, therefore, usually lacking, whereas race purity and social homogeneity are nurtured. Such a habitat does not restrict its inhabitants into rigid provincialism as do mountains and hill country, but it does tend to foster a certain amount of solid conservatism.

For generations, the small Judean Plateau was the stronghold of racial homogeneity, re-

ligious purity, and simple austerity of culture in the Hebrew world. As a consequence, the descendants of the plateau tribes of Judah and Benjamin have fathered the Jewish kith and religion, while the ten outlying Israelitish tribes were long ago swallowed up in the general racial polyglot of the Near East. Similarly, the Spanish Meseta today contains the purest elements of the Spanish people, and the distribution of the Osmanli Turks is now practically coextensive with the Anatolian Plateau.

The stronghold of modern Buddhism is not on the fertile Indian lowland which gave it birth, but upon the high, inhospitable and nearly inaccessible Plateau of Tibet. The primitive Abyssinian church, alongside serfdom, slavery, and an outworn feudal structure in society, survives upon the highest tableland in Africa. The Mormon church, while essentially a product of nineteenth-century frontier America, harks back to such ancient social elements as patriarchy, polygamy (no longer practiced), and a simple rural motivation for society. Today the practice of Mormonism survives most vigorously not in the state of New York where it originated, nor on the plains of the Midlands where its organization was wrought, but in the insular integrity characteristic of the Snake River and Great Basin plateaus of the West.

POLITICAL ASPECTS

Plateaus frequently play important political roles in human history. For instance, the political activities of the early Hebrews were centered at Jerusalem on the Judean Plateau. After the Captivity, the resurgent Jewish state was founded upon this same central tableland. Similarly, the plateau states, Castile and Leon, formed the nucleus of the modern Spanish nation, and Madrid in the center of the Meseta is today the capital of the country.

For centuries the Ottoman Empire was a more or less ramshackle agglutination of racial elements loosely held together by Moslem traditions and a corrupt political influence emanating from Constantinople. The recent revival of the Ottoman state, however, has not come from Constantinople (Istanbul) nor from the commercial littoral of Asia Minor, but from the interior plateau. The new state is a purely Turkish creation, even the capital having been removed to Ankara (Angora) in the interior.

Throughout all tropical Spanish America there are white populations living on plateaus. These are in most instances isolated from one another by intervening lowlands or mountains. Despite the community of race, language, and tradition, nothing approximating political unity has existed in tropical America since the Spanish colonial period. Rather, each plateau has developed its own specific set of local political interests and has become the center of a separate national state.

When a country is subjected to a powerful racial or commercial invasion, the lowlands may rapidly lose their political independence. At the same time fragments of political autonomy may survive on plateaus. Thus, in India, the British formerly exercised direct control over the peoples of the coast and the easily penetrated Indo-Gangetic Plain, but the native states of the Deccan maintained a semi-independent status.

Nowhere is the relation between a plateau habitat and political independence better shown than in the instance of Ethiopia (Abyssinia). The nucleus of this country was Amhara, an African state which not only possessed a venerable history but whose ruling dynasty actually claimed descent from the queen of Sheba, a contemporary of King Solomon. During the latter part of the nineteenth century, the Amharic state began a remarkable expansion and welded together the Empire of Ethiopia at the very time when the remainder of Africa was fast succumbing to European conquest. Ethiopia was attacked several times but managed to repulse her enemies successfully. In this she was greatly aided by her location upon a nearly inaccessible plateau which rises high up into a zone of cool and energizing climate. The surrounding less valuable lowlands were speedily parcelled out among France, Italy, and Great Britain, who used them for bases from which to make constant attempts

Figure 24–4   Coffee cable car in Highland Colombia. Most of the coffee is grown at an altitude of 2,500 to 6,500 feet above sea level on slopes often having 25 to 30 degree angles. The aerial cable, which often is employed for transporting the coffee down steep slopes and over deep ravines, is an adjustment to rough terrain. (Photo courtesy of the Colombia Information Service)

Figure 24–5   Aerial view of Bogotá, Colombia, a remote center of civilization flourishing on a plateau deep within the Andes. (Photo courtesy of the Colombia National Tourist Board)

at securing economic concessions in Ethiopia. Finally in 1935, Italy, still smarting from a crushing defeat received nearly forty years before, resolved to attempt once more the military conquest of the plateau. The points of attraction were (1) a large population, (2) many undeveloped natural resources, and (3) a zone of cool climate (the *woina dega,* between 4,800 and 8,000 feet elevation) suitable for white colonization.[1] The physical obstacles facing the Italians were appalling; they were confronted by a complete lack of roads and bridges, and ringed about far below by a scorching thirsty desert. Moreover, the terrain was almost totally unknown to the invaders, whereas the natives were thoroughly familiar with every foot of their plateau. Foot by foot the Italian army climbed to the plateau by building bridges and improved roads, reconnoitering from airplanes and drenching the countryside with poison gas and a hail of machine gun bullets. Despite nature's aid, excellent morale, and the utmost physical courage, the Ethiopians were finally defeated. Even a relatively impregnable plateau location proved to be no longer a defense against airplane, poison gas, armored trucks, and modern engineering skill. Thus Ethiopia, almost the last independent native state in Africa, was taken over by an ambitious Italy. But because Italy, a member of the Axis in World War II, was defeated, Ethiopia again enjoys her independent status.

[1] H. Scaetta, "Geography, Ethiopia's Ally," *Foreign Affairs* (October, 1935), p. 65.

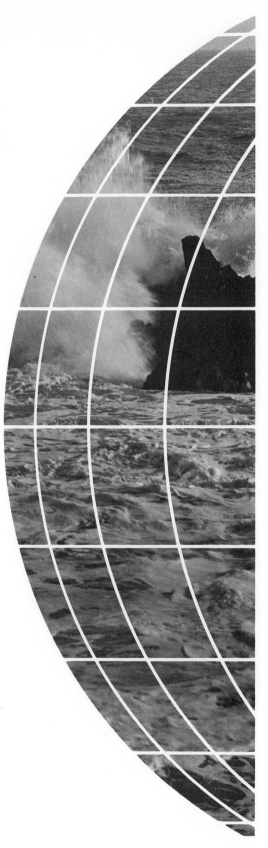

V

The Hydrographic Factors

Next to air, water is man's most necessary resource; without these he cannot survive. Therefore, well-watered places, where quality, quantity and an even, or reliable, distribution exist, are among the choicest spots for human habitation. Wherever, and whenever, the pressure of population upon certain areas of the earth becomes great, concern for the water supply has high priority.

With the "drift to towns" in evidence today, the swelling populations, and the great burgeoning of metropolitan areas and their suburbs, there is an increasing interest in the planning of multiple and interlocking uses of water. Regionalizing is being done with drainage basins as the basic units.

25

Ground Water— Occurrence and Utilization

Water is found on the planet earth, in three[1] major forms—ocean waters, surface waters of the land, and underground waters. Water is involved in nearly every aspect of human endeavor, but the bearing upon human affairs of each of its three major forms of occurrence is quite different. It has, therefore, become customary to regard each major form of water occurrence as a separate and distinct element of man's natural environment. Not the least among them are underground waters.

ORIGIN

The term *ground water* is applied to all waters found beneath the surface of the earth. Ground water is commonly of three types from the standpoint of origin—*magmatic, connate,* and *meteoric.* Magmatic ground water is present in volcanic eruptions and some geyser eruptions. Because it is formed by the union of hydrogen and oxygen as these gases are liberated from the hot magmatic materials deep in the earth, it is sometimes known as nascent water. Connate ground water occurs in strata of sedimentary rocks or beds of loose, unconsolidated sediments. These sedimentary materials were long ago laid down in bodies of either fresh or salt water, a portion of which becomes entrapped in the sediments and may remain in it for ages. Meteoric ground water is, of course, by far the most common generic class because it is derived from the various forms of precipitation in the atmosphere. It is estimated that one-sixth of all rainfall soaks into the ground (in contrast to the one-half which evaporates and

the one-third which runs off the surface of the land). This meteoric "soak-in" not only constitutes the major source of ground water but is also a permanent means of its replenishment.

In regions of deep soil and open penetrable rocks, meteoric waters may soak in freely and ground water is abundant. In instances where hard impervious bedrock lies at or close to the surface, ground-water resources are apt to be meager or absent. Even the hardest of crystalline rocks, however, if filled with cracks and fissures, or if old and deeply weathered, may locally contain water in abundance.

MODES OF OCCURRENCE

Ground water occurs in great variety of situations. For the purpose of geographical analysis, however, these may be grouped into some six types.

VADOSE WATER

The commonest mode of occurrence of ground water is in the vadose or subsurface zone. Another name for this is *soil water.* It is derived from rain or melted snow which soaks into the soil and, to a much lesser extent, from the absorption of moisture directly from the atmosphere.

Vadose water occurs in the soil in three principal ways: (1) hydroscopic moisture held by adhesion to the surface of the individual soil

---

[1] It is also found in the atmosphere, but as vapor rather than as liquid water. Accordingly, atmospheric water has been treated under weather and climate.

409

particles, (2) capillary moisture held loosely in the smaller pores or interstices of the soil by surface tension, and (3) free moisture in the larger pore spaces, in process of gradually percolating downward under the pull of gravity.

The amount of vadose water in a soil at any given time and place depends upon a number of variable factors: the average annual rainfall, manner of rainfall occurrence, time elapsed since the last rain, rate of evaporation, temperature, land slope, vegetation cover, texture and structure of the soil, humus and colloidal content, and several others.

The amount of vadose water within a soil in a humid climate ordinarily varies from 23 percent of the total volume in cultivated land up to 40 percent in pasture land. After a prolonged drought these percentages fall to 17 and 22 respectively. In semiarid and arid climates, the percentages are, of course, much smaller.

THE WATER TABLE

Below the vadose or shallow soil water zone usually lies a water table. The free water normally found in the shallow zone is actually in process of slow percolation downward under the pull of gravitation. It originates as rain or snow which, after soaking into the soil, seeps slowly downward until it encounters an impervious layer or until it reaches a depth where the weight of the overlying formations becomes great enough to seal all fissures in the rock. There it comes to rest as a deep-lying zone of gravitational water, where it saturates the ground below a certain level, filling the pores of the subsoil and the cracks in the underlying bedrock. The lower limit of this zone is rather indefinite, but its upper limit is a definite surface known as the *water table* (Fig. 25–1).

The depth below the surface at which the water table is encountered varies greatly. In regions of heavy rainfall it may lie only a few inches below the surface, whereas in extremely arid ones it may lie at a depth of scores of feet, or it may be absent altogether.

The water-table level also depends upon the character of underground drainage. Where the soil and bedrock are pervious and underdrainage

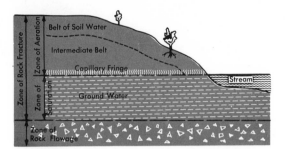

Figure 25–1   Cross section showing the water table in relation to the surface of the land. The broken line indicates the water table.

is rapid, ground water is apt to be deep-lying. On the other hand, where underdrainage is poorly defined, the water table may stand at a high level.

The configuration of the land influences the water table considerably. Indeed, the latter may be thought of as a warped surface which tends to follow the undulations of the physiographic landscape. The relief is much less and the gradients much more gentle, however, in the water table than in the land surface itself. In low-lying areas, therefore, ground water approaches closer to the surface than under hills or ridges. Where it intersects the surface of the land, swamps or lakes occur. Where rivers incise their valleys below ground-water level, they become permanent streams and thus maintain their flow independent of seasonal alimentation by rain or snowfall.

The depth at which the water table stands in any locality is not fixed but fluctuates from time to time in response to both natural and man-made causes. It rises after each rain and lowers during the intervals between rains. Similarly it rises and falls during the year in accordance with seasons of wet or drought. Fluctuations of longer periods are occasioned by cycles of unusually wet or dry years.

Man himself may lower the water table locally by pumping, ditching, or tiling for drainage, or by denuding the surface of its vegetation so as to augment the rainfall runoff. For example, the early settlers in Iowa obtained good supplies of water from dug or bored wells ten to thirty feet deep, but later, drilled wells ranging from sixty to one hundred feet, or in some cases even two hundred to three hundred feet, became necessary. Records covering forty or fifty years indicate a mean lowering of ten to twenty feet, or perhaps even more in the water table of Iowa.[2]

On the other hand, man may locally raise the gravitational water level either by irrigation or by the building of such structures as may interfere with subsurface drainage. On many irrigation projects in the arid West, a too lavish application of water has so raised the water table as to render much good land swampy. Low-lying land in frequent instances has been made uselessly alkaline by rising ground water. Expenditures for drainage in some of the irrigation districts of Utah have considerably exceeded the initial cost of getting water onto the land.

SUBTERRANEAN STREAMS

While vadose water is practically omnipresent and even a water table is found in most areas, subterranean streams are of comparatively rare occurrence. In humid localities underlain by soluble limestone, caverns and subterranean channels often result from prolonged solution. Such cavities may contain well-defined streams of water. At times these possess large volume and considerable velocity. Continued erosion by an underground stream, in some instances, causes the roof of its cavern to collapse, thereby forming a sinkhole at the surface. Areas marked by subterranean drainage, caverns, and sinks are said to possess *karst* topography.

In arid or semiarid regions, underground flows of a quite different sort may be encountered. Where canyon streams descend from the uplands and debouch onto alluvial fans or detritus-filled basins, they are soon lost in the loose sands and gravels. Such waters, however, usually

continue to flow as slow-moving subsurface streams below the dry stream beds, locally known as *wadis, arroyos, sand creeks,* or *washes,* which seam the surface of arid regions. A shallow well put down in the *thalweg* or axial drainage line of a dry wash will usually encounter flowing water at no great depth. Evidence of the presence of ground water of this type is often amply afforded by the natural vegetation.

SPRINGS

Ground waters frequently emerge at the surface as springs. Such phenomena are particularly numerous on hillsides and on the lower slopes of mountains. They also occur on plains where they are usually found on the walls of stream valleys or at the base of outcropping strata of resistant rock. Two types are common; gravity or contact springs, and fissure springs.

The downward progress of meteoric waters is often impeded by an impervious layer of rock or subsoil, in which case the waters seep slowly down the dip of the impervious layer, to emerge as a gravity spring at the point where the layer in question outcrops (Fig. 25–2). Should the impervious layer not outcrop, the downward seeping waters may develop a slight head of pressure. This may be sufficient to force the waters upward to the surface along a fissure or crack in the overlying materials, thereby creating a fissure spring. Gravity springs and simple wet-weather seeps are ordinarily the products of vadose water. Fissure springs are more often fed by gravitational water from below the water table; in some instances they are artesian in character.

Springs have a direct bearing on the location of human habitations in both arid and humid lands. The practiced observer everywhere recognizes the level of springs in the neighborhood of Paris by the alignment of villages on the hillsides. Springs, as natural sources of domestic water, were of great importance in the early settlement of eastern United States. Owing to their restricted occurrence and their frequently uneconomic

Figure 25–2 Cross section illustrating conditions necessary for springs. GS represents a gravity spring, and FS a fissure spring. Dotted layers represent porous strata (aquifers).

[2] For a more detailed discussion of fluctuations in the water table and the problem of a declining water level, see Harold E. Thomas, *The Conservation of Ground Water* (New York, McGraw-Hill Book Company, 1951), 327 pp.

location, however, they are today of only slight import save in backward mountain and hill country districts. In all arid regions, springs are of capital importance. In many desert portions of western United States, they are of considerable significance as watering places for livestock or as sources of drinking water for the use of itinerants.

ARTESIAN WATER

Water trapped in deep-lying rocks in such manner as to develop considerable hydrostatic pressure is termed *artesian*. A well drilled into such water-bearing rocks is known as an artesian well, provided the water flows from it; if the water rises in the well but does not flow, it is termed sub-artesian.

The natural conditions necessary for artesian water are (1) a porous layer of sand or rock known as the aquifer or water bearer, (2) a catchment area formed by a high-lying outcrop of the aquifer, (3) considerable slope or dip of the aquifer in order to accumulate a head of pressure, (4) an impervious layer of cap rock overlying the aquifer for preventing the escape of the water under pressure (Fig. 25–3).

In rare instances, artesian water may contain an abundance of salt or alkalies. Artesian water is often of great ecological significance in determining the economic possibilities of an area. The Dakotas, northeast central Australia, most of the oases of eastern Algeria, and many of the desert basins of western United States are exam-

ples of areas where settlement has been largely dependent upon this resource.

THERMAL AND MINERAL WATERS

In certain localities where volcanic or igneous action has formerly occurred or where faulting on a major scale has taken place, ground water may penetrate far down into the earth along cracks and fissures. Under such circumstances, it may come into contact with heated rocks and be blown out as steam and hot water in a geyser eruption, or it may well up quietly as a hot spring. In their passage upward, the heated waters may encounter soluble materials and become highly mineralized, resulting in either hot or cool mineral springs.

Mineral and thermal waters are of considerable economic significance. They may occasion a tourist industry as do the geysers and hot springs of Yellowstone National Park, or they may be the locating factor for bottling works as at Colfax, Iowa. Most important of all, by reason of their real or imagined therapeutic value, hot springs and mineral springs have caused the growth of health resort communities. Baden-Baden and other spa cities of Europe illustrate such centers of activity. In the United States, Hot Springs, Arkansas, is perhaps the outstanding spa and therapeutic bath center (Fig. 25–4). The entire city of Hot Springs is a creation of the long line of uprising hot waters along a fault line transecting one of the Ouachita Mountain ridges. So important has this spot become that it has been made a national park and put under the control of the federal government.

SIGNIFICANCE OF GROUND WATER

HUMID REGIONS

The significance of ground water varies greatly in accordance with general climatic conditions. In humid regions, it is utilized almost universally for domestic purposes in both rural and urban communities. In addition, the latter make heavy demands upon it for industrial uses. Since ground water is plentiful in regions of moderate to heavy rainfall, it is used carelessly and waste-

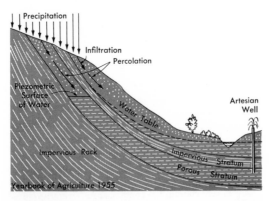

Figure 25–3 Cross section illustrating water conditions necessary for an artesian well.

Figure 25–4 The downtown section of Hot Springs, Arkansas, showing some of the city's many resort hotels. Hot Springs owes its importance as a health resort primarily to the occurrence of ascending hot waters. (Photo courtesy of the Hot Springs Chamber of Commerce)

fully. It is, in fact, frequently too abundant, creating serious problems in mining and quarrying operations and rendering drainage necessary on many low-lying lands (Fig. 25–5).

SEMIARID REGIONS

Ground water is also used for domestic and industrial purposes in both town and country in lands of semiaridity. Here, however, it is often far from abundant and must be used carefully. For example, in many towns of the American Great Plains, ordinances have been enacted forbidding the watering of lawns and gardens during the summer months. Despite these and like precautions, the supply of ground water often runs low during the dry season. In drought years, it may become completely exhausted. Hence, most homes are equipped with cisterns in which rain water is stored for auxiliary use.

DESERT REGIONS

It is in arid lands that ground water attains its most crucial utility, however, for through its control of local variations in the natural vegetation, it has a vital bearing upon pastoral adjustments. In addition, many oases depend completely upon ground water for their existence. The latter is, accordingly, distributed with great care and is used sparingly for water supply and irrigation.

DEVICES FOR PROCURING GROUND WATER

SPRING WATER

Spring water usually reaches the surface through either hydrostatic pressure or gravity flow. Consequently the water is dipped out at the spring or led by pipe or ditch to the point where it is desired. In case it be needed above the point of

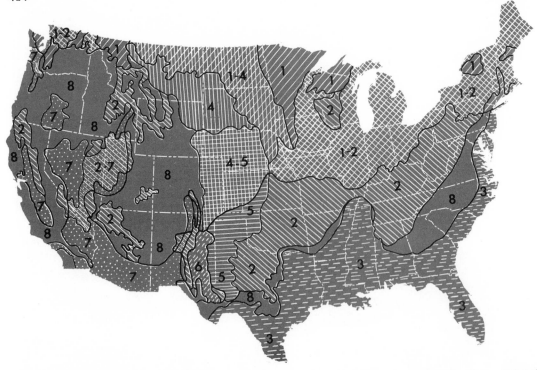

Figure 25–5 Ground-water sources in the United States: (1) Glacial moraine: abundant supplies from sand and gravel beds, (2) paleozoic rocks: potable water from sandstones and limestones, (3) sedimentary beds of the Coastal Plain: good supplies from sands and from limestones in Texas and Florida, (4) mesozoic rocks of the northern Great Plains: mineralized artesian water from underlying sandstones, (5) tertiary beds of the southern Great Plains: abundant water from sands and gravels, (6) Roswell Artesian Basin: abundant supplies from Permian limestones, (7) western filled basins: large supplies from sands and gravels, and (8) areas of complex rock structure with local deficiencies in ground water. Note: where two numbers occur together, two sources—at different depths—are indicated. (Map adapted from the U.S. National Resources Planning Board)

issue, it may be elevated by such crude devices as the "go fetch it" of the Appalachian hill districts, or by the pump or hydraulic ram of more advanced localities.

WELLS

In order to obtain ground water, man usually finds it necessary to construct wells. Dug or driven wells may satisfactorily attain a depth of thirty to forty feet, while bored ones may reach a depth of one hundred feet or more. Those of greater depths, however, must be drilled.

Ancient man drew water from open wells by a wooden, earthen, or metal bucket attached to a rope or leather thong. Today this means of obtaining it persists in some backward areas and is used occasionally as a makeshift device anywhere. A modification of this method is the *sheduf* or long handled dipper. Two improve-

ments upon the simple rope-and-bucket device were the *well sweep* of northern Europe and the *noria* in Mediterranean Europe. In the former, a long lever equipped with a counterweight is made to do the work of hoisting; in the latter, the rope is run over a pulley and hitched to a draft animal.

Until a few decades ago, open curb wells were in almost universal use. The "old oaken buckets" of which there were two in each well, were attached to either end of a rope. The rope hung over an iron pulley supported from a crossbar above the well. In this arrangement the empty bucket as it descended acted as a counterweight to aid in elevating its filled mate.

Toward the end of the nineteenth century, hand pumps came into general use throughout the United States. These were simple mechanical devices based upon the principles of the lever and of the cylinder and piston, and they hoisted water either by suction or compression. Such hand pumps are still employed in elevating water all over the civilized world, but where a continued flow is necessary, pumps are operated by windmills or by gasoline, electric, or steam engines.

ARTESIAN WELLS

Wells which flow under their own pressure are to be desired from the standpoint of economy. Many artesian waters emerge under a head sufficient to carry them through pipes to points of consumption. Even subartesian wells, where the water rises part way to the top of the casing, usually necessitate much less pumping than wells drawing on the water table.

COMMUNITIES AND THEIR WATER SUPPLIES

RURAL COMMUNITIES

In the majority of instances, the homes of rural communities in the United States depend for their water supply upon individual dug or bored wells. Water is procured by pumps operated by hand, windmill, or small gasoline engine. If the wells are located properly in relation to barns and other outbuildings, there is usually small danger of water pollution.

HAMLETS AND VILLAGES

Where people are grouped into hamlet or clustered village patterns, there is increased danger of well pollution. Such semirural communities cannot, therefore, safely continue for long to depend upon individual shallow wells. As a consequence, the village, if it be a progressive one, takes over the control of the water supply. A larger and deeper well is put down in a situation least liable to be reached by contaminating materials, a village pumping station is installed, and a standpipe is erected for water storage. Consequently, the tall standpipe is one of the outstanding features of the American village.

TOWNS

When villages grow into incorporated towns, the population becomes locally so dense as to create two critical problems, pollution of the town well or wells, and occasional peak demands upon the water supply for fire protection. The town, therefore, drills deep wells in an effort to tap artesian sources. These usually yield abundant supplies of water and are, if properly cased, free from contamination.

CITIES

As towns develop into cities, even artesian sources become inadequate. Wells may decline in yield or the rate of pumping may prove incapable of meeting growing domestic and industrial needs. Fortunately, most cities are, mainly for historical reasons, located in river valleys. A city may, therefore, construct large infiltration chambers in the lenses of sand or gravel under the nearby river floodplain, in order to provide an abundant water supply. More commonly, ground water is abandoned altogether as a source, and water is pumped directly from the river or is transported hundreds of miles from a distant source, as for example, at San Francisco and Los Angeles. All water destined for domestic use must, of course, be purified before it goes into the city mains.

METROPOLISES

Occasionally cities become very large, developing into veritable urban metropolises or conurbations. The population of metropolitan New York is 11 million, that of greater London, 8 million, that of metropolitan Chicago, approximately 6 million, and that of Los Angeles, $6\frac{1}{2}$ million. Such giant urban concentrations demand enormous quantities of water for drinking purposes, baths, swimming pools, the washing of city streets, manufacturing plants, laundries, fire departments, dilution of sewage, and other uses. New York City consumes more than one billion gallons daily, and each year brings an increase in consumption.

To maintain an uninterrupted water supply of this magnitude has proved one of the chief ecological problems of modern urban areas. Some of the larger cities have found it necessary to take over the control of whole drainage basins, build many square miles of storage reservoirs, construct scores of miles of tunnels and aqueducts, reforest extensive areas, and maintain a forestry service and a board of engineers and geologists.

ECOLOGICAL CONSIDERATIONS

In addition to its major significance as a source of water supply, ground water exercises considerable influence over the cultural landscape. Among the items affected are land utilization, distribution of population, size and shape of landholdings, and routes of travel.

LAND UTILIZATION

The depth to ground water frequently affects land utilization. For example, in the Aquitaine Basin of France, the valleys with their high water table and abundant springs are prosperously devoted to the production of maize, wheat, and fruit. By way of contrast, the intervening calcareous uplands, standing at an elevation of perhaps six hundred to seven hundred feet, are permeable and dry. These areas support but meager cultivation in the midst of preponderant pastoral activities.

POPULATION GROUPING

The early settlers in most parts of the American Midlands found ground water abundant and easy to obtain. As each settler was able to dig his own well, population spread uniformly over the countryside. The isolated farmstead, therefore, became the usual form of rural establishment.

In Picardy and other portions of northern France, the water table lies far below the surface of the high limestone plains. As a consequence, the construction of deep wells was difficult and costly and with other factors compelled the grouping of several farm homes about common wells, leaving the intervening countryside largely devoid of habitations. Indeed, the arrangement of farm houses into hamlets and clustered villages, which is so often encountered in various parts of Europe (a survival from medieval times), may possibly be a response to a common well as often as to the protection afforded by the lord's castle.

SIZE OF LANDHOLDINGS

In the arid Northern Basins of Mexico, points where water may be procured are often far apart. In most instances, a well, water hole, spring, or *tanque* has become the nucleus of a *rancho* or *hacienda*. Since the intervening waterless country is of little value, the size of the landholdings usually depends upon the distance between wet points. Most *ranchos* and *haciendas* are, therefore, huge. Following the Mexican Revolution of 1910 some haciendas were broken up into *ejidos* on which several families worked the land cooperatively. There is an experiment of this nature near Torreon in northern Mexico.

ROUTES OF TRAVEL

In lands of marked aridity or low water table, trails and caravan routes follow rather closely the points where ground water is available. To a certain extent, railways and motor highways similarly tend to avail themselves of such points of supply.

SUGGESTED USEFUL READINGS

See also the texts suggested for Chapter 26.

Ackerman, Edward, and George O. G. Lof, *Technology in American Water Development* (Baltimore, Johns Hopkins Press, for Resources for the Future, Inc., 1959), pp. 384–406.

Durfor, Charles N., and Edith Becker, *Public Water Supplies of the United States, 1962,* Geological Survey Water Supply Paper 1812 (Washington, D.C., Government Printing Office, 1964).

Fair, Gordon Maskew, and John Charles Geyer, *Elements of Waste–Water Disposal* (New York, John Wiley & Sons, Inc., 1958), pp. 98–137.

MacKichan, K. A., and J. C. Mammerer, *Estimated Use of Water in the United States, 1960*, Geological Survey Circular 456 (Washington, D.C., 1961).

Strahler, Arthur, *Introduction to Physical Geography* (New York, John Wiley & Sons, Inc., 1965), Chapter 19, pp. 267–285.

Thomas, Harold Edgar, *The Conservation of Ground-Water; a Survey of the Present Ground-Water Situation in the United States* (New York, McGraw-Hill Book Company, Inc., 1951), 327 pp.

Tolman, C. F., *Ground Water* (New York, McGraw-Hill Book Company, Inc., 1937), 593 pp.

United Nations, Economic Commission for Asia and the Far East, *The Development of Ground-water Resources with Special Reference to Deltaic Areas*, Water Resources Series No. 24 (New York, United Nations, 1963), 244 pp.

U.S. Department of Agriculture, *Water,* Yearbook of Agriculture, 1955 (Washington, D.C., Government Printing Office, 1955), 751 pp.

U.S. Department of Health, Education, and Welfare, *Statistical Summary of Municipal Water Facilities in the United States, January 1, 1963*, Public Health Service, Publication No. 1039 (Washington, D.C., Government Printing Office, 1965), 66 pp.

Surface
Waters
of the Land

Rivers, creeks, fresh and salt lakes, swamps, marshes, and canals constitute the surface waters of the land. Everywhere throughout the world people are adjusting themselves in one way or another to these features of the landscape, depending upon their waters for household, municipal, and industrial use, navigation, disposal of sewage and industrial waste, irrigation, hydroelectric and steam power, minerals, drainage, and food. Obviously no single body of water can serve all these varied uses locally at one time, but some do run the gamut along their courses from source to mouth.

A direct relationship exists between the distribution of surface waters and population density. Many of the world's outstanding cities are situated on rivers and lakes. In order to fully comprehend the subtleties of man's adjustments to surface waters of the land, it is desirable to know the salient physical factors connected with the life history of streams, since they play the dominant role in determining the contour of the land.

STREAMS AND VALLEYS

Stream valleys are not the result of cataclysmic or catastrophic movement during the geologic past; rather are they the slow handiwork of running water. Rivers have simple beginnings—rain, falling on sloping terrain, forms a small gully which increases in size with each additional shower (Fig. 26–1). The water entering at the upper end lengthens the gully by headward erosion, while that entering laterally starts new tributary gullies. Thus are most valleys made.

Every stream during its life cycle has a definite task to perform. This consists of reducing the land to sea level. Streams pass through the same stages as human beings—*youth, maturity,* and *old age,* each being distinguished by definite characteristics. Some rivers, like the Mississippi, combine all three stages from source to debouchure, being youthful in the upper course and old at the outlet, maturity prevailing midway. Completion of the cycle is not a matter of time but of accomplishment: no two streams work at precisely the same rate (Fig. 20–7).

FLOODS

A flood is a flow of water over a stream's banks. It occurs in mature and old valleys where the distribution of precipitation is seasonal (Fig. 26–2). Additional physical factors are (1) excessive rainfall, (2) rapid melting of snow, (3) frozen ground, impervious to the water of spring rains and thaws, (4) scarcity of vegetation for retarding runoff, and (5) breaking of dams and levees. Man contributes by cutting down forests, plowing the land for crops, building dams, changing the courses of streams, and paving roads.

Floods have geographic significance because of their baneful effect upon the swarms of people who often occupy the floodplains. Because such plains are apt to be comparatively level and fertile, they are among the most densely populated and most intensively tilled areas in the world. In the lower Hwang-Ho valley, the population is estimated at 700 persons per square mile, though in certain sections it is said to approximate 6,880; in parts of the lower Ganges plain it is estimated at 1,000 to 2,000. Such pressure of population necessitates a low level of living, especially when nearly all the people are farmers. That the density in the Orient is greater than the land can support is indicated by the fact that every serious flood brings famine, pestilence, and death in its wake.

FLOODS AND THEIR CONTROL

To date man has been only partially successful in his attempts to stem the floods along the world's great rivers: the Hwang, Yangtze, and Mississippi all break through their levees periodically. In so-called primitive and backward countries, the people make no effort to prevent floods, accepting them as inevitable as they do disease. They build their dwellings on stilts, work a little when they can, and fish when the country becomes inundated. In advanced countries, however, man definitely strives to prevent floods. He carries on reforestation, employs strip-cropping and contour plowing, builds artificial levees atop those of nature, straightens and constricts channels (thereby shortening the distance, increasing the velocity of the current,[1] and enabling the river to scour out its channel), and he constructs dams and reservoirs for storing surplus waters during the flood period.

In a study submitted to the Select Committee on National Water Resources of the U.S. Senate

[1] By constructing jetties for narrowing the Mississippi River near its mouth in 1875, James B. Eads, engineer in charge, so increased the stream's velocity as to force it to clean out its own channel. Not until this was done could large ocean vessels reach New Orleans.

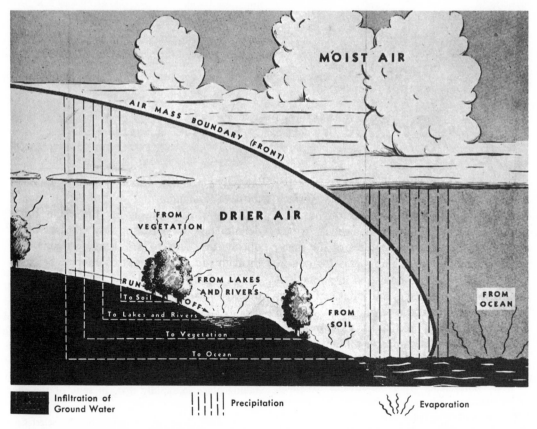

Figure 26–1   Diagrammatic representation of the hydrologic cycle in nature. The ocean is the primary source for most of the moisture in the atmosphere, and most if not all moisture eventually returns to the ocean. Only three-tenths of 1 percent of all the rain that falls on the earth is available *when* and *where* it is needed for man's use. The total runoff is 2,600 times the total withdrawal for use. (Adapted from the Environmental Science Services Administration)

Figure 26–2 Swelling floodwaters of the Mississippi River nearly isolated the town of Wabasha, Minnesota, in April, 1965. (Photo from Wide World Photos)

in June, 1960, the Army Corps of Engineers[2] reported the following facts.

The flood problem in the United States results from the conditions of hydrology and topography of our river basins which produce the runoff that appears in streams and rivers as floodflow, from the capability of channels and floodplains to pass such flows, and from the extent to which river valleys are used and developed. . . . But there was no flood problem until the white man began to settle in the river valleys, and thus gave floods something to damage.

Thus, in a real sense the flood problem is caused by people. If man had left the flood plains to the streams that created them, there would be no flood damage, and no flood problem. But man has had very good reasons for his unrelenting efforts to wrest valley lands from the streams to which, under the laws of nature, they belong. Bottom lands are normally more fertile and easier to till than uplands, and it is less costly for man to build his cities and other works on relatively flat valley bottoms. In addition, when the country was first settled, the rivers constituted the main avenues of

commerce. There are still advantages to be gained by locating cities on navigable waterways and certain industrial developments are attracted to river valleys by a readily available water supply.

There is good reason to believe that these highly advanced regions will take positive steps to control floods in the future, but millions of dollars will have to be spent to bring this about.

The battle between man and streams for possession of flood plains lands has been long and costly. It has been costly to those who settled on the flood plains and have had to suffer the damages inflicted by floods. It is proving costly to nations to make it possible for the owners of flood plain lands to utilize them as intensively as they desire. At this time the development of flood plain lands is taking place so rapidly that, in spite of the effec-

[2] U.S. Army, Corps of Engineers, for the Select Committee on National Water Resources, U.S. Senate, *Water Resources Activities in the United States: Floods and Flood Control* (Washington, D.C., Government Printing Office, 1960), pp. 1–2.

tiveness of Federal flood control works, the flood damage potential in unprotected or in partially protected areas appears to be increasing.[3]

WATER SUPPLY AND DEMAND

In the brief span of a century and a half, American farms and cities were extended from the Appalachian Mountains to the Pacific Ocean. In this westward movement, Americans destroyed forests, overplowed and overgrazed the lands, dangerously increased soil erosion, and contaminated rivers with mud, sewage, and industrial waste.

In this expansion, water became a key resource because of its varied uses and the vast amounts required. The quantities utilized for irrigation, manufacturing, and so on, depend largely upon the climates, the populations, and the principal economic pursuits carried on (Fig. 26–3). With a population of roughly 200 million and a total withdrawal of water estimated to exceed 340 billion gallons a day, the per capita consumption of water for all purposes in the United States is over 1,700 gallons daily. This includes water withdrawn for domestic, municipal, irrigation, power, and industrial uses, and represents 30 percent of the nation's potential supply. About half the total, excluding water power, is claimed for industrial uses, two-fifths for irrigation, and one-tenth for domestic rural and municipal use.

Consumption is based on the difference between intake and discharge. In industry, where a total of 14,055 billion gallons of water were withdrawn in 1964, 13,171 billion gallons were discharged. This amounts to an annual consumption of only 884 billion gallons of water, or 6.3 percent of all intake. The actual proportion varies with the particular activity, ranging from less than 3.3 percent in the meat industry to ten times that amount in the food processing industry. In irrigation, from 50 to 60 percent of the intake is consumed. Less than 20 percent of the withdrawals for public supplies is consumed. On an overall basis, about 23 percent of water withdrawals for various purposes is consumed in the United States.

Although it is considered a nonconsumptive

use, waterpower accounts for the largest volume of withdrawals. In 1960 alone, two trillion gallons of water a day, or 2.2 billion acre-feet of water for the year, were used to develop waterpower. From 1950 to 1960, withdrawals for waterpower increased by 33 percent. Changes in intake in other categories are indicative of increasing demands for water. Self-supplied industries had a 27 percent increase in 1960 withdrawals over 1950. Public supplies during the same period increased by 23 percent, from 17,000 million gallons daily in 1950 to 21,000 million gallons daily in 1960![4]

Major water-use regions are shown on the map, Figure 26–3. A fairly clear picture of the number of people who drew water daily from these regions in 1960 is given in Table 26–1.

Almost every large city faces a truly great problem in supplying itself adequately with water. If a city cannot get sufficient stores of water to meet its needs, its future will be affected adversely. Doubtless, then, the expansion of all the great cities will depend upon this resource. Some statisticians already predict that the ultimate population of New York City will be limited by the total amount of water available to it. Until recently the safe yield of the existing supplies was only a few percent above one billion gallons per day.

The municipal supply, serving more than eight and a half million people, is obtained from nearby sources, the Catskill Mountains, and the Delaware River Basin. In 1961, four-fifths of the city's water supply came from sources in the Catskill Mountains and the Delaware River. The Pepacton Reservoir, where waters of the East Branch of the Delaware are impounded, has a capacity of 143,700 million gallons, and is the largest storage reservoir supplying water to the city.

New York's water supply is believed to be ample except in emergencies; the city would be vulnerable if (1) a drought should last through two successive years; (2) the per capita consump-

---

[3] *Ibid.*, p. 2.

[4] See K. A. Mackichan and J. C. Kammerer, *Estimated Use of Water in the United States, 1960,* Geological Survey Circular 456 (Washington, D.C., 1961).

Water-use Regions	Area (1,000 Square Miles)	Population (1,000's)	Average Runoff (Mgd)	Withdrawals 1960 (Mgd)	Per Capita Use (Gpd)
New England	59	9,921	67,000	6,400	640
Delaware-Hudson	31	23,796	32,000	20,000	830
Chesapeake	57	8,663	51,000	7,100	820
South Atlantic	170	14,539	110,000	13,000	910
Eastern Gulf	109	6,933	99,000	5,900	860
Tennessee-Cumberland	59	4,184	59,000	7,500	1,800
Ohio	145	17,950	110,000	24,000	1,300
Eastern Great Lakes–St. Lawrence	47	12,424	40,000	13,000	1,000
Western Great Lakes	81	13,183	42,000	16,000	1,200
Hudson Bay	60	666	4,600	170	260
Upper Mississippi	182	12,359	62,000	11,000	920
Upper Missouri	458	5,382	24,000	20,000	3,700
Lower Missouri	62	2,451	23,000	1,600	640
Lower Mississippi	64	4,735	49,000	5,300	1,100
Upper Arkansas–Red	153	3,309	11,000	5,500	1,700
Lower Arkansas–Red-White	117	3,884	79,000	4,900	1,300
Western Gulf	341	10,029	52,000	22,000	2,200
Colorado	258	2,027	13,000	14,000	7,000
Great Basin	200	1,204	10,000	7,000	5,800
South Pacific	112	15,412	64,000	33,000	2,100
Pacific Northwest	257	5,412	159,000	29,000	5,400
Hawaii	6.4	634	—	1,600	2,500
Alaska	586	226	—	200	870
Puerto Rico	3.4	2,385	—	1,200	510
United States excluding Alaska, Hawaii, and Puerto Rico	3,022	178,463	1,200,000	270,000	1,500
Grand total	3,618	181,708	—	270,000	1,500

Table 26–1. Water-use regions of the United States.

Figure 26–3   Water utilization regions in the United States.

tion should rise over an extended period; and (3) the population should increase sensationally.[5]

New York City now consumes in excess of one billion gallons daily; the per capita consumption is almost 150 gallons. Among the outstanding uses, aside from drinking, are cooking, bathing, washing, and sprinkling of lawns.

Everywhere large cities become increasingly concerned about their water supply and reach deeper and deeper into their hinterlands to acquire it. San Francisco has already spent many millions of dollars and is constantly investing more on its water system which reaches back some two hundred miles into Yosemite National Park in the Sierra Nevada to get the 166 million gallons it uses daily. Fast-growing Los Angeles taps several sources (Figs. 26–4 and 26–5), chiefly the Colorado River, 392 miles distant. The problem of water—too little or two much (floods) at the wrong time and place—has vexed human beings down through the ages.

Water from public sources is relatively cheap —usually costing the consumer less than five cents per ton or less than two cents per capita per day; probably one-half the residential water takers in the United States pay less than one cent per capita per day for their water.

FREEDOM FROM BACTERIA

The aim is to fill the mains with water free from bacteria. To succeed is an Herculean task. Yet every city faces this problem, since possibly not one gets a supply that is absolutely pure. No river in the country has water hygienically safe without treatment. Cities, by dumping their sewage into a river, pollute the water withdrawn by those downstream. These waters literally swarm with the germs of such infectious diseases as typhoid

[5] In 1965, after two years of prolonged drought, eastern New York, New Jersey, and eastern Pennsylvania were declared a "disaster area."

Figure 26–4   Open lined section of the Los Angeles–Owens Valley Aqueduct. (Photo courtesy of the Los Angeles Chamber of Commerce)

fever, dysentery, and others. These streams might eventually aerate themselves, thus purifying their waters, were they permitted to flow long distances without continually receiving additional waste from sister cities. The possibility that a water polluted with sewage might be fully purified by flowing for "a dozen miles or so" becomes too remote for serious consideration. No modern river city dares use water without first chlorinating it, thereby destroying disease bacteria.

Strange as it may seem, cities on the Great Lakes face serious problems. Chicago and Cleveland, to mention but two, have been forced to erect their intakes (cribs) two to eight miles out as a means of avoiding the contaminated waters near shore.

A recent study conducted by the World Health Organization[6] provided a survey and analysis of urban water supplies in seventy-five developing countries. The report revealed that 70 percent of the urban population in the seventy-five countries—more than 200 million people—have inadequate piped water service, unsafe water, or both. In addition, about 450 million urban inhabitants will need new, extended, or improved pipe water supplies by 1977.

For people who live in well-developed parts of the world the obtaining of water from piped house connections is taken for granted. In many parts of the world, however, water is obtained from public outdoor outlets and not from outlets such as faucets and taps in household interiors. For example, in 1962 of the total urban population in Africa supplied by water 34 percent had house connections and 30 percent had public outlets; the remainder were not served by either. In Asia, the percentages were 18 and 25 respectively. Certainly the decision makers regarding water supplies on these continents face sobering, even staggering, moments when assessments are being made for future needs of not just water but ways of sanitary delivery.

In parts of China and Japan where human waste is used for fertilizing the fields and where the population is extremely dense, raw water for drinking is dangerous because of the deadly disease germs it contains. Hence long ago the people began to boil their drinking water, a practice which destroys active disease germs. Boiled water, however, is not palatable. Centuries ago, no one definitely knows when or by whom, leaves of the tea shrub were placed in the boiling water, which added a pleasant flavor. That started the practice of tea drinking which is widespread throughout the Far East and means much to the health of the people.

FREEDOM FROM CHEMICAL IMPURITIES

Water in many parts of the world is impregnated with lime, gypsum, and other harmful chemicals. The natural waters of all limestone areas are hard and ought to be softened to render them really suitable for domestic and industrial uses. Often such waters must be softened before certain types of industries can use them. Distilled water is necessary in the manufacture of some chemicals and drugs and of storage batteries. And the nature and amount of impurities are of great significance in the pulp and paper, textile, soap, food canning, and tanning industries.

[6] Bernd H. Dieterich and John M. Henderson, *Urban Water Supply Conditions and Needs in Seventy-five Developing Countries,* Public Health Papers No. 23 (Geneva, World Health Organization, 1963).

Downstream cities frequently suffer by reason of "trade waste," a name given to refuse from certain types of industries. Organic matter discharged into streams in large quantities frequently proves objectionable because it furnishes food for the rapid multiplication of disease bacteria, if these are present. The discharge of undiluted mineral waste also creates a serious problem for downstream cities, because it hinders the natural purification of the stream and adds substances that oxidize very slowly. Such waste kills fish; it also makes water foul smelling, ill tasting, and dangerous for livestock and human beings. If an urban center's domestic water supply is so threatened, prompt measures should be taken to prevent such pollution; a city's demand for drinking water should have precedence over all other requirements. Thus recently the city of Prince Albert in Saskatchewan discovered that a chemical was polluting the North Saskatchewan River on which it is located. Careful investigation disclosed that the substance was waste from a factory in Edmonton, Alberta, nearly 400 miles upstream. The offending plant was ordered to divert the waste to an outlet other than the river.

INDUSTRIAL WATER USE

Few people, even in highly industrialized communities, have the remotest idea regarding the huge requirements of water for manufacturing, shown in the following table.

WATER INTAKE IN MANUFACTURING FOR 1964[7]

Industry	Gallons (billions)
Primary metal industries	4,577
Chemicals and allied products	3,897
Paper and allied products	2,072
Petroleum and coal products	1,397
Food and kindred products	760
Other industries	1,352
United States total	14,055

Future predictions, while not entirely reliable, do point to a considerably greater industrial water usage. Yet in terms of potential supplies and

[7] "Water Use in Manufacturing: 1964," *1963 Census of Manufactures* (Washington, D.C., Bureau of Census, 1964).

Figure 26–5 Jawbone Canyon inverted siphon, a part of the Los Angeles Aqueduct. This section is one of several steel pipelines which cross deep canyons traversed by the aqueduct. This pipe is 7½ feet in diameter and is made of steel plate 1⅛ inches thick. There are six types of construction along the course: (1) open unlined canal, (2) open concrete lined canal, (3) covered concrete conduit, (4) concrete lined tunnel, (5) reinforced concrete pressure pipe under low heads, and (6) riveted steel pipe. Note the dry aspect of the country and the type of vegetation. This is a land where the sun shines with great intensity and where rain may not fall for months at a time. Hence, the densely populated Los Angeles area with its great demand for water has constructed this aqueduct 338 miles long in order to draw a part of its supply from the heavy snowfall of the high Sierra Nevada. (Photo courtesy of the Los Angeles Department of Water and Power)

the growing number of industrial recirculation systems, the estimates are not unduly alarming. Besides, projected needs do not take account of possible revision in the patterns of production or of the detailed differences in local or regional conditions.

Even today, access to good supplies of water has not been an overriding concern in the location of industrial activity.

It may be argued from the evidence now available that physical supply of water has not in fact been a major factor in the location of industry in the United States and several other industrialized countries during recent years: that water has been plentiful in many areas, and where it is not readily available in suitable amount and quality, industry has made the necessary investment in supply, treatment, and recirculation facilities to correct deficiencies. There is now strong ground on which to challenge the assertion that water's role in industrial location will become more important.[8]

About 66 percent of the total water used in American industry is for cooling purposes; for the most part this can be returned to its source without appreciable changes in quality except for a rise in temperature.

Cooling water is generally confined in pipes where it does not come in contact with the process or suffer deterioration in quality. Where water is plentiful, inexpensive, and of suitable quality, a once-through system might be installed. The water enters the plant . . ., performs its duty once, and is discharged to a receiving body of water. Sometimes the discharged water is of higher quality than when it entered the plant.

In many instances, water is scarce, expensive, or of poor quality. An engineering feasibility study may point to re-use as more desirable than a once-through system. Then the closed internal circuit . . . is built. The heart of the system is a cooling device: a tower or the less efficient pond. Cooled water is pumped from the tower or pond to the equipment, where it extracts heat from other substances. The heated water returns to the cooling tower or pond, is cooled by evaporation of a small portion and is pumped out to start the next round trip.[9]

As an example of industrial consumption of water, the American iron and steel industry is used because of its great need for water. When operating at full capacity, it utilizes in an average day enough water to supply a city several times the size of New York City. In 1964 the steel industry used 4,051 billion gallons of water. (From 80 to 90 percent of this is surface water.) Forty-five percent of this water is used to make steam, to cool furnace doors and rolls, operate hydraulic machinery, and wash away scale which forms when hot steel is rolled. Twenty-nine percent is used to cool blast furnaces and quench white-hot coke as it comes from the by-product ovens, and to perform miscellaneous duties.

Each district, of course, adjusts to its particular water situation in its own way. Plants on the Great Lakes (Fig. 26–6), where the supply of good water is unlimited, use larger quantities than those plants at Youngstown or Fontana. Youngstown straddles the Mahoning River, which is called "America's dirtiest and hottest river." Youngstown's mills long suffered from a water supply that in summer was both inadequate and hot (as much as 130° F). This is due to the water being used and reused over and over again —possibly as many as twenty times. This handicap was partially overcome by constructing Lake Milton, with a capacity of nine and a half billion gallons. Recently Army engineers found that the temperature of the water at the surface of Lake Milton was 65.5° F. (and so was the water flowing from the dam's outlets), whereas that at the floor of the lake at the same level as the outlet was four or five degrees cooler. Since water even a few degrees cooler saves the mills much money, a way was found for diverting the cooler water into the Mahoning River. In summer also when the temperature of water in an open stream may reach 100° F., algae multiply rapidly. These tiny organisms, adhering to the pipe walls, clog the system in a short time. The steel companies accordingly use chlorine and other chemicals to destroy the algae, thereby insuring more economical furnace operation.

[8] Gilbert F. White, "Industrial Water Use: A Review," *Geographical Review*, XXXIX, 1960, pp. 421–422.
[9] National Association of Manufacturers and the Chamber of Commerce of the United States, *Water in Industry* (January, 1965), p. 12.

Figure 26–6 Bethlehem Steel Corporation's plant in Lackawanna, N.Y. Its situation on the shores of Lake Erie is ideal for meeting its huge industrial water requirements. (Photo courtesy of Bethlehem Steel)

The Fontana plant, situated in a region of small total rainfall and desertic summers, is the most effective reuser of water in the entire industry. It is said to be the only fully integrated steel plant in the United States not located on or near a river, lake, or bay. Accordingly, it purchases part of its requirements from a local water company which it supplements from wells on its own property. Both of these together, however, are of limited capacity. However, an ingenious water-recovery system involving the successive treatment of wastes and of passage of water through cooling towers where by trickling down it releases its heat to the atmosphere, permits the manufacture of steel with only 1,400 gallons of water per ton compared with 20,000 to 25,000 gallons for the industry as a whole.

It seems certain that as industrial water requirements soar, drastic measures for conserving it will have to be taken, not only in the arid, semiarid, and subhumid areas, but also in the humid ones. Much water is wasted because of carelessness. In fact, Americans are considered to be the most wasteful people in the world in their use of water. The American Iron and Steel Institute, surveying 271 member companies, found that 31 plants were using 97 percent of the total intake. Each of these required over 10 million gallons of water a day. The survey also indicated that the reuse of water accounted for fully 60 percent of the withdrawal for all the companies combined.

The cost of industrial water is small indeed. It is believed that the average is between four and five cents per one thousand gallons in the United States. But there are areas where the cost is as much as ten dollars for the same amount. Variations occur by reason of location and type of industry.

Another way of viewing the water needs and uses is to select certain manufactured or processed items and find the number of gallons per unit. For example, to produce one ton of pulp and paper, 57,000 gallons of water are needed; for one net ton of steel (blast furnace smelting), 24,798 gallons of water are needed; for distilling one proof gallon of whiskey, about 150 gallons of water are required. It is significant to note that even the creation of one automobile requires 10,000 gallons of water, and for 1,000 pounds of "finished" meat, 2,750 gallons of water are used. Add to these the needed water for refining petroleum, tanning leather, making detergents, soaps, and a host of other finished products and the figures are quite overwhelming as indicators of modern societies' water demands.

DISPOSAL OF SEWAGE AND INDUSTRIAL WASTE

Since most cities and innumerable factories are situated on rivers, lakes, and bays, they obviously drain their sewage and industrial waste materials into these bodies. They could not exist if such bodies were not available to carry away their waste water. As long as cities were relatively few in number and small in size, with agriculture heavily outweighing manufacturing in importance, the rivers and lakes could handle the waste. In short, when one or two small industries dumped their waste into a stream there were no appreciable ill effects. But when one hundred large industries begin to do so, a river becomes a menace to public health and the very foundations of the economic and social structure and a liability to all those occupying its basin. In a study made several years ago in the United States, it was found that there were in excess of 22,000 sources of waste pollution, divided almost equally between 11,800 municipal small systems and 10,400 independent industrial waste outlets. It is significant that today there is not a single major waterway in the nation that is pollution free.

POLLUTANTS: SEWAGE

When surface waters could no longer safely receive all the untreated domestic sewage dumped into them, artificial processes of treatment began to be adopted. In the United States in 1954 the sewage of approximately 95 million urban dwellers was collected and that of about 60 million was processed to some degree of purification. The filthiest American river from municipal pollution has been the Ohio, into which some 1,100 cities and towns drain their sewage and waste. However, in 1948, eight states joined together to grapple with this common problem. Installation of municipal sewage treatment facilities has greatly improved the situation and now well over 25 percent of the sewage drained into the basin is adequately treated. Pittsburgh has built at a cost of about 100 million dollars a huge sewage plant that cares not only for its own needs but for those of sixty county communities and is capable of handling 150 million gallons of sewage daily.

Everywhere modern plants are being in-

stalled, but still more municipal plants are needed. The cost runs into billions of dollars, but the task is so essential that nothing must stand in its way.

POLLUTANTS: INDUSTRIAL WASTE

The wastes of factories (including acids, oils, chemicals, and animal and vegetable material) in a country growing industrially can, if untreated, contaminate surface waters. Moreover, much of such waste is poisonous. This problem did not become nation-wide until about 1930. It was believed the best way to get results would be through the enactment of laws. However, these laws contained many unwise provisions. Now we know that the overall public interest is best served by cooperation between representatives of industry and technical staffs of regulatory bodies.

Hundreds of millions of dollars have been spent and are still being spent to learn how much waste can be diverted to a stream and on methods of making solids and sludge harmless. Nearly every large company employs at least one waste specialist. Pulp and paper makers, who have been among the worst offenders in this respect, have been making an effort to avoid pollution of waterways and in 1964 maintained waste treatment facilities valued at $150 million. Some of their waste products now have economic value and are being used as textile dyes, road surfacing materials, food flavoring, and fuel. One large rayon plant in Virginia's Shenandoah Valley was so successful in treating its metallic poisons that seventy miles of river formerly polluted again contain fish. Many rivers whose fish had been disappearing from streams for decades are again capable of being fished as a result of control of industrial waste and sewage disposal problems.

To restore rivers, lakes, and bays after a century's orgy of pollution is a tremendous and expensive task. However, some industries have installed systems that are more elaborate than the sewage disposal plants of many large cities. The steel industry spends about $10 million annually to clean the streams it uses.

WASTE WATER RECLAMATION

So scarce is water becoming that the reclamation of waste is now well developed. Obviously this is most important in arid and semiarid regions. Thus the state of California applies to its soils for agricultural purposes or for underground water recharge some 350,000 acre-feet per year of sewage plant effluents from municipalities and institutions.

An example of waste reclamation in humid United States is found in the huge Bethlehem Steel Corporation plant at Sparrows Point. Since the Patapsco River on which the plant is located is tidal and hence is brackish (satisfactory only for cooling purposes), a large supply of fresh water is needed for sprays. The wells that once sufficed to meet these needs do so no longer. Hence, since 1942 the plant has been using treated effluents of the entire city of Baltimore (over 1,700,000 inhabitants). This waste, which is first passed through the municipal sewage treatment plant of Baltimore and then further processed by the company, amounts to approximately 150 million gallons per day and is reputed to be the world record for industrial use of reclaimed waste.

SUPPLY OF SURFACE WATER IN A DRY REGION: WESTERN UNITED STATES

While the acquisition of an adequate supply of pure water is no mean task in a humid region, it is obviously intensified in dry ones. Thus water problems loom large in most parts of the United States west of the "Dead Line"—the 100th meridian, which coincides with the twenty-inch isohyet. This region comprises about 34 percent of the area of the country. The presence or absence of water determines the extent of agriculture and manufacturing and the distribution of population. In short, water is the determinant of the economic and social life there. The region of greatest deficiency includes much of California, Arizona, New Mexico, Colorado, western Utah, Nevada, and part of Texas. Here lack of water is perennial, not temporary. It is interesting to note that most of the water—at least 85 percent—comes from outside the area, from the humid mountains and foothills where the headwaters of most major streams have their sources.

Into the West a great migration has been going on for more than one hundred years. The Pacific Coast, particularly California, is the fastest-growing part of the nation. With increasing population go increasing agriculture and manufacturing. These enterprises require more water: it is their lifeblood!

It is easy to understand why southern California, which has a disproportionate share of the agriculture, industry, and cities, and two-thirds of the population, but receives a small rainfall (two-thirds of the available water is in the northern half of the state), wages an unceasing struggle for more water. No wonder Los Angeles gives serious thought to distilling ocean water and building an 1,100 mile aqueduct to tap the Columbia River. It is easy to understand also why industrial reuse of water is so common in this area as well as in the entire West.

We have seen the importance of irrigation to the West. Thus if the American people should decide that in the future they want to make more use of the drier, sunny, climatic regions for manufacturing and residence, then what is to be done about the scanty water resources? A distinguished Stanford University group, in responding to the President's Water Resources Policy Commission, recommended that urban and industrial use should get priority and that agricultural production in excess of its present output must increasingly rely on the East where there is a great surplus of precipitation. If irrigation to expand western farm production should be given priority, the region's population could not increase as it otherwise might.

There is much loss of water even in western United States. It is estimated that two-thirds of the ten thousand larger reservoirs in the United States (the largest are in the West) have an estimated useful life of less than one hundred years due to silting. Elephant Butte Dam on the Rio Grande in one-third of a century has, as a result of silting, lost 20 percent of its capacity. More than 100,000 acre-feet of silt pass into Lake Mead, behind Hoover Dam, each year.

INLAND WATERWAYS FOR NAVIGATION

RIVERS

Except in deserts and on ice caps, streams are among the most widespread natural features of

Figure 26–7 A view of the busy Rhine River as it flows by the famous Lorelei hills. (Photo courtesy of the German National Tourist Office)

the land. Hence it might be inferred that these waterways would be great inland arteries of transportation; with few exceptions, however, such is not the case. Most rivers are characterized by certain natural hindrances to navigation—insufficient depth or length, swift current, irregular flow, crooked course, wrong direction, ice, shifting sand bars, or sparsely settled, unproductive tributary area. Notwithstanding, throughout the civilized world, the largest cities and the densest populations, and the greatest development of industry and commerce, are to be found on streams and lakes.

Mature rivers have fewer obstacles to navigation than young or old ones. Not a single river on earth is free from all the impediments just enumerated. When a stream gets a high rating for navigability, it is only after man has spent much labor and money on its improvement—for example, the Rhine (Fig. 26–7).

Some of the less advanced countries such as Brazil, China, Colombia, and the Soviet Union, rich in great rivers but poor in railway facilities, make much use of their waterways for transportation. Towns situated on Siberian rivers emerge

from hibernation only during the few months of summer when the streams are free from ice. The Amazon Basin, despite its continental proportion, is almost lacking in railway lines. The use of rivers is not restricted to undeveloped countries,

Figure 26–8 A diesel towboat of the Island Creek Fuel and Transportation Company, Huntington, West Virginia, pushes a sixteen-barge load of coal on the Ohio River. (Photo courtesy of the National Coal Association)

however; the most advanced nations—Belgium, France, Germany, Great Britain, the Netherlands, and the United States—also utilize them (Fig. 26–8).

In order to comprehend adequately the principles involved in the utilization of rivers for transportation, the hindrances to navigation are reviewed.

INADEQUATE LENGTH

Only occasionally is a river navigable for a great distance by larger ships. The Amazon is exceptional in this respect, for small ocean-going vessels can ascend 2,300 miles to Iquitos in Peru. The Mississippi, on the other hand, even after the expenditure of many millions of dollars, is navigable for ocean vessels only to New Orleans; from there to the Twin Cities, large barges are used.

UNRULY CURRENT

Rivers with swift currents facilitate down-river traffic but retard that going upstream. On the upper reaches of the Yangtze, craft constructed especially for going against the current occasionally find it impossible to make headway and do well to hold their own against it. In contrast, the Amazon has a very low gradient, which is a distinct aid to navigation. Several hundred miles from the Atlantic, the river is only thirty-five feet above sea level.

FREEDOM FROM SEASONAL CHANGE

No navigable river on earth has a very enviable record in this respect. If it is free from ice, it suffers from floods or low water. Even the Amazon has floods which inundate the country over thousand of square miles, forcing those who gather forest products to suspend operations during the rainiest months (November to May).

The Rhine is among the most fortunate: melting snow and ice give its upper course maximum flow in summer, while winter rains make winter the high-water season for the middle and lower course. Hence, with two seasons of maximum supply, the flow in all except the upper course is quite steady.

Most poleward flowing streams in the Northern Hemisphere suffer from floods caused by ice; the Mackenzie, Lena, Ob, Yenesei, and others, are ice-bound for more than half the year; in spring, their upper courses thaw, while their lower reaches are still frozen. The Yenesei rises thirty or thirty-five feet and inundates an area about thirty miles wide at its mouth. The St. Lawrence is frozen five months of the year; that this seriously affects Canadian commerce is indicated by the fact that Atlantic ports of the United States export more Canadian wheat than does Montreal. Seven-tenths of the exports from American ports move during Montreal's closed season. On the other hand, the St. Lawrence is quite unusual in its steadiness of flow. Records kept since 1860 indicate that the maximum flow is only 2.2 times the minimum flow, compared with 33.1 at Bonneville on the Columbia and 115.1 at Florence, Alabama, on the Tennessee.

MEANDERING COURSES

Few rivers are straight; even those considered so are rather crooked and increase greatly the distance between points over the airline route. The great bends in the lower Mississippi more than double the distance between St. Louis and the Gulf of Mexico (Fig. 21–4). Moreover, they increase the danger from floods. After the devastating flood of 1927 in the lower Mississippi, the federal government realized that unified action was imperative in dealing with this problem (the river's banks lie in six states) and began a long-time program of channel straightening by dredging cutoffs. These have reduced distance and simultaneously, by increasing the velocity of the river, have reduced flood hazards.

Bends may hinder navigation in another way, especially where the river is small but much used (Fig. 26–9). The Cuyahoga at Cleveland has long presented difficulties to shipping, its glaring defect being its tortuous course. This factor was of little importance until 1900 because small vessels predominated. Now, however, large lake carriers are employed for the most part, since they are far more economical to operate. The concentration of iron and steel mills along the lower five and a half miles of the course made this factor especially serious. In 1939, the city "streamlined" the lower river, cutting back nine of the worst bends, widening the channel at critical

Figure 26–9 The Cuyahoga River winding through Cleveland. The Cuyahoga is a great physical obstacle confronting the city of Cleveland. It has presented difficulties to navigation almost since the founding of the city, and these difficulties have become intensified as lake vessels have increased in size. The river is so narrow and so tortuous (its name of Indian origin means *crooked*), the bends are so abrupt, and bridges so numerous and many so low that navigation has become extremely slow and difficult. Vessel owners and captains have testified that they would rather take a cargo to any other port on the lakes than to Cleveland, providing the cargo is bound up the river. Only in recent years, as a result of the cutting back of the sharpest bends, have the largest lake carriers been able to ascend the Cuyahoga. (Photo from Ewing Galloway)

points, and removing and rebuilding old narrow bridges to permit the largest freighters on the Great Lakes to navigate the river safely and with reasonable speed.[10]

WRONG DIRECTION

When rivers flow in the wrong direction, as do those of the northern Soviet Union and Canada, their commercial value is greatly reduced. They flow away from the populous and productive regions and into a great sea of ice water, the navigation of which is costly and hazardous. Ships carrying machinery, metal goods, and other items to the Yenesei River settlements, for example, must be accompanied by ice-breakers.

UNPRODUCTIVE AND SPARSELY POPULATED TRIBUTARY AREA

A waterway may rank high in several of the conditions enumerated above, but if it flows through a region of few products and few people, it will

be little used. The Amazon, mightiest of all rivers, flowing across South America near its widest point, is of only slight importance because it traverses a great wilderness (Fig. 26–10). The Yangtze-Kiang, on the other hand, flows through a region estimated to contain more people than the entire Western Hemisphere; nowhere else does a river serve so many people.

THE GREAT LAKES

The Great Lakes give the United States and Canada the finest system of inland waterways in the world. From the standpoint of traffic, they have no equal, excelling because they

1. Are large and deep
2. Penetrate the interior of the continent for some 1,700 miles
3. Extend generally east-west—the direction in which traffic naturally flows
4. Do not experience the severe storms and tides of oceans and seas
5. Lie in the midst of great storehouses of bulky products which are fabricated somewhere on the lacustrine periphery
6. Have given birth to and nurture numerous great cities

The lakes suffer from several handicaps however. They have (1) a paucity of first-class natural harbors; nearly all lie at the mouths of small rivers and must be protected by breakwaters, (2) rapids and falls which obstruct continuous transportation, though these have been overcome by canals and locks, and (3) their transportation interrupted by winter ice on the connecting rivers and straits (Fig. 26–11).

TRAFFIC ESSENTIALLY IN BULKY PRODUCTS

Great Lakes traffic consists almost entirely of bulky products—iron ore, coal, grain, and limestone. All, except wheat, have relatively low value in proportion to weight. In order to move them from place to place, man has devised a special

[10] C. Langdon White, "After 100 Years of Vacillation, Cleveland Solves Its River Problem," *Annals of the Association of American Geographers*, Vol. XXX (September, 1940), p. 207.

type of vessel which is a triumph of human design. Lake carriers have blunt ends, straight sides, great length, and flat bottoms and are

"glorified canal boats"; they have their wheelhouse forward and their engine rooms, stacks, and quarters aft; midship the deck is lined with

Figure 26–10 Although the Amazon is in many respects the greatest of all rivers, it is little used because it flows through a region with few people. Sparse population is the region's outstanding problem. Most of the people who do live in the Basin eke out a precarious livelihood by fishing, hunting, gathering forest products, and subsistence farming. This photograph shows the Rio Negro, one of the major northern tributaries of the Amazon, Brazil. (Photo courtesy of the American Geographical Society)

Figure 26–11 A Coast Guard icebreaker escorting a lake carrier through heavy ice near the Soo Locks, which connect Lakes Superior and Huron. (Photo courtesy of the U.S. Coast Guard)

hatches. These craft are built for speed and capacity.

Lake freighters move bulky commodities at a low cost, the average for 10 mile-tons being one cent. Well equipped ports, typically handling over 1 million tons of freight a year, have facilities for loading ships in less than five hours. Some carriers, conversions from conventional bulk freighters, are built to unload themselves. This group handles 90 percent of all the lake-borne limestone. From Lake Erie ports, these vessels often return with coal which they can deliver to ports lacking unloading facilities.

Lake carriers average in excess of thirty round trips per season,[11] aggregating some 40,000 to 45,000 miles. The rate for coal is lower than for ore, since westbound traffic is always much lighter than that eastbound. Loading and unloading are facilitated by labor-saving devices which enable Great Lakes traffic to be

the cheapest in the world when calculated on a ton-mile basis.

THE GREAT LAKES— ST. LAWRENCE SEAWAY

For more than a third of a century this project was widely discussed in both the United States and Canada. It now links the Great Lakes and the St. Lawrence River with the Atlantic and permits the harnessing of an enormous amount of hydroelectric power. At the present time the seaway permits small ocean-going vessels to penetrate the continent 2,350 miles to Duluth over a continuous twenty-seven-foot navigational passage. Today it is not expected that any large number of such ships will journey in and out

[11] The season of navigation extends from about May first to about the middle of December.

Figure 26–12 An excellent example of a chamber lock is the Eisenhower Lock in the International Rapids section of the St. Lawrence Seaway. Locks of this type are used to lift and lower ships. (Photo courtesy of the Power Authority of the State of New York)

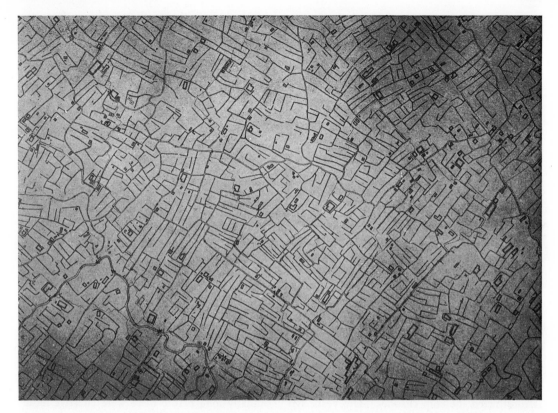

Figure 26–13 Part of a net of closely spaced canals southeast of Shanghai. In few other areas of the world is there a comparable development of canals. The average distance between waterways is only 380 feet. The area shown is approximately three and a half miles long by two miles wide. (Courtesy of George B. Cressey)

of the heart of the continent, for lake vessels can carry larger cargoes, can operate with less draught, and can function more economically.

In 1954 contracts were awarded for specific segments of the seaway. Each country was responsible for certain phases of the work. The cost ranged from $800 million to $1 billion. The project involved canalization and deepening, with the major portion of the work falling in five sections—most of it in the International Rapids.

The building of the Seaway has meant a continuation of the economic development that has thus far distinguished the Great Lakes region of both countries, and promises to be an investment in the future progress of both as well as in the ability of two good neighbors to work together in harmony.

CANALS

Canals are man-made waterways through barriers in natural routes of travel. They have existed since antiquity—the early Egyptians, Babylonians, and Chinese all used them. Early canals were adjusted solely to level terrain; elevated land was shunned until the invention of the chamber lock—a device for lifting or lowering ships (Fig. 26–12). Throughout the world, canals have been dug to facilitate transportation in the following ways:

1. To prevent delta dwellers from being marooned from the outside world during the rainy season when the land becomes a sea of mud. The canal boat means to the Dutch and Chinese gardener what the horse means to the *estanciero* of the Argentine Pampa and the automobile to the Corn Belt farmer: it is his indispensable ally (Fig. 26–13).

2. To shorten long voyages by connecting oceans, seas, gulfs, or large bays. Comparing the journey from New York to San Francisco via Cape Horn and via the Panama Canal, a saving is noted in the canal route of 60 percent or 6,059 miles.

	Nautical Miles	*Statute Miles*
New York to San Francisco via Panama Canal	5,262	6,059
New York to San Francisco via Magellan	13,135	15,126
New York to San Francisco via Cape Horn	13,328	15,348

3. To avoid falls and rapids which interfere with easy and safe navigation. The Welland Canal built around Niagara Falls and the canal constructed around the "Falls of the Ohio" at Louisville exemplify this principle.

4. To cut off headlands. The Kiel Canal enables vessels to go from the North Sea to the Baltic Sea or vice versa without having to go around Denmark.

5. To make inland cities seaports. Manchester's cotton industry was retarded as long as the raw cotton had to be handled via Liverpool. The Manchester Ship Canal greatly stimulated the city's trade by making it a seaport. Houston, Texas, did not become an outstanding city until it constructed the ship channel. Sixty years ago it was about the same size as Galveston; now it is sixteen times larger and the chief city of the state. Not only is it a great ocean port, but its fifty-mile-long channel is lined with manufacturing plants.

6. To serve as links in an otherwise continuous transport chain. The Soo Canals, connecting lakes Superior and Huron, handle about two-thirds of all the trade of the Great Lakes and more tonnage than through the Suez and Panama canals and the Rhine River combined.

7. To enable a nation to handle its own traffic within its own borders, when its rivers have their debouchment in a foreign land. Germany, feeling keenly Holland's control of the Rhine mouth, built the Dortmund-Ems Canal to connect the densely populated, coal-producing, highly industrialized Ruhr with the North Sea.

8. To facilitate inland intercourse between two parts of a country otherwise separated. The Grand Canal, begun in 540 B.C., not only links Hangchow in Middle China with Tientsin in north China, but connects all the rivers going to the sea from the interior. It was built, presumably, to enable the north to get rice from the south in time of famine and to bring tribute rice to the court at Peking.

IRRIGATION

Irrigation is the artificial application of water to crops, without which they would perish. Many people think that irrigation is practiced only in arid or semiarid regions but this is not so, for in southeastern Asia, the great rice bowl of the world, flooding—a kind of irrigation—has been practiced by the people from time immemorial and still is.

It is in the dry regions of the world, however, that water is of ever-present interest, for there it means life. Only through his ingenuity in bringing water to the desert has man been able to create an existence there. Deserts the world over are dotted with man-made oases. The art of irrigating the soil must be almost instinctive in man, for throughout the far corners of the earth, whether in Egypt, Iraq, Iran, India, China, Peru, Mexico, or southwestern United States, he reacted similarly long before there were effective means of communication. Irrigation sprang up among peoples who knew nothing of its development elsewhere.

Though irrigation has been practiced since antiquity, only a fraction of the world's desert wastes has been, or ever can be, reclaimed.[12] Probably not more than 10 percent of such regions can become productive, a consequence of inadequate water supply, rugged topography, poor soils, drainage problems, and dearth of sites for storage reservoirs.

In deserts, control of the water supply implies control of the land.

Many of the world's outstanding irrigation projects depend upon surface streams which have their origin in mountains where there is heavy snowfall during the winter. If the fall is adequate, the supply of irrigation water during the summer will be sufficient; if it is light, a scarcity

[12] A detailed map of the world's irrigated lands accompanies Richard Highsmith's article, "Irrigated Lands of the World," *Geographical Review,* LV (July, 1965), pp. 382–389.

is felt during the critical season. The probable amount of water for irrigation is of primary importance, for upon it depends what crops shall be grown. In parts of arid America, farmers anxiously watch the amount of snowfall in the mountains and select their crops according to the quantity and time of occurrence. If it begins early, they feel confident of adequate water for late crops; but if it begins late (in the spring), they fear a shortage for summer and autumn and plant accordingly.

When the snows fall on slopes garbed with forests and closed to the grazing of sheep, melting occurs more slowly, less water is wasted in spring floods, and more is available for agriculture. A crying need throughout western United States is for more storage reservoirs. Some, of course, have been constructed, but mostly by the Reclamation Service, for example, behind Hoover Dam and Grand Coulee Dam.

The oasis of Egypt lies along the Nile River, which rises in equatorial lakes in a region of heavy and well-distributed rainfall. The river is perennial, flowing through the desert for almost 3,500 miles. It is Egypt's lifeblood, its banks and delta sustaining 95 percent of the nation's more than 28 million inhabitants. Here is one of the densest populations in the world—almost 2,000 persons to the square mile of inhabited area. The average farmer (*fellah*) has only two or three acres of land to support his family and to pay rent and taxes. Numerous dams have been built across the Nile since 1861—dams that have increased the cultivable area and the harvests. Newest and most important of these is the new High Aswan Dam, 430 miles south of Cairo, and one of the world's most impressive works of man. Ultimately it will bring to the thirsty desert enough water to irrigate an additional one and a half to two million acres. Nevertheless, the stern fact is that *97 percent of the country is unirrigated desert!* The arable area was expanded by only 12 percent during the past half century, while the population was doubling. Food crops and cotton occupy most of the irrigated land. The rapid increase in population—about 800,000 per year—combined with the already high density per square mile of arable land, gives Egypt a population problem that appears to be in-

soluble. The per capita intake of calories has been declining in recent years. Thus Egypt portrays better than almost any country in the world the true meaning of water.

SOCIAL SIGNIFICANCE OF IRRIGATION

Because of the high value of water, land, and improvements, cultivation must be intensive. Dwarf farms ultimately characterize nearly all irrigated landscapes, irrespective of the continent on which they are found.

Social conditions are unique: individualism is suppressed, cooperation prevalent. Community thought and community action permeate everything from building dams and canals to regulating the water supply. This cooperation was a mighty factor in fostering civilization which was cradled in regions of irrigation—Egypt, Iraq, Iran, and elsewhere.

In the United States annual ground water and surface water requirements for irrigation have been estimated for the year 2000, based upon those for the year 1957. Such estimation, of course, has to take into consideration the efficiency of use now and the assumed greater efficiency in the year 2000. Of interest to many people, however, will be the fact that so-called "well-watered" regions use much water for irrigation. It is not only the arid regions which have irrigation as a common practice. Selected water resource regions illustrate the above points.

ESTIMATED ANNUAL WATER REQUIREMENTS FOR IRRIGATION 1957 AND 2000 (*Thousand Acre Feet*)

Water Resource Regions (*Selected*)	1957	2000
New England	54	297
Delaware-Hudson	220	583
Southeast	1,743	12,196
Lower Mississippi	1,592	4,409
Western Gulf	11,840	15,689
Great Basin	9,444	9,742
Pacific Northwest	16,182	21,053
South Pacific	5,044	4,635

Shifts in population, better transportation, increased efficiency in use, transmission, and application of water all enter in these prognostications.

WATER POWER

Centuries before man appreciated the value of coal or conceived the idea of the steam engine, he was using hydraulic power to supplement the feeble energy of his own body. Then water power was a geographic control, because an industry, in order to use it, had to move to the power site. Power was the all-important factor! This was a distinct handicap, for frequently the falls lay in an isolated, inaccessible area, far from raw material sources and from marts for the finished articles. Transportation facilities were invariably inadequate.[13]

Water was used to turn a great wheel, the supply emanating from a river tapped some distance upstream in order to bring it above the wheel. The momentum of the water falling on the wooden cups turned the wheel, thereby generating power. Often a dam was built above the mill to equalize the flow throughout the year. Fortunately, small streams could be utilized efficiently; indeed, they could be used more advantageously than large ones.

With the invention of the steam engine, coal displaced water power and for the most part the moss-covered wheel became a romantic memory. Later, the invention of hydroelectric power by turbine, generator, and transmission line enabled power from falling water to return, but this time the users, if not too distant, could break away from the shackles of isolation and locate with especial regard to raw materials, markets, and transportation.

TECHNIQUE OF WATER-POWER DEVELOPMENT

In order to harness a river's energy, a dam is usually built at a narrow place. A lake is then formed behind the dam and this ponded water is drawn into the plant as required by means of tunnels or pipes. It turns great turbines which operate generators, changing the energy of running water into the energy of electricity (Fig. 26–14).

WATER POWER AND NATURAL ENVIRONMENT

From the standpoint of the natural environment, water power depends upon steep gradient, huge volume of water, and regularity of flow. Fortunately, these conditions occur widely over the earth, especially in mountains and hill country. Potential sources lie in such sharply contrasted environments as rainy equatorial Africa, Norway, northwestern Arizona, and New England.

If all other conditions be favorable, an irregular rainfall may be overcome by man through the construction of dams such as at Hoover Dam.

Many rivers have one or more of the requirements for power development, but few possess all. The ideal is a river that has its source in a lake or a field of melting snow and its course through a forested region. Generally speaking, areas of former glaciation offer superior conditions for development, since they are characterized by numerous falls, lakes, swamps, and clear water. They also receive moderate to heavy rainfall, well distributed. To be sure, water power occurs in nonglaciated regions, but the flow of water is usually variable, save in the Rainy Tropics.

ECONOMIC FACTORS IN WATER-POWER DEVELOPMENT

A region may have ideal physical conditions for water power, but if it is located far from dense and progressive populations and from raw materials for industry, and if it lacks good facilities for transport, it may be ignored. Water power must be economically accessible. In few places is it transmitted more than three hundred miles through one system of lines.

Two of the world's greatest power sites, from the standpoint of potential horsepower, are Niagara Falls and the lower Congo River: the energy of the former is estimated at 6 million horsepower, and that of the latter at 114 million horsepower. So far as utilization is concerned,

---

[13] Occasionally water-power sites could not be utilized, because the valleys were so narrow and the slopes so steep as to preclude room for a factory. Electricity changed this.

Figure 26–14 The Hoover Dam and Power Plant on the Colorado River is an important source of low cost hydroelectric power for Los Angeles. (Photo courtesy of the Los Angeles Chamber of Commerce)

however, Niagara is the best site in the world; the Congo, until recently, was one of the less favored.

Niagara Falls

Because it lies in one of the most populous and highly industrialized portions of North America, because it has a great fall, and because it lies on a river unrivaled in the regularity of its flow, Niagara has no economic equal among waterfalls. It has the greatest concentration of generating equipment in the world (Fig. 26–15). With the attraction of a magnet, it has drawn about itself a large coterie of industries—fabricators of chemicals, alloys, abrasives, aluminum, and scores of other electrochemical and electrometallurgical products which need both abundant and cheap power. Niagara is their lifeblood. Its power also supplies the innumerable industries located on the Niagara Frontier and beyond.

The Congo

In the heart of Africa, along the lower Congo River between Kinshasa and Matadi, a series of rapids, capable of producing 114 million horsepower—more than that of the whole of North America—interrupt the gradient. Some technical snags, such as too much silt, must be overcome, but the big drawback has been the scarcity of large power users. Less than .05 percent of the potential power is being used.

Until the political chaos following independence of the Republic of the Congo, it appeared that considerable hydropower might be developed. The outlook is presently not bright.

WATER POWER VERSUS COAL

Contrary to public opinion, hydroelectric power is usually not cheap power. This misconception is doubtless the outgrowth of the widespread publicity given Niagara's cheap energy and of

Figure 26–15 The Niagara Power Project of the Power Authority of the State of New York. In the foreground is the Robert Moses Niagara Power Plant and in the background, the Lewiston Pump-Generating Plant and reservoir. The total capability of the project, 2,400,000 kilowatts, places it among the largest in the world. (Photo courtesy of the Power Authority of the State of New York)

the political notoriety so widely disseminated in connection with such projects as the Tennessee Valley Authority and Hoover Dam. The installation of a hydroelectric system is tremendously expensive—about double that of a steam plant of identical output. Moreover, hydro sites are seldom strategic industrially and, if developed, must be connected with large consumers by very costly high-tension lines. Line loss frequently amounts to 15 percent of the power-plant energy. A steam plant has the advantage not only of cheaper installation but of location near the market for its energy. The only two possible limitations are fuel and water for condensing steam. From four hundred to five hundred tons of water must be supplied for each ton of coal for condensing purposes.

Coal and water power have long been com-petitors. In the future, however, they will become partners. Since coal is exhaustible and water power is permanent, each must supplement the other as a conservation measure. Though the original purpose of the TVA was to generate cheap hydroelectric power (electricity) for the people of the region, today 75 percent of all the energy generated is from coal, not falling water.

Workers in a region burning coal enjoy fewer amenities than those in a region utilizing water power, for coal grime defaces buildings and ruins furniture and clothing, while smoke injures health. The death rate from pneumonia increases proportionately with smoke density. Pittsburgh, formerly known as the "Smoky City," had for many years one of the highest constant pneumonia death rates of any community in the world.

SUGGESTED USEFUL READINGS

ATLAS

Miller, David W., *Water Atlas of the United States: Basic Facts about the Nation's Water Resources* (Port Washington, New York, Water Information Center, 1963), 8 pp. and 40 plates.

GENERAL WORKS

Ackerman, Edward, and George O. G. Lof, *Technology in American Water Development* (Baltimore, Johns Hopkins Press, for Resources for the Future, Inc., 1959), 710 pp.

Dieterich, Bernd, and John M. Henderson, *Urban Water Supply Conditions and Needs in Seventy-five Developing Countries*, Public Health Papers No. 23 (Geneva, World Health Organization, 1963), 92 pp.

Durfor, Charles N., and Edith Becker, *Public Water Supplies of the United States, 1962*, Geological Survey Water Supply Paper 1812 (Washington, D.C., Government Printing Office, 1964).

Fair, Gordon Maskew, and John Charles Geyer, *Supply and Waste-Water Disposal* (New York, John Wiley & Sons, Inc., 1958), 615 pp.

Hirshleifer, Jack, James DeHaven, and Jerome W. Milliman, *Water Supply Economics, Technology, and Policy* (Chicago, University of Chicago Press, 1960), 378 pp.

Kuenen, Philip H., *Realms of Water: Some Aspects of Its Cycle in Nature*, trans. and rev. by Max Hollander (New York, John Wiley & Sons, Inc., 1955), 327 pp.

MacKichan, K. A., and J. C. Kammerer, *Estimated Use of Water in the United States, 1960*, Geological Survey Circular 456 (Washington, D.C., 1961).

National Academy of Sciences—National Research Council, *Waste Management and Control*, Publication 1400 (Washington, D.C., 1966), 257 pp.

United Nations, Department of Economic and Social Affairs, *Integrated River Basin Development* (New York, United Nations, 1958), 60 pp.

United Nations, Division of Water Resources Development of the United Nations Economic Commission for Asia and the Far East (ECAFE), *Flood Damage and Flood Control Activities in Asia and the Far East*, Flood Control Series No. 1 (New York, United Nations, 1951).

United Nations, Division of Water Resources Development of the United Nations Economic Commission for Asia and the Far East (ECAFE), *Methods and Problems of Flood Control in Asia and the Far East*, Flood Control Series No. 2 (New York, United Nations, 1951).

United Nations, Division of Water Resources Development of the United Nations Economic Commission for Asia and the Far East (ECAFE), *Multiple-Purpose River Basin Development*, Parts 1, 2A, 2B, 2C, and 2D, Flood Control Series Nos. 7, 8, 11, 14, and 18 (New York, United Nations, 1955, 1956, 1959, and 1961).

United Nations, Division of Water Resources Development of the United Nations Economic Commission for Asia and the Far East (ECAFE), *Proceedings of the Regional Conference on Water Resources Development in Asia and the Far East*, Flood Control Series Nos. 9, 13, and 19 and Water Resources Series No. 23 (New York, United Nations, 1956, 1959, 1962, and 1963).

U.S. Army Corps of Engineers, Department of the Army, "Future Needs for Naviga-
    tion," *Water Resources Activities in the United States*, Committee Print No. 11
    (Washington, D.C., Government Printing Office, for the Select Committee on
    National Water Resources, 1960), 28 pp.

U.S. Army Corps of Engineers, Department of the Army, "Floods and Flood Control,"
    Water Resources Activities in the United States, Committee Print No. 15 (Wash-
    ington, D.C., Government Printing Office, for the Select Committee on National
    Water Resources, 1960), 77 pp .

U.S. Bureau of the Census, Department of Commerce, "Water Use in Manufacturing,
    1964," *1963 Census of Manufactures* (Preliminary Report, 1966), 11 pp.

U.S. Department of Agriculture, *Water*, Yearbook of Agriculture, 1955 (Washington,
    D.C., Government Printing Office, 1955), 751 pp.

U.S. Department of Health, Education, and Welfare, *Statistical Summary of Municipal
    Water Facilities in the United States, January 1, 1963*, Public Health Service Pub-
    lication No. 1039 (Washington, D.C., Government Printing Office, 1965), 66 pp.

27

The Ocean and the Coast Zone

THE OCEAN

Aside from climate, the ocean is the most extensive element of man's natural environment. Its waters cover 140,000,000 of the earth's 197,-000,000 square miles of surface. Since this exceeds 70 percent of the surface of the globe, the ocean must be regarded as an environmental element of great importance. Certainly it is considerably more than a mere filler between the continents.

OCEANS AND THEIR SEAS

In common parlance, the great world ocean is usually divided into four separate oceans, the names and areas of which are as follows (Fig. 27–1).

Pacific	63,900,000 square miles
Atlantic	31,700,000 " "
Indian	28,400,000 " "
Arctic	5,400,000 " "

These four oceans are of very unlike size. Among them, the Pacific is by far the largest. It is roughly elliptical in shape and measures nearly 12,000 miles from east to west along the equator. It contains nearly half of the water of the globe and is, therefore, often referred to as the *water hemisphere*. Were all the seven continents combined into one large land mass, it could be placed within the Pacific Ocean alone, and there would still remain a rim of water 430 miles wide completely surrounding it, in addition to the other three oceans. Along the western border of the

Pacific Basin proper, there are several semi-detached seas of considerable size, as follows.

Malayan Sea	1,998,000 square miles
Tasman Sea	1,740,000 " "
Coral Sea	1,655,000 " "
South China Sea	895,000 " "
Bering Sea	876,000 " "
Okhotsk Sea	590,000 " "
East China Sea	482,000 " "
Yellow Sea	405,000 " "
Japan Sea	405,000 " "
Ross Sea	348,000 " "

The Atlantic Ocean is little more than half the size of the Pacific and is relatively narrow. It is roughly shaped like an hourglass, the bulbous portions being about 4,000 miles wide but the narrow waist measuring only 1,600 miles. The northern half of this ocean possesses six semidetached seas, as follows.

Mediterranean Sea	967,000 square miles
Caribbean Sea	775,000 " "
Hudson Bay	476,000 " "
North Sea	222,000 " "
Black Sea	178,000 " "
Baltic Sea	163,000 " "

Third in size is the Indian Ocean. It is roughly circular and is about 5,000 miles from east to west at its widest point. It differs from

443

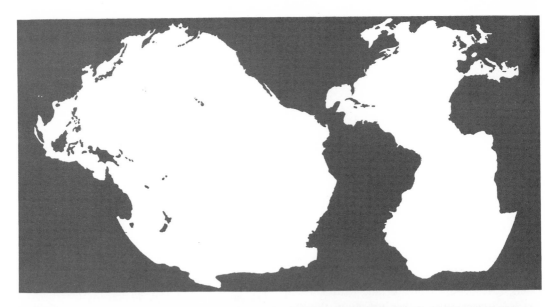

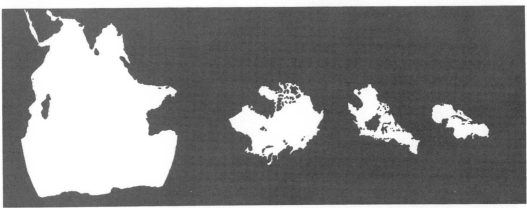

Figure 27–1   The oceans and seas arranged in order of size.

both the Pacific and Atlantic oceans in being completely landlocked at one end. It has only two semidetached seas, as follows.

Andaman Sea   285,000 square miles
Red Sea   169,000   "   "

The Arctic is the smallest of the oceans. It is a roughly oblong body of water lying be-

tween Eurasia and North America. It thus forms a sort of "polar mediterranean sea." It is less than twice the size of the Asiatic Mediterranean (Indo-Malayan Sea) and only about three times the size of the American Mediterranean (Caribbean[1] Sea). Consequently, some authorities choose to regard the Arctic as merely a large sea belong-

[1] Including the Gulf of Mexico.

ing to the Atlantic Ocean. In its narrowest portion it is about 1,500 miles wide; in its widest, about 3,000 miles.

It possesses four large semidetached seas. They are as follows.

Norwegian Sea[2]	770,000 square miles
Barents Sea	575,000 " "
Kara Sea	225,000 " "
Baffin Bay	224,000 " "

PHYSICAL CHARACTERISTICS OF THE OCEAN

THE OCEAN SURFACE

Sea level is a monotonous surface of slightly convex curvature. To the eye, it appears flat except when disturbed by waves varying in height from a few inches to perhaps sixty-five feet in extreme instances. At periodic intervals, the water in mid-ocean is lifted and lowered eight to twenty-one inches by tide-producing cosmic forces. In shallow water near shore, the rise and fall of the tide may be increased to four or five feet or more. In bays, estuaries, and other partially landlocked portions of the ocean, the tidal rise may be as great as fifty or even seventy-five feet in exceptional cases.

THE OCEAN BOTTOM

The portion of the earth's solid shell concealed by oceanic waters is surprisingly varied in its configuration. Submarine topography is known in detail throughout only a trivial fraction of the area of the world ocean, but enough information has been gained from soundings to indicate that the major relief features of the sea floor are bigger than those of the lands. On the other hand, the minor relief features are fewer and less pronounced than are the minor features of the lands. The reason for this is that the sea floor is not exposed to erosion as is the land surface. In the shallow marginal areas, there is some erosion by waves and currents; but weathering and action by stream, wind, and ice is, of course, lacking. Submarine topographic features owe their general appearance principally to the

action of the constructional forces which produced them. Even the original contours of submarine topography are continually being reduced and rounded by the deposition of sediments. These sediments are generally of two kinds: first, the *terrigenous* deposits consisting of gravels, sands, silts, muds, and coral fragments eroded by wave action from the shore or washed out from the land by rivers; and second, *pelagic* deposits far from land, consisting of clay formed from volcanic dust and oozes formed from the bodies of dead plants and animals settling from the ocean surface.

THE CONTINENTAL SHELF

Nearly everywhere around the margins of the continents, the ocean bottom slopes gently downward from the shore through a zone which varies from a few miles to a few hundred miles in width (Fig. 27–2). At the outer margin of this zone there is generally a fairly abrupt change in gradient; beyond it, the sea floor slopes downward at a rate several times as great as that displayed nearer shore. This change in gradient occurs at depths which vary from 30 or 40 fathoms on down to 300 or even 400 fathoms, and this, rather than the shoreline, marks the real edge of the continents. Between this continental edge and the shore stretches the submerged part of the continents known as the *continental shelf*. Beyond the continental edge, the bottom descends more steeply in what is known as the *continental slope* to the ocean basins. In other words, the actual ocean basins are more than filled by water, and consequently the water of the world ocean overlaps some ten million square miles of the lower and outer edges of the continents. Moreover, any vertical movements of the continents are immediately reflected in the increase or decrease in the amount of continental shelf which is overlapped by the ocean waters.

The continental shelf possesses relief features in great number and of large scale, some of which baffle explanation. Soundings reveal the presence of well-defined valleys, deep gorges,

[2] Including the Greenland Sea.

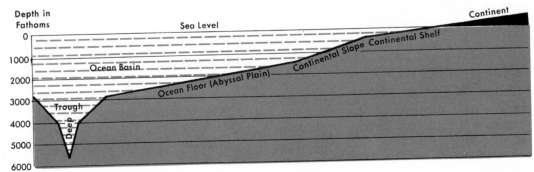

Figure 27–2   Ideal cross section of the ocean floor from the edge of the continent to the depths of an abyss or "deep."

submerged hills, shoals, and reefs. Some of the valleys are cut deep below the general level of the shelf and descend far down the slopes which lead toward the bottom of the ocean basins. Along the northeast coast of North America, there are submarine canyons which exceed in depth and grandeur the Grand Canyon of the Colorado. The hills and plateaus of the continental shelf project in places above sea level and constitute the *continental islands,* such as Nantucket, Martha's Vineyard, and Long Island, on the eastern margin of the United States, Catalina Island and the Farillons on the western margin.

THE OCEAN BASINS

Descending the continental slope, the relatively steep gradient continues until depths of 1,000 to 1,200 fathoms are reached and the ocean floor flattens out into the vast level plain or gently undulating surface of the *ocean floor.* These great submarine plains occupy more than 75 percent of the whole oceanic area and average about 2,000 fathoms in depth. In places, the bottoms of the oceans are interrupted by swells or rises which form mid-ocean plateaus and dividing ridges. From many of these rise *pelagic islands,* which are of volcanic origin, as for instance the Hawaiian Islands, or are constructed in whole or in part of the remains of corals and associated organisms as are the reefs and atolls of the Pacific (Fig. 27–3).

Scattered about over the ocean bottoms are some sixty-five more profound depressions known as *troughs.* About fifteen of these are large in

area; about fifty are small. In depth they vary from 3,000 to 4,000 fathoms. All told, these depressions or troughs cover approximately 7 percent of the ocean bottom. The Tuscarora Trough off Japan, the Philippine Trough off Formosa and the Philippines, and the North American Trough east of the Bahama Islands are perhaps the best known of these (Fig. 27–2).

Within some of the submarine troughs are narrow depressions of still greater depth. These are known as *ocean deeps* or *abysses* and lie below 4,000 fathoms; a few exceed 5,000 fathoms in depth. In the Swire Deep, just east of the Philippines, a sounding has been recorded which indicates a depth of more than six miles. Thus the ocean deeps descend much farther below sea level than the loftiest mountains rise above it.

OCEAN WATER

The most familiar characteristic of ocean water is its salinity (saltiness) which makes it unfit for drinking or culinary use. During the long eons of earth history, the rivers of the land have been flowing down to the sea over rocks which are composed in part of soluble minerals. These are constantly being leached out and carried in solution to the ocean in an amount computed to be nearly three billion tons each year. When evaporated, ocean water leaves these minerals behind and hence they have gradually increased in concentration. Some of the soluble salts are used by animals and plants in their life processes, but others have simply accumulated in the sea until today the ocean waters carry in solution an amount of mineral matter ranging from 3 to 3.7 percent by weight. The Baltic with less than 1 percent and the Red Sea with more than 4 percent represent extremes in mineral content.

Upon analysis, the salts held in solution in the sea are found to consist chiefly of chlorides and sulphates of sodium, magnesium, and calcium. In addition, nearly half of the ninety-odd elements known to modern chemistry are represented, at least in minute traces. More than three-fourths of the total is common table salt (sodium chloride). Were the oceans to be evaporated to dryness, the salts would cover the entire area of the ocean with a layer two hundred feet thick. This would be enough material to equal in volume the entire continent of Africa above sea level.

OCEAN TEMPERATURES

The surface waters of the ocean vary strikingly in temperature from place to place, but not nearly so much as does the ground at the surface of the continents. In equatorial regions, the surface waters average 80° F., or above; both toward the south and north from the Tropical Zone, the temperature gradually decreases as the latitude increases. In latitude 40°, or thereabouts, the temperature is somewhere in the neighborhood of 60° F.; in subpolar areas it is approximately 30°.

There is very little fluctuation in the temperature of the surface waters in the Tropical Zone from one part of the year to another, but the seasonal variation may be considerable in extratropical waters. At no place, however, is there any appreciable seasonal change in the water at depths below 150 fathoms.

Thus far, consideration has been given to the temperature of surface water only. Very different conditions prevail throughout the great body of oceanic water as a whole. Temperatures decrease rapidly with depth; below the comparatively shallow depth of 700 fathoms, the temperature is almost everywhere less than 40° F. The oceans, therefore, constitute a vast reservoir of cold. In the ocean depths, however, there is a significant relation between latitude and temperature. In tropical regions, the water on the ocean floor has an average temperature of 40°; in inter-mediate latitudes, bottom temperatures range between 30° and 35°, and in high latitudes, between 28° and 30°.

MOVEMENTS OF OCEAN WATER

Ocean water ordinarily manifests three types of movement. First, periodic vertical rise and fall known as the *tide* and caused by the gravitational force of moon and sun. Second, aperiodic oscillatory movements known as *waves,* caused by the brushing effect of the wind. And third, continual forward movement or flow known as *currents,* caused by a combination of several factors.

The low temperatures found everywhere upon the ocean floor suggest that cold water from the polar seas sinks and creeps equatorward along the bottom, and is replaced by warm equatorial water flowing poleward on the surface. While such a general exchange does take place, the actual pattern of currents upon the surface of the oceans is a very complex one.

In general, the circulation of surface water in each ocean is arranged into two enormous eddies or gyrals, those of the Northern Hemisphere revolving clockwise and those of the Southern Hemisphere counterclockwise about comparatively motionless central areas. Thus in each ocean there is a warm current moving pole-

Figure 27–3   A coral reef—one type of pelagic island. (Photo courtesy of the U.S. Navy)

ward along the western side, and a cool current moving equatorward along the eastern side (see Chapter 7).

CLIMATES OF THE OCEANS

The general decrease in ocean surface temperatures from the equator toward either pole produces a distinct climatic zonation over the oceans. The Tropical, Subtropical, Cyclonic, and Polar zones are easily recognizable, but they are less markedly differentiated than on land. Their boundaries do not follow a direct east-west direction across the oceans but instead are deflected either poleward or equatorward by prevailing winds and currents (Fig. 27–4).

Within each zone there is differentiation into recognizable types of climate. In the Tropical Zone, there is a wide strip of year-round convection rains along the equator. Bordering this on either side is a zone of seasonal rainfall. Within the trade wind belts, the rain-shadow effect of the great land masses is evidenced in the arid and semiarid areas over the oceans.

In the Subtropical and Cyclonic zones, continental influences are carried to leeward for considerable distances eastward over the ocean. There they gradually dwindle, and are replaced by marine conditions over the central and eastern portions of the ocean basins. In the Polar Zone, there are an outer region of cold water infested seasonally by drifting ice and an inner region of ice packs. All told, there are ten easily recognized major types of climate over the oceans.

MARINE FLORA AND FAUNA

Like the lands, most of the ocean is rich in plant and animal life. These fauna and flora are in the main quite unlike those of the lands.

The flora or native plant life is varied both in form and habit, and it differs considerably from one maritime region to another. Part of it is anchored or sedentary, and part is free and floating in habit. The forms present in any oceanic area depend on temperature, salinity of the water, amount of water motion, amount of silt in the water, and many other factors.

The fauna or native animal life of the ocean is extremely varied, involving species of every phylum from protozoa to mammals inclusive. In general, marine fauna is of four types. First, there are the anchored forms found about the shores and on the shallow bottoms. Second, there are the *plankton* or floating forms. Third, there are the *nekton* or swimming forms. Fourth, there are the *benthos* or deep-sea forms whose structural and functional adaptations to darkness, cold, and great pressure usually preclude their migration out of a very restricted abyssal zone.

THE COAST ZONE

Intimately associated with the ocean is a second element of the natural environment—the shore or littoral. It consists of that part of the earth's lands that touch the ocean. By most persons, this is regarded as a narrow irregular line to which the term *coastline* is appropriately applied. When examined in detail, however, it is seen to be a strip of considerable width, for which the term *coast zone* is more fitting than coastline.

CHARACTER OF THE COAST ZONE

The coast zone consists of a coastal strip with its physical relief features—its bays, estuaries, coves, and sounds and its capes, promontories, and peninsulas. It includes also a shore of varying width and the adjacent waters, together with their offshore bars, shoals, and islands.

TYPES OF COAST ZONES

All coast zones possess certain traits in common, but they differ markedly in their detailed characteristics. When classified as to the kind of shoreline which they possess, some four types are recognizable: *submergent, emergent, neutral,* and *compound.*[3]

Coast zones with submergent shorelines

One major class of shoreline is formed by the slow sinking of the land (or the rising of the ocean level, whichever may be the case). Shorelines thus formed by the surface of the sea

[3] Such a classification is based (1) upon the relative movements undergone by land and sea in producing the present shoreline, and (2) upon the character of the land surface against which the sea has finally come to rest.

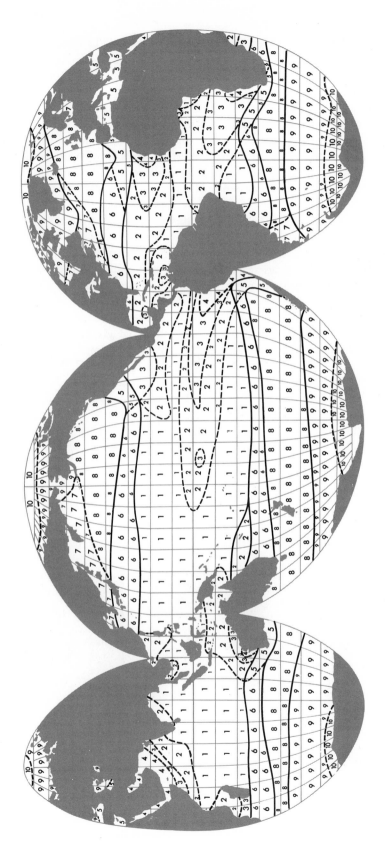

Figure 27—4 Generalized climatic regions of the oceans (compare this map with that for the continents): (1) Rainy Tropical, (2) Monsoon Tropical, (3) Semiarid Tropical, (4) Arid Tropical, (5) Mediterranean Subtropical, (6) Humid Subtropical, (7) Humid Continental (modified), (8) Temperate Marine, (9) Subpolar, (10) Polar Icepack.

coming to rest against a partially submerged land area are known as submergent shorelines. The submerged land may, of course, be either a plain or a rugged upland. If the land area in question is a low flat plain, the sea will enter far up into the main river valleys, converting them into wide, shallow estuaries. Into these, the tides enter once or twice a day, causing the river water to back up for varying distances upstream. This periodically inundates low-lying areas and converts them into tidal marshes.

Sometimes an entire main valley is submerged leaving the former tributaries as "detrunked" separate streams, each with its individual tidal estuary. The divides between rivers remain unsubmerged as long ragged peninsulas or necks. In places, the sea spills across these divides and cuts off portions which form low, flat islands. Examples of such *estuary coasts* are the Baltic coast of Germany, the Hudson Bay region, western France, the Cape Cod–Nantucket–Martha's Vineyard area of southern New England, and eastern England (Fig. 27–5).

Where a hilly or mountainous land is submerged, the stream valleys are drowned to form reentrants with hilly sides. To these reentrants the name *rias* is sometimes applied. The unsubmerged interstream areas form bold, high peninsulas, and the offshore islands are rugged and rocky. A ria usually forms an excellent harbor, affording good protection from winds and storm waves. Erosion by waves produces marked cliffs along a ria coast. Where rock structure is homogeneous, the cliffs may be high and overhanging as are the white chalk (limestone) cliffs of southern England. Where rock structure is variegated, the weaker members are rapidly excavated to form sea caves and guts; the stronger are left as chimneys, stacks, and offshore rocks. Examples of ria coasts are afforded by the Puget Sound area, northwest Spain, Brittany, Wales, Japan, Maine, and Greece (Fig. 27–5).

Where the land in question was glaciated in past ages, submergence has produced a somewhat different outline. The dominant characteristic is the existence of long, narrow, roughly parallel, steep-walled reentrants of the sea known as *fiords*. These would seem to be the result of the drowning of a topography carved by glacial erosion. A fiord, therefore, is apparently a partially submerged glacial trough. They are often very deep but sometimes have a relatively shallow sill at their seaward end. Their walls are steep, often rising almost vertically from the water. Tributary streams fall as cascades from hanging valleys on either side of the typical fiord. Such coasts are noted for their scenic beauty and many of them are visited by great numbers of sightseers. Examples of fiord coasts are furnished by Norway (Fig. 27–5), southern Alaska, Iceland, Labrador (Fig. 27–6), southern Chile, western New Zealand, and many other areas.

Thus submergent coasts, whether they be of the estuary, ria, or fiord type, are characterized

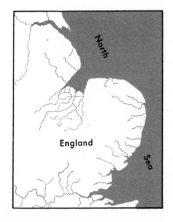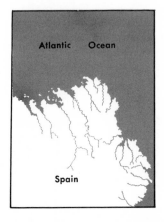

Figure 27–5   Outlines of three kinds of submerged coasts: left, estuary subtype, center, ria subtype, right, fiord subtype.

Figure 27–6 A fiord on the Labrador coast. (Photo courtesy of the Geological Survey of Canada, Ottawa)

by reentrants of the sea alternating with peninsulas, promontories, necks, and capes. Low-lying areas are transformed into coves, bays, and sounds. The result is a long and irregular coastline with comparatively deep water offshore. The adjacent sea bottom is highly irregular, exhibiting the inequalities of the former hills and valleys of the now submerged portion of the land. Such coasts are exposed to the erosional attack of waves. Wave-cut cliffs develop, crescent-shaped beaches are thrown up at the inner end of bays, and finally bars are built from headland to headland and from islands to the mainland.

Submergent coast zones frequently have a considerable percentage of their population engaged in fishing. In part this may be owing to the paucity of land for agriculture—the lower, more fertile areas having been submerged—and in part to the sheltered waters which encourage fishing activities. It is certain that fish and other sea food, both as a basis for cash income and as a substitute for meat, enable many a littoral to support a population far beyond the limits set by its land resources.

The harbors of a submergent littoral frequently become the loci for important seaports. The inhabitants become interested in commerce, ship-building may develop, and large numbers of people become involved in the carrying trade. Those nations, therefore, which possess well-located submergent coasts often become important merchant and naval powers. Norway is such a country. With a population of only 3,750,000, she possesses the largest merchant fleet per capita in the world.

Coast zones with emergent shorelines

A second class of shorelines is formed where the margins of a continent slowly rise (or perhaps the level of the sea is lowered), allowing the surface of the sea to come to rest against a partially emerged land area. Where such emergence of the land occurs, the coast advances seaward and the new shoreline is formed by the intersection of sea level with a former portion of the continental shelf. This leaves some of the former continental shelf exposed as a new coastal plain. Since the continental shelf is continually being smoothed by waves and currents into an approximately plane surface, the new coastline will possess a simple and regular outline, and the newly emerged area will be low, flat, poorly drained, and often quite sandy.

The streams, which are extended outward from the old land, wind and wriggle their way sluggishly across the new coastal plain. They are usually shallow and not navigable. The waters of the sea are also shallow, sometimes for many miles offshore. Harbors are few, sometimes altogether lacking. If one is desired, it must be

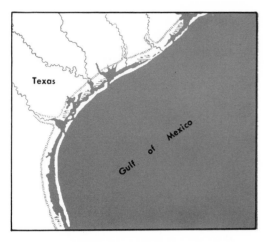

Figure 27–7   Outline of an emergent coast. Note former shoreline, offshore bar, and lagoon.

constructed by building moles, breakwaters, and long piers. A channel for small ships can readily be dredged, but in many instances large ships must anchor offshore and have their cargoes transferred by lighters and barges.

Owing to the shallowness of the water offshore, waves do not ordinarily reach such a coast but instead break at a considerable distance out from shore (Fig. 27–7). There, the action of the waves soon casts up an offshore bar composed of sand, and wind action often piles this sand into a line of dunes atop the bar. The bar runs roughly parallel to the coast and incloses a narrow lagoon of quiet water. Into this lagoon the coastal streams discharge their waters which in turn escape through narrow breaks in the offshore bar known as *tidal inlets*. Silt brought in by streams, sand carried in by the tide, and the growth of marsh vegetation gradually cause the lagoon to become filled.

Waves break directly upon the seaward face of the bar producing considerable erosion, particularly during periods of storm. Thus, as the bar grows on its landward side, it is eroded on its seaward side. The net result of this is to produce a slow shoreward migration of the bar. Thus, an offshore bar and a lagoon are earmarks of youth in coasts of emergence. Physiographic maturity is reached when the lagoon has been obliterated and the bar has been driven against the shoreline. In old age, the bar has been re-

moved and the peninsulas and other coastal irregularities destroyed by prolonged wave erosion.

Owing to the shallowness of water and the paucity of harbors along an emerged coast zone, seaports are not numerous. The few commercial cities situated upon emerged littorals are frequently served by lighterage from ships anchored in open roadsteads, as in Peru, northern Chile, and portions of West Africa. Other ports may depend upon the inlets through the offshore bar which are kept open by the currents of large streams. Still others may construct artificial harbors by building expensive breakwaters.

Figure 27–8   Miami Beach, Florida, located on an offshore bar, is one of America's most famous pleasure resorts. (Photo courtesy of the Miami Beach News Bureau)

The maritime life of an emerged coast zone is small; fishing usually, but not always, is relatively unimportant, and commerce is at a minimum. The population, therefore, is apt to be occupied in agriculture. Where accessible to densely populated areas, emergent littorals sometimes develop important recreational activities. The offshore bar may be lined with the summer cottages of well-to-do migrants, with resort cities at intervals (Fig. 27–8). The sand and shallow water are admirable for bathing, while full exposure to the sea breeze affords relief from summer heat. Examples of emerged coasts are afforded by Florida, South Carolina, Georgia, and Texas in the United States. Eastern Mexico, the Guinea coast of Africa, eastern Spain, and Israel also provide examples.

Coast zones with neutral shorelines

A third type of shoreline is seen in coast zones where there has been neither positive nor negative change of the land in relation to sea level. To such, the term *neutral shoreline* is usually applied. Volcanic coasts, deltas, fault-line coasts, and coral islands usually possess neutral shorelines. The characteristics of coast zones possessing such shorelines are, therefore, quite varied, each constituting a special case.

The most familiar variety of neutral coast zone is that formed by the deltas of rivers. For example, the great delta of the Hwang-Ho is growing seaward through the deposition of silt at a rate of three feet or so per year. It is extremely low, flat, and poorly drained. A large proportion of it is intensively cultivated for agriculture—diked, ditched, and canalized to provide drainage. There is, however, not a harbor and only one seaport on the whole of the delta from the hills of Shantung southward. On the old delta north of Shantung there is not a harbor or a seaport town for two hundred miles.

On the Nile Delta there are similarly only a few small port towns. It is only on the margins of the delta that the great commercial city of Alexandria and the canal-entrance city of Port Said have developed. In both instances, considerable harbor engineering has been necessary.

Sometimes, where a stream is large, it is able to keep the channels through its delta scoured free of silt. Ships can, therefore, enter and a seaport may develop up the river at the first point where relatively high and firm ground is encountered. This is exemplified by New Orleans on the Mississippi Delta.

In the western part of the Netherlands and adjacent portions of Belgium, the coast is formed by the huge Rhine Delta. By diking and draining the surface, this area maintains a high degree of agricultural occupancy. It is, however, only through constant and costly dredging of the river channels that the ports of Antwerp and Rotterdam are kept open to ships and the commercial life of the Low Countries maintained.

Another variety of littorals with neutral shorelines consists of volcanic coasts (Fig. 27–9). These possess rather regular coastal outlines, at least in the early stages of their physiographic history. This regularity is broken by small indentations which are either coves at the mouths of creeks or irregularities produced by initial inequalities in the lava flows. These are the loci of villages, the inhabitants of which may divide their interests between fishing and farming. The former frequently is hazardous because offshore bars are lacking and the waters near shore are usually deep. The latter is limited to small spots of decayed lava or scoria, or to alluvium along the creeks. The Island of Hawaii, for example, rises abruptly from deep water but has no good harbors. There are tiny fishing villages on the small coves but no major seaports. Quelpart Island off Japan, Santa Lucia and Saint Vincent in the West Indies, and several islands in the southwest Pacific are similar.

Coasts formed by faulting or fracturing of continental or island margins exhibit another variety of neutral shoreline. The west coast of peninsular India, the margins of the Red Sea, and the east coast of Malagasy (Fig. 27–9) are examples of fault-line coasts. They are usually straight, steep, and devoid of many indentations.

Many South Sea islands and a few islands in the West Indies and elsewhere exemplify the

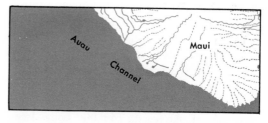
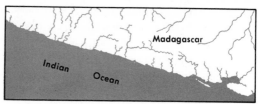

Figure 27–9 Outlines of two kinds of neutral coasts: top, the volcanic subtype, bottom, the fault-line subtype.

coral reef variety of coast. In some instances, entire islands are built by coral colonies. In others, already existent islands are simply rimmed by a fringe or collar of coralline materials. Such islands are usually lacking in harbors and approach to them by ship is rendered dangerous by the presence of submarine reefs and pinnacles of coral.

In cases of slow submergence, the original island itself may disappear, but the coral colonies on the fringing reef may be able to build up as fast as subsidence occurs. In that event, the fringing reef may continue to exist even though the central island has vanished, leaving a ring of coral limestone inclosing a lagoon of protected water. Such a coral ring is known as an *atoll*. If the reef is breached, the inclosed lagoon may form an excellent harbor for ships. The lagoons of atolls also furnish ideal havens for transoceanic seaplanes. The atoll, however, would seem to represent shoreline of submergence formed from the original neutral coast of island and fringing coral reef.

Coast zones with compound shorelines

The fourth and last type of coast zone comprises those littorals whose shorelines show the features of both emergence and submergence. This probably includes the great majority of coast zones over the earth. For example, the Atlantic Coast of the United States from the Carolina capes northward to Long Island Sound seems to have undergone both submergence and emergence. It is quite possible that there have been several oscillations of the land in relation to sea level in this general region.

In the northern New Jersey–New York section there seems to have been a profound submergence of the coast, forming Long Island Sound and drowning the mouths of the Hudson, Passaic, Hackensack, and Raritan rivers to make New York, Newark, and Raritan bays. Later there was a small emergence exposing the coastal plain of southern Long Island and causing the offshore bars of Rockaway Beach, Long Beach, and Fire Island, and the curved spit of Sandy Hook to be formed. The amount of emergence has been relatively slight, however, because the tides enter far up the Hudson and cause the river

water to back up as far as Albany, 150 miles inland, and the extensive Hackensack Meadows are so low as to be very poorly drained.

Man's use of this compound coast zone shows adjustments to both submergent and emergent features. For example, the rias of the drowned mouths of the Hudson, Hackensack, Passaic, and Raritan rivers have collectively become the greatest port of the world, lined with piers, shipyards, and docks. Nearby on the lower areas a great industrial district has developed. On the newly exposed coastal plain of southern Long Island an area of apartments, market gardening, and miscellaneous agriculture has grown up. The offshore bars are largely given over to boardwalks, bathing beaches, several waterfront amusement installations, hotels, and summer homes. The lagoons, such as Jamaica Bay, Sheepshead Bay, and Great South Bay are the seats of a fishing and shellfish industry and the anchorage for almost countless small pleasure craft. In this area, however, the submergent features dominate, whereas the emergent features are decidedly secondary.

On the Pacific coast, the shores of Puget Sound and of the Bight of Southern California likewise show mainly submergent features but they do give evidence of a later slight emergence (Fig. 27–10). On the contrary, the coast of New

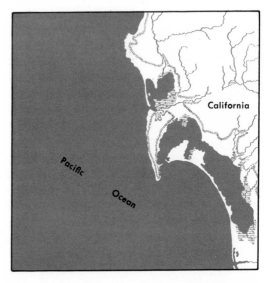

Figure 27–10 Outline of a compound coast. Note that both submergent and emergent features are in evidence.

Jersey south of Sandy Hook exhibits, in the main, emergent features, with only minor evidences of drowning. Strictly speaking, these are compound coast zones, but to the geographer this term is usually reserved for littorals where both sets of characteristics are strongly in evidence.

One of the best examples of a compound littoral is furnished by the Chesapeake Bay area. The shallow waters of this bay are the seat of an important oyster and fishing industry, while the newly emerged sandy plain supports an important truck-farming industry. At the same time, the submergent features furnish the excellent harbors of the port cities of Norfolk and Baltimore.

Other examples of compound coasts are those of northern Poland (formerly East Prussia), southern France, western Denmark, and northern Holland.

GEOGRAPHIC ASPECTS OF THE COAST ZONE

The various physical, hydrographic, and biotic features which occur along the margin of the land combine to make up a unique habitat for man known as the *coast zone* or *littoral*. There the dual factors of land and sea meet, and there man may develop marked maritime interests even while maintaining his land connections. The coast zone, however, is a limited rather than a universal factor because it is not, like climate, relief, or location, present in all geographic regions.

RACIAL CONTRASTS

The littoral constitutes a habitat markedly different from adjacent interior regions. When man from the hinterland, therefore, overflows into the coast zone, he assumes new interests, is induced to enter new occupations, and gains a new means of travel and communication. Culture items from distant lands find their way into his life and perhaps even foreign blood may enter into the veins of his descendants.

More often than not the littoral attracts by way of the sea peoples entirely unrelated to those of the interior. Thus Phoenicians and Philistines inhabited the coast of a land otherwise possessed by Hebrews, Canaanites, and Arameans. In Asia Minor, the ancient Greeks inhabited the littoral

while Lydians populated the interior. More recently Asia Minor exhibited a contrast between littoral Greek and interior Turk. The largest city in the modern Greek world was Smyrna, not Athens. In 1922, however, the Greek armies were crushed by the Turks and the entire Greek population expelled. In the eastern Adriatic, the South Slavs, an interior group, are divorced from the sea by a narrow zone of Italian blood and culture. Finland, still another example, is Finnish only in the interior; in the coastal zone, it is Swedish.

POLITICAL DETACHMENT

Coast zones are frequently detached politically from the areas which lie behind them. In part this is due to the external peoples and cultures which they attract, but in larger part it is resultant upon their ease of invasion and conquest.

The coast lands of Ethiopia were early conquered by Britain, France, and Italy. Saudi Arabia is almost rimmed by such independent and semi-independent states as Yemen, Aden, Trucial Oman and Kuwait. British Columbia in western Canada is deprived of half her littoral by the Alaskan "panhandle," while the province of Quebec in eastern Canada is excluded from nearly a thousand miles of Labrador coast by the province of Newfoundland.

STRUGGLES FOR COAST LANDS

The commercial and strategic value of coast zones causes them in many instances to be hotly disputed. Generations of warfare were required for Spain to eject the African Moors from her southern margin. Today Spain herself holds precariously the adjacent coast of Africa.

The "War of the Pacific" (1879–1883) was fought with the Bolivian littoral as the prize, the loss of which forever relegated Bolivia to the rank of a third-rate interior country. The Second Balkan War was largely an outgrowth of the dispute over the Macedonian and Thracian coast zone. The Italo-Yugoslav quarrel over Dalmatia was more than a mere wrangle over a piece of territory. This latter was essential to Yugoslavia as an outlet to the world ocean, but its possession by Italy would have converted the Adriatic into an "Italian lake." The outcome, as so often eventuates, was a compromise. The coast proper went to Yugoslavia after World War I, while certain offshore islands and enclaves of the mainland went to Italy. At the close of World War II, Yugoslavia gained the entire coast zone, ending the attempt by Italy to surround and hence dominate the Adriatic Sea.

For nearly a thousand years, the Poles and Germans contended for possession of the Prussian coast. During most of that time, the Poles were confined to an interior situation. After World War I, a Polish Corridor was bored through West Prussia to the sea. After World War II, the matter was presumably disposed of for all time by removing the German population and awarding all of the coast zone on the Baltic Sea between Frisches Haff and Stettin to Poland (Fig. 38–9).

Over a period of more than a thousand years, the Russians have sought possession of an ice-free littoral, but they were long thwarted by Byzantine, Turkish, Swedish, British, and Japanese arms. More recently eastern European ports have been used by the U.S.S.R., especially Stettin, Danzig, and the smaller ports of Estonia, Latvia, and Lithuania.

The desire of all nations for a piece of coast zone and the constant pressure of great nations to possess such areas are one of the keys to history. It is a result not so much of the intrinsic value of the littoral itself, but of its indirect value in affording a "window on the world ocean" to its possessor. The resources and facilities of the ocean are very great and, moreover, these are traditionally available to any nation enjoying access to them.

THE OCEAN AS AN ENVIRONMENTAL FACTOR

CLIMATIC INFLUENCES

The ocean exercises a significant influence upon climate. The habitability of the trade-wind shore, the mild temperatures of west coasts of continents in the Cyclonic Zone, and the distribution of rainfall and cloudiness over the continents are three of the most obvious examples of its influence. To these might be added the effects of ocean currents, sea breezes, monsoon winds, and the hurricanes off the subtropical seas.

ECONOMIC SIGNIFICANCE

Raw materials and power

The ocean is an important factor in man's economic life, for it furnishes him with many resources and makes possible many extractive and processing industries.

The extraction of salt from sea water is an important mineral industry in numerous coastal localities. The gathering of kelp and other seaweeds is likewise a significant activity. A few seaweeds are edible; others yield potash, iodine, agar, and lesser products.

The oceans are currently the scene of much study for minerals, since a number of new ocean techniques are expected ere long to provide minerals to mankind from this little-understood portion of the globe. Of course, some minerals have been taken from below the oceans for a considerable time, for example, petroleum and natural gas from the continental shelves of the Gulf of Mexico, the Pacific Coast of the United States, the Persian Gulf, the North Sea, and others. Magnesium is a mineral being won from ocean water in increasing amounts. It is known that deposits of ilmenite, magnetite, monazite, diamond, zircon, manganese, and phosphate are present, but for all practical purposes, so little is known about their location and size that most ventures are at present not regarded as economically feasible.

Fisheries

Ocean fishing is an important industry, supplying man with a not inconsiderable amount of food and furnishing employment for many. Statistically, more than 100,000 of Norway's 3,750,000 inhabitants are engaged in fishing. This figure is doubtless too small, since a large proportion of the farmers who dwell along the fiords are really as much fishermen as farmers. Equipped with one of the world's most modern fishing fleets, Norway took in over 1.6 million metric tons of fish in 1964. She is the leading supplier of marine fish in the Northeast Atlantic and the world's largest exporter of fish and fish products.

Japan for decades boasted the most productive fisheries in the world (Fig. 27–11). In 1964, her great bank and open-sea fisheries yielded over 6.3 million metric tons of fish. The fisheries are

Figure 27–11   A Japanese fishing vessel with an enormous catch. (Photo courtesy of the Consulate General of Japan, N.Y.)

fact that plankton is more abundant in cold water than in warm, a consequence, no doubt, of smaller amounts of denitrifying bacteria. Plankton consists principally of algae and diatoms. Conditions for fishing are found in most nearly ideal combination on the submarine plateaus of the North Atlantic. The Grand Bank of Newfoundland, Nantucket Shoals, Dogger Bank, and other similar localities are therefore preeminent fishing grounds.

Four areas are outstanding for their fisheries (Fig. 27–12): (1) the New England–Grand Bank region, which yields cod, haddock, mackerel herring, and numerous other varieties of fish (Fig. 27–13), (2) the north European region, comprising the Bay of Biscay, the Baltic and North seas, and the Norwegian coastal waters, which yields mainly herring, cod, and haddock, (3) the Pacific Northwest region (North America), extending from California to the Bering Sea, which is noted primarily for salmon together with lesser amounts of halibut, tuna, and cod, and (4) the northeastern Asiatic region, which produces herring, haddock, bonito, and salmon.

Lesser fishing grounds are provided by the Tasman Sea, the western Mediterranean, the Gulf of Mexico, and South African waters. Oysters are obtained chiefly from cultivated *parks* in Chesapeake Bay, Long Island Sound, Puget Sound, and the coastal waters of the Netherlands, Japan, and western France. The sealing industry is largely in the hands of Americans and Russians in the neighborhood of the Commander and Pribilof islands (Fig. 27–14). The largest and most important herd of fur seals uses the Pribilof Islands in Bering Sea as a breeding ground. Here by international agreement a certain proportion of the total seal herd is killed each year. Whaling, once a widespread industry, now centers in Antarctic waters, the whale's last great sanctuary. Of the 63,000 whales caught in 1963, 30,000 were from the Antarctic region. The industry is carried on mainly by Japan, Norway, and the Soviet Union.

large and modern. Huge floating canneries, designed to catch, process, and can the fish, are becoming popular. Although a relatively small proportion of the working population is engaged in fishing activities, fish is an important food staple and protein source of the Japanese diet. In the 1960's, however, Peru moved into first place among the fishing nations of the world but most of her catch, consisting of anchovies, is converted into fish meal and exported to be used as animal feed.

Maritime fisheries fall into three classes— *inshore, banks,* and *pelagic.* A score of nations participates in banks fishing but only a few prosecute the pelagic fisheries of the open ocean. Inshore fishing is practiced to a greater or lesser extent by every people possessing a coastal zone.

Fish are widely distributed through the ocean but are particularly numerous and palatable in shallow or epicontinental seas. It is these areas that are the great feeding and spawning grounds. Besides shallow water, a very significant factor seems to be cold water, though authorities do not yet fully agree on this point. Nevertheless, it is a

Ocean commerce

Man's conquest of the ocean has transformed it from an almost insuperable barrier to a world highway of trade, travel, and communication.

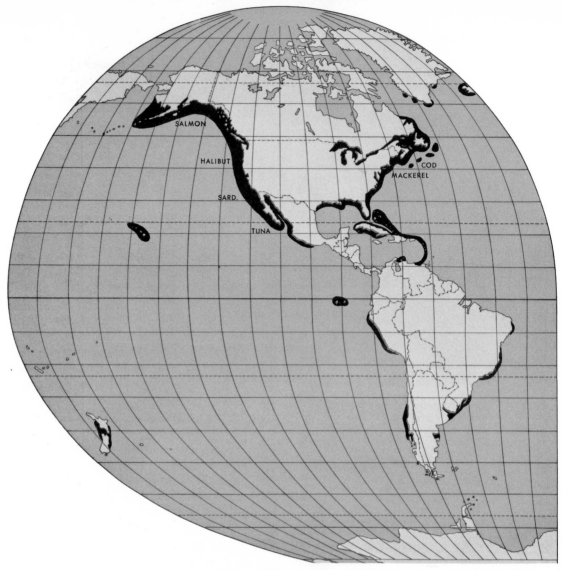

Figure 27–12 Black areas show the commercial ocean fisheries of the world. The most important products of these areas are labeled.

This was not a rapid accomplishment but a slow process continuing even now.

A millennium before the Christian era, the Greeks navigated the Ægean Sea and the adjacent waters, finally voyaging into the Euxine and across the Ionian Sea to Italy. Later, the Romans carried their commerce from one end of the Mediterranean to the other, even venturing timidly out into the Atlantic. The dawn of modern times saw the Hanseatic League spreading its commercial network over the Mediterranean, Black, Baltic, and North seas. Its traders visited the Madeira and Canary islands, the coast of West Africa, and by traveling on Arab vessels visited even the Indies.

After Columbus, all four oceans were rapidly opened to trade. Today, however, commercial activities center in the Atlantic. Indeed, the present has aptly been termed the "Atlantic Era." There are many who predict the advent of a Pacific era of commerce. Certainly the vast population and potential buying power of the Pacific Rim would seem to suggest such a possibility, but too many ecological variables are present to permit a reliable forecast.

During the Mediterranean commercial period, goods were carried largely by galleys. Such a vessel was a one-, two-, or three-storied rowboat, usually equipped with an auxiliary sail. From ten to one hundred rowers were employed

for motive power. In some instances these were laborers for hire, in others they were slaves chained to their benches and urged on with whips. Later, galleys were supplanted by caravels, rather small and clumsy sailing vessels. Columbus required approximately seventy days to cross the Atlantic in his caravel, the *Santa Maria*.

In the early part of the nineteenth century, clipper ships were making Atlantic crossings in twelve to fourteen days. The clipper, evolved in New England, was a trim variety of schooner carrying a veritable cloud of canvas. It represented a marked advance in navigation, but it vanished from the seas nearly a century ago. Sailing vessels were replaced by steamships which could carry enormous cargoes and were able to cross the Atlantic in seven to ten days. The

"tramp" steamer was the standby for decades, carrying two-thirds of all maritime commerce in the years just preceding World War I. Tramps are in turn being superseded by liners of the cargo-passenger type, which appear to be more practicable.

Trade routes cross the oceans in almost every conceivable direction. Among these, however, are a few channels of preeminent importance. The tendency of commerce to follow definite paths across the oceans is owing to several factors: (1) the need to approximate Great Circle paths, (2) the location of areas of large population and surplus production, (3) the shape of the continents and the location of their major points of access, (4) deviation to touch islands and peninsulas, and (5) avoidance of navigational hazards.

As a result of these restrictive factors, nine routes carry most of the world's transoceanic trade, and, of these, the North Atlantic Route is the greatest, since over it nearly one-fourth of the tonnage of the world's merchant vessels finds employment. A map of ocean trade routes (Fig. 27–15) shows that most of them radiate like giant tentacles from European waters, creating what has often been aptly called the "trade octopus" of north-west Europe. No other region on earth is so dependent on foreign trade or ranks so high in it.

Seaports

Seaports, and their hinterlands, are both the creations and creators of such routes. It is an interesting and significant fact that the world's largest cities have water connections with the sea (Fig. 6–7). In the United States, virtually all of the largest cities or metropolitan districts possess important means of water transportation—ocean, lake, or river and canal. This would seem to indicate that for a city to attain first rank in the United States, it must be located strategically on navigable water. An unfavorable site may become the locus of a seaport if it possesses a superior geographical location. Seaports are, therefore, often far from ideal in their environmental qualities and are forced to operate under physical handicaps. An ideal port should have the following characteristics.

1. A deep and commodious harbor
2. A bottom suitable for anchoring
3. Protection from storms
4. Freedom from ice during winter
5. Location on an arm of the sea extending inland as far as possible
6. Space for docks and warehouses
7. Level land on which to build a commercial city
8. Access to a rich and populous hinterland

The ocean is a highway par excellence. Along with the Great Lakes of North America, the ocean supplies the world with its cheapest means of transportation. By way of comparison, railway haulage is about nine times as costly.

Figure 27–13 New England fishermen sorting their catch. (Photo courtesy of the Bureau of Commercial Fisheries)

Figure 27–14 On the Pribilof Islands in the Bering Sea is the largest and most important herd of fur seals in the world. These islands comprise the breeding grounds and the animals never go ashore at any other place. Until 1956 only three-year-old male fur seals were killed, because they could be spared without decreasing the birth rate. These immature seals do not mingle with the breeding animals but herd together nearby. After breeding is over, the seals leave the islands, the females going as far south as southern California, the younger males going not quite so far, and bulls going only as far as the Gulf of Alaska and the waters south of the Aleutian Islands. The industry is under government management; before World War II, 15 percent of the skins were turned over to Canada and 15 percent to Japan in accordance with provisions of the North Pacific Sealing Convention of July 7, 1911, which was entered into in a desperate effort to save the herd from extinction. The skins are sent from the islands to St. Louis, Missouri. Today the herd is increasing to the extent that the islands are becoming overcrowded. (Photo courtesy of the Bureau of Commercial Fisheries)

Shipbuilding and merchant marine

When ships were constructed of wood, shipbuilding was a widely disseminated industry. During the nineteenth century, steel ships came into vogue, whereupon Great Britain with its industrial maturity assumed the lead in shipbuilding.

For years, the United Kingdom occupied the leading position in world merchant shipbuilding. More recently, however, she has been displaced by Japan, who launches over one-fifth of the world's total registered tonnage annually. The tonnage totals of Japan and the United Kingdom, combined with that of West Germany, account for over half the merchant ship tonnage built in the world. Other major shipbuilders are Sweden, the Netherlands, France, Norway, the United States, and Italy.

The locative factors for this industry appear to be a supply of steel, an abundance of skilled labor at a moderate wage scale, nearness to a market for ships, plentiful fuel, and a favorable coast zone.

The world's most important shipbuilding districts are as follows: the Clyde River (Scotland), the Tyne, Tees, Thames, and Wear rivers (England), Belfast (Ireland), the Delaware River (United States), and Stettin (Germany). Other areas of importance are New York Harbor and Chesapeake Bay (United States), Hamburg and Kiel (Germany), Bordeaux and Le Havre (France), Genoa and Naples (Italy), and Kobe, Kure, Nagasaki, and Yokohama (Japan). Japan, enjoying a shipbuilding boom, is making many of the world's largest oil tankers, particularly the supertankers.

The carrying trade of the world is concentrated in the hands of comparatively few nations. All of these possess littorals which are highly favorable to maritime activity. In a few instances, the nations involved possess no shipbuilding industry but depend upon foreign shipyards for their vessels. In 1939 the merchant marine of the world was distributed as follows.

Country	Percent
British Empire	31
United States[4]	15
Japan	9
Norway	8
Germany	7
Italy	6
Holland	5
France	5
Others	14

[4] Two-thirds of this tonnage was engaged only in domestic trade. It therefore consisted chiefly of coastal, intercoastal, and Great Lakes carriers. Few nations equal the United States in size, and no other equals it in coastal development. Hence, in no other instance can so much of a nation's needs be met through domestic commerce.

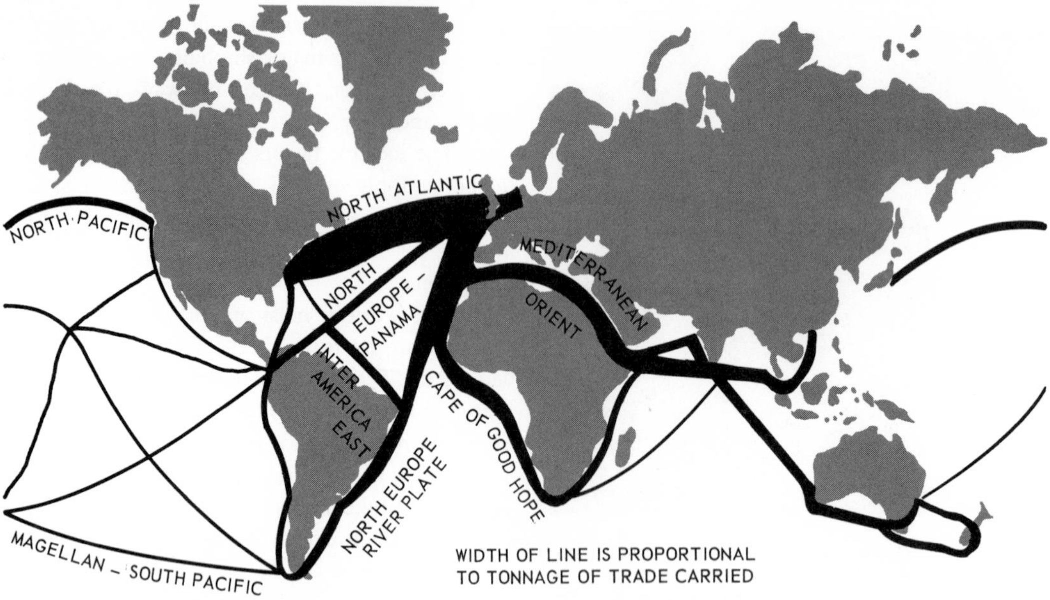

Figure 27–15 World ocean trade routes.

During the ensuing six years of World War II, however, great numbers of merchant vessels were sunk, burned or bombed into uselessness. Germany's merchant fleet was practically obliterated, while the merchant fleets of Japan, Italy, France, Norway, the Netherlands, Belgium, Greece, and others were greatly reduced. In the later years of the war, the world's tonnage actually increased over the prewar total by some 23 percent. This was largely the result of the unprecedented rate of construction by the United States and to a much lesser extent to construction by Britain and neutral Sweden. At the close of the war, the relative standing of the eight leading countries was roughly estimated to be as follows.

Country	Percent
United States	60
British Empire	21
Norway	4
Japan	3
Holland	2
Sweden	2
Italy	1
France	1
Others	6

Ten years later, some sort of approximate equilibrium had again been established among the maritime nations. The enormous wartime lead of the United States had largely disappeared. Britain and Norway had regained their ranks. The lesser carrier countries were jockeying for relative positions below them. Germany had not yet recovered. The relative standing was then as follows.

Country	Percent
United States	30
British Empire	22
Norway	7
Panama	5
France	4
Italy	4
Netherlands	4
Japan	4
Others	20

In 1965, the world merchant shipping fleets shared a gross registered tonnage of 160 million

[5] United Nations Statistical Office, Department of Economic and Social Affairs, *Statistical Yearbook, 1965* (New York, United Nations, 1966), pp. 436–37.

tons.[5] The proportions claimed by the leading countries were as follows.

Country	Percent
United Kingdom	13.4
United States	13.4
Liberia	10.9
Norway	9.8
Japan	7.5
Republic of South Africa	6.6
Greece	4.5
Italy	3.6
West Germany	3.3
Netherlands	3.1
Others	19.1

SOCIAL AND POLITICAL SIGNIFICANCE

Great as is the ocean's influence upon economic affairs, its bearing upon man socially and politically is even greater. Throughout most of human history, the ocean has been an almost insuperable barrier. It has effectively separated peoples and prevented the free contact of cultures. This has had both good and bad results. Britain has always had occasion to rejoice at the comparative isolation given her by the sea, for it has kept her partially aloof from Europe's chronically recurring troubles. New Zealand, on the other hand, is not so benefited by the ocean, for it separates her from outside markets by some 12,000 miles.

Today the ocean has become a great highway and the entire civilized world is interested in maintaining the safety and freedom of the seas. Nations have risen and fallen in attempts to control the ocean, but by common consent it is now accepted as one of the world's most valuable international possessions.

Diving bells, long cylindrical tubes, and even hydrographic and meteorological stations on "sea mounts," are becoming quite commonplace in the news. Prolonged underwater stays (over several weeks) by observers in windowed water vehicles are providing us with vast amounts of information about animate and inanimate sea materials. "Escape hatches" are used not only for emergence from but also for reentry into these undersurface laboratories.[6]

[6] For additional information on Oceanographic research, see M. J. Dunbar, "The Surge of Oceanographies," *The Geographical Review*, Volume LV, Number 3 (July, 1965).

SUGGESTED USEFUL READINGS

ATLASES

U.S. Hydrographic Office, *Oceanographic Atlas of the Polar Seas*, United States Hydrographic Office Publication No. 705 (Washington, D.C., Government Printing Office, 1957).

U.S. Weather Bureau, *Climatological and Oceanographic Atlas for Mariners* (Washington, D.C., U.S. Weather Bureau, 1959).

GENERAL WORKS

Carson, Rachel L., *The Sea Around Us*, rev. ed. (New York, Oxford University Press, 1961), 237 pp.

Coker, Robert E., *This Great and Wide Sea: An Introduction to Oceanography and Marine Biology* (New York, Harper & Brothers, 1962), 325 pp.

Defant, Albert, *Physical Oceanography* (New York, Pergamon Press, 1961).

Guilcher, Andre, *Coastal and Submarine Morphology*, trans. from French by B. W. Sparks and R. H. W. Kneese (New York, John Wiley & Sons, Inc., 1958), 274 pp.

Johnson, Douglas, *Shore Processes and Shoreline Development* (New York, John Wiley & Sons, Inc., 1919), 584 pp.

King, Cuchlaine, *An Introduction to Oceanography* (New York, McGraw-Hill Book Company, Inc., 1963), 337 pp.

Miller, Robert, ed., *Papers in Marine Geology* (New York, The Macmillan Company, 1964), 531 pp.

Walford, Lionel Albert, *Living Resources of the Sea* (New York, Ronald Press Company, 1958), 321 pp.

VI

The Edaphic Factor

Soils reflect many significant physical attributes of place. Among them are temperature extremes, adequacy and frequency of precipitation, and the nature of the underlying rock. The upper horizons give evidence of leaching and the level of the water table, as well as the plant cover and of organisms, both living and dead.

Soils also reflect many significant cultural attributes of place. The impacts by man—by his plowing, planting, grazing, cropping and rotating crops, and fertilizing—cause differences in soil appearance, fertility, and productivity and create, indirectly and directly, economic and social changes quite apparent to those who wish to and are competently trained to see them. While soil may be regarded as a "stationary" factor in the earth's "life layer" it is a most necessary one for it is the physical and chemical earth attribute where lithosphere, hydrosphere, atmosphere, and biosphere mesh.

Mankind's food supply would diminish sharply, perhaps disastrously, with the loss and deterioration of soil.

28

Soils—
Their Origin and
Characteristics

Soil is one of mankind's most important assets. Indeed, ever since man invented the first primitive form of agriculture, near the beginning of the Neolithic period of prehistory, it has probably constituted his most valuable natural resource. Today, soil is intimately involved to a major degree in the geography of nearly all peoples of the world. Despite this fact, soil is practically unknown in any scientific sense to the majority of people. To the average man, a soil is merely "dirt"—dead material in which plants grow. Even many students of geography who are accustomed to dealing with soil as an environmental factor possess little real knowledge of its intricate characteristics or of the processes involved in its origin and evolution.

The general lack of knowledge concerning soil has hindered the proper evaluation of that factor in most studies of human ecology. A brief discussion of the various kinds of soil per se is therefore presented in the present chapter as a prelude to the succeeding chapter wherein they are treated geographically.

Soil may be defined nontechnically as the unconsolidated covering of the earth's surface that is capable of supporting life. It is apparent to the most casual observer that this loose mantle of surface materials is derived directly or indirectly from two sources: (a) the weathering of exposed masses of rock, and (b) the accumulation of dead and partially decayed organic materials. A cursory examination of the soil blanket reveals striking differences in character and depth from place to place over the earth. Many varieties of soil are easily recognized. To a certain extent, these varieties are owing to differences in the rocks from which they have been weathered

and to differences in the character and amount of organic matter which has been added.

SOIL FERTILITY

The most important characteristic of any soil is its fertility. The early view was that soil fertility was a result of the kind of parent material from which the soil was derived. Fertility, however, is not that easily accounted for. Rather, it is a resultant of many variable factors, such as texture, structure, aeration, and so forth.

TEXTURE

The fineness or coarseness of the particles composing a soil constitutes its texture. Commonly four main textural grades are recognized—gravel, sand, silt, and clay. The first two are coarse in texture and form *light soils,* whereas the last two are fine-textured and form the chief constituents of *heavy soils.* In size these particles are as follows: gravel is 2 mm. up to several cm. in diameter; sand, $\frac{1}{2}$ mm. up to 2 mm. in diameter; silt, $2\ \mu$ up to $\frac{1}{2}$ mm. in diameter; and clay, less than $2\ \mu$ in diameter.

Gravel, sand, and silt are rock particles, but clay is a chemical product of weathering and is composed of crystals $2\ \mu$ ($\frac{1}{12,000}$ of an inch or less in diameter). Clay particles are so small that they exhibit the special physical properties of a colloid.

Texture governs the water-holding quality of a soil. Gravelly and sandy soils tend to drain too rapidly. In clay, on the other hand, the soil openings are so small that drainage is retarded. Silt mixed with varying amounts of sand and clay is usually of most advantage in agriculture.

Since a soil rarely contains particles falling entirely into one textural grade, many transitional types and subtypes have been recognized and designated by such terms as *sandy loam, silty clay, coarse sand, fine sand, silt loam, fine sandy loam,* and others.

STRUCTURE AND TILTH

Structure refers not to the size of soil grains but to arrangement of these into physical aggregates. *Tilth* is a term applied to a soil in order to describe its behavior when stirred or tilled. Soils possess various structures, some simple and some complex, and hence behave very differently under tillage. Some are indurated or caked, some are mealy and friable, some form clods, some roll up into lumps, and some are held together in soddy chunks. Still others are flocculated so as to break into crumbly, loamy particles.

COLOR AND TEMPERATURE

Color, one of the most obvious properties of a soil, frequently may be correlated with fertility and other properties. This, however, is apt to be true only within a restricted area, for in widely separated localities the correlation may be reversed. For example, a black soil indicates high fertility in Iowa, whereas lighter colors indicate lower fertility and often poor structure. In western Washington, however, brown soil may be preferred to black because the latter frequently is acidic muck. In like manner, a red soil in Kansas may be of relatively low fertility, while one of similar color in Georgia is apt to be of prime quality as compared to other soils of the region. A gray desert soil of favorable texture and structure usually needs only water to render it highly productive; a gray forest soil may be so infertile that it can hardly be made to produce even after being heavily fertilized.

Color does, however, bear a rather reliable relation to soil *temperature*. Light colored soils behave very differently in regard to heating and cooling under insolation than do dark colored ones. Hence, some are "cold soils" whereas others are "warm soils."[1] Some are ready for production earlier in the spring than others. Some radiate their heat rapidly at night even during midsummer, while others retain theirs.

DEPTH AND PERMEABILITY

The soil mantle varies in depth from a few inches to scores of feet in exceptional instances. Some localities possess such a thin veneer mantling the underlying bedrock that cultivation is rendered precarious or impossible. Even where the soil mantle is deep, it may be relatively impermeable to the roots of plants by reason of an indurated subsoil or the presence of compacted layers within the soil.

AERATION AND MOISTURE

The amounts of air and water in a soil are factors which partially control its fertility. The amount of air present in the interstices depends upon the factors of texture, structure, and depth of the water table. Air in the soil is necessary for the germination of seeds and for insuring the thrifty development of most plants of economic value. Water is present as film coatings upon soil grains, as a capillary filling of the interstitial spaces between grains and, to a certain extent, as chemically combined water. The moisture content is controlled by much the same set of factors as the aeration.

COMPOSITION

Soil contains in general three groups of constituents—relatively insoluble mineral materials, soluble mineral materials, and organic matter. The main body of a soil normally consists largely of silica, alumina, and compounds of iron. The large glassy grains of sand are mostly quartz, a form of silica. The finer particles of silt and clay are predominantly composed of silicates of iron and alumina. Such ingredients may be regarded as largely inert and serve to provide bulk and framework to the soil.

The soluble mineral materials are much less in total quantity but are more important in function, since they comprise the majority of plant nutrients—calcium, potassium, magnesium, and so forth. Not all soluble mineral matter, however, is desirable; sodium salts, for example, are deleterious in any save small amounts.

Organic matter is present in or upon most

---

[1] Other physical properties, of course, are important also in this connection.

soils and is composed chiefly of dead and partially decomposed plant life. Animal forms, too, add their smaller quota. Such plant and animal accumulations are known as *humus*. Soils rich in humus are characteristically black or dark brown in color. Light colored soils are usually poor in humus.

A soil composition making for fertility is one which is relatively free from injurious ingredients, and contains an abundance of available plant nutrients, both mineral matter and humus.

MICROORGANISMS

A physical aggregate of mineral particles, plus chemical plant foods, plus dead organic matter, does not in itself produce fertility. This last is to a considerable degree the function of soil microorganisms, the number of which is incredibly large. "For example, as many as one million protozoans, 800,000 algae, one million fungi, and 20 million bacteria may inhabit a single grain of soil." Since the topsoil upon a single acre (down to the depth usually reached by a plow) weighs about 2 million pounds (about 1 billion grams), it is apparent that the total number of microorganisms in it is about 23 quadrillions. The combined weight of these invisible living organisms "is from 10,000 to 50,000 pounds."[2] Since that same acre of soil in a warm humid climate could support on its grass and other herbage three to five cattle or fifteen to twenty sheep, it is apparent that the soil supports as much (or perhaps even more) life below ground as above ground. Moreover, the constant activity of these soil microorganisms is necessary in order to help create, to maintain, and to augment soil fertility.

AGE

The age of soil controls in large measure its fertility and lasting qualities. Soils pass through a regular sequence of stages in their evolutionary life cycle, a circumstance which causes them to exhibit distinctly different characteristics at each stage. This, however, will be discussed at greater length later in the chapter.

PHYSICAL ENVIRONMENT

The usefulness of soils varies according to certain aspects of their physical environment. The climate above and the drainage below the soil, the slope of the surface, and the vegetative cover all have a bearing upon a soil's utility.

GEOGRAPHICAL LOCATION

Lastly, the geographical location of a soil (its relative position and accessibility) may be and frequently is the deciding factor in determining utilization. There are still areas of otherwise excellent soil which lie untouched because of unfortunate location. On the contrary, many areas of relatively infertile soil are utilized and given a high valuation because of their central or adjacent location.

CLASSIFICATIONS OF SOILS[3]

LITHOLOGIC CLASSIFICATION OF SOILS

The fact that soil materials ordinarily consist mainly of small fragments of rocks and minerals shows that there is an important relation between soils and their parent geologic formations. Two similar sandstones in widely separated places may, therefore, yield roughly similar soils; and the same may be said for two shales, two limestones, or two conglomerates. Early observers, therefore, concluded that most of the observable differences among soils were caused by differences in the rocks from which they were derived. One textbook[4] pointed out that,

Among stratified rocks, most sandstones weather into poor soil. Shales produce clay soils of greater average fertility, but in some cases they are heavy and hard to work. Limestone soils are, as a class, very fertile, but if their limey constituents are dissolved out, as they may be, the soil is less fertile.

Such clay, if derived from phosphate limestone, may be highly phosphatic and fertile; if derived from cherty limestone, it may be filled with and

[2] F. L. Wynd, "Feed the Soil," an address presented at the annual convention of the Plant Food Producers of Ontario, at Tadoussac, Quebec, June, 1950.

[3] For the soil classifications of the U.S. Department of Agriculture see *Soil Science Proceedings 1965* (Washington, D.C., U.S. Government Printing Office, 1965), p. 332.

[4] R. D. Salisbury, H. H. Barrows, and W. S. Tower, *Elements of Geography* (New York, Henry Holt and Company, Inc., 1913), p. 264.

in places almost covered with obnoxious chert nodules.

The igneous and metamorphic rocks yield as great a variety of soil types. In general, granite, rhyolite, quartzite, or granogneiss yield soils which are usually infertile and acidic because of their high silica content. On the other hand, a basic eruptive rock (such as basaltic lava) or the ultrabasic gabbro among the plutonic rocks may weather into highly fertile soils.

All the facts readily led to the classification of soils on the basis of the lithology of the parent material. Soils were commonly designated as granitic soils, limestone soils, shale soils, lava soils, and so forth. However useful such geologic or lithologic designations may have been, modern pedologists have found that so many of the characteristics of a soil are determined by other factors that this method of classification is of limited value.

ATTRIBUTIVE CLASSIFICATION OF SOILS

If the soil map of a county in the United States is selected at random it will, upon examination, reveal from eight to fifty soil types mapped areally. Such a map is the result of close study of the several soil attributes in the area and a careful attempt to classify soils into series.

Soils are frequently classified as to color, texture, place location, physical environment, or a combination of several or all of these characteristics. Such a classification may be termed *attributive*, because it is based upon specific attributes. This kind of classification should be regarded highly for some purposes, but it is of limited value for beginning students in geography.

PHYSIOGRAPHIC CLASSIFICATION OF SOILS

It is a fact of common observation that some localities possess deep soil while others have but little. Moreover, within a given locality, if it be at all diverse as to relief, there is a spotted distribution of soil types.

Depth is to be explained by the balance between the rate of soil formation and the rate of its removal by the agencies of erosion. The local diversity or patchy occurrence is apt to be puzzling until the physiographic agents are in-

voked to provide an explanation. When the work of these agencies in erosion, transportation, and deposition of the soil-forming materials is recalled, considerable light is shed upon the problem.

From the physiographic standpoint, three classes of soils may be distinguished.

Figure 28–1 Cross section of a residual soil. (Photo courtesy of the Soil Conservation Service, USDA)

Residual soils

Soils formed by the weathering of rocks and the addition of humus *in situ* are known as residual. While there may be small additions of colluvial materials through creep, slumping, talus fall, and slope wash, such soils reside essentially where formed. A cross section shows a regular gradation in texture downward from fine material through coarse subsoil into broken rock with unaltered bedrock below (Fig. 28–1).

Cumulose soils

Cumulose soils are, in one sense, special forms of the residual type in which the humus content is exceptionally high. *Peat* runs 70 percent or more organic matter without discernible inorganic constituents. *Muck,* a heavy black earth, possesses an organic content of 15 to 50 percent.

Transported soils

In many instances, soils do not reside where formed but occur in locations to which they have been brought by stream, wind, or glacier. Such transported soils may be recognized by the fact that they do not grade into the underlying materials but overlie them unconformably. Representatives of this type may be designated according to the physiographic agent by which they have been borne to their present location and are as follows:

Alluvial soils are those which have been transported and deposited by running water. Their materials are usually sorted more or less carefully as to size and laid down in layered or stratified arrangement. Soils of this class are to be found on deltas, river floodplains, river ter-

Figure 28–3 Vertical cut through a soil of glacial origin showing the unsorted condition of the materials. (Photo courtesy of the Soil Conservation Service, USDA)

races, lacustrine plains, and sometimes on peneplanic uplands (Fig. 28–2).

Morainic soils are the result of glacial transportation and deposition. The materials of a moraine are unsorted as to kind or texture and constitute a veritable jumble of varied ingredients (Fig. 28–3). The surface of moraine is sometimes thickly strewn with boulders and cobbles and sometimes is singularly free from such coarse debris. Morainic soil occurs in formerly glaciated mountain valleys as local deposits and as till sheets on open plains country.

Æolian or wind transported and deposited soils are of two kinds: (1) coarse sands formed by dune accumulation (Fig. 23–2) and (2) loess or layers of fine silty material consisting of wind-blown dust. Migrating sand dunes and ridges may form on the ocean's coast, near the margins of lakes, in river valleys, or in arid regions. Such sand formations may migrate considerable distances and completely cover an area

Figure 28–2 Cross-section view of an alluvial soil. (Photo courtesy of the Soil Conservation Service, USDA)

Figure 28–4 Loess standing in a vertical bluff near Vicksburg, Mississippi. Loess is a yellowish-brown substance of such fine texture that it disappears into the pores of the skin when rubbed between the fingers. (Photograph courtesy of the U.S. Geological Survey)

with a hummocky blanket of sand. Sooner or later, however, such deposits become anchored by vegetation and begin their evolution into soil.

Areas located to the leeward of deserts, large floodplains, or surfaces denuded of vegetation by continental glaciation are subject to heavy dust storms, after each of which a layer of loess is left upon the surface of the region. Such loessial deposits may accumulate to great thickness. In the Missouri Valley, deposits of 40 to 50 feet in thickness are not uncommon. In northwestern China, loess deposits have locally reached a thickness of more than 330 feet.

In texture, loess is intermediate between silt and clay. In structure, it is crumbly and blocklike in its cleavage. As a result, where transected by river valleys, canals, or road cuts, loess deposits form almost vertical cliffs, usually yellow in color (Fig. 28–4). Because of this peculiar cleavage habit, loess will not slump under erosion as do most soils. The loess-covered hills of western China are, as a result, carefully terraced to provide barley and millet fields. Many of the peasants in the treeless areas of Shansi and Shensi have built homes by digging caves into the loess cliffs. In the United States, bank swallows com-

monly evidence similar troglodytic characteristics.

PHYSIOLOGIC CLASSIFICATIONS OF SOILS
The life cycle of soils

Regardless of geologic origin or physiographic history, all soils within a given climato-floral region tend to develop certain traits in common. Any soil has going on within it certain chemical and physical processes; soils pass through cycles of development resembling those of other changing natural phenomena.

One may, therefore, recognize young soils, mature soils, and old soils. Such a classification is obviously *physiological,* depending as it does upon the stage reached by the developmental processes within the soil itself. These processes include oxidation, hydration, solution, the addition of humus, eluviation or the removal of materials from the upper levels of the soil, and illuviation or the deposition of materials at a lower horizon. As time goes on, they give to a soil characteristics entirely different from those which it possessed initially—characteristics which are in harmony with the climatic and vegetative environment. In other words, soils, like human beings, become adjusted to their environment.

Young soils

Wherever material is being removed rapidly by erosion, or conversely, wherever it is being deposited at an appreciable rate, the evolution of the soil is constantly retarded or set back as the new materials repeat the changes of youth.

In youthful soils the chemical elements have not been extensively changed from those in the parent materials, humus is usually inappreciable in amount, and the original parent structure is not wholly broken down. Hence such "soils" are frequently merely raw sands, silts, and clays (*regosols*), or stony mountain soils (*lithosols*). Under the petrographic microscope the grains still record much concerning the physical geological history of their area of derivation.

Mature soils

If soil material is subjected for a long period of time to a certain climatic regime, it slowly progresses from youth toward maturity. The climatic regime in question controls the vegetative cover, the amount of water entering the soil, and the temperatures to which it is subjected. Thus the evolution is from the start directed toward specific characteristics to be attained in maturity.

As time goes on, the chemical structure of the original material is more and more broken down, chiefly through the disintegration of the complex silicates. Iron is oxidized, alumina is hydrated, and the lime, potash, and other substances are taken into solution. Meanwhile organic litter is accumulating on the surface and roots are penetrating the upper reaches of the soil.

Where the climate is humid, the iron is oxidized to a red color and both the iron and aluminum compounds are carried downward and deposited as a matrix about the grains of the soil material, or as coating upon them, or even as concretionary nodules. Simultaneously the lime and other soluble alkaline materials (soda, potash, and magnesia) are taken into solution, carried downward, and eventually removed by ground water. This may be described as a lime-losing, iron-alumina-accumulating soil and is usually acid in reaction. This type of soil is called a *pedalfer*.

On the other hand if the climate is arid or semiarid, the iron and aluminum compounds are, because of a paucity of soil water, but little

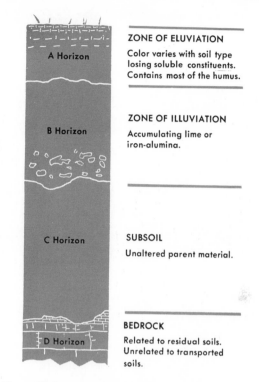

ZONE OF ELUVIATION

Color varies with soil type losing soluble constituents. Contains most of the humus.

ZONE OF ILLUVIATION

Accumulating lime or iron-alumina.

SUBSOIL

Unaltered parent material.

BEDROCK

Related to residual soils. Unrelated to transported soils.

Figure 28–5   Generalized profile of a mature soil.

Figure 28–6   Profile of a mature black-earth or chernozem soil in the North Dakota portion of the American Spring Wheat Belt. This very fine sandy loam shows a fairly deep, dark-colored surface or "A" horizon, a brownish lower "B" horizon, and a light gray zone of lime enrichment in its lower "B" horizon. (Photo courtesy of the Soil Conservation Service, USDA)

Figure 28–7 World map of principal soil types. Pedalferic group: (1) laterites, (2) red and yellow soils, (3) gray-brown forest soils, (4) podzols, (5) tundra soils, (6) prairie soils. Pedocalic group: (7) chernozem or black soils, (8) chestnut soils, (9) brown semidesert soils, (10) sierozem or gray desert soils. Zero indicates high mountain areas.

altered. The descending meteoric waters, however, are sufficient to take into solution the lime and carry it downward a distance varying from a few inches to several feet. There the lime is deposited as a grain coating, a matrix filling, or as concretions within a layer of variable thickness and depth. During spells of wet weather, the lime may be carried down, only to be brought back up by ascending capillary water, and deposited in the zone of illuviation. Such a soil, lime accumulating and alkaline in reaction, is called a *pedocal.*

In either case the youthful soil is slowly becoming a mature soil possessed of definite hori-

zons or layers. A vertical cross section of these is known as the *profile.* When mature, a soil shows the following profile development (Figs. 28–5 and 28–6). In some localities where exceptional conditions prevail, such as in playas—desert lake beds, bogs, half-bogs, or wet meadows—special types of soils (intrazonal soils) develop.

Old soils

These processes finally build definite types of soil out of heterogeneous parent materials. But the processes finally run down and may actually bring about degeneration in old age. Soils surviving from a past physiographic cycle, as on undissected

remnants of an uplifted peneplain, may advance far into senility. The soils of any area which is undisturbed for prolonged periods of time finally reach old age and are known as *planosols*. Their A horizons become entirely leached and impoverished. Their B horizons become compacted, indurated, and in places even cemented. Such objectionable features as hardpan, gumbo, iron crust, and mortar-bed occasionally manifest themselves in old age.

CHARACTERISTICS OF MATURE SOILS

THE PEDALFERS

As was pointed out in the previous section, soils fall into two physiological classes—*pedocalic* and *pedalferic*.[5] Of these, the pedalfers are characteristic of a humid climate and develop under a vegetation cover of forest, savanna, or tall grass. They are, as a rule, low in humus and are iron-alumina accumulating. In the following description of the six types of pedalfers, only those which are mature, that is, possess fully developed profiles, are mentioned.

Laterites

Typical of the most humid portions of the Rainy Tropical regions is a soil known as *laterite* (Fig. 28–7). If the forest is destroyed, the soil no longer receives the organic material so necessary

---

[5] The syllable *ped* means "earth"; while *al* indicates aluminum; *fe*, iron; and *cal*, calcium.

for the formation of humus. Moreover, the high temperatures of the surface layer of soil causes the humus (organic nitrogen) to deteriorate. Also, the penetration of air and water into the bare soil is harmful to it. Finally the heavy rainfall causes percolating water to leach the soil of the bases and nitrates.

In areas of slightly less rainfall (sixty to eighty inches), lateritic earths of several kinds develop. These more or less resemble true laterites and may be grouped with them as related soil types. Laterites and lateritic soils thus cover most areas having a Rainy Tropical climate and, in addition, extend into the rainier portions of the Monsoon Tropical climate.

Tropical and subtropical red soils[6]

Over large portions of those regions which lie in the Monsoon Tropical and Humid Subtropical climates, the characteristic soils are red soils (Fig. 28–8). Like the laterites, the red soils develop under a forest cover in a hot, humid environment (thirty to sixty inches of rain per annum). They are low in humus, phosphate, and the alkaline earths, but are less leached of such materials than is laterite. They are usually red in color because of the presence of abundant ferric hydroxide, but they may vary considerably in color from one locality to another. The yellow soils which occur over parts of southeastern United States are similar to the red soils except that they have probably evolved from materials either so deficient in iron as to preclude the attainment of the normal red color, or so poor in drainage as to permit of only imperfect hydration.

Gray-brown podzolic soils

Poleward from the red soils of the Tropical and Subtropical zones, lie the gray-brown podzolic soils. These are brown or grayish-brown soils with brown or yellowish-brown subsoils. The gray-brown podzolic soils develop under forest or woodland cover in the milder portions of the Cyclonic Zone. Their characteristic environment manifests from thirty to fifty inches of rainfall

[6] Red soils also occur in a few places in the Cyclonic Zone.

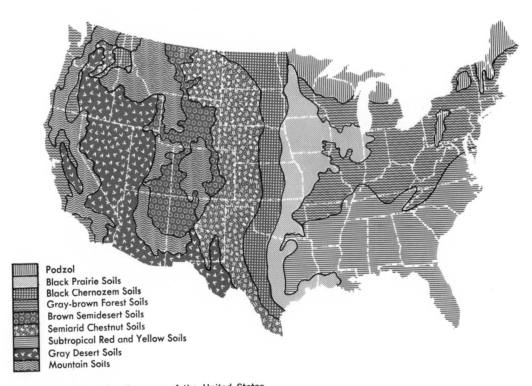

Podzol
Black Prairie Soils
Black Chernozem Soils
Gray-brown Forest Soils
Brown Semidesert Soils
Semiarid Chestnut Soils
Subtropical Red and Yellow Soils
Gray Desert Soils
Mountain Soils

Figure 28–8   Principal soil groups of the United States.

annually, a hot or warm summer, and a distinct but not severe winter season. The vegetation of their habitat is usually hardwood forest: in some localities it may be coniferous forest or a mixed stand of conifers and hardwoods. A thin layer of leaf mold overlies these soils and a small amount of humus is present in the A horizon. They are not so thoroughly leached as the lateritic soils and red and yellow soils of the warmer climates. The gray-brown soils are one of the better soils of the pedalfer group.

Podzols

The podzols are light-gray soils occurring in regions whose characteristic natural vegetation is northern coniferous forest. They are thus characteristic of the humid poleward portions of the northern Cyclonic Zone, extending far northward until they meet the rather characterless soils of the tundra. The environment of the podzols is one of cool, moist summers and long severe winters. These conditions permit the accumulation of a thick surface layer of raw humus below which lies the gray or grayish white A horizon, underlain in turn by brown subsoil. Podzols are light textured; the surface soils are leached of soluble plant foods and are acid in reaction. They are among the poorest of soils.

Tundra soils

Poorest of all the pedalfers are the tundra soils. The type of environment in which tundra soils develop is that of the Subpolar climate which characterizes the coasts and islands of the Arctic and Antarctic areas. There, long, very cold winters keep soil moisture locked up most of the year. During the few weeks of the summer, the ground thaws out only to a shallow depth, and below this lies the *permafrost* zone. Chemical action is slow; hence the mineral matter in tundra soils is mostly mere broken particles of parent material.

Bacterial activity is feeble, plant decomposition is slow, and much humus accumulates. Tundra soils, therefore, lack any real vertical profile. Their surface may be covered with a sod layer of mosses, lichens, and grasses two or three inches thick.[7] Below this lies a thin layer of peaty humus, underlain in turn by a layer of sandy clay.

Prairie soils

Excelling all other pedalfers in fertility and lasting qualities are the prairie soils. Unlike them, too, the latter have a wide zonal distribution, although they are limited in actual areal extent. In the Cyclonic Zone, this soil is black in color and occurs in areas having 25 to 30 inches of rainfall annually. In the Subtropical Zone, the color is dark-brown and the rainfall limits are 35 to 40 inches. In the Tropical Zone, prairie soils develop under a rainfall of 25 to 50 inches; their color is reddish brown.

These rainfall amounts would indicate a natural vegetation of forest in the prairie environment. Actually, the vegetative cover is one of tall prairie or savanna grass which, for some reason either natural or man made, exists in an environment for which the normal climax should be forest. This has led some investigators to conclude that the prairie soils are probably immature soils in the process of becoming either red soils or gray-brown soils. Their dark color is owing to deep penetration of grass roots—a trait in which they resemble the pedocalic group. There is, however, no lime accumulation in the B horizon. Neither is there any marked tendency to accumulate iron and alumina. The prairie soils are high in humus, of good structure and tilth, and rather rich in soluble plant foods. They are one of the most valuable types of soil for agriculture.

THE PEDOCALS

Pedocalic soils evolve in an arid, semiarid, or subhumid climate. They accumulate lime carbonate in their subsoils even though the rocks from which they derive contain very little. They are nonacid in reaction and develop under a cover of short grass, steppe, or desert vegetation. They fall into four rather distinct types which in maturity present the following characteristics.

Chernozems (black soils)

The chernozem or black-soil type of pedocal ranges from Tropical to Cyclonic Zone. The en-

---

[7] Arthur N. Strahler, *Introduction to Physical Geography* (New York, John Wiley & Sons, Inc., 1965), p. 185.

vironment suitable for the development of a chernozem or black soil is a vegetation cover of prairie grass or short grass, a hot temperature during at least part of the year, and a subhumid rainfall. Areas whose average annual precipitation is less than twenty inches usually develop a chernozem soil. Chernozem is considered a soil aristocrat; it is very fertile and contains abundant grass-root humus and much mineral plant food. It is black to dark chocolate-brown in color, with yellowish, brownish, or reddish subsoil. It is neutral or limy in reaction and contains a noticeable but deep-lying zone of lime accumulation (Fig. 28–6). Chernozems are perhaps the most desirable soils known to man.

Dark-brown soils

The dark-brown soil type, like all the pedocals, is distributed through all temperature zones of the earth except the Polar. It exists under 10 to 15 inches of rainfall in the Cyclonic Zone and under 10 to 20 inches in the Subtropical and Tropical zones. Thus, it is distinctly a soil of semiarid lands whose natural vegetation is steppe or short grass. These soils are dark-brown to chestnut in color, for which reason they are fre-

quently known as chestnut-colored soils. They contain only a fair amount of humus but are rich in plant food. A marked zone of lime accumulation occurs at a moderate depth in the B horizon. The C horizon or subsoil is brown in color.

Brown soils

In better watered desert areas where short grass with low density of cover is the vegetation, the prevailing soils are brown to light brown in color and show a marked zone of calcium carbonate and similar materials at shallow depth. The light annual rainfall of eight to ten inches prevents leaching; hence these brown soils are fertile, despite their low humus content which is expected of soils developed under poor grass or shrub cover. Very little of these soils is under cultivation.

Gray desert soils

Poorest of all pedocals are the gray desert soils. They are gray in color with brown subsoil. Their A horizon is light and porous, often powdery in structure. The soil profile is poorly developed, the humus content is very low. The lime accumulation is heavy and close to the surface.

SUGGESTED USEFUL READINGS

Buckman, Harry O., and Nyle C. Brady, *The Nature and Property of Soils*, 6th ed. (New York, The Macmillan Company, 1960), 567 pp.

Bunting, B. T., *The Geography of Soil* (Chicago, Aldine Publishing Company, Inc., 1967), 190 pp.

Eyre, Samuel R., *Vegetation and Soils* (Chicago, Aldine Publishing Co., Inc., 1963), 324 pp.

Kellogg, Charles E., *The Soils that Support Us* (New York, The Macmillan Company, 1947), 370 pp.

Millar, C. E., L. M. Turk, and H. D. Foth, *Fundamentals of Soil Science*, 3d ed. (New York, John Wiley & Sons, Inc., 1958), 526 pp.

Robinson, G. W., *Soils: Their Origin, Constitution and Classification*, 3d ed. (New York, John Wiley & Sons, Inc., 1959), 513 pp.

U.S. Department of Agriculture, *Soil*, Yearbook of Agriculture, 1957 (Washington, D.C., Government Printing Office, 1957), 784 pp.

29

Soils— Culturally Defined

Man's record of abusing and destroying his heritage of soil is indeed a dismal one. "After man, the desert" is a saying unhappily true of human geography in all climes and ages. The sites of ancient empires are today scenes of desolation. The Mediterranean margins of Asia and Africa are dotted by ruins and sprinkled with the debris of cities great in the days of the Roman Empire. Today many parts of this area support only an occasional Bedouin and his flock. The Mesopotamian valley of the Tigris and Euphrates rivers, once so flourishing as to mythologically suggest a site for the Garden of Eden, is today a depleted and well-nigh deserted terrain. Beyond the Great Wall of China, uncounted ruins testify to the land's former bounty in what is now the Gobi margin. Climatic changes perhaps have played their part in this encroachment of the desert upon former productive cultural landscapes, but man's ruin of the soil cannot have been a negligible factor.

Short as has been the period of man's use of soil in the United States, approximately 50 million acres of soil on flat, rolling, and hilly landform have been destroyed and 50 million acres more are almost as seriously damaged. About 100 million additional acres are in very bad condition. This soil destruction is proceeding at a rate of about 200,000 acres per year. Much of this land has been ruined so thoroughly as to compel complete or partial abandonment. This, if allowed to proceed unchecked, may result in nothing short of a national debacle. American soil loss by man-induced erosion already exceeds the total area of Connecticut, Illinois, and Massachusetts (Fig. 29-1). No people, civilized or barbaric, on the face of the globe have impover-ished and ruined their farm lands faster than Americans.

ECOLOGICAL IMPORTANCE OF SOIL

Aside from certain forms of aquatic life and very lowly forms of terrestrial plants and animals, no life of any consequence would be possible upon the earth were it not for soil. Plants grow in it, some animals live in it, and practically all animals depend upon it for food. Man likewise derives all but a minute portion of his food from the soil through the medium of either plants or animals. In addition to food, the soil supplies a host of other articles to man; in all, these amount to something more than 80 percent of the total annual production of raw materials in the world.

The soil as an element of the natural environment is of interest because it constitutes the basis of three major forms of economic-geographic adjustment—agriculture, pastoralism, and forest industry. In agriculture, the adjustment is, however, based directly upon the soil itself, whereas in pastoralism and forest industry it is aimed only indirectly at the soil through the medium of the natural vegetation which it supports, grassland or forest respectively.

Ecologically, the soil involves probably eight-tenths of the human race. In nearly every portion of the world a large percentage of the labor force is engaged in agriculture or in allied pursuits. Many underdeveloped portions of the earth show very great percentages of soil-adjusted populations.

Britain alone of the so-called highly industrialized countries shows an apparent escape from the soil. Approximately 5 percent of the British

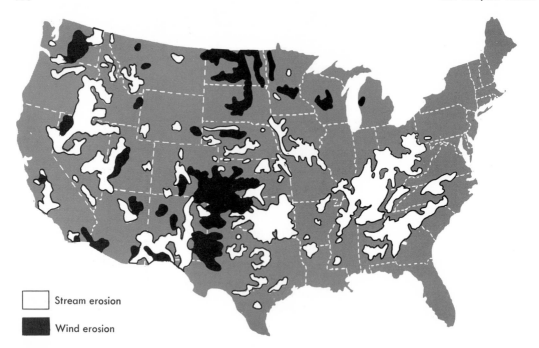

Stream erosion

Wind erosion

Figure 29–1   Areas in which much of the soil has been either severely damaged or completely destroyed by erosion.

population may be said to be agricultural. But even here, for every Englishman who has been released from agriculture, an additional increment has been necessitated from outside sources.

GEOGRAPHIC PROBLEMS IN SOIL USE

The adjustment of man to soil, in order to be satisfactory, entails the proper solving of three problems—initial selection, maintenance, and utilization. That these problems have been met incorrectly more often than not is frequently evidenced by the uneconomic status of soil-supported industries, by the need for protective tariffs, and by temporary abandonment or permanent ruin of land.

INITIAL SELECTION OF SOIL

The United States was settled by land-hungry Europeans. These early settlers were of many kinds, but for the most part they were city and village dwellers drawn from the middle classes of northern Europe. They knew little about farming and even less about land. Consequently, they settled upon lands with soils of all grades of fer-

tility. Some of this settlement prospered, some of it failed dismally and was abandoned. Much of it just managed to maintain itself under economically marginal conditions.

When marginal land deteriorates under careless handling, when auxiliary resources of timber and wildlife diminish, or when markets decline, economically marginal lands become economically submarginal. In time of depression, people living on submarginal lands are the first to apply for public assistance or relief. If economic conditions remain poor, settlement of the poorest lands is abandoned. Even in prosperous times, much agricultural settlement does not produce enough besides providing the bare necessaries of life, to pay for schools, roads, rural mail delivery, public health, forest fire protection, and other governmental services.

In the course of the history of land settlement in the United States, many Americans did gain considerable empirical knowledge of land and soil. The United States, however, never developed anything approaching a national land policy nor even a system of land classification to govern land settlement. Today, there are millions of acres in farms in the United States which are unsuited for agriculture and which would be more profitable or more enduring if devoted to some other use. There are perhaps 650,000 economically submarginal or otherwise undesirable farms in the United States. What the magnitude of this problem in the other countries of the world is cannot even be estimated.

SOIL MAINTENANCE

Proper maintenance of the soil is not a single problem. Rather it challenges man along three distinct lines—*desiccation, destruction,* and *depletion,* each or all of which may become crucial under certain environmental circumstances.

THE PROBLEM OF DESICCATION

In the Cyclonic Zone, an annual precipitation of twenty inches is normally the minimum under which permanent agriculture may be carried on. There are, however, extensive tracts in the world where it is prosecuted under rainfall conditions which are below this safe minimum. In such subhumid and semiarid lands, soil desiccation may be a serious problem.

In the opening years of the twentieth century large areas in the Columbia Basin of northwestern United States were settled and sown to wheat. In localities where the annual precipitation was from twelve to twenty inches, huge yields per acre were obtained for several years. Then, rather rapidly the yield began to diminish and failure after failure in crops occurred. County organizations were reduced to skeletons and whole townships were abandoned. Crops during the first few years had utilized not only the rainfall but had drawn upon the stored water in the soil. When this stored water had been depleted, the annual rainfall proved insufficient to support further crops. So desiccated had the soil become that, even where abandoned, it usually has not regained its grass covering. In many localities, the topsoil still has the appearance of dust or fine dry sand. Great dust storms occur during which much soil is removed by deflation, to the land's permanent detriment and to the acute discomfort of the remaining inhabitants.

Some such results as these must have attended all of man's preliminary ventures into lands of marginal rainfall. In some localities, however, he has satisfactorily adjusted himself to the soil under semiarid conditions.[1] Such adjustments are usually termed *dry farming* and include some three types of common practices. The first consists of deep plowing followed by summer fallowing. During the fallow interval the soil is harrowed to destroy moisture-consuming weeds and to keep the surface loose. Water may therefore soak into the soil, its escape being retarded by the mulch. Thus sufficient moisture is stored to make possible successful cropping in alternate years. The second type is used in regions where the soil is light and friable and strong winds are prevalent; here the maintenance of a loose surface mulch in summer fallowing is impossible. Hence, dry farming must consist of careful selection of drought-resisting plants which make modest demands upon soil moisture. Millets, sorghums, and Sudan grass are examples of such crops. The third type of dry farming seeks to concentrate soil moisture into certain restricted spots at the expense of extensive intervening stretches. This is a common practice along the northern margin of the Sahara. Broad holes are excavated and partially refilled with fine, fertile, and moisture-retaining soil. The soil water over a wide area drains into this depression where it is used to support perhaps an olive tree and a patch of barley. Similarly, a dry gully may be blocked by an earthen or stone dam behind which fine moist silt slowly accumulates. This, too, is made to support its cereal patch or tree crop, but no attempt is made to utilize the surrounding land.

THE PROBLEM OF DESTRUCTION

While soil desiccation is a problem peculiar to lands of marginal rainfall, water erosion is the curse of agriculture in humid regions. On every type of land, save that which is perfectly flat, water erosion, the physical destruction of soil,

[1] G. A. Fuller, United States Soil Conservation Service, states that a lack of nitrification is as great a limiting factor in dry areas as a dearth of moisture. Personal communication.

Figure 29–2 Soil erosion of gully type in Carroll County, Mississippi. (Photo courtesy of the Soil Conservation Service, USDA)

occurs.[2] As raindrops fall upon the land, they proceed to run off if the land possesses appreciable slope. Each droplet carries away to the nearest stream and, perhaps eventually to the ocean, a tiny grain or so of soil. After each rain, a plowed field is seen to be covered with rill marks or tiny channels created by the erosive power of running water. If this is allowed to continue, these rills grow into gullies that constantly become wider and deeper. These, forming on fine, gently rolling farm land, may become as deep as 100 to 200 feet within sixty or seventy years. Eventually a field becomes too rough to cultivate and in addition loses its entire soil covering (Fig. 29–2). At best the soil is but a few inches to a few feet deep, and the average depth of the more productive top soil is only seven or eight inches; below it lie the coarse, infertile materials of the subsoil. Thus has man during his short history ruined millions of acres of good land. One is led to wonder how long he will or can perpetuate this folly.

The remedy is twofold: prevention of sheet washing or soil planation which precedes gullying, and eternal vigilance and constant warfare on the gully where it has formed. There are several ways to prosecute a warfare of this kind. Gullies which have already formed or are in process of formation may be checked by damming or filling with straw, logs, rocks, cement, or brush and by protecting the sides against further washing by planting them with Bermuda grass (Fig. 29–3). Further gullying may be prevented by correct land utilization, a change in methods of plowing (Fig. 29–4), and avoidance of overpasturing.

In the United States, all kinds of land have been devoted to a wide variety of crops on the fallacious assumption that all of it, good and bad, steep and level, was equally well suited to these diverse uses. The solution of this problem must

[2] The Soil Conservation Service reports that more than 75 percent of the United States consists of sloping land, all of which is subject to erosion in some degree when used for intertilled crops or when overgrazed.

Figure 29–3 Wire fencing and brush dams in a gully near Ralston, Nebraska. This is one of several effective methods being employed in the United States to control gullying. With every rain gullies grow longer by headward erosion; as soon as they get down into the friable material, the land "melts away" almost like sugar. It is patent that much study and research are necessary to solve this problem—one of the biggest confronting farmers over large parts of the world. (Photo courtesy of the Soil Conservation Service, USDA)

depend on the scientific coordinated action of the best land-management specialists in the country.

The moderately sloping lands are being protected by a new system of strip cropping whereby the clean-tilled crops, such as corn, cotton, and tobacco, which really cause most of the erosion, are alternated with strips of close-growing crops such as grass, lespedeza, sorghum, and others. All of the crops are planted along the contour of the land. By this method, a strip containing dense crops not only catches rain water and suspended soil from the clean-tilled strip above but also protects the soil of the intertilled strip below. On some slopes, strips of permanent protective cover consisting of shrubs, trees, and vines are being planted. This excellent procedure not only retards water erosion but also makes advantageous use of plants of economic value—nut trees, persimmons, honey locust, and briar. In the Old World, tree crops have long been used on slopes. The tea and mulberry groves of the Orient and the olive, chestnut, and carob groves of the Mediterranean realm are familiar examples of this type of slope land utilization. In the New World, the coffee plantations of Latin America present an outstanding example. The rather recent development of

Figure 29–4 Low terraces (dark vegetation) laid out on contour with crop rows on contour between them near Red Oak, Iowa. Sloping land, if used at all for crops, should be plowed in conformity to the contour of the land; that is, the furrows should be winding and level rather than straight. This practice permits each furrow to function as a soil-preserving dike. (Photo courtesy of the USDA)

apple orchards in parts of the northern Ozarks and in the hill country of southeastern Ohio has brought about a greatly improved adjustment to soils in these areas.

Where tree crops are not in demand, much can still be done to reduce erosion by planting the land to cover crops rather than to those which demand clean intertillage. As indicated heretofore, corn, cotton, and tobacco demand frequent cultivation and hence are enormous soil wasters on slope land. Pasture, hay, and certain small grains, on the contrary, demand only an initial plowing and thenceforth form an almost complete cover, their roots binding the soil together with varying degrees of effectiveness. In Missouri, it was found that clean-tilled crops lose two to three hundred times as much soil as close-growing crops and that bare ground loses four hundred times as much.

Overgrazing on slopes also permits erosion, for it destroys the young growth and the power of the vegetation to reproduce itself. Some improvement is being made in this respect in each of the major grazing regions of the United States. Effective weapons against gullying and erosion in these areas are (1) avoidance of premature grazing, (2) rotation grazing, (3) prevention of overgrazing, and (4) deferred grazing, which is a plan that allows a portion of the range to mature seeds before grazing is begun.

The fight against erosion is of far-reaching significance. Not only will it save soil, an irreplaceable resource, but it has a vital bearing upon the navigability of inland waterways, the value of streams for water power, irrigation, and municipal water supply, and upon the problem of flood control.

THE PROBLEM OF DEPLETION

Analyses of the dry matter in vegetation show that plants utilize some thirteen chemical elements in their growth. The elements in order of quantity present in plant tissue are: carbon, oxygen, hydrogen, nitrogen, potassium, sodium, calcium, magnesium, silicon, sulfur, phosphorus, chlorine, and iron. Of these, carbon, hydrogen, and oxygen are supplied in abundance by air and water. Three others, sodium, chlorine, and silicon, seem not to be absolutely essential for plant growth, but soil, to be classified as fertile, must contain the remaining seven in an available soluble form.

Of these seven essential elements or plant foods, iron, magnesium, and sulfur are almost always present in sufficient abundance to meet crop needs. A fourth, calcium, is frequently deficient in pedalferic soils, a circumstance which may be manifested in acidity, sourness, and poor tilth. Poverty in calcium, however, presents no great problem. Heavy liming, or the addition of crushed limestone or shell in quantity, will usually correct the most extreme cases of calcium deficiency at relatively low expense. The supply of the remaining three elements, phosphorus, nitrogen, and potassium, is often inadequate. Even in rich soils one or more of these three elements may be none too abundant and hence may be quickly depleted. Because of this, they have been termed the "crucial" soil elements.

Soil-forming materials usually contain in relatively insoluble form most or all of the elements needed by plants. Prolonged chemical weathering finally breaks down a portion of such potential plant foods into available soluble form. A virgin soil thus contains the accumulated results of a very long period of weathering. Each year an additional increment of available plant food is added, but the rate of liberation is, in the very nature of the process involved, exceedingly slow. It is not difficult, therefore, to exhaust the supply of certain of these plant foods. It should not be surmised that virgin soils contain all the elements, for many are notably deficient in certain ones. For this reason, extreme care should be taken in selecting soils for crops. This is particularly significant inasmuch as each crop demands a small quantity of many elements and usually draws heavily on one or two. For example, coffee and wheat exact a heavy toll upon phosphorus; tobacco rapidly consumes both potassium and phosphorus; corn makes heavy drafts upon phosphorus and nitrogen, while sugar beets deplete potassium and nitrogen.

Continuous planting of the soil to any one crop is therefore reckless mining of fertility. The first preventive of soil depletion, then, is *crop rotation,* so that the heavy demands are distributed among the several elements rather than concentrated upon one or two exclusively. Under such treatment, the soil is able to replenish its supply of available solubles at approximately the same rate as they are being removed. A scientific rotation always includes a legume which stores nitrogen in the soil.

Soils in humid climates also tend to lose fertility by the natural process of leaching. Downward percolation of meteoric water tends to remove the soluble substances such as calcium and magnesium. Fortunately, the soil is rather tenacious of its phosphorus, but eventually large amounts of even this element may be lost through natural processes. It is common, therefore, for many virgin mature soils to be low in fertility.

The second preventive against soil depletion is *mixed farming*. Under such a plan the land is devoted to the production of pasture and forage crops as well as of grain. As many domestic animals as possible are kept. The forage, pasture, and at least part of the grain are fed to animals, and these or their products are sold to provide the farmer's income. Meanwhile, the animal manures are returned to the soil, and crops such as clover, rye, or cowpeas may also be planted and plowed under in an unripe state as "green manure." Leaves, grass, garbage, and other organic waste materials may also be accumulated in piles or pits, made into compost, and applied to the soil. These practices not only maintain but may actually increase the fertility of the land.

Where it is neither possible nor desirable to practice crop rotation or mixed farming, there remains but the alternative of *commercial fertilization*. While expensive, the marked increase in per acre yield amply justifies the heavy use of chemical fertilizers and their purchases quadrupled between 1940 and 1960. Nitrate, phosphate, and potash are sold as common commercial items, and general prepared fertilizers consisting of mixtures of two or all of these plant foods are available (Fig. 29–5).

SOIL UTILIZATION

The selection of the proper crop or crops for each type of soil is a matter meriting the most careful attention. Throughout human history, land utilization has been directed mainly by mere chance or by scarcely less intelligent trial-and-error methods. At very early dates, however, attempts were made by the ancients to formulate

certain rules for the use of land. As early as the third millennium B.C., the Emperor of China laid down a ninefold classification of the soils in his domain. Among the Greeks and Romans rather detailed lists of soil types were also made in order to emphasize the different uses to which they should be put. In spite of this, it is only very recently that soil science has advanced sufficiently to supply man with generally valid principles to aid him in his adjustments to this element of the milieu.

The question of utilization resolves itself into two distinct problems: local land utilization or the selection of crops suited to local variations in soil, and regional land utilization or the determination of what part the soils of a region should play in the geographical division of labor.

THE PROBLEM OF LOCAL UTILIZATION

Within a small area, a variety of soil types is usually represented, some of which are young, some mature, and some old. Under pioneer conditions of human ecology, these various types

Figure 29–5 Effect of commercial fertilizer on the size of ears of corn in Honduras. A fertilizer program is being conducted here by the Food and Agriculture Organization in order to stimulate the interest of the government and the farmers in the efficient use of fertilizers. (Photo by S. Lampe, courtesy of FAO)

are occupied indiscriminately. Economic life is organized upon a subsistence basis, and each farm is made to yield as many as possible of those staples with which the needs of life have customarily been met. It goes without saying that under such pioneer ecology, many local varieties of soil may be planted to wheat, corn, potatoes, or whatever staple is in demand. Such relations to soil meet with varying degrees of success, some proving so uneconomic as to compel erstwhile pioneer farmers to engage in auxiliary hunting or forest industry adjustments in order to subsist.

As transportation and facilities for local trade develop, certain refinements in agricultural adjustment are made. Areas of sandy soil may be given over to potatoes, cold clays put in pasture for dairy cattle, stony patches on slopes planted in orchards, and fertile, mellow loams devoted to grain production. The mere ability to transport and market local surpluses first enables man to use and later drives him to a division of labor among the soils of a region.

Finally with the development of world transportation, any specific local area is faced with competition from a great number of distant ones. Under such pressure, the specific utilization of its soils is further refined. The old soils may, therefore, be abandoned and revert to grass or forest; such youthful soils as can be economically improved are fertilized; but the mature soils will more and more determine the characteristic aspect of the local agriculture and for such, careful crop associations and rotations will be worked out.

This increased refinement in adjustment to soils may finally reach the point where an area enters the stage of completely commercialized agriculture. A few staple articles, eminently suited to local soils, are then produced and marketed over a wide area. In return, many of the necessaries of life are imported. In this way a locality may become identified with a product—Aroostook potatoes, Wenatchee apples, Fresno grapes, Rocky Ford melons, Door County cherries, and Palouse wheat are examples. This suggests the larger questions of the regional utilization of soils.

THE PROBLEM OF REGIONAL UTILIZATION

Modern tendencies in economic production point to an ultimate geographical division of labor throughout the earth. Part of this consists of regional specialization in agriculture, no successful development of which can take place without careful regard for the edaphic factor. Mature soils over wide areas tend to possess characteristics in common, characteristics often so significant that whole regions would seem to exhibit soil predilections for certain crops while severely handicapping certain others. Because of this, an optimum geographic adjustment can obtain in any region only if the agricultural economy be in close harmony with its soil qualities.

The tropical rain forests

Man of the selva is primarily an agriculturist, but even so, he meets with scant success in cultivating the laterite and lateritic earths of his region. As a result of the heavy rainfall and constant high temperatures, these soils are low in humus and are leached of their essential mineral elements.[3] A native farm usually consists of a small forest clearing planted in cereals and vegetables and a scattering of fruit trees. Even these prove such a drain upon the soil that within a few years, crop yields decline to a point where the patches must be abandoned and new clearings made. All thought, then, of developing such lands into permanent commercial producers of sugar, rice, and other cereals must be abandoned. The natural vegetation is forest, and any commercial agriculture in such an environment must be based upon tree-crop staples. Cacao, coconuts, sago, spices, and bananas would therefore seem to offer possibilities for sustained use of the soil.

Tropical savannas and subtropical forests

The red soils of these regions are comparatively infertile. China maintains a huge population in a red soil environment but does so only at great cost of human labor and by constant fertilization. On the contrary, there is a huge export of products from some regions of red soil, but these surpluses from comparatively small areas are no index to a potential permanent future for these soils in general. The rice export of the Orient is, in the main, drawn from immature delta soils. In Cuba, the sugar export is maintained by the

[3] Raymond Bouillenne, "Man, the Destroying Biotype," *Science,* Vol. 135, March 2, 1962, pp. 706–712.

clearing of new fields for cane. The American South has witnessed the march of cotton production westward onto new land and the abandonment or excessive fertilization of the older areas. Even with the unusually fertile soils of Java, the Dutch found it necessary to regulate very carefully the crop system in order to establish and maintain a permanent agricultural adjustment.

The temperate forests

The forest and woodland regions of the Cyclonic Zone possess fairly good gray-brown soils. These, however, cannot maintain permanent commercial grain production for export. Exceptions to this are provided by certain localities where advantages in geographical location make commercial fertilization profitable. On the whole, the gray-brown soils should support balanced systems of mixed farming with here and there specialized areas of fruit, vine, or vegetable production.

The northern coniferous forests

The gray forest soils or podzols of this region are usually so unproductive as to fail to pay for agricultural effort spent upon them. They should support permanent forest on either a natural or a silvicultural basis. Certain immature clays, clay loams, and sandy loams may be utilized for a dairy and root-crop agriculture.

Subarctic tundras

The rather structureless soils of the tundras are so lacking in any simple and distinctive vertical profile that they are sometimes regarded as an intrazonal phenomenon rather than a real zonal soil type. They are, however, characteristic of the Arctic shores and of a few Antarctic islands and are very widespread in occurrence. These soils support growths of mosses, lichens, sedges, grasses, flowering perennials, and in favored localities growths of small shrubs. Because of their rigorous climate, tundra soils are non-agricultural. They do, however, produce vegetation suitable for the pasturing of reindeer, yak, and other meat animals.

Humid and subhumid grasslands

The prairie soils and chernozems of these regions constitute the preeminent soil resources of the world. They are almost universally possessed of good physical structure and high fertility. Moreover, they are so-called lasting soils and are able to sustain prolonged cereal production without appreciable deterioration. In addition, they include most of the so-called black cotton soil of the Tropical and Subtropical zones.

Semiarid grasslands

The dark-brown or chestnut colored soils of these regions are highly fertile and of good tilth, but they lie where the rainfall is wholly undependable. Thus, while tempting man to occupy them agriculturally, such soils do not reward him well. Within the tropics, the steppe soils constitute a periodic famine zone; in extratropical regions they form a one-crop gambler's fringe about the lands of dependable agriculture. On the whole, their destiny should lie in a combined system of forage crop production by dry farming and cattle ranching on range land.

Deserts and semideserts

Desert and semidesert regions seem destined to support pastoral adjustments, with an emphasis upon sheep as the animal husbanded. Locally, small areas support, and will continue to do so, an intensive irrigated agriculture. However, as in the Nile Oasis, such soils are usually immature in age. Irrigation on the mature brown or gray soils of regions having the semiarid or arid type of climate would seem not to promise the general success hoped for by the more sanguine promoters of irrigation. Experience in using mature and old soils shows that under irrigation they may quickly become waterlogged and alkaline by rising ground water.

ECONOMIC CONSIDERATIONS

The predecessors of modern European man were probably pastoralists on the dark-brown soils of the steppe and the brown soils of the better watered parts of the desert of central Asia (Fig. 28–7). Migrating in ox wagons into the forest lands of Europe, they learned agriculture in a gray-brown soil environment. This latter must have been a prolonged, well-nigh heartbreaking process. By Roman times, large portions of the continent had been won to agriculture and the soil was yielding quite satisfactorily.

The European colonists who settled the American East encountered the same familiar gray-brown soils of the "temperate" forest. Since these presented no new problems in adjustment, the early American pioneers migrated westward carrying with them the familiar European crops with corn and tobacco added. About 1830, the pioneers encountered the black prairie soils of Illinois. Although these were considered by many to be "too poor to grow trees," their main disadvantage lay in a tough sod which could not be turned with the iron plows then in use. With the invention of the steel plow, this difficulty was overcome and the westward advance of agricultural settlement was resumed.

Their tremendous success with the dark prairie soils led the pioneers to conclude that all dark-colored soils would prove equally adaptable to agriculture. As a result, settlement pushed rapidly out onto the pedocalic soils of the Great Plains. In central Kansas, the newcomers were severely repulsed in the seventies and again in the nineties. For a time settlement paused, only to be resumed when new dry-farming methods were introduced. At last, man had conquered the pedocalic environment, and land occupancy was extended far beyond the margin of climatic safety. Large-scale machine methods have provided man with the means of bringing into production extensive areas over the earth almost simultaneously. This rapid opening up of the prairie soils, chernozems, and dark-brown soils in various parts of the world has not proved an unmixed blessing. To be sure, it has given mankind an area of cheap grain, but it has also created a glutted world market. Already agricultural man is beginning to withdraw from the brown soils and from many portions of the dark-brown (or chestnut-colored), soils, fleeing drought, man-aided dust storms, and financial ruin.

European man in America has had much less success with the red and yellow soils of the South. For three hundred years, American farmers have been feeling their way toward a proper adjustment to these soils. Indentured labor, slavery, and cropper-and-mortgage systems have been tried and the former two have been rejected. Cotton, tobacco, and to a lesser extent rice, indigo, sugar cane, and other plantation staples have, from time to time, formed the mainstays of commercial production.

The system of cotton, corn, and tobacco growing by slave labor which finally evolved in the South early began to deplete the soil fertility. Hence, many old fields were abandoned and let go back to brush, and new fields were cleared each year. This process could not continue indefinitely, and so a steady westward migration of planters and their slaves to new lands took place.

Cotton, corn and tobacco are clean-tilled crops, leaving the soil unprotected against the heavy summer monsoon rains. The soil remains bare and unfrozen during the mild winters in this climate, exposed to the cyclonic winter rains. The result of this Southern system of agriculture has been an appalling amount of soil leaching, washing, and gullying. Today, one-half of the nation's eroded land lies in the South, and roughly half of all commercial fertilizer used each year in the nation ordinarily goes to the South.

The value of all the soil washed off Southern fields and sent down the streams to the sea since 1890 probably exceeds the value of all the cotton exported since that date. Such a system of farming is not profitable, to say the least. The South supports only 41½ million people today and yet it has, after only three hundred years, ruined more land than the whole nation of Japan had to start with. In comparison, the Japanese have farmed their land for more than thirty centuries and they have ruined none of their soils; instead, they have greatly improved them.

What is probably even more significant, there was, during this time, a unique rural American culture evolving in the East and Middle West based upon free labor and small middle-class land ownership. This latter gradually became antagonistic toward large land-holding, unpaid slave labor, and plantation agriculture in the South. After a long series of arguments, quarrels, debates, and compromises, the Civil War was the almost inevitable consequence.

The Civil War, of course, ruined the well-to-do Southern landowning classes; but since that war, a modified plantation system has ruined the small farmers and farm laborers, through the prevailing system of land leasing, tenancy, and farm credit. Obviously, Americans have not yet developed a sound economic geography of their subtropical red and yellow soils.

During this same period the American farmer has had almost no success with the podzols of the upper Great Lakes area, northern New England, and the higher parts of the northern Appalachian Highlands. Finnish, Norwegian, and French-Canadian settlers have brought about some developments on these soils, but on the whole the podzols remain unutilized. Aroostook County, Maine, is the one exception. It supports a nationally famous potato industry but only at a cost of fertilizer greatly in excess of that necessary to produce a comparable crop from the gray-brown podzolic soils farther south.

Settlement began fairly early on the New England podzols, but not until after 1870 on those of the Great Lakes districts. The land was originally covered by fine coniferous forests. When it was logged off, many lumbermen stayed on as farmers. Some of the lumber companies tricked thousands of people into buying this land for farms. Much labor is required to clear the stumps and glacial boulders. The soil is poor and the climate is cool and frosty even in summer. Farms are isolated and the supplementary income from woodcutting is now about gone. Many of these farms cannot produce a decent living. Much land is tax delinquent. State grants have to be made to provide roads and schools. Many counties and school districts there are bankrupt. Land abandonment is going on steadily.

Some of the northern counties of Wisconsin have attempted to zone their lands so that such unwise settlement will be corrected and in the future prevented (Fig. 28–8). The inhabitants of other states, however, refuse to adopt such a common-sense method of dealing with the problem. Maine, fortunately, never organized local governments for some of her northern areas, and so most of her podzol lands remain in producing forest. This has been the wisest and most profitable use of what should be permanent forest land. Some parts of northern New Hampshire, Vermont, and Michigan manage to retain farm settlement on podzol soils because the inhabitants help support themselves by the summer tourist business.

While agricultural occupancy was being pushed westward, large areas of podzols and gray-brown podzolic soils in the East were being abandoned, partly because of declining fertility but principally because of competition from the newly occupied pedocals of the Midland and Great Plains regions. Even larger areas of red and yellow soils were abandoned in the South. To many, this seemed unavoidable, since it was considered inevitable that soils should "wear out." This is, however, refuted when crop yields in Asia are examined. There, after four thousand years of use, similar soils in the Yangtze Kiang region are as productive as ever.

In the vast Western Intermontane Region, between the Sierra Nevada and the Cascades on the west and the Rocky Mountains on the east, the soils are mostly of two kinds. There are brown semidesert soils on the less arid lands, and gray desert soils on the more arid. Both these soils provide low-grade range for cattle and sheep ranching. Young alluvial soils in most of the valleys are suitable for irrigation; that is, provided that the water supply is adequate and the land lies low enough so that water can be led onto it.

Some of the Indians practiced irrigation here, but it was not until after the arrival of the Mormons in Utah in 1847 that irrigation agriculture really developed. After that, individuals, land companies, states, and the federal government developed scores of irrigation projects. Correctly irrigated young alluvial soil in the valleys gives excellent crops of alfalfa, grain, fruits, sugar beets, pasture grass, and vegetables. There has, of course, been considerable unwise irrigation development. Even the best localities are a long distance from market, and haulage costs eat up most of the profits.

The nonirrigated lands of the West (and this is perhaps 95 percent of the total area) remain mainly in desert and grass range. Most of this has been almost destroyed by overgrazing. The management of public range and the planning of a sensible irrigation policy are the two primary problems for America's desert and semidesert soils.[4]

The present uses of soils in the United

[4] For world view see Richard M. Highsmith, Jr., "Irrigated Lands of the World," *Geographical Review*, Vol. LV, No. 3 (July, 1965).

States may be summarized as follows. Subtropical red and yellow soils constitute the cotton and tobacco belt. Gray-brown forest soils are mostly used for general farming. The northern podzols are given over to dairying, potato growing, and cut-over stump land. The prairie soils specialize in corn, hay, soy beans, and livestock. Just west of these, the fertile black chernozems produce wheat and corn. Still farther west, the chestnut-colored soils produce wheat. The brown soils of the still drier western lands support cattle and sheep ranching and attempt to produce wheat by dry farming. The gray desert soils support some grazing and irrigation agriculture.

It is fairly apparent to any student of geography that certain general changes in American soil use are badly needed. For the red and yellow soils, more general farming and dairying and less cotton, tobacco, and corn are needed. For the gray-brown forest soils, more dairying, more truck and market gardening (using fertilizer), and much more forestry are mandatory. The prairie soils should reduce the amount of their cash-grain production. The podzols should be almost wholly devoted to forest production.

The black earths or chernozem soils should probably remain, as they now are, in wheat and corn production. The chestnut or dark-brown earths should produce less wheat and more grassland. In the brown soils, dry farming might well be eliminated altogether and grazing redeveloped. On the gray desert soils, all public range should be restored, public grazing reduced and controlled, future irrigation projects planned wisely and conservatively.

SOCIAL CONSIDERATIONS

Climate and landforms set the broad limits of economic life within a region but do not determine its specific character. Soils play a large part not only in the choice of local crops but in the development of man's local social traits as well.

ETHNIC CHARACTER AND POPULATION DENSITY

A large-scale map depicting population density in an agricultural area is apt to reveal surprising variations. When compared with the soil map of that area, a striking correlation between soil type and population distribution is often evident. Furthermore, soil type may actually reveal some relationship to the ethnic composition of the area. An example may be cited from Linn County, Iowa. Here the black prairie soils are occupied by the descendants of New Englanders or early German immigrant stock. The less fertile and rather sandy timbered soils along the Cedar River, on the other hand, are held by more recent Czech immigrants. As a second random example, Phillips County in Colorado shows a similar segregation of human stocks upon unlike soil types. The dark-brown soils of the county are almost entirely occupied by recent arrivals from Iowa, Nebraska, Illinois, and Kansas, whereas the sandy soils are worked mostly by farmers of southern stock, notably from Missouri.

CULTURE LEVEL

Profound differences in the cultural landscape are often traceable to soil variation. The porous, infertile, sandy soils in parts of New Jersey support a very mean landscape. The homes of most of the inhabitants are cabins and squalid shacks about which are small unkempt fields set in a background of pine trees and brush. The people are poor, uneducated, and backward, although their region lies but a few hours from metropolitan New York. This population has furnished the state with a disproportionate number of paupers, criminals, and delinquents.

In marked contrast to this is the area of fertile Hagerstown loam about Lancaster, Pennsylvania. Comfortable white houses, big red barns, and good roads are set among highly productive fields of corn, tobacco, hay, and small grain. The people are prosperous, educated, and public spirited. From among them have come many leaders in state and national affairs.

This is no mere chance comparison, for it may be duplicated in almost every region of the world. Similarly, the contrast between the cultural landscapes on the phosphatic soils of the Kentucky Bluegrass and the acidic, shaly soils of the Highland Rim is pronounced, as is that between the sandy lands of northern Wisconsin and the glacial soils of the Green Bay Lowland.

SOCIAL CLASSES

Fertile soils may be said to abet systems of tenancy, since they are able to support both a peasant and a landlord class. In the antebellum South, the areas of fertile soil were the strongholds of slavery, an institution meeting with scant support on the stony, shaly, or sandy soils. The present alarming increase of tenancy in the prairie soils of the Middle West, particularly in that part west of the Mississippi River, is in marked contrast to the lack of land renting and tenancy in the podzol belt of the Upper Great Lakes Region. Throughout history, rich soils were often associated with aristocracies, whereas poor ones have in many instances cradled democracies.

POLITICAL CONSIDERATIONS

Man's earliest civilizations were established in the desert areas of western India, Mesopotamia, and Egypt. The soils of these areas, especially the immature alluviums of the river valleys, are in general fertile; but they are often highly alkaline and support a drought and salt-tolerant flora. They become productive only under irrigation, the application of water being necessary to promote crop growth and to wash the alkalies from the soil. If left to their own devices, those cultivators located nearest the source of water would irrigate their lands profusely, leaving an inadequate amount of water for those cultivators farther away and inundating the latter's lands with alkali leached from their own soils.

To prevent such practices, rigid social regulation was necessary, and hence stringent water laws were evolved. To achieve these results, an absolute despotism was required, and the pattern of such a society, once fixed, was almost unalterable. Consequently, the early civilizations located upon these gray desert soils were naturally the seats of tyrannical governments.

In contrast to these early sites, Roman civilization developed upon reddish-brown sclerophyllous-woodland soils of the Mediterranean climate. There, soil use involved quite a different set of problems than in the desert oases. In the early days of the republic, agriculture seems to have been developed upon the basis of small proprietorship and independent yeoman farming. In the empire period, however, this seems to have been largely replaced by despotic systems of serf and even slave cultivation. The result was an inevitable decline in Mediterranean agriculture, a circumstance which contributed to the eventual collapse of the tyrannical Roman Empire.

From the Mediterranean, civilization spread to northern and western Europe. There, the humid marine and continental climates supported a heavy forest vegetation under cover of which normally develop gray podzols and gray-brown podzolic forest soils. The quality of these soils is relatively poor and they are adapted to producing trees and shrubs rather than grasses. Since man's principal agricultural crops are domesticated grasses, it is obvious that such soils are naturally poor for agriculture. The land had to be laboriously cleared and kept clear, stirred, manured, and gradually enhanced in humus and improved in tilth.

Such patient and not very profitable soil rebuilding could not be promoted under despotism. Moreover, the soils of the European forest areas are so diverse and variegated that no single set of rules could be applied to even a small district. Nevertheless, a despotic feudalism grew up in northern Europe after the era of Roman conquest, based upon the labor of villeins and serfs. This failed, for during the Middle Ages the productivity of soils over large areas declined to the irreducible minimum and Europe became relatively overpopulated. It remained that way until peasant uprisings and an eventual agrarian revolution succeeded in restoring land holding to the hands of the peasants.

After this, the productivity of the land rose rapidly. In other words, despotism on these soils failed, but widespread democratic land holding and small-scale capitalism provided the incentive necessary for the improvement and maintenance of such soils. Where this has been achieved, the productivity of European land is greater today than ever before. The old despotic order, however, retained its hold on the forest lands of Russia, the Junker-held lands of Prussia, and a few other parts of Europe. This persisted even into the twentieth century.

This same system of small-scale capitalistic democracy was transferred to northern United States, eastern Canada, and numerous other areas during and after the seventeenth century. There it was successful from the outset, although not always very profitable. In southern United States, a despotism using at first slavery, later exploiting tenant labor, has not proved successful. Instead, it has produced a terrible wastage of both soil and human resources.

Early in the nineteenth century, westward settlement in America reached the black and dark-brown (chestnut) soils of the grasslands. A little earlier, Russian settlement had reached similar pedocalic high-humus soils of the Ukrainian and Siberian steppes. A little later, similar soils in Australia, western Canada, and South Africa were settled. Such grassland soils are almost ideal for agriculture, requiring only plowing and sowing to yield immediate and sustained profits.

Very quickly, capitalistic ownership and farming for individual profits developed on these soils, with exploitive one-crop systems and careless methods of cultivation for quick cash returns. Large-scale holding by absentee ownership has increased appallingly. Desiccation, exhaustion and erosion by wind and water are reaching threatening levels. In short, the very political system seemingly necessary for the maintenance of fertility in forest soils promptly proceeds to destroy its basic foundation in the grassland areas.

In the early 1930's, Russia took note of this fact and began the application of state socialism to her chernozems and better-watered sierozems. She later applied it to the podzols and gray-brown soils of her forest lands, where it has not proved successful. On the Russian grasslands, on the other hand, it has provided a successful method of production maintenance and soil preservation. Apparently socialism is as suited to grassland soils as is capitalistic democracy to forest soils, or despotism to desert oases.

SUGGESTED USEFUL READINGS

Bennett, Hugh H., *Soil Conservation* (New York, McGraw-Hill Book Company, Inc., 1939), 993 pp.

Bunting, B. T., *The Geography of Soil* (Chicago, Aldine Publishing Co., 1967), 214 pp.

Eyre, Samuel R., *Vegetation and Soils* (Chicago, Aldine Publishing Co., 1963), 324 pp.

Higbee, Edward, *American Agriculture: Geography, Resources, Conservation* (New York, John Wiley & Sons, Inc., 1958), 399 pp.

Higbee, Edward, *The American Oasis* (New York, Alfred A. Knopf, Inc., 1957), 262 pp.

Higbee, Edward, *Farms and Farmers in an Urban Age* (New York, The Twentieth Century Fund, 1963), 183 pp.

U.S. Department of Agriculture, *Farmers in a Changing World*, Yearbook of Agriculture, 1940 (Washington, D.C., Government Printing Office, 1940), 1213 pp.

U.S. Department of Agriculture, *Soils and Men*, Yearbook of Agriculture, 1938 (Washington, D.C., Government Printing Office, 1938), 1132 pp.

VII

The
Biotic
Factors

The biotic factors exist and exert their major influence in that "life layer" of the earth referred to in Part V. In the ensuing chapters the accounts of flora or natural vegetation, fauna or native animal life, and microorganisms may be regarded by some readers as completing the story of the life layer. That would be erroneous, certainly short-sighted, for the earth's life layer, in total, must include human beings as well.

In this chapter, therefore, the human realm as well as the plant, insect, and animal kingdoms will be discussed. Chapters 2 and 3 might be reread beneficially at this time—concurrent with those on the biotic factors.

30

Flora or Natural Vegetation

In scantily populated parts of the earth, the natural vegetation is often the most conspicuous element of the environment. Because of this, it is common practice to refer to primitive folk as "forest peoples," "tundra peoples," and so forth. In rather densely peopled areas, the natural vegetation often survives to a considerable degree and lends a distinctive appearance to the landscape.

THE FLORAL REALM

The sum total of all native plants found growing in an area, excluding those domesticated or cultivated by man, constitutes its flora or natural vegetation (Fig. 30–1). The particular kind of natural vegetation in any area is largely determined by climatic factors. Thus every type of climate is characterized by certain general groups of floras, so that a climatic region, broadly speaking, is also a vegetation region. This is true, however, only in a general sense, for locally, within a climatic region or province, the character, appearance, and richness of the flora vary strikingly. This is so because local differences in soil, drainage, and other natural factors in addition to climate affect the natural vegetation. Thus climate determines the broader limits as to kind and amount of native vegetation within a region, but local factors (edaphic, physiographic, and biotic) determine its specific makeup and composition in the various parts of that region.

CLIMAX VEGETATION

In response to the climatic factor but more specifically to the minor factors, generally plants group themselves into local formations or societies. When, after a long period of migration,

accommodation, and contest for supremacy among species, a plant association has become thoroughly adjusted to its environment, it is termed the *climax vegetation* of the area which it occupies. For example, a cover of buffalo grass with an occasional clump of wild sage and a sprinkling of mallows, wild gerania, windflowers, and ironweeds constitute a plant association which may be regarded as the climax vegetation for certain parts of the American Great Plains. Elsewhere in this region are slightly different associations but all are composed of plants belonging to the steppe or dry grassland group characteristic of a semiarid climate.

PLANT SUCCESSION

Commonly man has wrought great havoc upon the natural vegetation; he has obliterated old species, introduced new ones, and upset the ecological balance between antagonistic species, thereby giving certain recessive plants a chance to become dominant. The more intensively man occupies an area, the greater the havoc he wreaks upon the flora. Nevertheless, he never quite succeeds in exterminating it entirely, for whenever he abandons a cultivated field, a great number of pioneer replacement forms spring up. These are followed in turn by an ecological succession of different species until finally the area is again occupied by a vegetation climax. This may not be identical with the original climax, but it is apt to resemble it in general form and function. Thus natural vegetation is an obvious and persisting factor, even in long-settled and intensively cultivated parts of the earth. Everywhere, however, one must carefully distinguish between native or natural plants on one hand and cul-

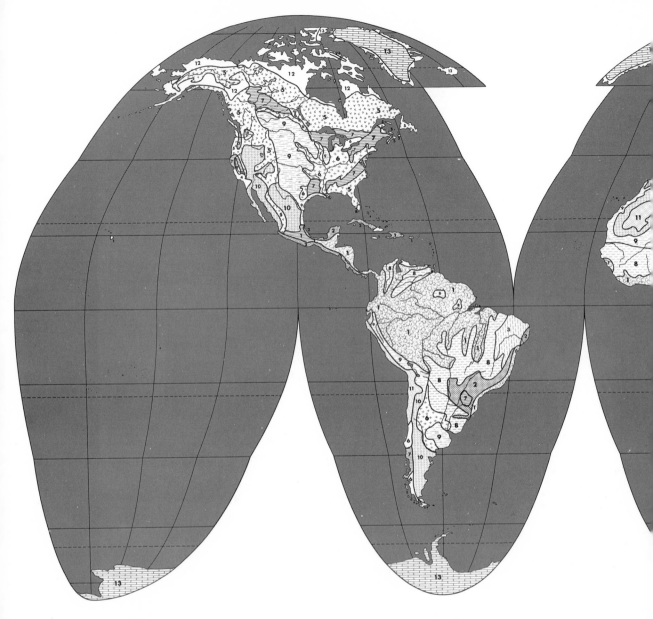

Forests

1. Broadleaf Evergreen Tropical Rainforests

2. Broadleaf Tropical Forests: Mixed Deciduous and Evergreen

3. Lighter Tropical Forest and Thorn Forest, Mainly Deciduous

4. Mediterranean Forest and Brush Land, Including Chaparral and Maqui

5. Evergreen Needleleaf Forests, Mainly in Middle and Higher Latitudes, Including Taiga

6. Broadleaf Deciduous Forests of Low and Middle Latitudes

7. Mixed Broadleaf Deciduous and Needleleaf Evergreen Forests of Middle Latitudes

Grasslands

8. Tropical Savanna, Including Tree Savanna

9. Middle- and Low-latitude Steppe and Prairie; Few Large Bare Areas

Desert Vegetation

10. Desert Shrub and Semi-arid Shrub

11. Scattered Sparse Grass or Shrubs, with Extensive Bare Soil or Rock Areas

Cold Region Vegetation

12. Tundra Areas, and Heaths in High Latitudes

13. Highland or Upland Areas with Much Bare Rock or Soil, and Bare Glacial Ice Caps

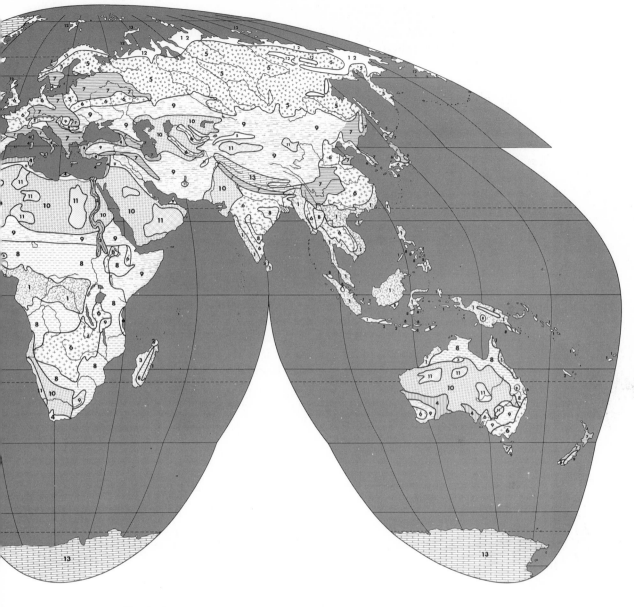

Grasslands

8. Tropical Savanna, Including Tree Savanna

9. Middle- and Low-latitude Steppe and Prairie; Few Large Bare Areas

Desert Vegetation

10. Desert Shrub and Semi-arid Shrub

11. Scattered Sparse Grass or Shrubs, with Extensive Bare Soil or Rock Areas

Cold Region Vegetation

12. Tundra Areas, and Heaths in High Latitudes

13. Highland or Upland Areas with Much Bare Rock or Soil, and Bare Glacial Ice Caps

Figure 30–1 Major world vegetation types, broadly generalized. (Map adapted from Kuchler and others, from William E. Powers, *Physical Geography*, New York, Appleton-Century-Crofts, 1966)

tivated plants or crops on the other, for the latter can in no wise be regarded as part of the floral environment.

FLORAL HABITATS

The floral realm contains such diverse plants as algae, mosses, lichens, grasses, weeds, shrubs, vines, and trees. These vary in size from almost microscopic molds to veritable giants such as the sequoias, banyan, or ceiba trees. In spite of this seemingly endless variety of form and size, the fact that species group themselves into associations or societies enables one to classify easily the floral environment. From the standpoint of the kind of habitat with which the plant world provides man, four general types may be recognized: forest, savanna, grassland, and desert (Fig. 30–2). The importance of recognizing such types becomes quite apparent when the ecology of various peoples is examined. To be specific, the type of vegetation which prevails in a region largely determines the ease or difficulty of settlement, the problem of clearing land, the materials

immediately available for food or the building of houses, barns, and fences, the possibility or impossibility of certain industries, and to some extent the nature of the landscape to which the inhabitants must psychologically and esthetically adjust themselves.

FORESTS

A forest is an association of plants dominated by trees. Forests occur under a wide range of climatic conditions but are, in general, limited to areas whose midsummer temperatures average 50° F. or above. Along the outer or equatorward margins of the Polar Zone, approximately 15 inches of rainfall are required for forest growth; in the Cyclonic Zone more than 30 inches with more than half falling during the warm months are essential, and in the Tropical Zone roughly 45 to 90 inches for deciduous forest and 90 to 150 inches for the selva are necessary. Forests originally covered perhaps one-fourth of the lands of the earth but have been destroyed by man until they now cover a scant 16 percent. The Rainy Tropical, Humid Subtropical, and

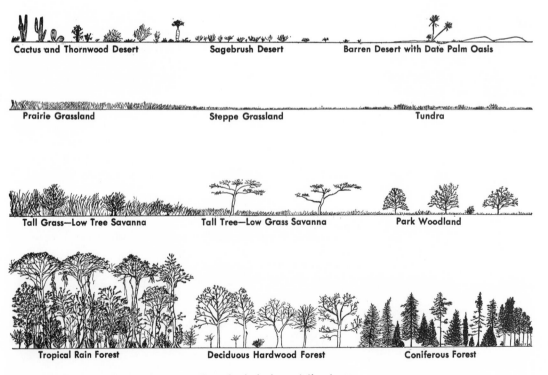

Figure 30–2 Conventionalized cross section of principal vegetation types.

Temperate Marine climates are forest producers par excellence. In addition, the wetter phase of the Humid Continental and the Monsoon Tropical climates favor forest vegetation.

The selva

The tropical rain forest or *selva* (sometimes incorrectly called "jungle") is perhaps the most striking and mysterious of all forest types. It is a thick-set forest of tall trees, such as rubber, ceiba, rosewood, cedar, mahogany, Para-nut, oil palm, and a multitude of others (Fig. 8–4). The cycle of growth is uninterrupted by drought or cold so that the selva shows a riotous medley of species and forms. Trees contest for sunlight by growing to great height, a circumstance which calls for immense buttresses at the base and results in an almost complete canopy of foliage. Vines and creepers climb up and over everything; lianas hang like ropes from trees and parasitic and saprophytic forms are abundant. Toward its northern and southern margins, the selva thins out into open monsoon forests and tree-dotted savannas.

The selva has proved a most disadvantageous habitat for man. In its confines lurk some of the least advanced members of the human species. Even the more advanced native peoples who inhabit it are confined to small tribal villages set in the midst of tiny clearings, surrounded by the forest which ever threatens with lurking danger and active encroachment. Scant wonder that even religious and social rites of such peoples are colored by the forest. In only a few places, as for instance the Caribbean lowlands of Central America, western portions of Malaysia, Indonesia, and the Guinea Coast, has man finally routed the rain forest. Here he has succeeded in establishing large plantations of wet-land crops—bananas, cacao, coconuts, rubber, and others.

The subtropical forests

The subtropical forests somewhat resemble the selva, except that they lack the grandeur and wealth of species found in the latter. The presence of a short winter season causes them to show a slight rhythm in growth and verdure. In southeastern United States, which may be used as an excellent example of this type of forest, the growth consists in general of (1) mangrove thickets on the southwestern shores of Florida that are overflowed by salt water, (2) almost impenetrable growths of tupelo, gum, and cypress on bottom lands where fresh water stands during most of the growing season, and of tupelo, upland cypress, ash, cottonwood, and red and white bays on bottom lands that are inundated for only a few weeks or months, (3) ash, black gum, hickory, red gum, and water oak on the drier ridges (seldom more than six feet in elevation) within the bottom lands, (4) a mixed forest of southern hardwoods (mostly oak) and pines (shortleaf and scrub pine on the poorer soils and loblolly on the heavier moister soils) on the broad Piedmont from Virginia to North Carolina and in the northern half of Georgia, Alabama, Mississippi, and Louisiana, most of Arkansas and eastern Oklahoma and Texas, and (5) longleaf, loblolly, and slash pine on the Coastal Plain from southern Virginia to the Trinity River in Texas. The longleaf pine is especially abundant and occupies extensive areas (Fig. 30–3). It shares with the shortleaf pine an ability to grow well on the deepest sandy soils.[1]

Since 1899 these southern pines have furnished up to 50 percent (now 20 percent) of the timber cut of the nation as well as practically all of the naval stores. Moreover, they are the source of a steadily increasing proportion of the country's pulpwood. No soils are too poor for these pines, a fact that is especially significant in a region where about one-fourth of the land is hopeless for agriculture. Cypress is a major source of wood for shingles and interior work but its area of exploitation has shifted notably owing to what may justly be called "cypress mining."

The temperate marine forest

The western margins of continents in the Cyclonic Zone are clothed with tall, dark forests consisting

[1] Coniferous forests are mostly found where the annual precipitation and temperature are too low to support deciduous forests. An exception to this statement, however, occurs in Humid Subtropical United States; here coniferous forests occupy extensive areas where the annual rainfall is fifty inches or more. The major limiting factors appear to be the high evaporation rate and the sandy, infertile soils.

Figure 30–3 Longleaf pine forest. Pure stands of longleaf pine characterize the uplands in southern United States. So useful is the tree that many lumbermen consider it the most valuable in North America today. Note how tall and straight the trees grow without a branch to break the evenness of the boles for many feet above the ground. (Photo by B. W. Muir, courtesy of the U.S. Forest Service)

mainly of beech and oak with occasional coniferous trees. Often these forests are rendered impenetrable by ferns, large-leaved shrubs, alders, and thickets of broom or similar plants. In the Pacific Northwest of America this type of forest is composed almost entirely of conifers—firs, spruce, cedar, and hemlock (Fig. 30–4)—and in places, redwood, which is comparable in size to the giants of the tropical selvas (Fig. 17–5). The temperate rain forests of Europe have been largely cleared after having been attacked for centuries by a struggling peasantry. The virgin forests of New Zealand which consist of ever-

green beeches, kauri pine, rimu, matai, totara, and tawa are three-fourths gone. The forests of Oregon and Washington are now being attacked. Dark, wet, rugged southern Chile has remained largely untouched, but exploitation is now beginning.

Humid continental forests

The Humid Continental forests are deciduous and in the so-called North "Temperate" Zone occur where the annual precipitation exceeds thirty inches, more than half of which falls during the warm months. In the main, these forests show from dense to fairly open stands of mixed hardwoods, with oak and hickory as the dominant species (Fig. 30–5). Maple, ash, elm, walnut, beech, poplar, and many others are, however, quite common. Haws, elderberry bushes, sassafras, sumac, and other shrubs are numerous and a thin carpet of grass is often present. Such forests are comparatively easy to penetrate and clear. As a result, large areas have been cut and won for pasture, cropland, and town site. Toward the north, these deciduous hardwood forests gradually give way to mixed hardwoods and conifers, and finally these pass into almost pure stands of pine, hemlock and spruce, with only a sprinkling of birch and poplar.

The taiga

The taiga, or northern coniferous forest, occurs (in North America) where the precipitation varies from 40 inches in the East to less than 15 inches in the Yukon and is generally below 20 inches in the interior. It is the most extensive coniferous forest in the world and extends over much of Alaska, northern Canada, Norway, Sweden, Finland, and the U.S.S.R. Although botanically very poor, this forest is one of the better in the world commercially. Unlike the equatorial forest, where one can scarcely find more than two or three trees of the same species on a given acre, the taiga consists primarily of pines, firs, spruces, and larches intermingled here and there with such leafy trees as aspen, balsam, poplar, and birch. In its northern reaches, the forest growth becomes scattered and dwarfed and is dotted here and there with meadows, moors, and stretches of tundra (Fig. 18–3). The taiga is an important timber producer as well as a great potential source of soft lumber and of wood pulp. Exploitation of the forest constitutes the chief human activity, though fur hunting and mining are also carried on. Farming is pursued with some success only along the equatorward margin where the soils are fairly fertile. Here such hardy crops as vegetables, fodder, barley, oats, and rye are grown. The low value of most of the soil and the long period of winter isolation, however, offer man slight inducement to win the taiga from nature; hence for the most part, it is very sparsely populated.

SAVANNAS AND PARKLANDS

Savannas are plant associations composed of both grass and tree forms, arranged frequently in such manner as to produce a park landscape or open woodland. The majority of plants, however, are grasses which grow tall and in tufts and which have coarse stiff leaves. The savanna is best developed in the Monsoon Tropical climate where high temperatures are combined with an annual rainfall of twenty-five to fifty inches distributed in marked seasons of rain and drought (Fig. 30–6).

Several varieties of savanna may be noted. At one extreme is the deciduous monsoon forest with a grass undercover, while at the other is the dry thorn forest with a steppe undercover. Between these are the tall-grass–low-tree savanna, tall-tree-low-grass savanna, bush savanna, cane and bamboo-brake savannas, and many other variants. Somewhat analogous to the tropical savannas are the chaparral (sclerophyllous woodland) and the piñon-juniper woodland which characterize the wetter phases of the Mediterranean Subtropical and Dry Subtropical climates respectively. Similarly savanna-like are the prairie woodlands or park meadows of the Cyclonic Zone, which occur in the drier phase of the Humid Continental climate and of the Temperate Marine climate where the rainfall is twenty-five to thirty-five inches annually.

The value of tropical savannas for settlement, especially by white people, is uncertain.

Figure 30–4   Spruce and hemlock trees in a Temperate Marine forest. (Photo by H. L. Shantz, courtesy of the U.S. Forest Service)

Figure 30–5 A Humid Continental forest of hardwood trees. The large trees are all white oak. (Photo by L. J. Prater, courtesy of the U.S. Forest Service)

Tropical grasslands everywhere are unattractive to primitive tillers of the soil, who with their few and inefficient implements experience extreme difficulty preparing the land for crops. They are also unattractive to most advanced agriculturists but obviously for different reasons. One outstanding disadvantage of savannas for highly civilized peoples is the prevalence of insect pests that are the carriers of some of the most serious infections of man and beast. In this respect the African savannas are especially bad because they have, in addition to the insect pests of savannas in other continents, the dreaded tsetse fly that transmits sleeping sickness to man and nagana to animals. The cattle tick abounds everywhere and causes Texas fever, which affects the rearing of cattle adversely. In addition, the natural

grasses provide poor forage for livestock. Only on the higher savannas, as in Brazil and South Africa, are good range cattle raised on native grass. Moreover the rhythm in rain and drought complicates man's agricultural and pastoral adjustments; drainage is a problem in the rainy season, irrigation in the dry season.

By superimposing a world map showing the distribution of population upon one showing the distribution of natural vegetation, it is seen that over most of the earth, savannas are only sparsely settled; this would seem to indicate that they do not constitute a highly favorable habitat for human beings. All the savannas in the Western Hemisphere are thinly settled, as are those in Australia and most of Africa. The Sudan is thought by many to be densely populated, but relatively speaking it is an empty land with a low population density. One area, India, which supports a truly dense population is the exception. It does this, however, at the expense of a low standard of living and occasional famine.

GRASSLANDS

Perhaps one-third of the earth's land surface is or was originally covered with grass. Grassland formations are normally the result of semiaridity, or of an extremely short growing season, or both.

Prairie grassland

This is a luxuriant type of grassland wherein the grasses grow to a height of one to three feet. It is a sea of waving grass and appears almost monotonous in its general uniformity of floral cover. Trees are scarce or practically absent (Fig. 30–7); the only ones in the American prairie are the deciduous species on the wide Missouri River bottoms and those in the postclimax woodland along lesser streams. Shrubs are scarce. Through thousands of years the species have become so well adjusted to their environment that they successfully meet even the most severe conditions of wind, heat, cold, and hail.

Prairies occur frequently on uplands in the Semiarid Tropical climate where the soil is a rich loam. Scattered patches frequently lie also along the transition belt between the Humid and Dry Subtropical climates. Prairie grassland occurs as a transition form between the Humid and Dry Continental climatic regions (Fig. 30–8). In America, which perhaps best exemplifies this floral form, the prairie characterizes that vast area having a rainfall of 20 to 25 inches in the north and of 35 to 40 inches in Texas.[2] Prairies are disappearing rapidly before the agriculturist who is both plowing and grazing them. Formerly they presented ecological difficulties to man, for they lacked shelter, building materials, and firewood. Moreover, the tough sod was practically unplowable. The railway, the steel plow, and coal, however, have enabled modern man to conquer the prairies which have become the great granaries of the world.

The steppe

The steppe is primarily an association of short grasses. Some of these lie in a soft, fine mat on the ground; others stand as hard wiry tufts.

Locally thorny shrubs and low, coarse bushes are dominant. Cacti and other succulent plants become numerous in some portions. Steppe vegetation is typically developed in lands receiving less than twenty inches of rainfall annually, providing there be a cold dry winter and a hot summer. So far, the steppe habitat has defeated man's attempts toward close settlement except in spots where it has been possible to develop agriculture by means of irrigation. The subhumid margins have been won by systems of dry farming, but owing to the cyclical recurrence of drought, such adjustment is precarious at best. Pastoral activities are and probably will remain the dominant utilization of the steppe habitat. Here again droughts periodically play havoc with man's adjustment and livestock either perish or

[2] John E. Weaver and Frederic E. Clements, *Plant Ecology* (New York, McGraw-Hill Book Company, Inc., 1929), p. 460.

Figure 30–6   Tropical savanna in South Africa. (Photo courtesy of the South African Information Service)

Figure 30–7 Tall-grass prairie covering loess hills near Ponca, Nebraska. Note how uniform the vegetation is. Prairies, as a rule, are flat to slightly rolling. (Photo courtesy of J. E. Weaver)

must be transported to better watered regions of grain and forage production. Since rapid transportation is a matter of comparatively recent development, pastoral steppe man throughout most of human history has been denied this form of economic relief, and hence from time to time has been thrown into seething unrest. Even now, economic coordination has not been perfected to

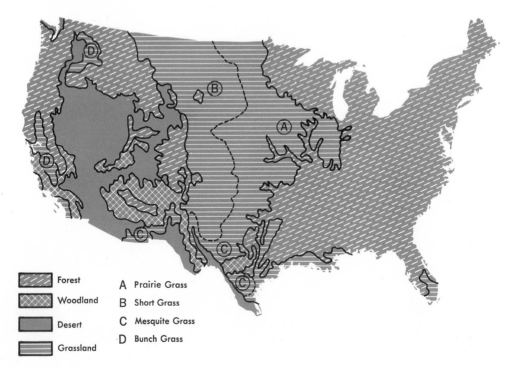

Forest A Prairie Grass
Woodland B Short Grass
Desert C Mesquite Grass
Grassland D Bunch Grass

Figure 30–8 Natural vegetation provinces in the United States.

the point where it will enable the steppes to be politically stable and to be steady producers of meat, wool, and livestock.

The tundra

Large portions of the Polar Zone are devoid of forest and are clothed with a special pseudograss-land formation known as *tundra*. This formation, which varies considerably from place to place, is consequent upon long, cold winters and short, cool summers (the growing season is only about two months long); in summer the soil temperatures are too low for trees. The subsoil is continuously frozen. During summer, the surface thaws out but the water cannot drain away. Ten inches of precipitation annually are sufficient, under a low evaporation rate, to produce tundra, of which there are three major kinds. The first of these is called *grass tundra* (Fig. 30–9). The drier sections are occupied by grass along with dwarf shrubs and perennial herbs, though in rocky places mosses and lichens are present. In the moister areas many *sphagnum* bogs occur. The "reindeer moss," which in reality is composed of fluffy, feathery lichens, is especially characteristic of the tundra in the Western Hemisphere. Poleward from the *grass tundra* lies the *desert tundra*, consisting of great expanses of bare rock with bits of *grass tundra* here and there in protected pockets; southward near the northern limit of the taiga and coinciding roughly with the Arctic Circle lies the *bush tundra*, the flora of which consists chiefly of dwarfed alder, birch, juniper, and willow trees.

This type of habitat is uncompromising so far as human adjustment is concerned. Agriculture is impossible and many other occupations nearly so. Wood is extremely scarce, being available to man only as driftwood along the shores, or through long journeys southward to the margins of the taiga. The scattered groups of Hyperborean peoples who inhabit the tundras have evolved a very ingenious but primitive culture. Most of them depend primarily upon hunting, trapping, and fishing, and to a certain extent upon the gathering of berries and edible leaves during the summer. The more advanced among tundra folk have perfected a nomadic pastoral adjustment wherein the reindeer (or domesticated caribou) is the animal husbanded. Already rein-

Figure 30–9 Tundra vegetation in Nushagak, southwestern Alaska. (Photo courtesy of the U.S. Geological Survey)

deer rearing is being prosecuted on a commercial scale in Lapland, which has about half a million head. Alaska, where herds once numbered 250,000, now supports 28,000. The U.S.S.R. has 2½ million reindeer. The carrying capacity of the tundra is estimated at 35 million reindeer. As meat becomes scarce in the Cyclonic Zone, the tundras may possibly become the seat of important pastoral industries.

Closely allied to the subpolar tundras in appearance and makeup are the alpine meadows that are found all over the world near the tops of high mountains. Most places of this kind are too cold and snowy for winter habitation, but few are without their summer *transhumants* who drive their flocks up from the lower valleys as soon as the snow begins to melt.

DESERTS

Deserts, which cover perhaps one-sixth of the earth's land surface, occur where there is low rainfall in both summer and winter and where the rate of evaporation is high. From many standpoints, they are the least favorable type of floral habitat for man. Large areas are practically devoid of vegetation, in places being encrusted with salt or alkali. Most desert surfaces carry a scattered grass growth, dotted with thorny shrubs and succulents. Less than ten inches of annual rainfall in the Tropical Zone usually results in true desert flora. In the Cyclonic Zone, the upper rainfall limit varies usually from six to eight inches, whereas in the Polar Zone deserts are lacking unless the barren surfaces of the polar ice caps be so classified.

The ecology of desert man is chiefly pastoral, save locally in irrigated oases where it becomes agricultural. The scantiness of pasture and browse afforded compels pastoral man into a wholly nomadic habit and greatly restricts the density of population.

PASTORAL ADJUSTMENTS TO FLORA

In the economic history of most regions, pastoralism has occurred in the early stages of development. This is true even of many forest regions. The early Gothic invaders of western Europe probably lived by herding swine in the dark oak-beech forests and by pasturing cattle in the clearings. Today, long after the forest has disappeared, their modern descendants intensively farm the land, retaining swine, cattle, and sheep only as items in their agricultural adjustments. Similarly, the tropical savannas and the temperate prairies and park meadowlands are, or have been, the seat of transitional adjustments in pastoral economy. Many forest lands, savannas, and park meadows as well as all prairies seem destined ultimately for agricultural occupancy. It is in the deserts, steppes, and tundras that pastoralism would appear to be the climax of human adjustment. Even there, man faces certain problems in his permanent use of the natural vegetation, as is clearly shown by examples from the grasslands of the United States. Overpasturing on the Edwards Plateau of Texas has destroyed the grass and permitted its replacement by a growth of small trees and bushes. Farther north, in the Great Plains and on the Columbia Plateau, large areas of the range were plowed during unsuccessful attempts at dry farming but were later abandoned. Fields thus relinquished do not reseed to bunch and buffalo grass but do reseed

to sagebrush and other undesirable species. Moreover, migrations of livestock and shipments of seed have introduced a host of undesirable plant immigrants—Russian thistle, cocklebur, sandbur, devil's claw, tumbleweed, and others, most of which seriously damage the floral covering or impair the condition of the animals which graze it.

EXPLOITIVE ADJUSTMENTS TO FLORA

The pastoral industries represent direct adjustment to grassland habitats or partial adjustment to a habitat wherein grass is present. On the other hand the exploitive forest-using industries represent direct adjustment to a forest habitat or to the tree elements in a composite habitat. They commonly appear in three forms: forest hunting, logging, and silviculture.

FOREST HUNTING

In the remote past, probably many peoples lived entirely by hunting the wild fruits, nuts, roots, and berries of the forest. Even at the present time, there are fragments of primitive forest peoples who live almost entirely by this means. The Veddahs of Ceylon, the Pygmies of central Africa, the Punans of Borneo, and several tribes of Amerindians in the Paraná-Amazon region are examples of such primitive forest folk. The "Digger" Amerindians of California, the Navajos who annually gather nuts in the piñon forests of Arizona and New Mexico, the several tribes of the Pacific Northwest delving for camas roots, and the Winnebagoes gathering wild rice in the swamps of the Great Lakes forest splendidly exemplify such ecological relationships.

The gathering of forest products on a commercial scale constitutes an outstanding phase of the economy of many regions today. Particularly is this true of the tropical forest lands. Many of the trees of the selva yield a juice or latex which may be made into valuable products. Rubber, gutta-percha, gutta-jelutong, and many others are of considerable significance. Several, marketed under the name of gums, are gathered in large quantities—gum arabic, gum chicle, and gum copal. Another product of importance is rattan, the dried stem of a vine from the tropical forest. The gathering of nuts is yet another form of forest hunting. Brazil nuts from Brazil, and oil-palm nuts from the Guinea Coast of Africa are excellent examples, but the annual harvest of acorns and chestnuts from the forests of Mediterranean Europe, and of hickory nuts, butternuts, hazelnuts, and black walnuts from those of eastern United States is not inconsiderable.

Another class of minor forest products is herbs and barks for medicinal purposes. Cinchona (quinine) from the selva, asafœtida and licorice root from the subtropics, and ginseng, sassafras, and slippery elm from the cool temperate forests, all are well-known examples.

The cork oak of the western Mediterranean Basin yields a valuable annual harvest of bark. The extraction of naval stores (pitch, resin, and turpentine) is another interesting minor forest-based industry, from two-thirds to three-fourths of the world's supply emanating from the forests of southeastern United States. Until quite recently this industry was so destructively prosecuted by too early working of small trees, by too deep chipping, and by working too many faces on the tree that speedy extinction was feared. A new method introduced from Les Landes in southwestern France, however, is likely to make "turpentining" in this region a permanent industry.

Charcoal burning is one of the most interesting of the minor forest activities. During medieval and early modern times, this was of immense importance in Europe. Whole communities of people lived in the remote recesses of the forest pursuing this smoky and disagreeable trade. Entire forest areas were denuded for the purpose of making charcoal until western Europe lay on the verge of a fuel famine. Fortunately, the discovery of coal relieved the situation. The preparation of charcoal, however, is still an important industry in many coal-poor lands throughout the world, as for example, Iran, Italy, and Greece.

LOGGING

The most important phase of forestry use in the modern world is logging. This industry takes on a variety of forms from place to place depending upon the local character of the forest and various other contingent environmental factors. In the tropical rain forests, logging is attended by many difficulties. The great variety and mixture of species, the high specific gravity of many trees which prevents floating logs on streams, the rank undergrowth which renders operations difficult and which quickly overruns trails and clearings, the remoteness from markets, the dearth of labor, the enervating climate, and the abysmal mud prevailing through most of the year, all conspire to retard logging developments. Accordingly such activities are confined usually, though not entirely, to the intermittent and haphazard operations of a few groups of individuals along the rivers or near the coasts. Nevertheless, a constantly increasing volume of mahogany, tropical or "Spanish" cedar, ebony, rosewood, and ivorywood is finding its way out to Cyclonic Zone markets. Most of these woods are destined for cabinet use, veneers, and special construction purposes. From the monsoon forests come open-grained mahogany, Moulmein cedar, logwood, sandalwood, boxwood, ironwood, and the immensely important teak.

The so-called "Temperate" Zone forests are the seats of large-scale and highly organized logging industries. In many instances there exist a considerable number of temporary camps and semipermanent company-owned towns whose sole *raison d'être* is the annihilation of the forest. Particularly is this true in the virgin softwood areas where growth is sufficiently uniform to permit *clean* logging. This large-scale type of operation is seen at its best in the United States. Under its regime, the white pine and cypress have become practically extinct in certain regions, but large quantities of yellow pine, fir, hemlock, and other less desirable softwoods still remain. The hardwood forests have been depleted quite generally and much of the present supply is furnished by part-time cutting from scattered forests and farm woodlots.

The vast northern forests of the Cyclonic Zone are being attacked largely by pioneer logging camps under the control of corporate enterprise in Canada, Sweden, and Finland. In Russia, the government maintains semimilitary camps in the northern forests for the same purpose. The winter cover of snow greatly aids the handling and collection of logs, but rail facilities are still inadequate. The major contribution of these forests so far has been to furnish pulpwood, but even this industry has been retarded by competition from second- and third-growth cuttings in more southerly forests.

SILVICULTURE

The serious inroads which man has made upon the forests of the Cyclonic and Subtropical Zones have compelled him to develop a permanent form of forest industry known as *silviculture*. Silviculture is, in short, the systematic growing of timber on a crop basis. This calls usually for state ownership, schools of forestry, trained foresters, fire and insect protection, systematic cutting of areas in rotation, and careful replanting.

Reforestation has been practiced to a limited extent in Japan since about A.D. 900 and, since 1868, has been a definite state policy. France established forest laws in 1827 and now has an annual increment of timber growth which just about balances the annual cut. This does not mean, however, that France is self-sustaining in its wood requirements; many items are procured through trade, particularly lumber and wood pulp. The creation in southwestern France, through reclamation and planting, of an artificial pine forest on about two and a half million acres of what had been an unhealthful waste of swamp and shifting sand dunes, is perhaps the most spectacular silvicultural adjustment yet accomplished in any land. Here where sheep and goat rearing was formerly the outstanding activity now dwells a population of over 1,500,000 people, many of whom are engaged in lumbering and turpentining.

The United States, Canada, the U.S.S.R., and Brazil, with their tremendous resources, have done very little along silvicultural lines, but most other advanced countries have of necessity established definite forest policies. By the end of the twentieth century, however, even the taiga and tropical forests will probably have been placed under strict regulation.[3]

RELATION OF FLORA TO OTHER HUMAN ADJUSTMENTS

The pastoral and forest-using industries represent direct ecological adjustments to natural vegetation. But many agricultural, manufacturing, and commercial industries also are related ecologically to this element of the environment.

AGRICULTURAL ADJUSTMENTS

The patch-agriculturalist of the Rainy Tropical lands is constantly encroached on by the forest. Pioneer species move into his gardens from the forest's edge; seeds, roots, and stumps sprout into life; vines, creepers, and bushes spring up with amazing celerity. Soon the clearing is inundated by the rising tide of jungle. Many tribes prefer the labor entailed in periodic migration and clearing of new areas of virgin forest to that engendered by the constant struggle against the overwhelming jungle growth.

In the Cyclonic Zone, stumps may persist for one hundred years or more in an area once occupied by softwood forests. Pastures, fence rows, and fallow fields are quickly expropriated by replacement forms of vegetation. Gardens are constantly threatened by weeds and grasses. Grain fields and meadows are often completely ruined by the upspringing wild plants. Mustard, quack grass, sourdock, and others have locally changed entire systems of agricultural adjustment.

MANUFACTURING ADJUSTMENTS

In the early stages of the development of manufacturing, the forest played an important ecological role as a source of fuel. The early iron industry of Britain depended entirely upon charcoal from British forests. Depletion of these caused the temporary collapse of the industry, a collapse which might possibly have been permanent had the country not possessed immense coal resources.

The lumber-sawing industry is localized directly in forest areas, but there are a large number of secondary industries which owe their existence in a country to its forest resources. Shipbuilding, pulp, paper, match, and furniture

[3] For further background in tropical silviculture see Joseph Tosi and Robert Voertman, "Some Environmental Factors in the Economic Development of the Tropics," *Economic Geography*, XL (July, 1964), pp. 189–205. Also suggested is Pierre Gourou, *The Tropical World: Its Social and Economic Conditions and Its Future Status*, trans. by E. D. Laborde (London, Longmans, Green & Co., Ltd., 1959).

manufacturing are outstanding examples. Still other industries owe their existence to wild shrubs, roots, nuts, tannin materials, fruits, fibers, grasses, and other items in the floral environment.

COMMERCIAL ADJUSTMENTS

Forests as sources of raw material for shipbuilding played no mean part in the commercial rise of the Phoenicians, Greeks, British, and Yankees at various times through history. Today, in an age dominated by steel ships, Norway and a few other countries with some forests but little iron ore continue to build a considerable number of wooden ships. Seattle, with softwood forests at its back, constructs small wooden craft for firms and individuals in a score of countries.[4]

Not only do the world's forests further trade by helping to supply materials for commercial carriers but they directly create trade as well. The annual world cut from forest lands amounts to some 71 billion cubic feet of wood, in addition to a large volume of minor products. This leads to a tremendous movement of commodities in both foreign and domestic commerce. It constitutes a large percentage of the exports from many countries, creates ports and port activity, and contributes to satisfactory trade balances. Moreover, the forest industries supply large populations with buying power.

The commercial significance of the grassland areas of the world is probably even greater than that of the forests. Whole civilizations have been built on grass as a primary resource. A large percentage of the livestock, wool, hides, and other pastoral products which enter trade (and their derived manufactures as well) are creations of the natural vegetation of the world's grassland regions.

[4] For a detailed description of trees and their uses, see Charles Sprague Sargent, *Manual of the Trees of North America*, 2d ed., 2 vols. (Gloucester, Mass., Peter Smith Publisher, 1962).

SUGGESTED USEFUL READINGS

GENERAL REFERENCES

Dansereau, Pierre MacKay, *Biogeography: An Ecological Perspective* (New York, The Ronald Press Company, 1957), 394 pp.

Dassmann, Raymond F., *Environmental Conservation* (New York, John Wiley & Sons, Inc., 1959), 307 pp.

Odum, Eugene P., *Fundamentals of Ecology* (Philadelphia, W. B. Saunders Company, 1953), 384 pp.

SPECIAL REFERENCES

Ames, Oakes, *Economic Annuals and Human Cultures* (Cambridge, Mass., Botanical Museum of Harvard University, 1939), 153 pp.

Anderson, Edgar, *Plants, Man, and Life* (Boston, Little, Brown and Company, 1952), 245 pp.

Braun-Blanquet, Josias, *Plant Sociology, the Study of Plant Communities,* trans. by George D. Fuller and Henry S. Conrad (New York, McGraw-Hill Book Company, Inc., 1932), 439 pp.

Cain, Stanley Adair, *Foundations of Plant Geography* (New York, Harper & Brothers, 1944), 556 pp.

Daubenmire, R. F., *Plants and Environment*, 2d ed. (New York, John Wiley & Sons, Inc., 1959).

Haden-Guest, Stephen, John K. Wright, and Eileen M. Teclaff, eds., *A World Geography of Forest Resources* (New York, The Ronald Press Company, 1956).

Polunin, Nicholas, *Introduction to Plant Geography* (New York, McGraw-Hill Book Company, Inc., 1960).

Richards, P. W., *The Tropical Rain Forest: An Ecological Study* (New York, Cambridge University Press, 1952).

U.S. Department of Agriculture, *Grass*, The Yearbook of Agriculture, 1948 (Washington, D.C., Government Printing Office, 1948).

U.S. Department of Agriculture, *Trees*, The Yearbook of Agriculture, 1949 (Washington, D.C., Government Printing Office, 1949), 944 pp.

31

Fauna or Native Animal Life

THE FAUNAL REALM

The fauna or native animal life of the earth is extremely varied in size, structure, complexity, appearance, and other characteristics. It consists of the totality of all living animal forms except man himself and those animals which he has tamed or domesticated. The whole realm of animal forms is divided into great groups of *phyla*. Some zoologists recognize fifteen phyla; others combine the various classes of animal life in slightly different ways and hence recognize only thirteen, eleven, or in some cases only eight. Regardless of the classification employed, however, these phyla, from the standpoint of organic evolution, range all the way from simple one-cell protozoa to the intricate chordata (vertebrates) of which man is the most highly developed. They may be subdivided in turn into classes, orders, families, genera, and species. All told, there are hundreds of thousands of species, many of which have some bearing upon man's life. The authors of this textbook prefer for the purposes they have in mind a classification of the faunal realm into the following eleven great phyla.

1. Protozoans
2. Porifers
3. Coelenterates
4. Ctenophores
5. Flatworms
6. Threadworms
7. Echinoderms
8. Annelids
9. Mollusks
10. Arthropods
11. Vertebrates

The protozoans were apparently the first forms of animal life to appear on the earth. Thereafter, each higher phylum appeared during later and later geologic periods of time. Meanwhile, the process of differentiation and subdivision has proceeded constantly. Many of these subdivisions have become extinct during the past but, nevertheless, members of all the great groups or phyla still exist and now live side by side to form a large and complex faunal environment over the earth. This faunal environment forms part of a total natural environment with which mankind must deal constantly in his geographical relationships.

Man is the dominant animal organism on the earth, although his supremacy is continually being disputed or challenged by the insects, the rodents, and other animal groups. Actually man is only one among thousands of faunal forms inhabiting the earth, his dominance being the result of his possession of an unusually large brain in proportion to total bulk. The intelligence resulting from such a brain has not so far enabled man to exterminate his animal competitors. He has, therefore, achieved his dominance through adjusting himself ecologically to fauna or native animal life. The geographic relation of man to fauna is quite obvious in so-called uncivilized regions but is often thought to be negligible in civilized communities. It is a mistake, however, to suppose that even in the most highly developed areas, man escapes reckoning with this persistent and ever-present element of his natural environment.

THE ELEVEN PHYLA

The great groups or major divisions of the faunal realm are significant for anyone interested in the geography of man and so some knowledge of them would seem to be imperative. Accordingly, a brief discussion together with a few examples of members is given for each phylum in the paragraphs which follow.

Protozoans

The protozoans are the lowliest and simplest forms of animal life. Common examples are the amoeba and paramecium. A detailed discussion of these microscopic animals is given in Chapter 32.

Porifers

The simplest many-celled animals (metazoans) are the porifers or sponges. They consist of triple layers of cells supported by a framework of limy, siliceous, or horny material and are found attached to rocks, shells, and other objects. Many varieties are gathered commercially and used for washing and other purposes.

Coelenterates

The next to lowest group of many-celled animals are the coelenterates. The jellyfishes and corals are the commonest examples. Among these, the corals have considerable importance because their colonies are responsible for building up many reefs, atolls, and low islands in tropical and subtropical waters. Coral limestone is often used as building stone. Some varieties of coral are much prized for jewelry.

Ctenophores

The phylum ctenophores includes such odd and little known animals as sea walnuts, comb jellies, and a few other forms found in tropical waters.

Flatworms

The flatworms include planarians, liver flukes, tapeworms, and similar forms. Some of them grow to enormous lengths and are almost indestructible by ordinary means. When these are broken or cut into segments, they promptly grow new terminal organs and become separate individuals. Many of them are parasitic upon higher animals and humans.

Threadworms

The nematodes or threadworms include such small animals as trichinellas, hookworms, and hair eels. Many of them are parasitic upon higher forms of animal life.

Echinoderms

The echinoderms include starfishes, crinoids, sea urchins, sea cucumbers, and a few other forms of life. They have little economic value, although some species of sea cucumbers are caught and eaten by the Japanese and Pacific islanders.

Annelids

The annelids or roundworms include earthworms, leeches, marine bloodworms, and so forth. The earthworms probably perform an important function in soil building. Up to a century or less ago, leeches were much used by physicians and veterinarians for bloodletting.

Mollusks

Slugs, snails, clams, oysters, octopuses, and a few other forms make up the phylum of mollusks. Most of these are edible and hence form important sources of food for man.

Arthropods

The phylum arthropoda includes the insects, the spiders, the centipedes, and the crustaceans.

Insects constitute an important group in the faunal environment. They are countless in number and variety; in fact, it is estimated that about one-half the species in the animal kingdom are insects; several common examples are ants, beetles, butterflies, fleas, flies, gnats, grasshoppers, and mosquitoes. Many insects are useful to man while others are unmitigated nuisances. Their presence or absence may determine whether an area is healthful or unhealthful, whether human beings live in comfort or despair, poverty or wealth. Their influence upon mankind, directly and indirectly, is far greater than is customarily realized. Without a doubt, insects comprise man's chief enemies and competitors among all native animal life. Closely allied to the insects are the crustaceans—crabs, lobster, shrimp, and others which furnish important sources of human food. In contrast, only a few varieties of insects are eaten (such as ants, grasshoppers, and grubs) by a few primitive peoples.

Vertebrates

In marked contrast to the ten phyla of invertebrates already discussed stands the phylum of vertebrates or chordates. The lowest class of these is composed of fish; in it are included hundreds of species which vary all the way from the huge sturgeon and tuna to the tiny sardine and even smaller forms. Some fish are both edible and numerous, circumstances which make them eagerly sought after for food. In addition to fish, other classes of chordates or vertebrates are amphibians, reptiles, birds, and mammals. Mammals vary in size from elephants to mice and are almost as diverse in habit as in size. Some vertebrates are herbivorous, some carnivorous, some insectivorous, some fructivorous, and a few omnivorous. Some crawl, as the snakes; some fly, as the bats and most birds; some jump, as the toad and jerboa; some swim, as the whale, seal, and manatee; still others run and walk, as the horse, antelope, and man.

The five classes of vertebrates arranged from lowest to highest are as follows. (Some subdivisions of the mammal class are shown in order to indicate man's position in the phylum of vertebrates.)

1. Fish
2. Amphibians
3. Reptiles
4. Birds[1]
5. Mammals
   a. Monotremes
   b. Marsupials
   c. Placental mammals
      (1) Beasts
      (2) Anthropoids
      (3) Men

AREAL DISTRIBUTION OF ANIMALS

Animals, like plants, are dependent upon their natural environment. They differ from plants, however, in possessing far greater mobility. In the preceding chapter, it was pointed out that in relation to climate, relief, and the lesser modifying factors, the plant realm tended to be grouped into rather definite floral provinces or regions. In the animal realm there is also an ecological relationship but it is less pronounced, except in the case of less mobile and inferior forms.

It is indeed significant that similarity in physical milieu does not necessarily mean similarity in fauna, and conversely. Thus, South America from north to south and from east to west, with almost every variety of physical conditions, exhibits a considerable unity in its fauna, whereas the grassy plains of South America and Africa, with rather similar environmental conditions, exhibit very little resemblance in their fauna.

The interpretation of the distribution of native animal life is so extremely complicated that even the zoologists do not agree regarding it. Hence, this volume, which concerns itself with human geography and not zoogeography, will not attempt so difficult a task.

Fauna, of course, does show some interesting ecology in distribution despite its general mobility. Among the microzoans, the trypanosome of African sleeping sickness is strictly tropical and the filaria of elephantiasis is tropical and subtropical.

In the insect realm, there is a tendency for certain forms, at least, to show geographical grouping. Some insects, such as woodticks, woodlice, driver ants, and certain varieties of mosquitoes are most characteristic of the forest. Termites or so-called white ants, cotton bollweevils, and tsetse flies are primarily, though not exclusively, savanna insects. Locusts and grasshoppers are steppe dwellers, whereas certain spiders and scorpions are confined to the desert.

The corals are purely tropical and the sponges mainly subtropical, but worms, starfish, crustaceans, mollusks, and many other groups are widely distributed.

---

[1] The birds (Aves) are difficult to place in the outline. In some respects they are almost as primitive as the reptiles; in other respects they are more highly evolved and certainly more specialized than many mammals. Indeed, some zoologists would include them under the mammals.

Fish, an extremely mobile faunal group, show some tendency toward latitudinal zonation. Cod, halibut, and haddock appear to be most numerous in the lower portions of the Polar Zone; salmon, halibut, butterfish, herring, and menhaden in the Cyclonic; shad, pompano, sardine, and tuna in the Subtropical; and red snapper, sailfish, true swordfish, flying fish, and many other species in the Tropical.

Most birds are able to fly and hence migrate long distances. Certain ducks, geese, plovers, and other species make yearly pilgrimages from tropical to polar regions and back again. But many birds show a fairly good geographical distribution despite this ability to fly. For example, hornbills, macaws, and parrots are tropical; bluejays, cardinals, crows, English sparrows, and starlings inhabit the intermediate zones; Greenland gerfalcons, ptarmigans, redpolls, and snowy owls are usually found in the Polar Zone. The flightless birds illustrate even a more exact environmental control over distribution: the true ostrich is largely tropical, the cassowary and emu, subtropical; the kiwi and the rhea, cyclonic; and the penguin, polar. The so-called "scratching and ground running" birds of the intermediate zones illustrate a fairly close adjustment to floral habitat: the partridge and woodfowl are primarily forest birds; the grouse, pheasant, quail, and turkey are perhaps most at home in deciduous woods and in the prairie; the bustard, prairie chicken, and sand grouse are most characteristic of the steppe, and the sage cock of desert areas.

The distribution of the higher land animals appears to be less a function of latitude and climate and more a result of physical factors permitting or retarding migration on land. The spread of land animals is checked by such impassable barriers as large bodies of water; high mountains, such as the Himalayas, by hindering migrations, separate two different faunas. The probable reason for the similarity in the native animal life of the Northern Hemisphere is that all the continents along the Arctic Circle are quite close together. This has facilitated migration. The dissimilarity in the fauna of the Southern Hemisphere, where each continent has its special types of animals, is largely the result of isolation of land masses. The resemblances of

certain species in India, South Africa, the Malagasy Republic and Australia suggest that those bodies were formerly parts of one large land mass which subsequently fractured into blocks, and that these latter have slowly drifted apart. The isolation of Australia and the Malagasy Republic has enabled them to harbor archaic forms which long ago disappeared elsewhere. This does not mean, of course, that Australia is especially adapted for marsupials and ill-suited for higher mammals; it means rather that the continent probably became separated from Asia, the large central continent which seems to have been the seat of evolution of species, before the higher mammals came into existence and hence was never reached by these later forms of animal life.

The land fauna of each continent is in the main distinct from that of the other continents. Within each great land mass, the various animals tend to group themselves in the type of floral habitat where they are best able to secure food. Thus each continent possesses fairly well-segregated forest, savanna, grassland, and desert faunas which constitute an integral element of man's natural environment in every part of the world, an element to which his life is adjusted in many ways.[2]

MAN'S WAR WITH THE INSECTS

The insect faunal group is the only one which seriously contests with man for world supremacy.[3] There are vast areas where the mosquito reigns as king undisputed by man. In the great northern forests, the white explorer endures the myriads of flies and mosquitoes during the summer only by wearing heavy clothing and by shielding his face and hands with netting and gloves respectively. In the depths of the tropical forest are large areas where mosquitoes are so numerous as to discourage settlement by even the aborigines. Native architecture in the Rainy Tropics is everywhere adjusted to an abundant insect life. Houses

[2] Marion I. Newbigin, *Animal Geography* (Oxford, The Clarendon Press, 1928).
[3] U.S. Department of Agriculture, *Insects,* The Yearbook of Agriculture, 1952 (Washington, D.C., Government Printing Office, 1952), see especially the section "Insects as Destroyers," pp. 141–191.

are so constructed as to allow for an inside fire, the smoke of which is not conducted out through a chimney but escapes below the roof in such manner as to drive out flying insects. One reason why hammocks are often used for sleeping quarters is to lessen the danger from spiders, scorpions, and centipedes. In highly developed areas, also, the mosquito, housefly, cockroach, and other insects become so numerous and pestiferous at times that cities are compelled to spend huge sums to check them.

INSECTS AND DISEASE

Many of the most dread diseases are noncontagious and would speedily disappear, were it not that the causative organisms are transmitted from person to person by insects. Examples of this are furnished by the Anopheles mosquito (malaria), the *Aëdes aegypti* (*Stegomyia fasciata*) mosquito (yellow fever), the rat flea (bubonic plague), the cootie or body louse (typhus fever), and the tsetse fly (sleeping sickness). Obviously man's problem of controlling this group of diseases rests largely on his developing ability to exterminate the vectors or carrier insects.

INSECTS AND AGRICULTURE

It is common experience to observe the annual havoc wrought in gardens by grubs, cutworms, beetles, plant lice, and earwigs. Similarly, moths and borers attack fruit trees and often almost destroy entire orchards. The *Phylloxera* for a number of years after 1870 almost completely destroyed the grape-growing industry of France; it reduced the area under grape culture by nearly 2 million acres and caused a loss of more than $2 billion. The army worm, chinchbug, Hessian fly, and corn borer have wrought so much damage to crops in the United States that the cultivation of wheat and corn has been temporarily abandoned over certain areas. The Mexican bean beetle has wrought similar havoc on certain vegetable crops. The Japanese beetle, introduced into eastern United States some years ago, has slowly spread westward despite quarantines and other restrictive devices. Encountering no major natural enemies in America, its ravages have been very severe.

Similarly, the migration of the cotton boll-

weevil from Mexico across the southeastern portion of the United States has occasioned losses of billions of dollars. This insect catastrophe has revolutionized the agricultural system of most of the American Cotton Belt and has aided in shifting the center of cotton production from the eastern to the western half of that region.

In the tropical forests and savannas, ants are a perpetual curse. Leaf-cutting or parasol ants often strip bare a field or garden in a few days' time. Against such depredations by insects the unorganized efforts of man are futile.

The dry lands of the world possess their insect pests in the form of locusts which breed in the steppes and desert margins and periodically become so numerous as to lay bare the country (Fig. 31–1). Occasionally they migrate into adjacent cultivated regions in such numbers as to darken the sky, leaving a trail of devastation behind. The Bible contains references to such locust plagues in antiquity. Older inhabitants of Kansas still recall the "Grasshopper Year" of the early days of settlement. Today frequent locust migrations constitute a major hazard to the grain farmer of the northern Argentine Pampa.

In many tropical and subtropical regions, ticks and burrowing grubs are so numerous that the cattle industry becomes negligible. The animals are rendered poor and scrawny and their hides nearly worthless except where maintained in fair condition by means of frequent "dipping" in disinfectant solutions.

Not all insects, on the other hand, are inimical to man and his crops. Bees and silkworms, for example, have been domesticated, the former supplying man with honey and wax and playing an important role in the successful pollinization of certain crops, the latter supplying him with one of his most highly prized fibers.

Against most insects, however, an incessant and costly warfare is being waged. Regional quarantines and national programs of offense and defense have been set up over wide areas; burning, draining, clearing of land, erection of sheet-iron barriers, and the large-scale use of traps, baits, and poisons are among the weapons used. Airplanes and helicopters are now being used to disseminate poisons in this warfare against the insect world (Fig. 31–2).

Figure 31–1   Locust invasion in Morocco. (Photo by Sudios du Souissi, courtesy of FAO)

American military forces, during World War II, encountered great difficulties from insects and other small animal forms in occupying various humid tropical areas. Accordingly, both the Army and the Navy sponsored researches in the field of insecticides. Out of these was developed a powerful new insecticide known as DDT, a single application of which can eliminate most of the insect life over a given area. Unfortunately DDT kills many insects which hold others in check. Hence with the predators eliminated, aphids, mites, and kindred pests soon flourish. The newer insecticide, TEP, marks as its victims these last and does not kill those which hold them in check.

HUMAN CONFLICT WITH HIGHER FAUNAL FORMS

In the earliest reaches of human history, man must have been largely at the mercy of his animal neighbors. An enormously long period of evolution in tools, weapons, strategy, and housing must have been necessary to guarantee his ascendancy over them. In general, the conflict today appears largely to the advantage of man, but locally he does not triumph in every clash. In parts of west Africa, troops of monkeys pull up the plants of garden and field almost as fast as they appear; herds of wild elephants sometimes trample to ruins native houses and fields while bush leopards and lions annually consume a number of children, women, and old men. In India tigers and poisonous snakes account for the deaths of many persons each year, while in certain parts of eastern Europe and northern Asia, packs of wolves terrorize many villages during exceptionally hard winters.

In central and western United States nearly a century of struggle was waged against the rattlesnake before it ceased to be a menace. Gophers, prairie dogs, and groundhogs still constitute an unsolved problem in many districts. Even the blind garden mole baffles man in some localities. Farther west, the jack rabbit contests with man (sometimes quite successfully) for possession of the short grass country. Probably the most destructive of the higher animals are rats and mice. They have succeeded in fastening themselves to man's establishments and continually devour his crops, attack his poultry, undermine his foundations, destroy his buildings, enter and raid his warehouses, and do an annual damage of many billions of dollars.

EXPLOITIVE ADJUSTMENTS TO FAUNA

Numerous faunal forms pursue and prey upon man and his works. Conversely, man also pursues and preys upon certain members of his faunal environment. This latter gives rise to a group of industries which collectively may be termed *besticulture* (exploitation of the *bestes* or native animal life). The three outstanding fauna-based industries are hunting, trapping, and fishing.

HUNTING

Hunting is one of mankind's oldest occupations. Along with the gathering of wild plant products, it must have supplied the ecological mainstay to most prehistoric populations. Among surviving primitive peoples, hunting often plays a dominant role in the economic ecology. Advanced peoples sometimes lapse into a hunting life as a temporary means of adjustment to a new environment. Examples of this are furnished by the American frontiersmen, the Russian *promy-shleniki,* and the advance line of Dutch Boers in the Transvaal.

Today, over most of the civilized world, hunting is prosecuted in a small way as a means for augmenting the local food supply. Particularly does this pertain to the United States and Canada, where considerable wild game survives in spite of close settlement. The original abundance of wild game in the United States almost exceeds the limit of comprehension. Despite the preceding long period of pioneer subsistence hunting, game was abundant enough to support almost a century of organized market hunting. Within the memory of men still living, nearly a million buffalo were slain each year for their hides alone. In 1869 the town of Hartford, Michigan, shipped for the market three carloads of passenger pigeons daily for forty days—a total of 11,880,000 birds. Obviously no creature could survive such slaughter. Not a single living specimen remains. In the closing years of the nineteenth century, it was possible for a market hunter to kill 1,000 golden plover, 200 prairie

Figure 31–2 Spraying banana plants against disease on a plantation in the Caribbean area. (Photo courtesy of Standard Oil Company, New Jersey)

chickens, or 400 wild ducks per week. At this time, game was to be had cheaply in all large city markets and hotels.

The lineal descendant of the market hunter is the modern "sportsman." Rod and gun clubs of the large cities, together with wealthy individuals in search of thrills, annually work tremendous havoc on the native animal life. The northern forests, the relatively inaccessible mountain regions of the Cyclonic Zone, and the big game lands of the tropical savannas are being overrun by these modern "savages."

TRAPPING

The prime fur-bearing animals, for obvious climatic reasons, are most numerous in the Cyclonic and Polar zones. The use of fur for clothing or ornament goes far back into antiquity, making the trapping industry a venerable economic pursuit. As the forests of the Cyclonic Zone have been cleared for agriculture, trapping has slowly retreated poleward. In spite of this, a surprisingly large quantity of furs is still obtained from these regions. Mountains, stream banks, swamps, and residual forest areas account for part of this annual crop. Moreover, casual winter trapping by farmers, even in well-developed agricultural areas, yields a still larger portion. Many people are surprised to learn that the United States ranks first among the countries of the world in the production of raw pelts (based on value). The northern forest belts of North America and Eurasia are also important sources of furs. In these regions, great fur companies operate farflung lines of trading posts where wandering trappers are outfitted each autumn. In spring the trappers return with their bundles of furs, whence the peltries are sent to collecting centers and finally to the great auction points—St. Louis, Seattle, Tacoma, New York, Chicago, Montreal, Vancouver, and Winnipeg in North America; and Copenhagen, Leipzig, Leningrad, London, Milan, Oslo, and Paris in Europe.

FISHING

Fishing ranks among the oldest of human activities, but despite its primitive origin it persists as one of the world's most modern industries.

It is estimated that man accounts for 10 billion fish each year. Fishing is very important ecologically in that it is the locative factor for hundreds of towns, villages, and smaller settlements. In addition, it engenders a large amount of commerce and manufacturing. For example, in 1964, the commercial fisheries of the United States yielded more than four and a half billion pounds valued at $390 million. More than 531,000 persons are employed in the American fisheries, a figure which suggests that over a million people are supported thereby.

Although their products are less valuable than the American output, the commercial fisheries of Peru lead the world in total fish production. Rich stores of fish, particularly anchovies, have contributed toward a lucrative export trade in fish meal. Japan, until displaced by Peru in 1962, was for a long time the leading world producer of fish. Today, she ranks second, supplying in 1964 some 2 percent of world output. Other countries where fishing is prosecuted on a huge scale are the Soviet Union, Norway, India, Canada, Spain, Chile, the United Kingdom, and Iceland. As a commercial industry fishing shows an interesting concentration in five areas: (1) northeastern Asiatic waters, (2) the Pacific coast of North America, (3) the New England-Grand Banks area, (4) North Europe, and (5) the coastal area of Ecuador-Peru. The preeminence of these regions is due to the combination of cold water for spawning, shallow banks for feeding, cold and warm currents for supplying abundant food and great variety of edible fish, highly indented coast lines for supplying bases and harbors, forest resources for boats and equipment, nearness to large markets, and poverty of the lands for agriculture. Some of these factors are, of course, not applicable to the west coast of South America.

DOMESTICATION OF FAUNAL FORMS

From parts of the foregoing discussion it must not be supposed that man's relation to fauna everywhere takes on the nature of a conflict. In many cases the exact opposite is true, for man has deliberately domesticated and propagated certain faunal forms. Some of these have been adopted by him largely for company or entertainment. The dog, cat, parrot, canary, white mouse, guinea pig, and goldfish fall primarily into this category. The majority, however, have been domesticated for utility.

WORK ANIMALS

A surprisingly long list of animals has been domesticated for draft or work purposes. One of the greatest aids to man in his socioeconomic evolution has been the draft animal. It is frequently asserted that the primary reason for the failure of the Amerindian generally to develop an advanced civilization was the lack of domesticable draft animals.[4] A similar lack of beasts of burden has kept the central African Negro in the stage of hoe agriculture and human porterage.

Among the draft animals, the horse, ass, and ox are very widely distributed, but most others are geographically limited to special areas: the reindeer (Fig. 15–21) is practically confined to the Polar Zone, the yak and llama (Fig. 22–11) to highland regions, the camel (Fig. 9–5) to tropical and subtropical sandy deserts and to dry continental hilly and rocky regions, and the carabao and work elephant to more humid tropical lands (Figs. 10–7 and 31–3).

CLOTHING

The use of fibers, skins, hides, and other animal products for clothing is of great antiquity. Such primitive materials, however, instead of being abandoned, are today of greater importance than ever before. Some of the domesticated animals supplying these products are alpacas, sheep, goats, silkworms, ostriches, and cattle.

FOOD

The dominant purpose of domestic animals is to supply man with food. The adoption of pastoral habits (or of animal husbandry in conjunction with agricultural habits) must have marked a tremendous stride in human ecology. It was probably engendered by the depletion of game locally. It gave to man, however, an enormous ecological advantage in rendering his occupancy independ-

Figure 31–3 Elephants are used in extracting and hauling teak logs in Burma. In the hot, humid climate of southeastern Asia horses do not thrive, and even donkeys are not numerous. Therefore, elephants are used as beasts of burden, especially for heavy work. (Photo courtesy of the United Nations)

ent of the natural food supply. As a consequence, the rearing of beasts for food has become one of mankind's leading industries. Among the food animals, poultry (chickens, ducks, geese, turkeys, and others) is perhaps most universal in occurrence, though beef cattle and sheep are widely distributed. Swine, dairy cattle, goats, and hares, too, are numerous but less widely distributed.

FAUNICULTURE

This varied array of domesticated animals has been derived by man from the native animal life of the environment, but it must not be regarded as now constituting part of the earth's fauna. Rather it forms part of the occupancy, being little more than ecological equipment in the hands

[4] At the time of North America's discovery, the continent had only one domesticated mammal—the dog.

Figure 31–4 A fox-fur farm in Prince Edward Island, Canada. The exploitation of wild fur-bearing animals went hand in hand with the exploitation of the forest. The resulting short supply and high prices along with a steady demand gave rise to a new industry—the production of fur from domesticated foxes. (Photo from Ewing Galloway)

of man—equipment which aids him in adjusting himself to his milieu. On the other hand, man can and does offer considerable encouragement and protection to wild animals without attempting to domesticate them and render them symbiotic with himself.

FISH PROPAGATION

The development of a world market for fish and of wholesale methods of catching them has resulted in the reckless destruction of many of the choicest fisheries. This has proceeded to such lengths that finally remedial action has been taken. International treaties, state and national laws, governmental bureaus of fisheries, and biological research are now seeking to rehabilitate this resource, and fish hatcheries and rescue commissions are accomplishing it with remarkable success.

An interesting alternative is suggested by the raising of carp and other species in ponds or on flooded rice fields. This is done both commercially and to augment the local food supply in China and Japan.

FUR FARMING

The reckless destruction of fur-bearing animals from the sixteenth to the twentieth century gradually brought about a critical situation in the trapping industry. Finally, furs were in the main obtainable only from remote sources and at high prices. About 1910, fur farming was started in Prince Edward Island, Canada. Within twenty years this had grown into an important industry in Canada, the United States, and a few north European countries (Fig. 31–4).

GAME PROTECTION

Wild game has steadily decreased in abundance over most of the earth. This is a necessary concomitant of the growth of population, but it need not result in the extermination of game birds and animals. It is now recognized that many desirable forms of wildlife are capable of maintaining themselves even in densely populated areas if they are accorded a reasonable degree of protection.

International treaties have been made in behalf of certain migratory birds, fish, and marine animals; much remains to be accomplished if they are to be afforded full protection. Game refuges and bird sanctuaries have been established, laws regulating the hunting of desirable types have been passed, and bounties for the elimination of undesirable species have been adopted. In many instances, wild animals and birds are propagated and used to restock depleted areas. Occasionally, exotic species are introduced into districts suitable for their occupancy. Over large areas, however, even in relatively advanced countries, no protection is afforded native animal life and much remains to be done toward that end.[5]

[5] In some areas pheasant farmers "sell hunting." They guarantee that birds will be found, and will be "fair game." Hunters are taken to areas which have been flooded with pheasants raised in captivity. Such birds are really not "fair game"—they do not even try to fly away!

SUGGESTED USEFUL READINGS

Darlington, Philip Jackson, *Zoogeography: The Geographical Distribution of Animals* (New York, John Wiley & Sons, Inc., 1957), 675 pp.

Farb, Peter and the editors of *Life, The Insects*, Life Nature Library (New York, Time, Inc., 1962).

Hesse, Richard, Warder C. Allee, and Karl P. Schmidt, *Ecological Animal Geography*, 2d ed. (New York, John Wiley & Sons, Inc., 1951), 715 pp.

U.S. Department of Agriculture, *Insects*, The Yearbook of Agriculture, 1952 (Washington, D.C., Government Printing Office, 1952), 780 pp.

32

The Realm of Microorganisms

There is a vast realm of small organisms which constitutes a very important part of man's natural environment. It consists of teeming trillions of life forms, most of which are too small to be seen. These tiny living things inhabit the air that man breathes, the food he eats, the water he drinks, and the surface of nearly everything he touches. Some of them, indeed, are found on his skin and on his mucous membrane at all times. Others of them occasionally invade his body and cause serious disorders and even death. Some are directly useful to man, whereas still others are neither harmful nor useful to him. The majority of these small organisms are, however, of some importance to man, to say the least.

Excessively dry or cold climates, sterile soils, rocky terrain, or ferocious beasts have retarded and, at times, prevented the development of certain parts of the earth. But microorganisms have probably been more effective in thwarting man than all these other factors combined. Despite the importance of the microorganic realm in the geography of human society, geographers generally have paid little systematic attention to it. Many college textbooks fail to treat it at all, even while discussing climates, landforms, soils, and other environmental elements in great detail— probably because it is not an obvious matter.

DISCOVERY OF MICROORGANISMS

Until quite recently man did not suspect the existence of microorganisms because most of them cannot be seen with the naked eye. A few are large enough to be seen with difficulty; some are barely visible against certain backgrounds— provided that the observer knows what to look for. Many can be seen only through the optical microscope. Still more of them can be seen only indirectly with the aid of the electronic microscope. It is not strange, therefore, that these small forms of life remained so long unknown.

Zaccharias Janssen, a Hollander, made the first crude microscope about 1590, and some twenty years later, Galileo also constructed such an instrument in Italy. In 1675, or perhaps a few years earlier, a Dutch naturalist, Anton van Leeuwenhoek, constructed a single lens microscope and used it to examine decaying matter, rain water, excreta, tooth scrapings, and other substances. In these he found both bacteria and microzoans which he called "animalcules."

Nearly two hundred years elapsed before others took up the study of microlife forms and the true nature and significance of bacteria and microzoans were determined. From these investigations, two sciences, bacteriology and protozoology, have grown up and assumed their present enormous importance in modern life.

The realm of microorganisms today is known to consist of several kinds of organisms: (1) microzoans or tiny animals, (2) microphytes or small plants belonging to the fungus class, (3) bacteria and rickettsias which seem to be of vegetable rather than animal nature (some biologists, however, do not classify them as either plant or animal), (4) the viruses whose precise nature is not yet known.

MINUTE ANIMAL LIFE
PROTOZOA

The protozoa are one-cell animals which can be found in the water of ditches and mud puddles and elsewhere. An ordinary gram of fertile soil may contain from 10,000 to 100,000 of these tiny animals, where they carry on important processes in making the soil suitable for plant life. By far the greater number reproduce asexually, that is, by some form of division of themselves. Very rarely some kinds of them are seen to reproduce sexually, that is, by conjugation. Some varieties, however, reproduce by sporolating. There are some four classes of protozoa, namely, *amoebae, flagellates, ciliates,* and *sporozoa.*

Amoebae

Amoebae and allied protozoa look like irregular particles of colorless animated jelly. They range from very tiny up to perhaps 1/100 of an inch in size. Each consists of but a single cell with a nucleus which controls nutrition and reproduction. The walls of the cell are not rigid, so that tiny particles of food may be encompassed or ejected. An amoeba is able to change its shape constantly and thereby produce movement (Fig. 32–1A).

Flagellates

A flagellate consists of a single elongated cell equipped with one or more tail-like filaments or flagella. Movement of a flagellum produces a swimming motion. One of the best-known flagellates is the *Gambian trypanosome,* about 1/800 inch long, which causes African sleeping sickness. Some flagellates, such as *euglena,* contain chlorophyll by which they manufacture their own food from carbon dioxide and water. Certain species of flagellates join together in great numbers to form colonies (Fig. 32–1B).

Ciliates

Elongated or pear-shaped protozoa covered with threadlike hairs or cilia are known as *ciliates.* The beating of the cilia propels the animal backward or forward and moves food particles into a mouthlike hole in the cell wall. Some, like *paramecium,* are free swimming cigar-shaped cells sometimes just large enough to be visible to the naked eye. A few ciliates lose their cilia in the adult stage and become anchored on a sort of stem (Fig. 32–1C).

Sporozoa

Sporozoa are round or oval cells without means of locomotion. They are parasitic upon higher animals and absorb their food through their cell walls. Reproduction is mainly by spore formation. In size they vary from extremely small up to about 1/100 of an inch. A well-known sporozoon is *plasmodium vivax* which causes malaria (Fig. 32–2).

HIGHER ANIMALS

A few of the higher forms of animal life (metazoa) should probably be included in the realm of small animal life. An example is the

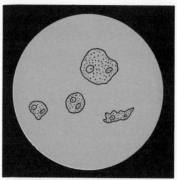

A. Amoebae

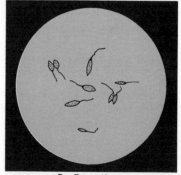

B. Flagellates

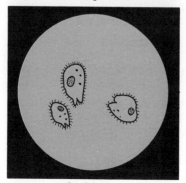

C. Ciliates

Figure 32–1 Some very small animal forms as seen under the optical microscope.

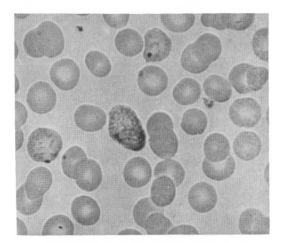

Figure 32–2   Photomicrograph of the malaria organism. The malaria parasite (benign tertian), known as *plasmodium vivax*, grows within the red corpuscles of the human blood stream. When the parasite is full grown within a blood cell, the cell breaks up to liberate young parasites and decomposition products into the circulating blood stream of the infected person, thus causing an attack of chills and fever. (Photo courtesy of the U.S. Public Health Service)

nucleus. Their common method of reproduction is by budding. They produce enzymes which create fermentation in starches and sugars. Two yeasts are of especial interest—*grape yeast,* the enzymes of which produce wine and vinegar; and *baker's* or *brewer's yeast,* whose enzymes produce fermentation in light bread and beer (Fig. 32–3A).

Yeasts are widely distributed in nature, their spores being found on the skin of every berry

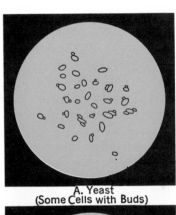

A. Yeast
(Some Cells with Buds)

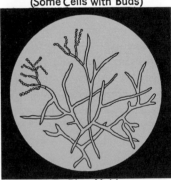

B. Blue Mold
Penicillium with Spores

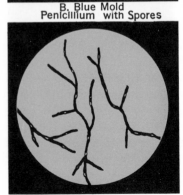

C. Actinomyces

Figure 32–3   Some very small plant forms as seen under the optical microscope.

vinegar eel, a microscopic threadworm often found in vinegar. Other threadworms of the *Anguillulidae* family cause galls and root knots in fruit and cotton plants and serch in sugar cane. One very small threadworm is the filaria which causes elephantiasis in man. Still another threadworm, *trichinella,* is parasitic upon pigs, rats, and a few other animals. When infected meat is eaten raw or in an undercooked state, the trichinellae are introduced into the human intestine. There, each mature worm lays several thousand eggs, the larvae from which burrow through the intestinal wall into the muscles. As many as fifteen thousand small parasites have been counted in one gram of infected muscle.

Liver flukes, a kind of small parasitic flat worm, are, at least during their immature stages, microscopic or submicroscopic in size. Certain very small arthropods might also be included in the realm of microzoans.

MINUTE PLANT LIFE

YEASTS

The yeasts are simple fungi—plants without roots, stems, leaves, or chlorophyll. They are single cells surrounded by a cellulose wall and containing a

and fruit, on many plants, in soil, and on dust particles. A few yeasts are often harmlessly present in the human digestive tract. One type, *monilia,* sometimes invades the human skin, intestinal walls, and other mucous membranes, causing a disease known as *thrush.* Other varieties of yeast invade lungs, nerve centers, lymph glands, bones, and other parts of the body, producing lesions, pus tumors, or pulmonary infections.

MOLDS

A mold plant is multicellular, with the cells lying end to end so as to form long branching threads or mycelia. An individual mycelium is often large enough to be visible. Some mycelia serve as roots; others bear fruits in the form of tiny spores. Molds can be seen growing on bread, cloth, jelly, fruit, paper, leather, dead wood, and many other substances. Some species are useful in making cheeses such as Camembert and Roquefort. Others cause disease in man, as for instance athlete's foot, ringworm, and scalp infections. Still other varieties are used in the preparation of the antibacterial medicine known as penicillin (Fig. 32–3B).

ACTINOMYCES

Actinomyces are microorganisms resembling molds but much smaller in size. Many varieties are present in the soil where they feed on dead organic matter and aid in the preparation of humus (Fig. 32–3C). A few species invade human tissue, producing actinomycosis or "lumpy jaw." Some varieties have recently been utilized too in the preparation of streptomycin, aureomycin, terramycin, and other antibiotic medicines.

ORGANISMS PROBABLY PLANTLIKE IN CHARACTER

BACTERIA

Bacteria are tiny microorganisms probably akin to the small plants known as algae. They are single-cell organisms which reproduce by fission, that is, by simple subdivision. Where environmental conditions are favorable, the number of bacteria may become astoundingly large. A gram of fertile soil may contain as many as 100 million bacteria. At that rate the top foot of soil over an acre of land would contain some 350 pounds of bacteria. If the weight of protozoa, fungi, algae, and other small organisms is added, the total reaches 500 to 700 pounds per acre foot of soil.

The bacteria are so small that it is impracticable to record their size in fractions of an inch. A new measure known as a *mu* (μ), equal to 1/25,000 of an inch, is used instead. Bacteria range in size from a fraction of a μ to 20μ or more. In general, there are four kinds of bacteria —*bacilli, cocci, spirilla,* and *spirochetes.* Some bacteria can achieve protection by surrounding themselves with a soft gelatinous capsule. A few species can survive very adverse conditions by forming a small resistant spore inside its cell which will live on after the cell dies.

Bacilli

One variety of bacteria is the bacilli. A bacillus is rod shaped and is usually immotile. Some kinds, however, are motile, being equipped with one or more threadlike flagella by which they are propelled. Bacilli average between 1 and 10μ in length. Some are aerobic, that is, they thrive in oxygen; others are anaerobic, that is, they cannot tolerate air. Some of the best-known bacilli are the colon bacillus, buttermilk bacillus, tubercle bacillus, typhoid bacillus, anthrax bacillus, and tetanus bacillus (Fig. 32–4A).

Cocci

The cocci are more or less spherical bacteria averaging in size between $\frac{1}{2}\mu$ to 1μ in diameter, and are nonmotile. Some common examples are the *streptococcus, staphylococcus, gonococcus, pneumococcus,* and *meningococcus.* There are several species of each. For instance, the staphylococci may be subdivided into *staphylococcus albus, staphylococcus aureus,* and *staphylococcus citreus.* Under the microscope the cocci assume different patterns. *Micrococci* usually exist singly, *diplococci* in pairs, *streptococci* in chains, and *staphylococci* in clusters (Fig. 32–4B).

Spirilla and vibrios

Spirilla are rigid spirals or corkscrews up to 10μ or more in length moving by means of flagella. The vibrios are shorter curved organisms. One

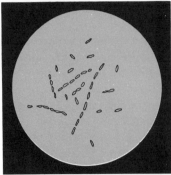

A. Bacilli

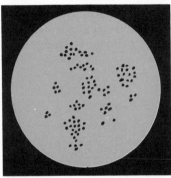

B. Cocci

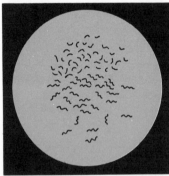

C. Spirilla and Vibrios

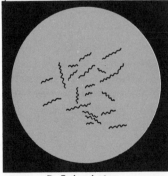

D. Spirochetes

Figure 32–4   Some common forms of bacteria as seen under the optical microscope.

spirillum is the causative organism in rat-bite fever; a vibrio is the causative organism in Asiatic cholera (Fig. 32–4C).

Spirochetes

The spirochetes are flexible spirals which move by rotating their coils. They vary in size up to 30μ or more in length. Various spirochetes cause syphilis, trench mouth, and hemorrhagic jaundice (Fig. 32–4D).

THE ROLE OF BACTERIA

The bacteria in general perform some four essential functions in nature: (1) some of them take nitrogen from the air and "fix" it in the soil; (2) they convert the animal waste product *urea* into nitrates which are plant foods; (3) they change the proteins in dead animal and plant matter into ammonia, nitrates, and nitrites so that they become usable as plant food; (4) they aid the yeasts in the processes of making bread, butter, cheese, vinegar, and alcohol, in the curing of leather, tobacco, tea, and cacao, in the retting of flax, and numerous other processes. Many bacteria have become partially or wholly parasitic upon animals and man and cause an untold amount of sickness and death. Despite this, the general role of bacteria in putrefaction and decay is essential in the lives of both animals and man. *If all the bacteria were suddenly destroyed, life on earth would probably disappear within ten or fifteen years!*

RICKETTSIAS

The rickettsias are very small microorganisms. They look like very small bacilli or cocci, but unlike bacteria, they cannot be cultured in artificial media in the laboratory. In size, a rickettsia is about $1/3\mu$ to $1/2\mu$ in length. Various rickettsias attack man, causing typhus of several varieties, Rocky Mountain fever, Australian fever, trench fever, and other maladies. They are transmitted from insect to insect, or from insect to higher animal, or from insect to man. They are especially apt to be carried by body lice, head lice, pubic lice, rat fleas, dog ticks, wood ticks, and rat mites.

VIRUSES

Viruses are extremely small particles probably ranging from $1/1,000\mu$ up to $1/4\mu$ in diameter.

Most of them are small enough to pass through the pores of the finest filter and hence it is practically impossible to segregate them by mechanical means. A mass of them clustered together can sometimes be seen under the optical microscope, but an individual virus is usually too small to be seen. The electronic microscope, which magnifies objects up to some 80,000 diameters (as compared to 1,000-2,000 diameters by the optical microscope), readily reveals the viruses.

Their extremely minute size hampers detailed study of the viruses. Some scientists believe them to be a special kind of very small bacteria. Others consider them intermediate between living and nonliving matter.

The viruses attack man and cause the common cold, influenza, and virus pneumonia, measles, infantile paralysis, smallpox, yellow fever, rabies, dengue, parrot fever, and other ailments. Some viruses attack plants, causing tobacco mosaic and other diseases.

MICROORGANISMS AND DISEASE

GROWTH OF KNOWLEDGE

Disease is as old as mankind. Some forms of disease are endemic, others epidemic. The nature and causes of disease, however, were not known until recent times. Disease was long accounted for by magical and religious explanations and was variously attributed to uncleanliness, bad air, sin, and divine displeasure.

Such explanations, however, did not satisfy inquiring minds, and the Roman scholar, Varro, as early as 116 B.C., postulated a vague concept of something on the order of germs as causes of disease. It was not until 1546, however, that Girolamo Fracastoro in Italy suggested that diseases might be the result of small living organisms. The discovery of such organisms was, of course, delayed until after the invention of the microscope.

Even after Leeuwenhoek's discovery of "microbes," there was a long, hot argument over whether such microorganisms were spontaneously generated from nonliving matter or derived from living parents of the same form. The French chemist, Louis Pasteur (1822–1895), did much to establish a knowledge of the nature of micro-

organisms. Among other things, he discovered the important fact that bacteria could be killed by heating and that such "pasteurized" substances would remain free of bacteria if kept from contact with the air. Concurrently, Joseph Lister (1827–1912), an English doctor, discovered the relation of bacteria to the infection of wounds and surgical incisions. His studies resulted in the development of disinfectants and antiseptics as means of fighting disease. Robert Koch (1843–1910), a German doctor, cultured bacteria in the laboratory and studied their life cycle. In so doing, he set a pattern for modern bacteriological research.

The work of these and other men started a period of scientific research. And so, by 1900, all the common bacteria had been discovered. Also most of the microzoans, yeasts, and molds had been found and described. The existence of some of the viruses has been pretty well established also. The discovery of the rickettsias by Ricketts followed in 1910.

Between 1910 and 1930, skin tests, vaccines, and serums were developed. The role of human and insect carriers was further studied and defined, and human allergies to fungi and bacteria were classified.

Then came the invention of the electronic microscope (first used in the United States in 1940), enabling man to study the viruses, rickettsias, and smaller bacteria. Meanwhile, the sulfa drugs were developed, and such substances as penicillin, gramicidin, and streptomycin were made by the biochemists.

MICROORGANISMS AND DISEASE

This brief survey of the realm of microorganisms is sufficient to show the important relation between the small forms of life and diseases in man. Many of the diseases, endemic and epidemic, over the world are caused by these various microanimals and microplants and plantlike forms. The viruses produce infantile paralysis, measles, yellow fever, and the common cold among men and foot-and-mouth disease among animals. The rickettsias cause typhus and Rocky Mountain fever. Bacteria cause bubonic plague, syphilis, typhoid, tetanus, whooping cough, and scarlet fever. The minute fungi produce thrush, athlete's foot, and other less well known infections. The protozoa and filariae give rise to malaria, sleeping sickness, elephantiasis, trichinosis, and numerous other ailments.

Very many varieties of the microorganisms are able to invade the human body through the respiratory system, the alimentary canal, the mucous membranes, cuts and abrasions, or in some instances through the skin itself. Once inside, they usually find an environment so favorable that they multiply with astonishing rapidity. Some varieties excrete poisonous toxins while others do a considerable amount of mechanical damage to the host. As soon as they become numerous within the human body, therefore, they usually cause illness and sometimes death.

SOME TROPICAL DISEASES

Cyclonic Zone man has already occupied and developed most of the habitable portions of the middle latitudes, and the high latitudes are rather inhospitable. Further world development, therefore, requires his expansion into the tropics. Tropical diseases, however, have greatly retarded and in some instances nearly prohibited such expansion because Cyclonic Zone man has had no resistance to them. Moreover, until recently, he has possessed no effective means of combating them. On the other hand, he has carried some tropical maladies back to his homeland where they have occasionally run rampant.[1] The tropical diseases include several ailments which are important enough for a brief description and discussion of each.

YELLOW FEVER

Yellow fever probably is endemic to tropical Africa and was brought to tropical America by the slave trade. Very shortly after colonization began in Middle America, yellow fever began to attack the Spaniards. Great numbers of Spanish colonists, traders, and soldiers died. Violent outbreaks of the fever also occurred among their African slaves. At times, trade was brought to a complete standstill and economic development in general was greatly retarded. In the course of time, yellow fever eventually spread during the hot months to parts of the American South and southern Europe. In these latter places, it always disappeared with the first frost of autumn, but

in the Tropical Zone where there is no frost, yellow fever remained a perpetual curse. No cure or preventive was found during the four centuries of Spanish control. During the Spanish-American War, yellow fever killed many more American soldiers than did Spanish bullets. So serious did the situation become that doctors began to study the disease closely. In 1881, a Cuban doctor, Dr. Carlos Finlay, had suggested that yellow fever germs were perhaps transmitted from sick persons to well persons by the *Aëdes aegypti* mosquito. An American Army surgeon, Walter Reed, with several assistants, volunteered to test the theory. They proved that yellow fever is not contagious, but that it is invariably transmitted from person to person by the *Aëdes* mosquito. One of the men lost his life in the experiment—a martyr to medical research.

After victory, the American Army remained in Cuba for some time, during which it undertook the eradication of yellow fever. Since the *Aëdes aegypti* is usually a "domestic" mosquito, the task was relatively easy. The American Army promulgated a set of highly restrictive measures, and then enforced them at the point of the bayonet. All uncovered water containers were destroyed; all mud puddles were filled; tin cans and trash heaps were cleaned up, houses were screened, and regular sanitary inspections were instituted. After the American Army of Occupation was withdrawn, Cuba continued these precautions, and hence there has been scarcely a single case of yellow fever since 1901. Continuing laboratory studies of yellow fever were made, but it was not until the year 1928 that a virus was identified as the causative organism in yellow fever.

More dramatic even than the success in Cuba was that attained in the Panama Canal Zone. This area had been one of the principal centers of the disease all through the Spanish colonial period and had retained its ill-repute under Colombian control. When the United States leased the Canal Zone, the Army was given com-

---

[1] Out of all fairness, it must be said that he has carried some of his own ailments, measles, mumps, gonorrhea, tuberculosis, and so forth to the tropics. When these were first introduced, the tropical natives, who had no resistance to such afflictions, often succumbed wholesale.

plete control and ordered to develop a long-time public health program. The latter was so successful that yellow fever has to all intents and purposes been eliminated.

The Rockefeller Medical Foundation has for several decades conducted a constant educational campaign against yellow fever and practically all tropical countries have cooperated in attacking the disease. By 1925, it was believed that yellow fever had been completely eliminated from the American Hemisphere. A few years later, however, it was found in numerous localities from Colombia southward into Bolivia and Brazil. However, this was not the classical urban yellow fever but the jungle type which is transmitted by insects other than *Aëdes aegypti* in tropical or subtropical forest environment. The disease is maintained chiefly by susceptible forest animals. A vaccination is now available which confers immunity for several years.

MALARIA

This disease is distributed throughout the Tropical, Subtropical, and Cyclonic zones, though it is most severe in tropical and subtropical regions. It is caused by a minute one-celled parasite which is introduced through the skin into the peripheral blood by an anopheline mosquito that has become infected by previously biting a person affected with malaria.[2] The organism, which multiplies asexually in the blood stream and in blood-forming organs of the body (Fig. 32–2), invades and destroys the red blood corpuscles and at the same time liberates poisons which cause the characteristic symptoms of chills and fever. Fortunately for man, not all species of anophelines transmit the disease. Malaria-bearing mosquitoes breed in such natural water bodies as brooks, lakes, ponds, pools, and swamps which are exposed to sunlight. Anopheline mosquitoes will fly a considerable distance—very often a mile or more—to get their blood meal. They are house haunters and bite mostly at night; seldom do they bite during the day, although recently the Gorgas Memorial Institute announced that one species of anopheline mosquito, *Anopheles bachmanni*, bites during the day and before 10 A.M.

Throughout the extensive tropical reaches of South and Central America, Africa, and Asia,

it long seemed incomprehensible that man could progress very far in sanitizing the lowlands against malaria because of the staggering cost.[3] Even in the Panama Canal Zone, where the United States government provided almost unlimited funds for antimosquito work and, in addition, was backed by treaty with absolute sanitary jurisdiction over a wide area, the disease has not been eradicated. To rid the area of malaria completely would require years of effort and the expenditure of additional huge sums of money. What the government has done is to eliminate the disease from the more important towns and their environs.

Malaria is far more difficult to eradicate than yellow fever, which also is mosquito borne but which is caused by a virus rather than a microzoan. The yellow-fever-bearing mosquito, by way of contrast to the one involved in malaria, is a short-flying species, developing almost exclusively in artificial containers—ant guards, bottles, cisterns, jars, tin cans, and vases in houses and yards. Hence man can triumph over it by eliminating these common breeding places. Colonel Weston P. Chamberlain[4] gives the following five reasons to account for the persistence of malaria.

First, the anopheles mosquitoes concerned are *rural* breeders, developing in swamps, brooks, ponds, or puddles over very great areas and then flying considerable distances (a mile or more) to obtain the blood meal necessary for the propagation of their species. *Second*, a large part of the indigenous population of the Isthmus living *outside of the*

---

[2] The discovery of the plasmodium of malaria (1880) was made by A. Laveran, a French army surgeon stationed at the time in Algeria, and that of the true relation of the mosquito to malaria (1897) was made by Ronald Ross, a surgeon in the Indian Army Medical Service.

[3] For many years antimalarial work consisted of emphasizing *control, not eradication*. The turning point came with DDT. Spraying the inner walls of houses left a residual poison that would kill any mosquitoes alighting over the next six months and in some cases in a year and at a cost of only twenty to fifty cents (U.S.) per capita per year.

[4] Weston P. Chamberlain, *Twenty-five Years of American Medical Activity on the Isthmus of Panama, 1904–1929* (Mount Hope, C. Z., The Panama Canal Press, 1929), pp. 15, 16.

sanitated towns is chronically infected with latent malaria, thereby affording abundant opportunity for newly hatched mosquitoes to acquire the parasites when they bite such individuals. *Third,* even when vigorously treated, those who contract malaria may remain infective for lengthy periods during which they cannot be shut up in a screened room as is the rule with the yellow fever patient throughout his brief three days of infectivity. *Fourth,* one attack of malaria confers no immunity to subsequent ones. *Fifth,* there is an insistent desire among many persons to leave sanitated areas at night for picnics or other purposes.

Today malariologists under the World Health Organization are waging an all-out war against malaria, spraying house interiors with DDT in infected areas wherever the disease is endemic. This is being done at very low cost. Hence, they believe they can wipe this scourge, which afflicts 250 million people, from the earth *if* the dramatic international campaign can be speeded up. Speed is imperative because some of the *Anopheles* mosquitoes that transmit the disease show a tendency to resist DDT.

AMOEBIC DYSENTERY

Dysentery, an intestinal disease, is caused by a parasitic amoeba. It is spread by ". . . careless contact cases, carriers (chiefly cooks), drains, dairies, dirty drinking water, the dust of dejecta, and the repulsive regurgitation, dangerous droppings, and filthy feet of fæcal-feeding flies fouling food."[5]

The amoebae attack the cells lining the wall of the intestine, break them down and cause ulcers and abscesses in the intestines and liver. Though dysentery is a severe and often fatal disease, it is being treated with considerable success with emetine.

For a long time, *Endomoeba histolytica,* which causes dysentery, was thought to be confined exclusively to tropical and subtropical regions; it is known now that this parasite is practically worldwide in its distribution, although amoebic dysentery is most common in the tropics. An efficient method for disposing of human excreta and provision of a pure water supply are probably the most effective means of combating this parasite and the disease it causes.

ELEPHANTIASIS

This dread disease seems to have been endemic to Oceania, but explorers and slave traders probably spread it to Australia, Asia, Africa, and the Americas. At one time, it became firmly established in a portion of South Carolina, but it seems to have died out there. It is very common in the Congo Basin, India, Indonesia, and the Fiji Islands. In certain districts of Southeast Asia about 5 percent of the population suffer from elephantiasis. Formerly it was very common in Barbados; and in 1921, some 5 percent of the people of coastal British Guiana were reported to suffer from it. In parts of Samoa, 48 percent of the population has it. In one of the Society Islands 70 percent of the adult male population is afflicted.

The disease can be caused by invasion of the body by several varieties of small thread worms or filariae. The filaria, *Wuchereria bancrofti,* is usually the offender in Africa, whereas *Wuchereria malayi* is usually the culprit in India, southeastern Asia, and the islands of the Pacific. When young, the microworms average 200 to 350μ in length, but the adult worms are 1 to 1.5 mm. in length. The microworms are transmitted by several varieties of *Anopheles* and *Mansonioides* mosquitoes.

After the worms grow numerous, the lymphatic system becomes blocked locally and enlargement of lymph glands and varicosity of the ducts occur. This is further aggravated by allergic reactions. In some cases the enlargement is painful; in others, relatively painless. It is usually found in adults rather than children, and males are much more susceptible than females.

The disease manifests itself in unsightly swelling of feet, legs, arms, the genitals and, more rarely, other parts of the body. A leg may swell and grow to three or four feet in circumference; the tongue may grow six to eight inches out of the mouth and dislocate the jaw. A scrotum may enlarge to a weight of two hundred pounds or more; and the breasts may enlarge to the waist and weigh twenty pounds or more apiece.

[5] Andrew Balfour, *War Against Tropical Diseases* (London, Wellcome Bureau of Scientific Research, 1920), p. 158.

There is no known way to kill the adult filariae, but sulfa drugs apparently will kill the young worms. Streptococcus and staphylococcus serums are also effective in many cases. Bandaging in the early stages often retards growth. Rest, laxatives, and dieting are usually helpful. Surgery relieves many of the worst cases.

AFRICAN SLEEPING SICKNESS

This dreadful malady is a "black cloud" hanging over the tropical parts of the African continent. The ravages of sleeping sickness among humans and the destruction of livestock by the closely allied disease, *nagana*, have interfered with the economic and social development of vast areas of Africa.

The Arabs found sleeping sickness (*Trypanosomiasis*) in Africa as early as the fourteenth century. Slave traders found it present in some Negroes and soon learned not to buy infected slaves. A British naval surgeon in 1734 described the malady on the Guinea Coast—where it is still rampant.

Sleeping sickness is a protozoan disease, being caused by a flagellate known as *Trypanosome gambiense* (a somewhat more virulent variety, *T. rhodesiense*, causes the disease in southern Africa). *Trypanosome brucei* is usually the causative organism for nagana in animals. These protozoans are transmitted by the bite of the tsetse fly (the *glossina*, a brownish bush fly, of which there are some twenty-three species).

The symptoms are fever followed by protracted lethargy, growing weakness, and gradual wasting of the body. The initial fever is succeeded by an inflammatory condition of the lymphatic system. Skin eruptions and severe swelling about the eyes are common. The disease may gradually disappear, but usually the tiny flagellates succeed in getting into the cerebrospinal fluid, whereupon congestion of the brain and sometimes hemorrhage occur. Eventually, most patients die. Even when an individual recovers, he is rendered mentally dull and apathetic.

Tsetse flies are indigenous over about half of Africa—from the Sahara southward to the Kalahari and High Veld. Sleeping sickness, however, is very spotty in its occurrence. In some districts, 90 percent of the population is infected;

in others only 5 percent; in still others the disease is totally absent. Areas of occurrence are scattered from Gambia and Liberia eastward to Eritrea and from Angola to Mozambique. The disease is particularly frequent in Chad, the Central African Republic, and western Sudan.

Nagana among animals is even more widespread than sleeping sickness among humans. Pigs, goats, sheep, horses, rats, mice, guinea pigs, rabbits, antelopes, monkeys, and apes are susceptible to it. *Trypanosomiasis* is a generic term covering a large group of related diseases that cause immeasurable losses of livestock.

The tsetse fly needs deep shade and moisture and hence breeds in woodland and brush along the watercourses. It usually is found within ten to fifteen yards from a stream, but it will follow a man or animal for a mile or more. It will ride upon a traveler for several miles or upon an auto for fifty or more miles.

Eradication of the disease seems impossible because it shows periods of latency or quiescence for several years, after which it breaks out virulently. White exploration and settlement and the development of trade have spread the disease markedly within recent decades.

Screening, trapping of Glossina flies, burning of brush, communal clearing of the land, and resettlement of the population will practically eradicate sleeping sickness locally; but in the wet tropics regrowth of the vegetation is discouragingly rapid. On the Island of Principe, where sleeping sickness mortality was formerly 83 per 1,000, the disease has been practically wiped out. But Principe is a small area much more easily dealt with than the huge continental expanses of Africa.

Extensive and constantly repeated surveys of large districts, early diagnosis of the disease, and use of pentamedine are helping fight the malady. The real problem, however, is elimination of the tsetse fly. It is believed that the day of great epidemics is past and that the disease is well under control, but control obtained only at the price of continued vigilance over the lives of millions of people.

Some progress is being made against nagana with antricide, a synthetic organic sulfur compound.

HOOKWORM

Laziness and extreme weakness are the symptoms of hookworm. In south China, some 50 percent of the total population is reported to have hookworm. In India, probably 60 percent have it. In Ceylon, it is said that in some areas nearly 90 percent have it. It has spread from the tropics into southeastern United States where some sections are highly infected.

The hookworm disease is caused by a very small roundworm which gets into the alimentary tract of human beings. It hooks into the walls of the small intestine, with a hooklike portion of its mouth cavity. There, it feeds on human blood, consuming about one-tenth of a cubic centimeter per day. Two species of this roundworm are parasitic upon man—*Necator americanus* in the Western Hemisphere and *Ancylostoma duodenale* in the Eastern.

As long as there are less than twenty-five hookworms in one individual, the results usually escape notice; but as the number increases the symptoms increase. The *A. duodenale* female lays some 24,000 eggs per day, *N. americanus* about half as many. These hatch and then, in the form of larvae, pass out of the human host in the feces. Hookworm larvae can enter the human body through the skin or be swallowed in drinking water or fresh vegetables. Since worms live in the human body up to eight years, their number can soon exceed the safe maximum, whereupon the victim is robbed of his strength. Chronic sufferers exhibit anemia and marked fatigue, and they may even show stunted growth and mental retardation.

The cure is relatively simple: a single dose of tetrachlorethylene will remove an average of 95 percent of the adult worms. To prevent reinfection, a person must take no raw food or unboiled water and must wear shoes, because hookworms can enter the human body through cracks and cuts in the bare feet.

OTHER TROPICAL DISEASES

Kala azar, blackwater fever, tropical leg sores, and many other diseases are serious threats to health in the frostless tropical lands. As man learns more about medical science, public health, and sanitary engineering, he is slowly bringing most of these ailments under control. In the Panama Canal Zone, the United States government has instituted such stern regulations that public health among white people is excellent and the urban death rate there is lower than that of most cities in the United States.

ONLY A BEGINNING HAS BEEN MADE

The example of the Canal Zone shows that tropical lands can be made healthful, but it also shows the enormous difficulties involved in achieving that result. Moreover, it reemphasized the necessity for constant vigilance in, and the huge cost of maintaining, sanitary standards after a healthful condition is once achieved. Moreover, the Panama Canal area is one of only a few small areas in the Tropical Zone which have been rendered relatively hygienic. The amount remaining to be done is really appalling. No better notion of the size of the problem can be gained than from the experience of the U.S. Army during World War II.

WORK BY THE U.S. ARMY

The Medical Intelligence Division of the U.S. Army was organized in June, 1941, when it became obvious that America was in for a global war. Army medical men realized that millions of young Americans would soon be sent on military expeditions into nearly every latitude on the globe. Maps were prepared showing the areal distribution of practically every known disease. Files containing an incredible amount of information on medical geography and the geography of disease were collected.

As a result of all this activity, American soldiers during World War II were supplied with very complete health information regarding the lands to which they were sent. They were given vaccines and hypodermic injections of serums, and supplied with sulfa drugs, penicillin, and various disinfectants. Those bound for the tropics were supplied with mosquito helmet nets, sleeping nets, and considerable quantities of quinine or atabrine.

Under the stimulation of global war, both the Army and Navy encouraged research into sanitation. One important achievement was the development of a portable water-purifying plant which can rapidly produce pure water from the most polluted sources. Another achievement was the creation of almost unbelievably effective insecticides such as the substance known as DDT.[6] Still another accomplishment was the development of a cheap process of making atabrine, a quinine substitute. Despite these advances in medicine and sanitation, there was a great deal of infection and sickness among American troops. The rate of sickness, however, was probably less than one-fourth of that established during World War I.

WORK OF WORLD HEALTH ORGANIZATION

This great organization operating under the United Nations has already recorded accomplishments that a few years ago would have been regarded as fantastic. It has written *finis* to the terrifying epidemics. As a result of its work, the tropical diseases are no longer feared by the white man; and although the native populations are less fortunate, they too have benefited. Various diseases, however, do not affect the white man and the native in the same manner, and the latter does not draw the same benefits from the new knowledge.

Yet WHO has eliminated malaria from countless areas and has saved tens of millions of lives; it has completely eliminated yaws from Haiti and is attacking it successfully on many other fronts; it has saved from death from sleeping sickness hundreds of thousands of Africans. Much the same thing has happened in the case of other diseases (Fig. 32–5).

Despite all that is being done, there are millions of natives, attached to the soil and to their tribal practices, whose lives are lived almost under the same conditions as those prevailing centuries ago. Their way of life has hardly been altered. For the native to benefit, he must be taught hygiene education, health education, transformation of living conditions, and better adjustment to nature. WHO is working on these and largely because it operates the world over, there is good reason to be optimistic regarding man's future in relation to the so-called tropical diseases.

Figure 32–5   A rubber worker in tropical Ecuador reads a notice of free medical treatment in front of dispensary. (Photo courtesy of World Health Organization)

SOME EXTRATROPICAL DISEASES

The really dread diseases are not all tropical in their occurrence by any means. Those discussed in the preceding section tend to be restricted to the tropics and subtropics because their causative organisms are not resistant to the cold winters of the Cyclonic and Polar zones. Some, however, are ubiquitous and are almost worldwide in occurrence. A considerable number of diseases tend to be most characteristic of extratropical regions.

DIPHTHERIA

Diphtheria is typical of the middle latitude diseases. It is caused by the *bacillus diphtheriae*. It leaves the body of one person and, floating in the air, enters the body of another through the respiratory system. As soon as it lodges in the mucous membrane, it begins to multiply. Soon a false membrane grows in the infected throat,

[6] The Naval Medical Research Institute also developed a powerful insecticide and repellent, NMR 448, and a very powerful repellent, NMR 1407.

sometimes clogging the larynx and suffocating the patient. The bacilli excrete a virulent toxin which attacks the brain, nerves, adrenal glands, heart, and kidney, often producing death.

Against this toxin, the body manufactures diphtheria antitoxin, although often at a rate insufficient to prevent death. If the patient recovers, he usually enjoys permanent immunity against reinfection. Unfortunately, some people become permanent carriers of the bacillus, infecting others.

For many centuries, diphtheria was a recurrent and dreaded scourge in civilized lands. The rate of incidence ran high, particularly among children. Quarantine was only partially successful in checking epidemics. In 1900, the death rate from diphtheria in the United States was about 40 per 100,000. Then the Schick test was developed to reveal susceptibility, and a toxoid was made. Injections of this toxoid usually bestow immunity. By 1950, the death rate had fallen to less than 1 per 100,000 persons.

OTHER EXTRATROPICAL DISEASES

Diphtheria is but one sample malady out of many. Tuberculosis, gonorrhea, infantile paralysis, meningitis, syphilis, chancroid, typhus, and typhoid are among the worst of these. Even mumps, measles, whooping cough, chicken pox, and scarlet fever are exceedingly serious in the damage which they occasion. The common cold is perhaps the most serious of all in terms of the total loss and discomfort which it causes.

MAN AND MICROBES

MAN'S WEAPONS

Man's first real step toward combating these microorganisms was to "discover" them. This was followed by years of intensive study in order to learn the habits and life cycles of the disease-producing organisms. Then came the devising of scientific methods of control. These latter involve segregation and quarantine where necessary, programs of rest, or exercise, or special diet, climatotherapy or physiotherapy where effective, improved public sanitation, elimination of insect and animal carriers where such are involved, vaccination and antitoxin treatment for diseases

against which immunization is possible, and direct chemical attack (medical treatment) in cases where the organisms are vulnerable to chemical and biological substances.

MEDICAL TREATMENT

Not all organisms are vulnerable to direct attack, but some of them are. Among the viruses, a very few respond to treatment by the sulfa drugs and ultra-violet light. Many of the bacilli yield to treatment by chemical poisons—disinfectants and germicides—the reaction differing for each variety. A substance known as *bacteriophage* also destroys some of them. Oxygen and ultra-violet light will destroy some varieties. Most of the cocci are destroyed by the sulfonamides, aureomycin, and penicillin. Gonococcus will yield slowly to a solution of silver salts. Many of the spirochetes, as for instance that of syphilis, are destroyed by arsenic compounds with mercury or bismuth injected into the blood stream. Most of them are quickly killed by penicillin and some other antibiotics if treatment is not delayed. The plasmodia of malaria are slowed down but not killed by large doses of quinine or atabrine. Chloroquine will kill *falciparum* parasites but *vivax* cases are more stubborn and will relapse after treatment ends.

CONSTANT VIGILANCE DEMANDED

The struggle is never won completely. Bacteria, when brought under control, frequently are able, either through selection or mutation, to produce different and hardier varieties. These multiply rapidly and return to the struggle against man. Man, himself, is often culpable; relaxation of quarantine, vaccination, or public health measures, or laxity in food, water, and tenement inspection is often the cause of renewed outbreaks of disease.

Every microorganism is part of a delicately balanced ecological system. Often, man upsets this balance, as evidence in his use of the airplane. Transoceanic air travel and cargo-hauling have already been instrumental in quickly transferring both bacteria and the insect carriers of bacteria and microzoans to continents where they were previously unknown. As air travel increases, this hazard will be greatly enhanced. New and powerful insecticides promise man the means of locally eliminating disease-carrying insects. But this may also eliminate some of the present enemies of microorganisms and permit them to increase at previously unheard-of rates. Only constant vigilance and scientific research can enable man to utilize successfully the beneficial members and to combat the noxious members of the realm of small living things.

Perhaps the greatest ally of disease is human ignorance. A very great amount of health educa-tion is needed to reveal to the masses how broad is the battle front of society against the micro-organic world, and how narrow is the margin of man's victory in his struggle to possess the earth.[7]

[7] The American Geographical Society has published maps showing the world distribution of many diseases and other afflictions mentioned in this chapter. The publications include material on cholera, dengue, elephantiasis, malaria, rickettsias, sleeping sickness, syphilis, and yellow fever.

SUGGESTED USEFUL READINGS

May, Jacques M., *The Ecology of Human Disease* (New York, MD Publications, Inc., 1959).

May, Jacques M., ed., *Studies in Medical Geography*, Vol. 2, *Studies in Disease Ecology*, and Vol. 3, *The Ecology of Malnutrition in the Far and Near East* (New York, Hafner Publishing Company, Inc., 1961).

Stamp, L. Dudley, *The Geography of Life and Death* (Ithaca, N.Y., Cornell University Press, 1965).

VIII

The
Mineral
Factors

The obtaining and harnessing of the world's minerals for use in agriculture, manufacturing, construction, and just the sheer creation of vast amounts of energy for multiple use are at the heart of today's story of civilization. The true magnitude of the use of such energy cannot be realized by a simple statistical account of the quantities of coal, petroleum, natural gas, uranium, and thorium. The transformation of the raw materials into energy is a technological marvel. Even the translation of fuel consumption into a measuring device of kilowatt hours represents man's attempt to make universal his recognition, discovery, implementation, and planning of the utilization of new energy to relieve himself of excessive burdens and endless toil. The bringing of these earth materials into the economic, social, and political life of people today illustrates clearly how "resources are culturally defined"; that "they are not, but they become."

33

The Mineral Realm

INTRODUCTION

Man lives today, specifically, in the age of the power machine. But there could be no such world without minerals, because it is the latter which make possible the power *and* the machines. Civilization and progress are based upon a determination to produce more powerful and better tools with which to harness more and more of the forces of nature and direct them toward providing increasing comforts, conveniences, and power. When ancient man wanted work done, he had to do it himself. Later he tamed animals and enslaved other human beings through conquest to do his work. Civilizations of the past were based upon a pedestal of human slavery; civilization of the present (as that in the United States) also is based upon slavery—slavery of the machine, *not* human slavery. More than 90 percent of the work performed in the United States today is done by mechanical means. It is estimated that each American on the average uses more than three thousand kilowatt hours of electricity annually. Another way of putting this is that he has at his bidding about 210 slaves.

The tools and machines which modern man uses are fashioned primarily from minerals taken from the earth. Lacking metallic minerals and the organic fuels, modern man would be little better off than his Stone Age ancestor. Progress, as we know it, was bottled up tightly as long as tools were made of bone, stone, and wood. Only metals can be manipulated with great precision. As soon as man comprehended the intrinsic value of minerals (especially of iron and coal), civilization swept forward like a mighty flood.

Nature probably required about two billion years to lay down what is now our mineral heritage. During all but one second on the clock, figuratively speaking, these reserves remained untouched by the hand of man. In short, it has been only since 1900 that he has really dug into this natural storehouse. Stated otherwise, man has mined more minerals in the past sixty-eight years than in all previous history.

Our particular civilization is inherited from southwestern Asia and the Mediterranean lands, regions very poor in most mineral resources. It is well known that intellectual progress far outran material progress in those lands. But the big question is: Which civilizations are superior, those of the past or ours of the present? According to some historians, ours lacks the beauty that characterized the civilization of Greece's "Golden Age"; the permanence of that of China; and the spirituality of that of the century of St. Francis of Assisi. But in man's relationship to the forces of nature and in all-around capability, our civilization indisputably outstrips anything of antiquity. Steam, electricity, radiant and nuclear energy, all have given modern man powers almost beyond the imagination of the ancients—powers that have enabled him to enter a new material world from that in which his ancestors dwelled.

Relatively few of the earth's three and a half billion inhabitants, even the intellectuals, realize that the growth of mining and the dependence of civilization upon its products mark the greatest change that has yet occurred in human affairs. Utilization of coal and iron ore made possible the railroad, steamboat, and many other inventions. With electricity came the mining of copper, which ushered in the telegraph, telephone, and the transmission line. With the development of steel came the use of the ferro-alloys which have given to steel properties hitherto undreamed. With the invention of the gasoline engine came the automobile and the airplane. And now nuclear and solar energy are on the threshold of new developments, the scope of which may be beyond present comprehension.

Mineral deposits, then, are among the most highly prized treasures on earth. Lacking an impressive array of them, a nation is inevitably destined for lesser rank; a nation positively cannot be in the "heavyweight" class of great powers unless it possesses great mineral wealth at home or abroad. In modern civilization, man draws upon minerals every minute of his life. Hence, it is both fair and accurate to say that we are living in a mineral age and that ours is a *mineral civilization*, and that we are on the verge of a nuclear age.

MINERALS AND ANCIENT MAN

Precisely how long ago mankind began using minerals for weapons and tools can only be conjectured, but possibly 500,000 years is a reasonable estimate. The making of flint weapons is believed to have been the first manufacturing industry. Through barter and theft these products were carried hundreds of miles from the sources of the flint.

Gold is believed to have been the first metal prize. Who the finder was, on what continent he lived, and how he came first to appreciate the value of his find never will be definitely known. While setting his fish traps in the river, primitive man's attention presumably was drawn to brilliantly colored grains or nuggets of native metal in the sand. Gold, along with silver, platinum and occasionally even copper and bismuth, is unique in that it occurs in metallic or native form. This results from its slight affinity for oxygen or other chemical agents. It was this fact that enabled it to be the *first* metallic mineral prize. Except for embellishment, however, gold possessed no value; it was too soft and pliable for weapons.

The first *useful* metal was copper, but it too was ductile and soft and poorly adapted for

weapons. Ultimately, however, some primitive genius learned the art of hardening it.

As with gold, the secret of iron's discovery will always be withheld from us. Possibly the most logical notion of its discovery is that a primitive man built his campfire on a patch of ground that happened to be rich in iron ore. Some of the ore was fused with the burning charcoal embers and when the fire went out, the savage discovered in the ashes a lump of heavy metal unlike anything he had ever seen before.

Unfortunately for ancient man, most minerals were useless as metals, since they were found in chemical compound. Not until metallurgical operations were perfected for extracting the metals from their ores did man climb the ladder of civilization at more than a snail's pace; a flint ax is superior to one fashioned from pure copper. But when early man melted copper and tin together, he got the metal—bronze—which was harder and stronger than either of its constituent metals. Bronze played so important a role in human life that it gave its name to the next rung in the ladder of advancing civilization. Actually, this substance was not sufficiently superior to copper to enable the Bronze Age greatly to surpass the Copper Age.

It is interesting to note that archaeologists and metallurgists dispute the priority of bronze and iron. The former insist the Bronze Age is the older, because they have uncovered bronze weapons in beds older than those containing iron, and because the smelting of iron required higher temperatures and greater skill than the preparation of copper and bronze. Many metallurgists, on the other hand, emphatically deny this second point—that the reduction of iron requires higher temperatures—and contend that the scarcity of early iron relics is consequent upon the metal's readiness to rust entirely away rather than being evidence of its nonuse. They add, as further support, that if the civilized world were to cease using iron today, few traces of its extensive employment could be found a few thousand years hence.

Despite the fact that iron's history taps antiquity at least four thousand years, the true Iron Age was delayed until the nineteenth century when processes were developed for the large-scale conversion of ore to pig iron and thence to steel—processes that necessarily had to await the development of chemistry and mechanical power as well as innovations in metallurgy.

MINERALS IN EARLY CIVILIZATIONS

History tells of the drawing power of minerals from very early times. In fact the legend of the gold of Ophir actually antedates history. As man became more highly civilized, he began to utilize more minerals and persisted in his search for them even though this led to war. Lack of space prohibits any treatment of this topic.[1]

WHAT ARE MINERALS?

In this chapter only those minerals having economic significance are considered. Minerals are of many kinds. They differ in distribution, mode of occurrence, physical characteristics, and economic usefulness. There are a number of ways of classifying them, several of which will be considered here. For geographical study they are grouped as follows: (1) the nonmetallic minerals, (2) the metallic minerals, and (3) the mineral fuels. Under each of these three groups, the individual minerals may further be classified as either "commercial" or "submarginal," though this grouping admittedly lacks precision. The term *commercial minerals* is used to represent mineral resources available under present technologic practices and economic conditions. The very rarity of some of these makes them of peculiar international concern. By *submarginal minerals* is meant deposits that are economically unavailable, that is, they cannot be profitably worked either because the deposits (1) are too small in size, (2) are of low quality, (3) are remotely situated, or (4) the techniques in use are too inefficient. Thus the iron deposits of the New Jersey Pine Barrens, which were used for making iron in colonial days, would definitely be classed as submarginal today. Contrast, for example, the mining of this bog ore, where tiny bits were brought up by an oyster-tong-like device with today's gigantic electrically operated machines which plunge into the ore and come up with many tons at each bite (Fig. 33-1).

Functionally, minerals are classed as *basic*

Figure 33-1 Open-cut mining of iron ore at El Pao, Venezuela. (Photo courtesy of Bethlehem Steel)

and *contributory*. The three basic minerals are coal, iron ore, and copper ore. These three, by combining and coordinating their peculiar properties, lay the foundations of man's attempt to control the forces of nature. Petroleum tends to supplement coal as the chief source of energy; the ferroalloys improve the quality of steel; and platinum as a catalyst is indispensable in chemical synthesis.

Minerals also are classed as *expendable* and *nonexpendable*. The former are those which are not abundant and which sooner or later will be gone: coal, petroleum, and natural gas are examples. Iron ore, copper, and clay are essentially nonexpendable, proof of which is their existence in relics representing the earliest cultures of man.

ORIGIN OF MINERALS

Whereas the origin of minerals is of primary importance to the geologist, it is of only secondary importance to the geographer. A brief discussion of the origin of nonmetallic and

[1] Any who are particularly interested in this aspect of the subject are urged to read T. S. Lovering, *Minerals in World Affairs* (Englewood Cliffs, N.J., Prentice-Hall, Inc., 1943), Ch. III, "Minerals in History Before the Industrial Era," pp. 34-55.

metallic minerals and of mineral fuels is, however, presented in the three chapters which follow.

SOME PECULIARITIES OF MINERALS

The following four idiosyncrasies of minerals result in putting a definite stamp upon mineral deposits. (1) Minerals are highly localized in occurrence and of limited availability. (2) Owing to the "hidden" nature of most minerals, their discovery is largely unpredictable. This more than anything else gives mining enterprises a speculative character. (3) All mineral deposits are exhaustible and continued exploitation is nearly always accompanied by increased difficulties in production. Improved technology may result in temporary improvement. (4) Most metals are durable and hence reusable. Thus "scrap" plays an important role in the conservation of iron ore, copper, aluminum, and some other metals. It has been estimated that about 40 percent of the charge of the open hearth furnace consists of scrap.[2]

WHERE ARE THE MINERALS?

Viewed in terms of their location, minerals are considered from three points of view: (1) location with respect to the nations of the world, (2) location with respect to topography, and (3) location with regard to degree of concentration.

UNEQUAL DISTRIBUTION

Viewed politically, the distribution of minerals is cruel and definite (Fig. 33–2). Minerals are not apportioned equitably among the nations. Moreover, man can do little about it; he cannot transplant or develop them in spots where they do not exist.

By far the principal supplies are tributary to the North Atlantic Basin. It is not accidental, therefore, that the world's leading industrial nations are located there. Nowhere else on the globe is there an area so compactly and strategically placed. The North Atlantic Basin countries appear to be marked off for permanent industrial leadership.

No nation has really adequate amounts of all minerals. Some, such as the Union of Soviet Socialist Republics and the United States, are rich; others like Italy and Japan are miserably poor. A nation as rich as the United States lacks adequate deposits of antimony, asbestos, bauxite, china clay, natural nitrates, nickel, mercury, platinum, fluorspar, graphite, magnesite, mica, quartz crystals, pyrite, tin, and tungsten. Even the British Commonwealth, with territory in every continent, covering the entire range of geologic structure from the oldest to the youngest and from sedimentary to igneous rocks, was not self-contained. It lacked entirely mercury and sulfur and had inadequate deposits of antimony, potash, and phosphates. Though it "controlled" much petroleum, the Commonwealth per se had relatively little.

LOCATION AND TOPOGRAPHY

Mining is primarily a pursuit of rugged regions. Hence most mining camps are to be found perched high on the sides of mountains or in steep, narrow canyons. The ignorant prospector, lacking knowledge of geology, nevertheless knows through experience that his chances of making a strike are far better in a mountain than on the level floor of a valley or on a plain.

This tendency for rugged relief and mining to go together does, however, have exceptions. Thus the Cascades, the California Coast Range, the Alps, and the Himalayas are of very minor importance in mining. There are also some areas of very low relief that are outstanding producers of minerals. Many of Canada's metals are being won from such terrain. Most of these, however, were formed many geologic ages ago when mountains towered high above the present surface. Through millions of years of geologic time, however, erosion, aided by the continental glaciers, mellowed the terrain. The flat plains of Louisiana and Texas also yield mineral riches and are huge producers of petroleum and natural gas.

[2] The relative amounts of pig iron and scrap in the charge are largely controlled by plant and market conditions, that is, the supply and relative cost of these materials. If both are available, the only factor considered in proportioning the charge is the carbon content the charge should have when melted.

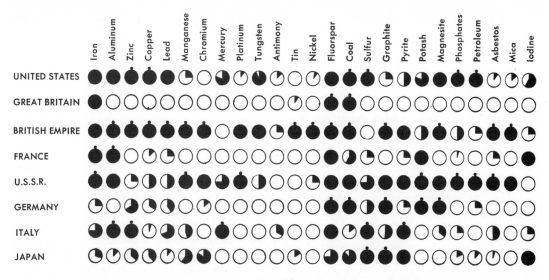

Figure 33–2   Prior to World War II, the seven so-called "Great Powers" were divided into the "haves" and the "have-nots." The diagram shows the self sufficiency of the several powers in minerals at that time. Black segments indicate the degree of self-sufficiency in each instance. The small protuberances above certain of the black circles indicate surpluses for export. This chart helps one to understand why international trade in raw materials is imperative: no country even approaches self-sufficiency in all minerals. (After the U.S. Army)

It should be realized and emphasized that minerals are not lacking in most plains; rather is it that they are inaccessible and hence cannot be won at a profit.

DEGREE OF CONCENTRATION

Few persons are aware of the degree of concentration of minerals. For example, over half the world's production of nickel comes from Canada's Sudbury district. All the Free World's cryolite is mined at Ivigtut in southwest Greenland. For many years about 75 percent of the world's molybdenum has come from a deposit in Colorado less than one square mile in size, and 95 percent of the anthracite of the United States is produced by ten counties in a small corner of northeast Pennsylvania. And Brazil supplies the entire world with quartz crystals.

Many of the nonmetallics, however, such as clays, sands, and stones—unlike the metallics, the mineral fuels, and even such nonmetallics as potash, nitrate, sulfur, and phosphate rock—are so widely distributed that their production almost anywhere is not a serious problem.

If man wants and must have minerals, and we know that such is the case, he must adjust himself to conditions laid down by nature when the earth was formed.

MINERALS AND MODERN GEOLOGY

Formerly, minerals were discovered by persons without real knowledge of the conditions under which they were formed; hence a "strike" was largely a matter of luck. Prospecting was and still is colorful and it actually reeks with glamor (for those who do not "prospect"), but the old-time bearded prospector is definitely passing from the scene. Even the geologist and the mining engineer do not operate alone. More and more those who seek minerals are beginning to work in groups as specialists. Coordinated group attack appears to be the key to the problem.

About 1900, a French geologist, De Launay, explained that during some periods of the earth's history certain unusual conditions prevailed that yielded valuable mineral deposits and that these conditions existed over larger portions of the earth. Thus the coal beds of England, India, and certain portions of eastern United States were laid down simultaneously when the climates there were much milder than now. Again, during times of long-continued aridity, extensive salt deposits were formed in innumerable places over the globe. A geologic revolution, during which mountain building occurs in narrow zones, may witness widespread intrusion within them and the intrusions may be accompanied by certain characteristic types of ore.

GEOLOGIC CONDITIONS AND MINERALS

Much in geology is immaterial to the geographer.[3] The authors believe, however, that beginning students in geography, many of whom may possibly never study geology, should know a few of the fundamentals of the relations of geologic conditions to the formation and deposition of minerals.

The metallic ores, the non-metallic deposits of economic value and the mineral fuels that are basic requisites for modern civilization occur under certain well-defined geological conditions. Their distribution is by no means haphazard or unpredictable. To assist in understanding their occurrence, the rocks of the earth's crust may be grouped in three categories. First there are the very old and generally much contorted or compressed rocks of the basement complex or Pre-Cambrian terrane. These include vast bodies of granite and other igneous rocks, many of them intensely metamorphosed, as well as sedimentary rocks that likewise have been greatly altered by heat and pressure during the many vicissitudes of crustal movement and volcanic eruption that have affected them throughout the long ages of geologic time. These ancient rocks contain many rich bodies of metallic ores, such as those yielding gold, silver, copper, nickel and iron. Nowhere do they contain coal, petroleum or the ores of such metals as aluminum and magnesium.

There are extensive areas of Pre-Cambrian rocks in every continent, and no large unit of these rocks, when adequately prospected, has thus far failed to yield essential metals. The Canadian shield surrounding Hudson Bay in North America and extending southward into the United States in the Lake Superior region is matched by the Scandinavian shield of northwestern Europe and the Angara shield of northcentral Siberia in Asia. In the Southern Hemisphere, the Brazilian shield of South America is matched by the extensive bodies of Pre-Cambrian rock in south and central Africa and the basement complex of Australia.

The second group of rocks in this very loose classification includes the sedimentary formations of Cambrian and Post-Cambrian age. These may be flat-lying beds beneath the plains and in plateaus or they may be wrinkled into mountains like the Appalachians. It is from these that the world's resources of coal and petroleum are secured, as well as much of the potash and magnesium and some of the iron and non-ferrous metals. Here, too, it is evident that every continent has its share. The widespread basin of the Mississippi Valley is matched by the extensive area of sedimentary rocks in central Europe between the Alps and the Scandinavian highlands. The vast lowland of the Amazon finds its structure counterpart in the interior basin of Australia and the broad plains of north-central Asia.

The third major type of geologic structure is that resulting from and associated with volcanic activity. Here the geologist has in mind not only the outpoured lavas and erupted cinders, ash and bombs of volcanic cones and plateaus, he thinks also of the intruded masses of igneous rock that crystallized in the conduits leading to volcanic vents or spread out in sheets or dome-shaped bodies in the upper part of the earth's crust without ever breaking through to the surface. Some of the world's most important reserves of precious metals, of copper, lead and zinc, and of tungsten, vanadium, molybdenum and manganese, essential in the production of modern steel alloys, are found in association with such rocks, especially those of Tertiary age. Here, again, we observe that *nature plays no favorites where continents are concerned.* The volcanic terranes of North America's western mountains have their equivalent in the Andes, the festooned arcs of the mountain systems in eastern and southern Asia, the plateaus and cones of central Africa.

Every continent displays almost the entire gamut of possible geologic structures and therefore may be expected to contain extensive deposits of almost every kind of mineral resource that might be useful as a raw material of industry. Although the United States alone has produced nearly two-thirds of the world's entire production of petroleum, it is because Americans have been more successful than other people in finding and using this type of fuel. A century ago two-thirds of the world's supply of petroleum was not concentrated beneath the surface of the United States. On the contrary, with the exception of Australia and the possible exception of Africa, every continent probably contained petroleum resources roughly proportional to the entire

[3] An excellent treatise on what in geology is and is not pertinent to geography is presented in Alan G. Ogilvie, "The Relation of Geology and Geography," *Geography*, Vol. XXIII (1938), pp. 79 ff.

total of the world's supply as the area of each continent is proportional to the total land of the earth.[4]

Thus knowledge of the general distribution of the rock groups throughout the world prepares one for the distribution of the important ore deposits and suggests the types that may be found in the future in specific kinds of regions. Moreover, applied geology reduces the hazard and eliminates much useless search. The experienced explorer for any particular mineral knows where in the world are his best chances of success. Thus he will not seek petroleum in the pre-Cambrian rocks of the Canadian Shield, in crystalline-metamorphic rocks, or in igneous rocks. He will attempt to follow certain favorable horizons, the general trend and distribution of which are quite well known; and he will test deep horizons in known fields. Enough is known about South America, for instance, to mark off the east slope of the Andes from Venezuela to Argentina as a region of probable discovery; the same holds for the great belt that extends from Romania into the Soviet Union, Iraq, Saudi Arabia, and Iran. The seeker of iron ore will explore in the late pre-Cambrian sedimentary horizons in Brazil, Australia, and India. Explorations for other minerals will suggest similar geologic possibilities and restraints.

SEARCH FOR MINERALS; KINDS OF MINING

The rewards of mining frequently are so great that mining operations are prosecuted in the most adverse climates and in extremely remote locales: in the bleak cold tundras of Siberia; in the disease-ridden jungles of Colombia; in the thirsty parched deserts of Australia; and in the thin cold air of Peru's lofty Andes. The difficulties attendant upon mining in these regions are great indeed, but if the mineral deposit is valuable, man will exploit it. Thus adverse geographic factors are a hindrance, not a preventive, to utilization.

Today's development is largely a matter of cooperation, scientific skills, ingenuity, and venture capital. The mining geologist appraises the size, quality, value, and potentialities of a given deposit. The mining engineer considers the mining possibilities, determines the location of mine openings, decides what methods of mining and beneficiation will be employed, and determines what mode of transport and power will be used. The metallurgical engineer decides the character and design of concentrating, smelting, and refining plants. The civil engineer designs and constructs aerial tramways, highways, and railways to make sure they are adjusted properly to the terrain and climate. The engineer also designs and constructs housing, public utilities, health and recreational facilities, making certain they are adapted to the specific milieu.[5] All of these activities depend upon financing; skills alone will not make the venture a success unless the costs of production and transportation can be kept lower than the selling price of the product.

FINDING MINERALS

The physical difficulties attendant first upon *finding* and second upon *developing* minerals may be great indeed. Hence, the old-time prospector, who spent so much time getting into and out of a region, is being replaced by the geologist, who frequently travels by plane or helicopter and utilizes highly scientific instruments. Among these are (1) the airborne magnetometer, which searches out large mineral deposits by recording the deviations they produce in the earth's magnetic field, (2) the airborne scintillometer, which determines radioactivity levels and is used to speed up the search for uranium, and (3) the aerial electromagnetometer, which can pinpoint certain kinds of mineral deposits. Recently two geologists using two helicopters surveyed 57,000 miles of territory in Canada's Hudson Bay region, accomplishing in a single season what a ground party would have required twenty-five years to do. Although adverse geographic factors are a hindrance to exploration in such an area as the Canadian Shield, they are not a preventive.

---

[4] Kirtley F. Mather, *Enough and to Spare* (New York, Harper & Brothers, 1944), pp. 73–76.

[5] Palmer W. Roberts, "Cold Weather Engineering," Parts I and II, *Military Engineer,* Vol. XLV (January-February, March-April, 1953).

Figure 33–3 Surface or strip mining in Ohio. The big shovel (background) is capable of removing 55 cubic yards of overburden at one bite after blasting has shattered the strata. The vein of coal is at the bottom of the cut, the roadbed on which the big shovel and the other machinery and vehicles rest. The small shovel (foreground) scoops up the coal and deposits it in trucks which carry it to the preparation plant. (Photo courtesy of the Consolidation Coal Company Hanna Coal Division)

KINDS OF MINING

Minerals are extracted in several ways. Where deposits are close to the surface, the soil and mantle rock are scraped off and the mineral excavated and lifted out. If rock itself is excavated, the process is termed *quarrying,* but where individual minerals are removed, the term *open-pit* or *open-cut mining* is applied (Fig. 33–1). If the mineral is coal, the term is *stripping* (Fig. 33–3). On the other hand, the working of placer gravels for their metal is known as *panning, rocking, sluicing, hydraulicking,* or *dredging,* depending upon the particular means used (Figs. 33–4 and 33–5). *Deep or hard rock mining* consists of driving tunnels, drifts, shafts, and stopes into the ore body. Some minerals, such as salt and sulfur, are frequently won by the process of drilling and pumping (Fig. 33–6).

WHEN SHALL ORE DEPOSITS BE EXPLOITED?

It is patent that many mineral deposits do not contain ore[6] and hence are not worked. But some potentially important ore deposits are also untouched, even though well known. Successful mining depends upon the harmonious functioning of a combination of factors.

 1. If the ore is of low grade, it should be

[6] *Ore* is a deposit of metallic minerals sufficiently rich to permit its profitable exploitation. Whether a given deposit constitutes ore or not may depend upon the concentration of the mineral in the rock, its price, proximity to transport facilities, cost of labor, and other factors. Thus it is possible for a lean deposit to comprise ore whereas a much richer deposit might not. Moreover, a given deposit may constitute ore at one time but not at another.

Figure 33–4 Hydraulic mining of phosphate rock in Florida. This type of mining is applicable almost exclusively to the procurement of metallic minerals; a notable exception is the winning of phosphate rock—a nonmetallic mineral—from the important deposits in Florida. (Photo courtesy of the National Plant Food Institute)

extractable at low cost, lie accessible to concentration mills and smelters, and be favored by efficient and economical transportation facilities to markets. The Birmingham district of Alabama typifies this situation: it handles successfully red hematite iron ore with a metallic content of only 37 to 40 percent. It is able to do this because the ore, coking coal, and fluxing dolomite all lie in close juxtaposition—all within a radius of twenty-five miles of one another. Hence, Birmingham enjoys one of the lowest assembly and manufacturing costs in the United States.

2. The size of the reserves is significant.

3. Transportation facilities are of vital importance. Only when it was assured that Cerro Bolivar had sufficient ore to last for many years did the United States Steel Corporation go ahead dredging the Orinoco, constructing a railway and a highway, building shipping facilities, a water system, and several towns.

4. Fuel and power are essential.

5. Capital is imperative for modern mining development. Mining has indeed become big business.

Figure 33–5 Dredging for gold. The dredge is ideally adapted to working low grade placers economically. It can sort many tons of material in a single day. This photo shows how fine material from the trommel passes over gold saving tables and tail sluices into the dredge pond directly at the stern of the boat, whereas the coarse material is conveyed up the stacker and dropped in huge piles on top of the fine material. (Photo courtesy of the Bureau of Mines, U.S. Department of the Interior)

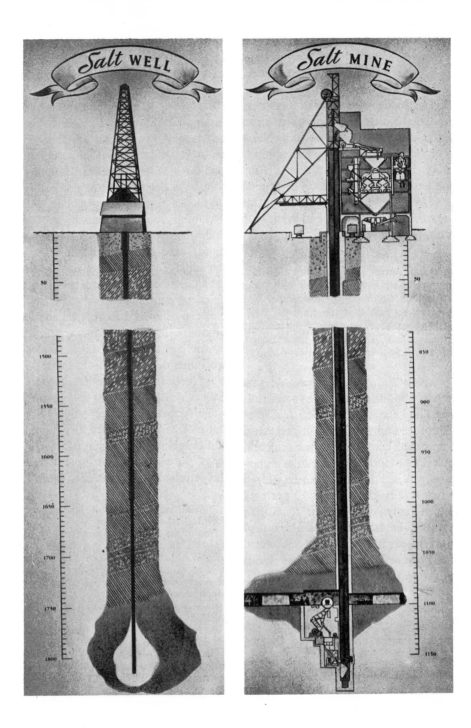

Figure 33–6 Two of the principal ways of getting salt are by evaporating salt brine and by mining rock salt. Left, brine from wells may be natural or it may be made artificially by pumping water into wells drilled deep into deposits of rock salt. The salt water is then brought to the surface where it is evaporated. Right, solid rock salt is mined and comes from the ground in large lumps which are crushed, screened, and graded. (After the International Salt Company)

6. The availability of labor may be an important concern. While the productivity of the average mining worker is steadily rising, certain phases of operation still require a significant labor supply. Modern technology, through the application of more mechanized techniques, has substantially reduced the number of employees engaged in mining. In less developed countries, the proportion of workers in the occupation of mining to the total labor force would be highest.

7. Natural conditions may hamper many enterprises. This is particularly true of the tropics, where dense vegetation, fevers, and pests are among the handicaps to be overcome.

8. Able management, in both engineering and business, is fundamental to successful mining operation, especially when handling lean ore. The Utah Copper Mine at Bingham is reputed to be the world's most profitable source of that metal, not because of rich ore, huge reserves, or large output, but rather because of able management.

9. Ore of extremely low metallic content may be mined profitably providing several of the above factors are favorable.

Whereas in the early days of mining, operators discriminated between rich and lean ores, major consideration today is given to size of the deposit, its uniformity, and its location. This puts a premium on human inventiveness. Thus the cyanamide process used in gold mining and the by-product process of coke making have greatly increased the range of commercially workable minerals. A similar result has come from the reduction of waste. Large amounts of coal, copper, lead, zinc, and other minerals, formerly cast aside as not worth the cost of recovery, are now being carefully reclaimed and utilized.

SOME ASPECTS OF MINERAL ECONOMICS

Mineral economics has been called the record of a battle, a battle between obdurate nature on the one hand, and determined mankind, with his technology and transportation, on the other. When nature is winning the battle, costs tend to increase; when man wins, costs tend to be reduced.

As the cost in terms of man-hours of pro-

ducing a mineral gradually increases, the mineral will be used more sparingly, more efficiently, and more selectively, for purposes for which it has distinctive value as compared with alternate materials. Or a substitution may be made. Thus since 1955, as repeated shortages in copper manifested themselves, some of the largest users of copper cable and wire began an engineering development program for substituting aluminum for copper. Mineral economics involves knowledge of tariffs, taxation, price movement, laws of property rights, production control, valuation, and other factors.

A new discovery frequently has world-wide repercussions. The great gold and silver discoveries in Spanish America precipitated a price revolution and caused Europe to pass from barter to a money economy. The discovery of platinum in the nickel mines of Sudbury broke the monopoly formerly enjoyed by Russia and Colombia.

It is strange that in a world so rich in mineral resources there should be so much quarreling and fighting for their control. There is actually no scarcity or even paucity of most minerals. The struggle for control, therefore, is not founded upon fear of exhaustion so much as upon fear that rival powers will extend their political control, thereby establishing monopolies that will be detrimental to excluded individual countries. The nations of the world, wanting economic security and perceiving the importance of access to mineral resources, may pursue policies in accord with this belief.

MINERALS AND MANUFACTURING

Most minerals play little or no role in the actual location of manufacturing, owing to the small quantities required and the necessity of using them in combination with other materials. Coal and iron ore, particularly the former, are notable exceptions, for there are few economic activities indeed that they do not affect. Thus the concentrated distribution, especially of coal and iron ore, largely controls the location of industry, and their concentration around the North Atlantic Basin seems to mark the nations of Europe and North America for permanent industrial leadership.

Let us consider briefly the section of England lying between Birmingham, Liverpool, and Leeds. When the factory system came into being, this area, richly endowed with coal, was altered in a few years from a

... peaceful green landscape devoted chiefly to herding sheep, into a gigantic factory district, with chimneys belching greasy smoke, and myriads of toilers herded into tenements. The population grew so fast that the English "Midlands" shortly became more densely settled than the Southeast which, from time immemorial, had been the principal center of English life.[7]

Steel,[8] which forms the framework that sustains modern industrial life, is synonymous with political and economic power: steel rules during both peace and war. Without great steel capacity, no nation can aspire to first rank and the concentration of productive facilities among the technically superior powers can be judged from the fact that approximately 90 percent of world production is confined to a dozen nations. The United States alone produces over one fourth of the world output. The power of the United States stands solidly on its enormous production of steel. Its steel capacity is in excess of 150 million tons, and is expanding at a rate of about 2 million tons annually. During World War II, it *added* a steel-making capacity four fifths as large as that of Great Britain and equal to that of Japan.

It is significant and interesting that the leaders of the Soviet Union, beginning with the first five-year plan, gave priority to heavy industry. They realized that the expansion of the iron and steel industry was a necessity if Russia was to reach higher levels of economic independence and if she was to become militarily impregnable.

SOCIAL ASPECTS OF MINERALS

The presence of minerals in any region exerts great influence upon human affairs, both in the area of occurrence and elsewhere, and therefore is a geographical fact of the first order. The state of Nevada is an excellent example of this: its history is largely that of its mines and miners —"now rolling in wealth and the next day penni-

less." Its population has to a large degree been determined by the lure of metals. Unlike its neighbor, Utah, which was built upon the solid base of agriculture and where the Mormon Church successfully discouraged mining until 1869, twenty-two years after the initial settlement, Nevada was built on a foundation of "sand"—minerals. The importance of petroleum to Venezuela, for example, can scarcely be overestimated. Oil is the economic lifeblood of the country. Probably nowhere else in the world is there greater dependence on a single commodity. Venezuela is a one-product nation: oil accounts for two-thirds of government revenue and nine-tenths of export earnings. The majority of the people do not benefit directly from the petroleum. To be sure the families of those who work for the oil companies do, but this industry gives employment to only 3 percent of the working population.

Often, where mining is important, it is the sole human activity. It alone fixes settlement for a period. But every existing mining locality sooner or later is deserted. This results from increasing costs through increasing difficulties in mining. Technical advance may triumph temporarily but ultimately it is engulfed by the rising tide of physical handicaps. Ugly scars then characterize the landscape—scars that are great or small depending upon the scale of operations and the methods of mining employed.

The social character of nearly all mining communities is much the same: there is little stability.

GHOST TOWNS

In comparison with urban centers based upon agriculture, manufacturing, and commerce, mining camps and towns are not permanent, for eventually the mines become exhausted and the people dependent upon them either migrate or turn to other occupations in the tributary area. In either event, the deserted camp becomes a

---

[7] W. D. Jones and D. S. Whittlesey, *An Introduction to Economic Geography* (Chicago, University of Chicago Press, 1925), p. 265.

[8] The word *steels* should be substituted for the word *steel*, for we refer to a *family* rather than to an individual.

ghost town. Since the majority of mines are situated in regions characterized by isolation, ruggedness, aridity, mugginess, or cold, where perhaps few, if any, other economic bases for livelihood exist, most of the people migrate. An evening spent around a campfire in any newly discovered mining region is almost certain to stir up reminiscences derived from the mining camps of every continent. Prospectors and miners, like storm waves, are continuously in motion.

Occasionally, the miners turn their attention to some other pursuit—a more lasting one, such as agriculture. Thus, many of the earlier irrigation farmers in Colorado and California were old-time prospectors or miners.

INTERDEPENDENCE A SOCIAL MANIFESTATION

"Interdependence is the most important single principle affecting the life of man today." No one continent can provide adequate amounts of the many minerals needed to satisfy the earth's more than three and a half billion inhabitants. The best use of the mineral heritage necessitates international trade. For example, the United States is now using far more mineral wealth than she produces, which means that she must import. The United States is self-sufficient in only nine of the most important minerals. Latin America possesses many of the minerals that the United States needs. Should these be exported or used within Latin America? Latin America needs balanced economic development for sound economic growth. In their determination to industrialize, too many of the countries have proceeded at an uneconomic pace—draining needed workers from the farms and substituting excessively high-cost local products for imports. Hemisphere interdependence thus brings with it an opportunity to each of the twenty-one republics—an opportunity to enlarge the profitable exchange of goods in a multitude of fast-growing markets.

POLITICAL ASPECTS OF MINERALS

Individual nations, like individuals in society, vary in the influence they wield. Many factors contribute to national prestige, but one of the most important is preeminence in mineral produc-

tion. Possession of coal, iron ore, and petroleum has played the major role in the economic and political strength of many a nation.

No state can be a great power unless it is important industrially—primarily in heavy industry (iron and steel), and no nation can attain such eminence unless it has a favorable heritage of mineral wealth. Inequalities in minerals mean inequalities in political power. Of all the factors which influence national policies, the possession of raw material resources, particularly minerals, ranks first.

MINERALS AND WAR

World War I proved how dependent are both industry and military power of nations upon mineral resources; it enabled statesmen to see that minerals were not everywhere available in adequate amounts. Since minerals are the essence of war and since they are maldistributed, *nations must have them.* A modern power may have the industrial capacity to turn out unbelievable quantities of tanks, armored cars, tractors, trucks, big guns, and airplanes but, lacking petroleum, its military machine will automatically collapse. To an extent unparalleled in history, World War II was fought *with* petroleum and *for* petroleum. General von Rundstedt, one-time Supreme German Commander in the West, and considered the ablest chieftain next to von Brauchitsch, asserted after Germany's surrender in 1945 that lack of oil, more than any other single factor, initiated the Nazi collapse.

The war minerals comprise three groups—*strategic, critical,* and *essential.*[9] *Strategic minerals* are those essential for war, for which the supply must be secured wholly or partly from sources outside the homeland. The list is not the same for all the powers and it changes from year to year for individual nations. *Critical minerals* are those essential for war, the procurement prob-

[9] In 1940 America's *strategic minerals* were antimony, chromium, manganese (ferrograde), mercury, mica, nickel, quartz crystal, tin, and tungsten; the *critical minerals* were aluminum, asbestos, graphite, platinum, and vanadium; and the *essential minerals* were coal, copper, iron ore, lead, molybdenum, petroleum, and zinc.

lems of which are less difficult than for the strategic ones either because they are less essential or are obtainable in more adequate quantities in the homeland. *Essential minerals* are those most vital to industry and which are produced in sufficient amounts to have normally an exportable surplus.

It was because Germany, Japan, and Italy feared the closing of foreign sources of the minerals which maintained the industrial base of their military machines that they resorted to war. They refused to accept a situation which enabled the "haves"—the United States, Great Britain, and the Soviet Union—to say "the gates are ours to close." Thus World War II became a contest between the "haves" and the "have-nots."

Even politically weak countries may wage war over minerals. Thus the boundary dispute between Bolivia and Paraguay which led to the terrible Chaco War of 1933–1934 was based in part on the possible oil resources.

Certainly one of the most interesting examples of the political influence of a mineral is the shifting of the center of gravity of the petroleum industry from the Western Hemisphere to the Middle East. Thus one of the most barren, unproductive, and poverty-stricken regions in the world has, since the 1930's, been shunted into a position of international significance.

Occasionally single nations have possessed the world's only large deposits of certain minerals, as for example Chile with nitrate and Germany with potash. Prior to 1919, Germany used her potash monopoly as a trade weapon, dictating to other nations and exacting in exchange for potash, supplies of copper, rubber, cotton, and other commodities. New important deposits of potash have been found in other countries since World War II, notably Canada and the United States.

One of the most interesting examples of political geography based upon minerals has to do with the iron and steel industries of Germany and France. The coking coal is in the Ruhr and the iron ore in Lorraine. An exchange of raw materials obviously would be helpful to both nations; nature ordained this but political reality made real cooperation difficult.

WASTE NOT—WANT NOT

Farm products may be seen and measured, but subterranean mineral deposits often remain unknown unless they occur in simple bedded deposits such as coal. Wheat and rice may be grown on the same land year after year—for even thousands of years as they have been in Egypt and China. By rearing livestock, considerable numbers of people may be sustained by the increase in herd. But minerals yield only "one crop": a ton of coal, a barrel of petroleum, or a cubic foot of natural gas, once burned, is gone for all time. Within limits, metals may be salvaged for repeated use. To be sure, the geological processes whereby minerals are formed and deposited are operative today, but the cycle covers millions of years so that practically speaking, there is no current replenishment of supply.

And yet, despite this fact, man continues to draw upon his mineral heritage as though it were a permanent resource. Once the minerals in a mine are removed or the mine can no longer compete economically with competitors, it is merely an ugly hole in the ground.

Improvements in mining technology may delay exhaustion by permitting utilization of low-grade ores but this is at best only an intermission. Therefore minerals should be conserved. Conservation is the wise use of resources—*not hoarding.* It is use without abuse. It is an economic and social problem, not a sentimental one. People all over the world must be educated to "substitute the psychology of conservation for the psychology of conquest." Conservation, however, cannot be taught by fiat; it must, on the contrary, be acquired essentially as a change in social attitude.

Nations everywhere, especially during wars, use up, burn up, and blow up the heritage of tens of millions of years. This has been true in Europe with increasing severity since the Neolithic Age. America too, especially since 1900, has been utilizing its minerals at an unprecedented rate: witness the fact that the Lake Superior region sent down the Great Lakes in 1944 approximately 100 million tons of iron ore —more than Japan per se had in reserves; also that the United States produced within its own confines about 67 percent of the world's oil during World War II.

SUMMARY

Having noted the distribution of world minerals, we were impressed by the fact that they are unevenly distributed and locally concentrated. We noted that among the great powers[10] there are the "haves" and the "have-nots" and that most of the world's serious conflicts have arisen among them. But we noted also that no single nation, not even the vast and rich Soviet Union is self-contained in all the necessary resources; that the United States is self-sufficient in only nine of the important minerals.

New and world-significant discoveries are still to be made. The past several years have witnessed important discoveries of iron ore in Canada, Venezuela, Gabon, Liberia, and Peru; of titanium and sulfur in Mexico; of petroleum in Saudi Arabia and Canada; and of uranium in many parts of the world. Numerous backward or underdeveloped countries are destined to leap into international significance as new mineral resources are discovered.

[10] A great power is a nation capable of waging active and autonomous war against another great power. For a country to be beyond doubt in this category, it must be able to fight with its own resources—not necessarily with those available in its own territories but with those it can be sure of getting. According to this definition, the United States and the Union of Soviet Socialist Republics are indisputably great powers.

SUGGESTED USEFUL READINGS

ATLASES

The Economist Intelligence Unit and the Cartographic Department of the Clarendon Press, *The Shorter Oxford Economic Atlas of the World*, 3d ed. (Oxford, Oxford University Press, 1965), Sections 7, 8, and 9.

Espenshade, Edward B., Jr., ed., *Goode's World Atlas*, 12th ed. (Chicago, Rand McNally & Company, 1964), pp. 35–41.

Van Royen, William, O. Bowles, and E. Pehrson, *Atlas of the World's Resources*, Vol. II, *The Mineral Resources of the World* (New York, Prentice-Hall, Inc., 1952), 118 pp.

GENERAL REFERENCES

Bateman, Alan, *Economic Mineral Deposits*, 2d ed. (New York, John Wiley & Sons, Inc., 1959), 916 pp.

Boesch, Hans, *A Geography of World Economy* (Princeton, N.J., D. Van Nostrand Company, Inc., 1964, Part 2.

Engineering and Mining Journal, Centennial Issue 1866–1966, *Mining's Dynamic Age*, Vol. 167, No. 6 (June, 1966). See especially sections on "The Miracle of Modern Mining," pp. 76–130; "The Challenges and Opportunities in Mining's Dynamic Age," pp. 132–168; "A Program to Assure Mining's Progress," pp. 169–190; "Exploration," pp. 192–232; "Open Pit Technology Is Ready for the Future," pp. 234–370; "Underground Mining," pp. 372–460; and "Mineral Processing," pp. 462–648.

Jones, Clarence Fielden, and Gordon G. Darkenwald, *Economic Geography*, 3d ed. (New York, The Macmillan Company, Inc., 1965), Part V.

Landsberg, Hans, and others, *Resources in America's Future; Patterns of Requirements and Availabilities, 1960–2000* (Baltimore, The Johns Hopkins Press, for Resources for the Future, Inc., 1963), 1017 pp. A shorter, less technical version was published as *Natural Resources for U.S. Growth: A Look Ahead to the Year 2000* (Washington, D.C., Resources for the Future, Inc., 1964).

McDivitt, James, *Minerals and Men* (Baltimore, The Johns Hopkins Press for Resources for the Future, Inc., 1965), 158 pp.

Riley, Charles M., *Our Mineral Resources.* (New York, John Wiley & Sons, 1959), 324 pp.

United Nations Statistical Office, *Statistical Yearbook* (New York, United Nations, annual).

United Nations Statistical Office, *World Energy Supplies*, 1957–1960, United Nations Statistical Papers, Series J, No. 5, 1962.

U.S. Department of the Interior, Bureau of Mines, *Mineral Facts and Problems*, 1965 ed., Bulletin 630 (Washington, D.C., Government Printing Office, 1965), 1118 pp.

U.S. Department of the Interior, Bureau of Mines, *Mineral Yearbook*, 4 vols. (Washington, D.C., Government Printing Office, annual).

Voskuil Walter, *Minerals in World Industry* (New York, McGraw-Hill Book Company, Inc., 1955), 324 pp.

White, C. Langdon, Paul Griffin, and Tom McKnight, *World Economic Geography* (Belmont, Calif., Wadsworth Publishing Co., Inc., 1964).

Zimmermann, Erich W., *World Resources and Industries: A Functional Appraisal of the Availability of Agricultural and Industrial Materials*, 2d ed. (New York, Harper & Brothers, 1951), Part III. See Henry Hunker's revision of the first ten chapters in Erich Zimmermann's *Introduction to World Resources.*

34

Bedrock and Nonmetallic Minerals

Rocks comprising the outer shell of the earth are almost infinite in variety. Each variety of rock consists of an aggregate of minerals in some definite proportion, and because the list of minerals is very great, the number of different rocks is also quite large. Collectively, these rocks, that is, the hard materials of the outer portion of the earth, constitute an important element of mankind's natural environment.

BEDROCK

The hard consolidated materials of the outer or crustal portion of the earth are usually termed *bedrock*. In many localities, bedrock is obscured by accumulations of soil or by a mantle of waste. Elsewhere, the evidences of its presence are both numerous and obvious. The rocky slopes of mountains, pleateaus, and mesas capped by resistant layers, outcropping ledges, and cuestas, and exposures of the rock foundation in river valleys, sea cliffs, quarries, and road cuttings, all testify to the widely evident presence of this element of the environment.

TYPES OF BEDROCK

Rocks differ widely in composition, appearance, and hardness. In general, however, they may be classified into four major groups—*plutonic, eruptive, sedimentary,* and *metamorphic,* each of which is described briefly.

Plutonic rocks

This class consists of igneous materials which have been derived from deep down in the earth. Such deep-seated materials in a molten condition have been forced upward and intruded into the outer portion of the earth where they have cooled into rocks of crystalline character. Granite, diorite, and gabbro are plutonic rocks.

Eruptive rocks

Frequently molten materials are ejected or spewed out from below through volcanic or fissure eruptions directly upon the surface of the earth. In this case, they cool so rapidly as to form rocks of noncrystalline character usually referred to as *lavas.* Basalt, rhyolite, andesite, and *tuff* are examples of eruptives.

Sedimentary rocks

Beds of gravel, sand, mud or marl, and shells become cemented and hardened into sedimentary rocks. The common sedimentaries are conglomerate, sandstone, shale, and limestone.

Metamorphic rocks

Rocks originally belonging to the plutonic, eruptive, or sedimentary groups may be subjected to heat or pressure, owing to earth stresses or other causes, and take on a new crystalline texture. In this event they so little resemble their original nature as to merit the name *metamorphic.* Marble, slate, quartzite, gneiss, and schist are outstanding examples of this class.

STRUCTURE OF BEDROCK

Rocks vary widely in structure (that is, in arrangement and attitude). Sedimentary rocks are originally formed in horizontal or flat-lying layers one above the other. They may retain this simple horizontal arrangement through eons of time (Fig. 34–1). They may, on the contrary, be subjected to such vicissitudes throughout earth his-

Figure 34–1 Limestone, a sedimentary rock, showing vertical joints and horizontal strata and laminae. (Photo courtesy of the U.S. Geological Survey)

tory as tilting, warping, folding, and faulting, in which event they assume a variety of arrangements or structures. Often these arrangements are further complicated by the intrusion of plutonic rocks or the addition of eruptive materials.

Bedrock may, therefore, be of simple horizontal or tilted structure or it may be exceedingly complex (Fig. 34–2). Often these complexities

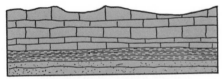

A. Cross Section—Simple Structure

B. Cross Section—Complex Structure

Limestone   Shale
Slate   Sandstone
Granite   Quartzite

Figure 34–2 Cross section of bedrock.

are reflected in the relief and configuration of the land, but in other instances, the initial relief may be so obliterated through long ages of erosion by the elements that all relation between underlying structure and topography will have vanished. For example, in a region whose physical landscape consists of a gently rolling plain whereon lies a deep mantle of soil, the bedrock may contain the truncated complex folds of what was once a mighty range of mountains (Figs. 34–2 and 34–3).

ADJUSTMENTS TO BEDROCK

Many ecological relations exist between man and the bedrock of his region. These are apparent in some of the minor phases of man's life, in his great engineering works, and in certain direct occupational adjustments.

In localities where bedrock approaches close to the surface, the cultivation of the soil may be seriously interfered with. Plows and other agricultural implements may be blunted or broken. The shallow soil dries quickly and crops are handicapped by lack of moisture. In such localities, too, wells must be put down to considerable depth, which makes their construction difficult and costly. Excavating cellars, basements, and drainage ditches, and the making of road cuts are also related to the depth and character of bedrock.

In the great engineering works of man, much depends upon the bedrock factor. In such cities as New Orleans or Chicago, which are situated upon a delta and lacustrine plain respectively, scores and even hundreds of feet of unconsolidated materials overlie the rock foundation. Excavations for tall buildings are easily made, but the loose materials will not support heavy structures. Accordingly, caissons must be sunk to bedrock and concrete pillars constructed. Where this is impracticable, buildings may be built upon huge supporting aprons or platforms of concrete and steel. In like manner canal walls, bridge piers, dams, and other major structures are apt to be insecure and require expensive reinforcement.

A contrasting situation is supplied by New York or Rio de Janeiro, which are built directly upon a rock foundation. Street grading, bridge construction, and excavations for building require costly drilling and blasting. New York's expenditures for tunnels, subways, sewers, and skyscraper basements have been almost unbelievably large. The firmness of the foundation, however, has enabled New York to develop the greatest assemblage of tall buildings to be found anywhere on earth (Fig. 6–7).

Mining

Bedrock is a source of many economically valuable materials known as minerals. These occur in a variety of forms. Some compose large irregular masses, others lie in beds or layers usually called strata, while still others are disseminated through rocks as fine particles. They also occur in veins (filled cracks in the rocks) or in stream gravels as placer deposits.

The various methods of extracting minerals have been discussed.

NONMETALLIC MINERALS

The term *nonmetallic minerals* is applied to a great number and variety of materials which man takes from the earth. In general, they fall into some four classes: building materials, gems, mineral chemicals, and mineral fertilizers.

BUILDING MATERIALS

No single cultural item shows a closer relation to the natural environment than do building materials. The palm thatched hut of the selva, the raffia or wattle home of the savanna, the skin, wool, or felt tent of the steppe, and the house

Figure 34–3   Basaltic bedrock in Yellowstone Park, Wyoming. (Photo courtesy of the U.S. Geological Survey)

of fir lumber in the Pacific Northwest are only a few examples of this relation. Building materials of mineral origin evidence as striking an ecological significance as those of nonmineral derivation. The adobe structure of Mexico and the Southwest, the stone cottage of Brittany, the loess home of northwestern China, and the building of glacial boulders in the glaciated portions of the American Midlands are clear evidences of the utilization of local materials in the environment.

Building stone

The quarrying and preparation of building stone, because of the great weight of the product, tend to be a local industry. The majority of building stones, therefore, are selected from the best varieties at hand, on the basis of such qualities as beauty, ease of cutting and trimming, strength, resistance to weather, and freedom from materials which produce stains.

Nevertheless, there are certain demands, chiefly those for tombstones, monuments, public buildings, and the private homes of wealthy persons, which are independent of local supplies and therefore create an interstate or even international trade in building stone. To meet such demands, certain rock-working communities grow up near occurrences of specific types of stone which are fashionable and hence are in popular demand. Such communities may develop huge quarry industries and enjoy an export trade to distant regions as long as their products remain in fashion. The so-called Bedford limestone from the Bedford-Bloomington district in Indiana, marble from Proctor and Rutland, Vermont, granite from Barre, Vermont, and other points in New Hampshire, Maine, and Massachusetts, sandstone from Amherst, near Cleveland, Ohio, and slate from Rutland, Vermont, and from eastern Pennsylvania are examples of widely used building stones. Quarrying industries were developed at such places at an early date and have been maintained against the competition of other potential producing areas by traditional skill, technological equipment, and effective advertising. The sandstone of the Connecticut Valley, commonly called "brownstone," was immensely popular in the United States during the period

known as the "gay 90's." A change in fashion, however, has almost entirely destroyed the demand for this once popular stone.

Sand and gravel

The extraction of sand and gravel constitutes the leading mineral industry of many localities. These materials are widely demanded for road metal, concrete, plaster, and a miscellany of small uses. Since they are of low value in proportion to weight and bulk, their extraction and preparation for market tend to become an almost wholly local industry.

Sand and gravel are easily obtained in glaciated regions where moraines, outwash aprons, and valley trains contain them in abundance and in relative purity. In nonglaciated regions, seashores, lake beaches, and river terraces are the chief sources. Frequently sand and gravel are won by dredging from the bottom of rivers and lakes. In areas where none of these sources exists, limestone, sandstone, basalt, or other rocks are quarried, crushed, and screened to provide these more costly, artificial products. Certain natural sands derived from the crushing of pure sandstones form the basis of the glass industry.

Clay

Clay is dug from open pits or shallow beds reached by shaft and tunnel. Based upon clay as a raw material are the brick, tile, pottery, porcelain, and terra cotta industries. Such activities are found in the vicinity of nearly every large city and, in addition, are scattered through all densely populated regions. High-grade pottery-making districts almost invariably develop upon deposits of fine kaolinic clays. Examples of districts noted for fine pottery wares are Shantung, southwestern England, Saxony, Bavaria, and central France. In the United States, the pottery industry centers in New Jersey and the Ohio Valley.

Cement

Certain calcareous shales, when burned to a clinker, reduced to powder, and mixed with water, will harden into a cement of rocklike firmness. Such material was known to the ancients and was used widely by the Romans in their building projects. Its modern large-scale use, however, began in the eighteenth century and has since increased rapidly. As an ingredient of concrete, it enters into bridges, dams, roads, skyscrapers, and a multiplicity of miscellaneous uses. Cement, today, may be regarded as one of the major materials possessed by mankind.

In America, the manufacture of Portland cement began in Pennsylvania in 1875, and the industry grew so rapidly that in 1963 the output was 478 million barrels. About 16 percent of the world's annual output is produced and consumed here, and it is estimated that production will reach over 500 million barrels by 1975. Most of the cement of the United States is made in many widely distributed districts throughout four major areas: (1) The Eastern Urban region which extends from the Hudson Valley westward to Chicago, (2) the Midcontinent area extending from Iowa to Texas, (3) the Southern Industrial belt of Georgia, Alabama, and Tennessee, and (4) the Ohio Valley. In addition, there are scattered areas of considerable production in the West, particularly in California and Texas.

In most instances, limestone and clay or shale are quarried, mixed in standardized proportions, and burned to fusion in reverberatory furnaces. The fused clinker is ground to fine powder, to which small quantities of gypsum or other retarding elements are added. The largest concentration of cement mills in the United States has developed in the Lehigh Valley of Pennsylvania. Here a natural cement rock is juxtaposed to coal and market, with the result that costs are reduced to a minimum. Such favorable geographical considerations, however, do not result in giving to the Lehigh Valley a monopoly in cement production. The product is so heavy that costs of transportation tend to drive the industry to the various market areas, providing coal is locally available. The trend is away from producing units which are small to the highly mechanized, very large cement works.

GEMS

The term *gem* includes a great variety of nonmetallic minerals. These may be grouped into three categories: precious stones, semiprecious stones, and certain base stones which bear some resemblance to the precious and semiprecious groups. Examples of the first class are diamonds (mainly from the Republic of South Africa, South-West Africa, Angola, Ghana, and Sierra Leone), rubies (mainly from Burma, Brazil, and Ceylon), and emeralds (from Colombia). Semiprecious stones, the second class, include such minerals as garnet, tourmaline, beryl, zircon, and sapphire and are derived from many widely scattered localities. Ranking below these in value is the third class consisting of such base materials as quartz, feldspar, flint, and obsidian.

Gem minerals are used for diverse purposes including jewelry, industrial arts, abrasives, drill points, and ceramics. In their resultant human ecology, the precious stones often produce social phenomena comparable to those occasioned by a gold deposit or an oil field. On the other hand, the human ecology of the other gems closely parallels that of drab mining and quarrying operations in general.

MINERAL CHEMICALS
Salt

So abundant is salt in the United States that most Americans fail to realize how precious an article it was to ancient mankind, or how difficult it is to obtain in many parts of the present-day world.[1] In some localities, salt is a government monopoly, in others the chief taxable item for government revenue. In certain types of environment, for instance, the forested lands of the Rainy Tropics, salt is almost universally a prized article of commerce. Among certain peoples, such as the salt-working Tibbus of the Central Sahara, this mineral is the ecological bond which ties whole communities to their environment.

Salt is commonly derived from three sources: (1) evaporation of sea water along desert coasts or on the leeward shores of trade wind islands

---

[1] Wars have been waged to gain possession of sources of salt and of the trade routes leading to and from them. Soldiers of the Roman Empire received an allowance of money to purchase their needed salt. This money was called *salarium,* from which we get our word *salary.* In the ancient world, salt was particularly valuable since it was the only known form of food preservative. Hence it was an important item of trade.

Some natives in the Rainy Tropics at times perform prodigious feats of labor for a mere handful of salt.

as exemplified by Southwest Africa and southern Puerto Rico; (2) extraction from the brines of desert salt lakes or from saline springs as on the margins of the Dead Sea, Great Salt Lake, and the lakes of Central Asia; (3) the mining of beds of rock salt which lie deep in the earth. Such rock-salt strata, being the residue of inland seas or salt lakes in the geologic past, are distributed widely and give rise to major mining centers. Rock salt may be mined by shaft and tunnel (Fig. 34–4) or it may be extracted by drilling down to the rock salt deposit. By this latter method a double casing is used—one pipe outside the other. Fresh water is pumped down the outer casing to the salt deposit, where a heavy brine forms and settles to the bottom of the cavity. This brine is then forced to the surface by compressed air.

In North America there are four chief areas of salt mining: (1) the Northeastern (extending from Central New York westward through Ontario, Ohio, and Michigan), (2) the Mid-continent (chiefly in Kansas), (3) the Gulf Coast, and (4) California. Six states—Louisiana, Texas, New York, Michigan, Ohio, and California—produce almost 90 percent of the total output in the United States. Approximately 30 million tons of salt are produced annually in the United States, the per capita consumption being in excess of 250 pounds yearly. This large per capita consumption is accounted for by domestic use (both human and animal), the salting of meat and fish, pickles and olives, and the demands of the chemical industry. It is used in making soap, softening and purifying water (chlorine is made from salt), bleaching paper, in manufacturing rolled steel, tanning leather, making pottery, glass, textiles, dyes, asbestos, and many other products.

Sulfur

Sulfur is one of the three or four most widely used minerals. The main uses include the vulcanizing of rubber, pulp and paper making, oil refining, and the manufacture of matches, insecticides, drugs, and sulfuric acid. The last named is itself an item almost unrivaled in the variety of uses to which it is put.

Commercial sulfur is obtained from four principal sources: native sulfur, which accounts for almost 70 percent of the total consumption based on sulfur content; recovered sulfur, produced from hydrogen sulfide obtained from sour natural and refinery gases; pyrites (metal sulfides, particularly those of iron); and by-product sulfur compounds such as smelter acid. Native sulfur is found in deposits near active or recently extinct volcanoes and in deposits associated with sedimentary rocks, especially in the cap rock overlying salt domes. Volcanic sulfur, which formerly was the principal source of the element, now makes up a relatively minor proportion of the native sulfur produced. Japan has a number of these deposits, most of them located on the main island and associated with a chain of volcanoes. The largest potential resources lie in a three-thousand-mile long zone of the Andes Mountains in South America. Mexico, New

Figure 34–4   Mining salt, Avery Island, Louisiana. The salt deposits here are so thick that chambers and corridors within the mine are of unusual height. In this picture the ceiling is 140 feet high. This is reputed to be the oldest salt mine in the Western world and also to have the thickest vein of salt yet discovered. (Photo courtesy of the International Salt Company)

Zealand, Iceland, and Alaska are among further potential sites. Deposits of native sulfur in salt domes are now the most important commercial source—the salt domes of Louisiana and Texas producing almost 75 percent of the U.S. output and meeting nearly half the world's needs of native sulfur. The United States as a whole supplies some 60 percent. In the Tehuantepec area of Mexico are important reserves of native sulfur, which have enabled Mexico to become a major world producer of this mineral.

Mining of the salt dome deposits is relatively easy; because crystalline sulfur has a low melting point of around 246° F., it can be fused underground by pumping steam heated above this temperature into the deposit. An air lift then brings the molten sulfur to the surface where it is pumped into huge bins to cool and crystallize or into liquid storage tanks.[2] Nearly all the native sulfur produced in this country is mined by the Frasch hot-water process from salt-dome deposits.

Lime

Lime is usually obtained by quarrying limestone and burning it in pits or kilns. It is marketed either as quicklime or slaked lime. Its manufacture is an ancient activity, the limestone outcrops of Europe still showing the quarries and lime pits of Roman or pre-Roman days.

Lime making is today a very widespread industry, existing wherever there is a market and a supply of fairly pure limestone lying adjacent to a fuel supply. In the United States the majority of the states are producers.

Of the 16,089,000 short tons utilized in this country in 1964, about 1 percent was consumed by agriculture, 9 percent in the building trades, and about 90 percent in chemical and manufacturing processes.

Asbestos

Asbestos is a mineral which shreds into a silky fiber. Because of this property, it may be spun and woven into textile form. In addition, its mineral nature renders it fireproof. Asbestos is becoming increasingly necessary in modern industry; it is being used for brake linings and clutch facings in automobiles, gaskets and packings in steam-driven machinery and, combined with cement, in the manufacture of roofing and other building materials.

Canada is the leading producer, supplying 40 percent of world output. The Soviet Union produces 38 percent, the Republic of South Africa 6 percent, Rhodesia 4 percent, and the United States 2 percent.

Mica

There are nearly a dozen kinds of mica, a common mineral characterized by a peculiar cleavage into thin sheets which are transparent, almost colorless, flexible, and resistant to corrosion. World production, however, is divided into two main categories: scrap[3] and flake mica, and sheet mica (block, film, and splittings).

Low-grade micas are widely distributed, but high-grade micas are limited in occurrence. From the latter are procured splittings and sheets. High-grade mica is used mostly in the electrical industry. Among the more important uses are for armature winding tape, rings, cones and transformers, spark plugs, radio, television, and radar tubes, and electrical computers. The world's leading producers of mica are the United States and India, followed by the Republic of South Africa, Brazil, the Malagasy Republic, and Canada. Most of the mica produced in the United States is scrap mica. The United States is dependent on foreign sources of both sheet mica and high-quality scrap. She imports much of her sheet mica from India (film mica and splittings) and Brazil (block mica).

Gypsum

In the United States, California, Michigan, Iowa, and Texas are the leading producers of gypsum. In addition, there are vast deposits yet untouched in the arid and semiarid West. Beds ranging from a few feet to twenty-five feet in thickness lie unexploited because of distance from market.

[2] In 1963, about 85 percent of the sulfur shipments were in liquid form.

[3] Scrap mica is ground and used as a filler or surface coating in such products as wallpaper, rubber, paint, roofing materials, plastics, and drilling muds.

When commercially prepared, gypsum is a white powder for which there is an important but restricted list of uses. Plaster of Paris, wall plaster, stucco, and plasterboard are the principal products which are derived from gypsum.

Minor minerals

In addition to the mineral chemicals already treated, there are many others which are important in varying degrees. Magnesite, fluorite, barites, borax, and soda are some of these. Year by year the list of commercially useful minerals grows, and the uses of each are extended. Among the mineral chemicals, three are of especial and crucial importance as soil fertilizers.

MINERAL FERTILIZERS
Nitrate

The loss of nitrate from soils under cultivation is heavy. As the rate of natural replenishment of this substance is very slow, the maintenance of a sufficient nitrogen content is a critical problem in soil use. Actually there is no scarcity of nitrogen in the world, for approximately 80 percent of the atmosphere consists of this gas. It is, however, chemically inert and does not combine readily with other elements, with the result that the soluble nitrates demanded by plants are far from abundant.

Plants contain large quantities of nitrogenous matter in their makeup. Even the ancients realized the necessity of spreading upon their fields and plowing under the stalks, straw, leaves, and chaff of the grains which they produced. Before returning such materials to the soil, they were sometimes "composted" or rotted in piles or pits. Animal manures were also carefully saved and applied to the soil. Today, manures, composts, cottonseed meal, tobacco stems, fish refuse, slaughterhouse waste, ammonium sulfate from gas plants and coke ovens, and other substances are all employed to replenish the nitrogen supply of the soil.

A few plants known as legumes have the power of taking nitrogen from the air and fixing it in nitrate form in the soil. This is done through the activity of certain symbiotic bacteria which such plants bear on their roots. Nitrogen may be supplied to a soil by planting and plowing under a legume crop such as clover, cowpeas, soy beans, or alfalfa. Where adverse climate, soil acidity, or economic pressure upon land preclude the planting of legumes, recourse must be had to artificial fertilizers in the form of mineral nitrate or synthetic nitrate.

In addition to its uses for fertilizer, a major need for nitrate is in industry, where much is employed in making explosives.

Most of the world's mineral nitrate is located in northern Chile where it occurs in beds of *caliche*. Five areas of nitrate deposits are scattered through the Atacama Desert for a distance of five hundred miles; these for many years supplied the world market. The *caliche* is quarried, the sodium nitrate is dissolved out, the brine evaporated, and the nitrate exported.

The Chilean government for more than half a century maintained a monopolistic control of nitrate, since the deposits were extensive and the nitrogen content much higher than in the deposits to be found elsewhere in the world. So important did the industry become to Chile that it furnished a livelihood to about 10 percent of the total population of the country. The government levied an export tax of twelve dollars per ton on nitrate which supplied considerably more than half the national revenue. Government officials considered this tax a permanent source of revenue. Such, however, was not to be the case. Since 1919, more than half the world's total nitrate has been of the synthetic type. The growth of competing sources became so great that from 1932 to 1935, the proportion of the total supplied by Chilean nitrate had dropped to 6.6 percent, while coal by-products had increased to 18.5 percent, cyanamid to 10.6, and synthetic to 64.3. Today the methods utilizing the nitrogen of the air account for more than 90 percent of the total output and are still increasing. The desire to eliminate dependence on a remote source of supply, along with the lower cost of atmospheric nitrogen, has been a major reason for the decline of Chile's industry. Crisis after crisis occurred following 1919 and the nation was paralyzed. Following 1929, the industry was completely reorganized, the export tax was removed, and more efficient methods were introduced. But still the cost of production is high.

Potash

Practically all soils contain at least a minute content of potash; some, indeed, show amounts as high as 50,000 pounds per acre. Potash is highly soluble, and hence pedalferic soils are usually poor in this element. Under continuous cropping, therefore, many soils are rapidly depleted and require fertilization. This has called into existence a large potash mining industry.

The value of this substance as a fertilizer was discovered in 1858, whereupon deposits were found and worked near Stassfurt at the margin of the Harz Mountains. Later, potash mines were opened in four other areas in Germany, in Alsace, in Poland, and in Spain.

Germany controlled almost the entire output between 1872 and 1914, with the result that this period saw numerous attempts at monopolistic control and price-fixing. During World War I, with the German supply entirely cut off from foreign markets, the world faced a potash famine. Frantic searches for alternative supplies were therefore instituted. At the close of the war, the Alsatian deposits went to France, resulting for a short time in competition and reduced prices. This ended finally with the creation of a Franco-German agreement for monopoly control. The search for supplies in other countries, stimulated by World War I, has therefore continued. In the United States, one of the largest consumers, the price jumped from $40 to $500 per ton during this war. Frantic efforts and large investments were made to establish a domestic potash industry. Small quantities were obtained from a number of saline lakes in the West, particularly from the dry Searles Lake in the Mojave Desert in southern California. Only this last plant continued to operate after the war.

It is in the Permian salt basin underlying parts of Colorado, Kansas, Oklahoma, Texas, and New Mexico, and in the Paradox basin of southwest Colorado and southeast Utah, however, that the major deposits of potash salts are to be found.[4] The United States is today the leading producer of potassium compounds but the deposits are being depleted rapidly. Development has been slow because the fertilizer-consuming districts of eastern United States are so far re-moved. Moreover, the rail haul of four hundred miles to Gulf ports is expensive.

The most sensational discovery of this important mineral has been made recently northeast of Esterhazy in Saskatchewan, Canada. Authorities are convinced that this will prove to be the largest and richest reserve in the world. Much capital is presently being invested in development and production.

Phosphate

Phosphorus is a very essential element to life, yet the average acre of soil contains only enough to produce grain crops for fifty to a hundred years. Commercial systems of grain farming, therefore, are not self-sustaining. The steady production and exportation of cereals from many regions constitute nothing short of organized phosphate robbery from the soil. Even where grain is grown for animal and human subsistence only, the phosphates must eventually be depleted.

There are several remedial devices possible in regard to the phosphate supply. They are

1. Practicing mixed farming rather than pure grain farming
2. Careful saving of all animal manures derived from meat and dairy animals and their return to the soil
3. Recovery of phosphatic slag from iron furnaces
4. Saving of bones from fish and slaughtered animals and converting them into bone meal
5. Protection of birds which make guano (as on the desert islands off the coast of Peru)
6. Saving human excrement and adding it to the soil rather than sending it as sewage to the ocean. (The wisdom of this method is challenged by many authorities on disease.)

One ton of human excrement will assay about two pounds of phosphorus (as well as four pounds of potash and thirteen pounds of nitrogen). Since an average human adult produces approximately forty ounces of excreta daily, the sewage from a city whose population is 1 million,

---

[4] U.S. Department of the Interior, Bureau of Mines, *Mineral Facts and Problems*, 1965 ed., Bulletin 630 (Washington, D.C., Government Printing Office, 1965), p. 721.

annually occasions a loss of nearly 1 million pounds of phosphate. On this basis, the world probably throws away approximately 1 million tons of phosphate per year. Victor Hugo in *Les Misérables* deals with this question, lamenting the fact that Paris casts 25 million francs annually into the sea (in the form of sewage). He scoffs at the idea of casting sewage into the sea and then sending ships at great expense into the Southern Hemisphere to get guano. To utilize this raw sewage, however, would create many difficult problems for public health officials. Sewage diversion onto lands of low fertility is being practiced, however, on a small scale in Germany. In agricultural China, human waste or night soil is carefully saved, and cities receive considerable revenue by granting concessions to collect it. George Cressey[5] states that in the early morning one may see canal boats and long lines of coolies with poles and buckets or with wheelbarrows transporting night soil.

Fortunately, the world possesses immense deposits of mineral phosphate upon which to draw in replenishing this element which it wastes so prodigally. More phosphate rock is mined than any other mineral-fertilizer product. The chief producing countries are the United States, Morocco, the Soviet Union, and Tunisia, which together account for three-quarters of world's output. The United States, the leading country, produced about 40 percent of the total in 1964.

She holds almost 30 percent of the world's known reserves of phosphate rock.

The enormous American deposits in Idaho, Montana, Utah, and Wyoming were scarcely exploited until recently, mainly because of their great distance from the important fertilizer-consuming areas in the South and East. With domestic and foreign demand expected to rise steadily during the coming decades, the western states, with 60 percent of the nation's reserves, will provide an increasing share of marketable production. However, the better located deposits of Florida and Tennessee, supplying over 85 percent of current American production, continue to lead in output.

The Soviet Union has deposits in northern Kazakhstan, the Kola Peninsula, in the region between the Dneiper and Volga rivers, and in Siberia. The world's leading reserves however, are in North Africa—Morocco, Tunisia, Algeria, and Egypt. Here are rich deposits located close to the surface and only 60 to 180 miles from ocean ports whence the product is shipped to European markets.

In addition to phosphate rock, other sources of phosphatic materials are phosphatic limestone, mineral apatite, basic slag, barnyard manure, and guano.

[5] George Cressey, *Land of the 500 Million: A Geography of China* (New York, McGraw-Hill Book Company, Inc., 1955), pp. 114–115.

SUGGESTED USEFUL READINGS

Bates, Robert L., *Geology of the Industrial Rocks and Minerals* (New York, Harper & Brothers, 1960).

Lukermann, F., "The Geography of Cement," *The Professional Geographer,* XII, 1960, 1–16.

Rau, John L., ed., *Second Symposium on Salt,* 2 vols. (Cleveland, Northern Ohio Geological Society, 1966). These volumes contain seventy-two of the papers presented at the Second Symposium on Salt held in 1965, and include sections of geology, geochemistry, mining, rock mechanics, geophysics, evaporated salt, solution mining, and underground storage.

35

Metals and Their Uses

Modern or industrial civilization is based to a large degree upon metal-yielding minerals. Up to the sixteenth century men worked with only seven metals—copper, gold, iron, lead, mercury, silver, and tin. During the next three hundred years seven new ones were added—antimony, arsenic, bismuth, cobalt, manganese, nickel, and zinc. These fourteen plus two newcomers—chromium and tungsten—completed the picture to the year 1900. Since 1900, however, the number known to man has more than tripled. The present is the "Age of Metals." This chapter is concerned with man's use of metals.

It is impossible to appreciate fully the potentialities of the various parts of the earth for human use without taking into account the metallic minerals. Therefore, the student of geography should understand in a general way the geology and the economics of metals; but more important he must have knowledge of the comparative supplies available in the world's major deposits and of the dominant features of their distribution. He should know what parts of the world were important in the past in the production of each metal, the present status of the various nations, and the probable future sources of production. Such knowledge will aid him in interpreting history and will prepare him for understanding many of the political enterprises in the future.

ORIGIN AND DISTRIBUTION OF METALLIC MINERALS

Metallic minerals are usually found in regions of former igneous activity, because under the intense heat, pressure, and flux accompanying mountain-making, waters and vapors bearing minerals in solution were formed.[1] The intrusion of molten magma from below into the rocks of the earth's crust brought up materials from which minerals were derived. Some of these were formed by the contact of magma with the native rocks, others by crystallizing directly from the molten materials themselves.[2] Most minerals are, therefore, disseminated in such fine particles as to be inaccessible; but here and there, hot or chemical-bearing waters and other volatiles have concentrated them into veins and irregular bodies. Rain water, too, has helped to concentrate metals by percolating through the rocks. As it has trickled downward during ages of time, it has dissolved them from upper levels and deposited them lower down in a zone of secondary enrichment. The intimate relationship existing between mineral formation and mountain-making means that most metalliferous deposits lie in mountainous regions.

The aggregate area underlain by all the mineral deposits of economic importance is "only an insignificant fraction of one per cent of the earth's surface, and the geographic position of the individual deposits is fixed by some accident of geology."[3] Thus the mineral possessions of any nation are fixed as to location and the distribution is definite and sometimes inequitable. If a nation is well endowed, as are the United States and the Soviet Union, it holds a potential advantage.

[1] Read pages 544–545.

[2] Field evidence appears to have established the genetic relation of a large number of ores—chromium, copper, nickel, platinum, and others—to molten intrusive rocks. Some deposits, however, such as iron ore, show a less obvious igneous origin.

[3] T. S. Lovering, *Minerals in World Affairs* (Englewood Cliffs, N.J., Prentice-Hall, Inc., 1943), p. 5.

Its technological and industrial development can be launched, its continued progress more readily assured. If, on the other hand, a nation is meagerly endowed, it must somehow compensate for its deficiencies.

ORE: WHAT IS IT?

Should the question "What is ore?" be asked, probably the majority of those responding would say, "It is rock containing bits of one or more useful minerals." Such a reply would be acceptable to the mineralogist, but not to the metallurgist. For instance, the mineral *hematite* (Fe_2O_2) always is an ore from the mineralogical point of view but not necessarily from the metallurgical one: in the Lake Superior region lie billions of tons of easily minable hematite (taconite) containing from 20 to 35 percent metallic iron ore, which for a long time was not considered ore in the commercial sense. Today, the taconite and jaspilite rocks of relatively low iron content provide over 45 percent of the iron from the Lake Superior region. They are rapidly outpacing ores which cannot match the economy and convenience of their processed concentrates. In the same region lie tons of ore containing 42 to 65 percent metallic iron, the supplies of which are being rapidly exhausted.

Other factors which help to determine whether or not an iron-bearing mineral deposit is ore are its content of phosphorus, sulfur, and titanium, the amount of moisture, and the relative amounts of acids (silica and aluminum) and bases (calcium and magnesium). Hence we may consider as ore any mineral (including the ore and the valueless earthy materials called gangue) whose extraction is possible at a profit. *Profit* is the important word in this definition.

Occasionally platinum, gold, silver, copper, and tin are discovered in native form (pure metal), but usually even they, as well as other metallic minerals, occur in combination with other substances.

THE POWER OF METALS

The precious metals have, since the dawn of civilization, exerted a mysterious fascination over man. They have enticed the adventurous of all ages to defeat, ruin, disillusion, or success.

One of the most feverish stampedes of all time was that to the Klondike following the discovery of rich gold placers in the Valley of the Yukon in 1897. Lured by the glitter of gold, thousands of prospectors rushed into the region during the following year; production mounted to 10 million dollars in 1898 and to 16 million dollars in 1899. The fame of the Yukon went all over the world.

The gold seekers landed at Dyea, on the western branch of the Lynn Canal, whence the trail led inland over the notorious and dangerous Chilcoot Pass. Here, trudging over the snow-clad waste, moved a black thread nearly two miles long—a thread consisting of human beings pulled forward by greed. When one could no longer continue because of illness, exhaustion, cold, or hunger, he fell out and his place was taken by the man from behind. It was a hard land, one to be shunned by weaklings, for not only was nature hostile but man himself was selfish and often depraved.

Before long came the discovery of White Pass, and in a day's time Dyea lost its entire population of 15,000 and Skagway gained it—Skagway, which until then had been only swamp. Henceforth, the line of men, drawn on by gold fever, went via White Pass. Today, he who goes by train from Skagway to White Horse via this famous pass sees fragments of the famous Trail of '98—that narrow rut clinging to the steep gulch. In some places it has been effaced by rock slides, but elsewhere it tenaciously records the steady tread of uncounted adventurers—seekers for quick fortunes.

But even after the army of men had successfully negotiated White Pass and Dead Horse Gulch, it was not at its journey's end. Ahead lay the so-called rock desert and the river rapids. It was indeed a bitter trail and it is little wonder that many perished.

TWO FAMOUS MINING CAMPS— ONE DEAD, ONE ALIVE

In every country where metal fever has attracted men, mining towns of a romantic character have come into existence. Occasionally they are long lived, but usually they are of only ephemeral duration—they wilt and die almost as quickly as they spring into existence. Virginia City, Nevada, typifies the mushroom type; Bingham, Utah, the permanent type.

VIRGINIA CITY

This town lay on the main highway to California near the western border of the barren desert and on the east slope of the Sierra Nevada. Over its fabulous wealth had trod thousands of weary feet enroute to California's *El Dorado*—beggars passing over a bag of silver. Ore was discovered in 1859 by placer miners who scratched and pecked at the surface and who washed the sand and gravel in their rockers. Seeking only the glitter of gold, they despised, cursed, and threw away the blue-black rock, some of which was later found to assay as high as $4,791 in silver to the ton.

As soon as the news of discovery became known (and no news of that period traveled so rapidly as that of a strike), a rush set in and claims were staked in all directions. Of the great influx of humanity, only a few experienced miners possessed sufficient knowledge to trace outcrops and claim valuable ground. Tent houses and saloons sprang up like mushrooms, where before had been only sagebrush. There was no economic basis for livelihood except silver; fuel and food were lacking and water was scarce. Fuel wood had to be cut in the Sierra Nevada and laboriously brought to the camp, and food and other necessaries had to be transported thither from California by pack train and wagon; it is estimated that in 1860 there were 450 wagons engaged in this transmontane trade. Wells supplied much of the water at first, but they dried up as the mines began to honeycomb the subterranean areas. Mine water obviously was foul and dangerous to use.

The population increased by leaps and bounds, reaching twenty thousand within a decade. Many of the men were bona fide miners but many others were mere adventurers—human parasites. The miners worked hard, endured many hardships, and had few amenities of life; their only recreations were gambling, drinking, and worse vices.

As the camp grew into a town, streets were graded, wards were established, wooden cabins superseded the canvas tents, mining corporations displaced prospectors (silver mining, unlike placer gold mining, demanded capital), wagon roads were built to California, a railway was extended to the camp, miners brought their families, and the community became more self-supporting. In order to assure itself an adequate supply of pure water, a tunnel thirty miles long was built to tap a lake in the Sierra Nevada.

Millions of dollars poured from the mines, and the town boomed as few others have. Men who several years before had rejoiced to get beans and bacon now ordered caviar, lobster, and champagne from the regular menu at the International Hotel.

As the mines reached greater depths, serious problems arose in the form of water and heat; in many instances overhead costs mounted to such a point that even the better ore bodies could scarcely meet expenses. Ultimately, mine waters were controlled by the nine-mile Sutro Tunnel. Temperatures exceeded 120° F., and great quantities of ice were taken below to help man and mule survive and work three shifts per day. But even with this aid, in some stopes, four picked men could not perform as much work as could be done by a single miner in a cool drift.

Finally, the accessible ore was worked out and Virginia City, most famous mining camp the world has ever known, wilted—its population for the most part deserted and its mines, mills, and buildings fell into decay.

BINGHAM

This city lies in a canyon of the same name in the Oquirrh Mountains (one of the Basin Ranges) about thirty miles southwest of Salt Lake City. It is both interesting and significant that the ore deposits (Fig. 16–13) here were not discovered by Mormons; Brigham Young, their leader, fearing that mining would break down his policy of systematic colonization in the Great Basin (Utah was the only state in the Union to be systematically colonized), played farming against mining.[4] So successful was he that Utah's

---

[4] In an address delivered at the Tabernacle, Young thus forcefully expressed himself: "I hope the gold mines will be no nearer than 800 miles. . . . If you elders of Israel want to go to the gold mines, go

minerals were scarcely touched until 1862 (fifteen years after the Mormons arrived) and then by soldiers stationed at Fort Douglas, who felt the lure of the Wasatch and Oquirrh mountains rising before them. The Mormons refrained from prospecting until the Church approved it, following the completion of the Union Pacific Railroad in 1869.

The Utah Copper Company's mine is one of the world's largest and most interesting projects, America's lowest cost copper producer, and one of the most profitable copper mines in the world. In output, it ranks first among the copper-producing mines of the United States. It is, in reality, a great mountain of low-grade ore, averaging less than 1 percent metallic copper, plus significant amounts of molybdenum and minute amounts of gold and silver. This mountain is being systematically torn down with great electric shovels; girdling the mountain are scores of levels or terraces, tracked and completely electrified. Electric locomotives haul the ore cars to the various benches over switchbacks and to the loading shovels; then the loaded cars are delivered to the foot of the mountain. Here they are made into trains and transported over the tracks of a steam railroad to concentration mills at Magna and Arthur where sufficient gangue (valueless material) is removed to permit the ore to be smelted. So low is this ore in copper content that it cannot go directly to the smelter. Two concentration plants handle the entire output of the mine.

The concentrate is then delivered directly to the great smelter at Garfield several miles distant on the south shore of Great Salt Lake and at the northern end of the Oquirrh Mountains, where it is transformed into blister copper for shipment to an electrolytic refinery also located in Garfield. The valuable refined copper is then transported to markets as far distant as the Naugatuck Valley of Connecticut, center of the nation's brass industry.

The site at Garfield was selected because of its excellent transportation facilities, its great stretches of cheap land, its adaptability for the economical handling of material by gravity, and the prevailing winds which carry the smoke either into the mountains or over the lake where it can have no deleterious effect upon farm crops.

The mountain's reserve of ore is still so large

(hundreds of millions of tons) that Bingham reflects a permanency not usually associated with mining camps.

KINDS OF METAL MINING

The method man will employ to win metals—whether it will be hard-rock or placer mining—will depend upon many circumstances but principally upon the geology.

PLACER DEPOSITS AND PLACER MINING

The concentration of relatively heavy minerals by a transporting agent produces what are known as placer deposits. Such deposits are to be found in the beds of streams where running water was the transporting and sorting agent, in ancient abandoned channels, and in alluvial deposits.

Three conditions are essential to the formation of such deposits: (1) the region supplying the metal to the placers must be one where the rate of erosion is rapid; (2) the metal must be resistant to decay and solution; and (3) the metal must be heavier than the valueless material (gangue) that is transported at the same time.

Being particularly heavy, the placer metals work their way down to the bedrock beneath the alluvium. Hence placer miners invariably attempt to get down to the zone of deepest gravel as quickly as possible.

Among the metals so mined are gold, platinum, tin, and tungsten. Placer gold is almost invariably discovered before the bedrock deposits. There are several methods of prosecuting placer mining—simple panning, cradling, sluicing, hydraulicking (Fig. 33–4), and dredging (Fig. 33–5).

VEIN AND HARD-ROCK MINING

Following discovery of the placer metal, for example, gold, comes the search for the "mother lode" from which it—the placer deposit—came. If the mother lode is sufficiently rich to justify exploitation, the vein may be mined for many years after all the alluvial deposits are exhausted.

A vein is a mineral body of tabular or ir-

and be damned. If you go, I would not give a picayune to keep you from damnation." His advice that they remain on their farms was religiously followed.

regular form, ranging in thickness from less than an inch to many feet and in length from less than an inch to many miles. It may taper out altogether. A system of veins roughly parallel to each other and occupying a restricted zone is known as a lode. Invariably there is more gangue than ore metal in veins.

Not all metals occur commercially in veins. For example, iron may be abundant in the vein, but it may occur elsewhere in deposits that are so large and of such high quality that it would not be economically feasible to extract it from vein deposits.

Vein mining may be semipermanent and is carried on by huge corporations with large capital resources and highly skilled personnel. An expenditure of 100 million dollars or even more at a single mining operation is not unusual.

Numerous factors must be considered before a hard-rock mine can be successfully opened and operated. Not only should there be a large reserve of ore but the place should be accessible, should have low transport costs to mill, smelter, and market, cheap power should be available, the climate should not be too trying on the working force, and a supply of labor should be present and eager to work. If the quality of the ore is high, that too is a big asset.

In hard-rock underground mining, where the minerals lie at considerable depths beneath the surface, shafts must be put down. Some of the gold mines in the Republic of South Africa's Rand are two miles below the surface. Artificial cooling is thus mandatory.

TRENDS

Present trends do indicate some marked advances in the direction of greater mechanization and efficiency in ore extraction and beneficiation. Technological innovations have enabled mines to combine various operational processes into faster, more integrated operations. This is particularly true in the United States.

MAN'S CHIEF ALLIES AMONG THE METALS

So dependent is modern civilization upon metallic minerals that one can hardly picture the organization of modern society without them.

IRON ORE

Iron is the most valuable and indispensable of man's metallic mineral allies. In fact it is the most important of the many minerals upon which modern civilization depends. While iron ores are widely distributed over the earth, they vary greatly in metallic content. Swedish magnetite contains more than 65 percent iron, whereas German hematite (brown ore) contains less than 30 percent iron. High metallic content, however, is occasionally offset by an excess of impurities, such as phosphorus and sulfur, whereas ores low in metallic iron may possess advantageous materials such as lime and manganese.

Although sixty-eight countries have iron ore deposits, only a small number of these deposits are commercially exploitable at present. Ten countries produce four-fifths of the combined output; they are the United States, France, China, Sweden, the United Kingdom, India, West Germany, and Venezuela. These nations are not equally favored. Ore does not attain its greatest value unless its location with reference to coking coal is strategic. Hence Sweden is far less fortunate than Great Britain, the Soviet Union, and the United States. The United States, on the other hand, has large deposits of iron ore (some of it of high quality) connected with large and rich deposits of coal and limestone and with huge markets on or near the Great Lakes. Over 75 percent of the iron ore produced in the United States is transported over the Great Lakes to markets in the United States. The carrying capacity of the United States fleet of 170 vessels is estimated at 76.3 million tons.[5] The St. Lawrence Seaway handles some 12 million long tons of foreign ore annually, most of this moving from the Quebec-Labrador mines to ports of the United States.[6]

TACONITE

With fast-dwindling deposits of high-grade iron ore, the American steel industry had either to locate such resources in foreign countries or find

[5] U.S. Department of the Interior, Bureau of Mines, *Mineral Facts and Problems*, 1965 ed., Bulletin 630 (Washington, D.C., Government Printing Office, 1965), p. 472.
[6] *Ibid.*

ways of converting economically the billions of tons of low-grade taconites into usable material. It has accomplished both tasks. The iron in taconites is scattered through the ore like specks of pepper. The task is to grind it, separate the particles magnetically from the gangue, and concentrate the powdered metal into small pellets capable of being used in blast furnaces. This transition from low-cost, direct-shipping, open-pit ores to greater reliance on taconites requires huge investments in technical research and plant development. Despite the large initial costs of experimentation, site processing of taconite ores into concentrates of high iron content has several advantages over high grade, direct shipment ores. Savings in transportation and greater efficiency in blast furnaces have advanced the demand for taconite to a level of 45 percent of all ores produced in the Lake Superior region[7] (Fig. 35–1). The future appears even more promising.

COPPER ORE

Next to iron, copper probably is the most useful metal. First to be of real service to man, it has nevertheless been relegated to a secondary position in its battle with iron for first place in man's economic estimation. It was copper that made possible "The Electric Age." About 50 percent of that used goes into various branches of electrical equipment, light and power industry, electronics, transportation, and complex weapons systems. Construction and the generation and

Figure 35–2   Copper mining in Butte, Montana. (Photo courtesy of the Anaconda Company)

transmission of power are the two largest consumers.

The ores of copper are generally more complex than those of iron and do not contain so high a metallic content. Some of the large companies are mining ores containing as little as 0.8 percent recoverable copper.

Although copper is widely distributed, production is mainly from seven regions—the Lake Superior area and western parts of the United States (Fig. 35–2), the Ural Mountains and Kazakhstan areas of the Soviet Union, the western Andes of Chile and Peru, central Africa (Zambia and the Congo Republic), and central Canada. These regions also hold about 85 percent of the world reserves in copper.

In the United States, about 85 percent of the ore is mined in the states of Arizona, New Mexico, Nevada, Utah, and Colorado. Arizona leads, contributing over 76 percent of the nationwide total.[8]

Although the United States still leads the world in production, its diminishing reserves and gargantuan consumption necessitate importation. While the copper industry claims that do-

Figure 35–1   Taconite pellets being loaded into the hatches of a lake carrier on Lake Superior. (Photo courtesy of Harkins Marine Photography, Duluth)

[7] See Clyde Kohn and Raymond Specht, "The Mining of Taconite, Lake Superior Iron Mining District," *The Geographical Review*, XLVIII, 1958, pp. 528–539.

[8] U.S. Department of the Interior, Bureau of Mines, *Minerals Yearbook, 1964*, Vol. 1 (Washington, D.C., Government Printing Office, 1965), p. 421.

mestic sources could meet current demand, prices have gone so high in the past several years that some large users are beginning to substitute aluminum, steel, and plastics for it for some purposes.

Possibly the largest single deposit in the world as well as one of the most productive and profitable mines is at Chuquicamata, Chile. Since the 1920's, Chile has been the second leading producer of copper in the world.

In the heart of the Republic of the Congo and extending across the frontier into Zambia lies Africa's important copper belt. The proved reserves comprise, according to estimates, more than one-third of the world's known deposits. Here is ore that may run as high as 6 percent metallic copper. While there is the additional advantage of ample water supply, production is sometimes hampered by inadequate labor, power, and transport, as well as political disturbances.

Canada is a large producer, with more than half the output coming from the nickel-copper ores of Sudbury. The rest of the copper is mined in Quebec, British Columbia, and Manitoba.

The largest consumers are the United States, the Soviet Union, Great Britain, the Federal Republic of Germany, and Japan. In 1963, world consumption was placed at 5,315,000 tons, and the figure is still rising. Many countries, including the United States, must import copper in order to bridge the widening gap between production and actual consumption needs.

LEAD

Lead has long been sought by man. The deposits in Spain were worked by those ancient mineralogists—the Phoenicians. And the Romans used lead pipes to carry water to their baths at Pompeii.

Lead is frequently substituted for more expensive minerals because of its low cost. It is one of the most versatile of all metals; several of its more important uses are in the manufacture of white lead, storage batteries, cable covering, ammunition, newspaper type, foil, bearing metal, and solder. Much lead is utilized in refining petroleum. Because lead is unusually resistant to the corrosive action of sulfuric acid, it is well suited to the manufacture of storage batteries.

Lead ore is mined in over fifty countries, with Australia, the Soviet Union, the United States, Mexico, Canada, and Peru the leading producers. Of the thirty-seven countries producing primary refined lead, the United States, the Soviet Union, Australia, Mexico, and Canada are the major world contributors.

Man has greatly increased his supply of this metal both by the discovery of additional lead deposits and by advancements in metallurgy, such as the invention of the selective flotation process.

ZINC

Zinc, like lead, was known to the ancients, who mixed it with copper to make brass. While still important as a component of brass, its chief use now is in galvanizing iron to protect the latter against atmospheric corrosion, for which purpose more than half the total output of the United States is normally used. Actually, zinc is only moderately resistant to corrosion but far more so than iron.

Other important uses are in battery cans, photoengraving plates, the automotive industry, paint, and pharmaceuticals. Substitutes can be found for nearly all of its uses except for brass.

Zinc is widely distributed on all the continents and each major manufacturing nation either possesses or has access to substantial supplies. Forty-two countries produce zinc, but the leaders are the United States, Canada, the Soviet Union, Australia, Mexico, Japan, and Peru. World reserves of zinc have been estimated at 85 million tons. Canada and the United States, who hold the largest shares, contain over 36 percent of the world reserves.

ANTIMONY

Antimony, a moderately hard brittle metal, is mostly used in alloys with other nonferrous metals, chiefly lead. Hence it is in great demand as an ingredient in storage batteries. Antimony is also employed in making type metal, cable covering, lead pipe, lead foil, babbitt and other bearing metals, chemicals, and pigments. It is not an expensive metal.

China leads the world in antimony production, mining nearly one-third of total world output. The principal producing countries, in addition to China, are the Republic of South Africa,

Bolivia, the Soviet Union, Mexico, Yugoslavia, and Turkey.

TIN

Tin, another of the ancient metals, was employed by prehistoric man in making bronze. Unlike many of the other metallic minerals, tin is not widely distributed. It occurs and is mined primarily in Malaysia, China, Bolivia, the Soviet Union, Thailand, Indonesia, and Nigeria, in about this order of importance. These countries produce almost 90 percent of the world output of tin. Malaysia and China alone provide from 45 to 50 percent of the total. In southeastern Asia tin is found largely in detrital deposits on or near the surface and is mined for the most part by hydraulicking and dredging. In Bolivia the mining is from veins—veins that are narrow and whose cost of mining is much higher than for the placer deposits of southeastern Asia. Bolivia is handicapped by having its deposits located at altitudes of 12,000 feet and more, where altitude imposes a problem. Working conditions at the mines are severe, but labor efficiency is improving. Food, fuel, timber, and machinery must not only be imported but must be transported over difficult terrain. In Nigeria, placer mining prevails.

Whereas tin is used to make bronze, alloys, bearing metal, foil, tubes, solder, and chemicals, it finds its greatest demand in the manufacture of tin plate—a response to our tin-can civilization which in turn results from industrialization and urbanization. Tin plate is made by dipping thin sheets of mild steel into a bath of molten tin. The United States, which produces no tin, uses about half the world's annual output. About 50 percent of this is converted into tin plate, most of which is used for containers of preserved foods. The uses of tin can be reduced only to a limited extent by substitution.

ALUMINUM

Aluminum is a late arrival, despite the fact that it outranks all other metals in quantity, comprising about 8 percent of the earth's crust. It is reported that as recently as 1883 only about eighty-three pounds were used annually. Aluminum's exploitation on a profitable basis depends on cheap power; twenty times as much coal is required to produce a ton of aluminum as a ton of steel. Accordingly aluminum is made with electricity generated usually at hydro sites which lie far from great power marts. However, there has been a marked increase in aluminum production and consumption in the United States because of the abundance of hydroelectric power, natural gas, and coal.

Because of the great expense of treating ordinary clay deposits, all of which contain aluminum, the world's supply of this metal is obtained from the ore bauxite which contains roughly from 30 to 35 percent aluminum. Most of the world's bauxite comes from Jamaica, the Soviet Union, Surinam, Guayana, France, the United States, the Republic of Guinea, Hungary, Greece, and Yugoslavia. The Western Hemisphere produces about half the world's output, and holds almost 20 percent of its proven reserves.

Aluminum is just beginning to realize its potential. It combines the properties of strength, malleability, conductivity, resistance to corrosion, and low density. It is used in a variety of products, and new applications are still being developed. Aluminum is most extensively used in the construction, transportation, electrical, and communications industries. It is also used in the manufacture of household items, including appliances, furniture, and utensils. Aluminum is cheaper than most metals with which it competes, this fact contributing to the accelerating demand for aluminum and aluminum products.

The United States, Canada, and the U.S.S.R. account for nearly 70 percent of the world output of aluminum.

The chief advantages of this metal are that it does not readily corrode, it can be made as strong as steel with only one-third as great weight, and it is ductile and highly conductive. Aluminum is widely used in the manufacture of aircraft, automobiles, and railway cars, in the electrical industry, and in a great variety of cooking utensils.

MAGNESIUM

The production of magnesium, one of the newer metals, was stimulated phenomenally as a result of World War II, when large quantities were used in airplanes, bomb casings, and incendiary bombs. A principal advantage of this metal is its lightness, it being only two-thirds as heavy as aluminum and less than one-fourth as heavy as iron. Accordingly, it has found widespread application in those industries, for example aircraft, where extreme lightness of weight is vital.

As in the case of aluminum, production of magnesium also is soaring; ten times as much was being made and used in the United States in 1968 as in 1940. The future of this metal is bright not only because of its many uses but also because of its limitless availability; the principal sources are the oceans and underground brines. The low-cost sea-water process requires power sites near the sea: in areas such as coastal Texas, electricity can be generated from natural gas, petroleum, or lignite, and in Norway from falling water. Not many nations are so highly favored as Norway, where hydroelectric generating sites are near the ocean.

TITANIUM

Titanium is one of the most abundant metallic minerals in the earth. Nonetheless it is rare. Its rarity results from the baffling problems encountered in its extraction with resultant high cost. While processes still cause it to be costly, more economical methods are being developed.

Titanium is obtained from ilmenite and rutile by laborious and costly methods. But since the metal combines the best features of many metals—high strength, light weight (40 percent lighter than steel), and good heat and corrosion resistance (even to salt water)—it is in great demand.

Those countries known to possess major deposits of titanium are Australia, the United States, Canada, Finland, Norway, India, Malaysia, Sierra Leone, and the Republic of South Africa. The United States and Canada produce almost half the world's ilmenite, and over 90 percent of all rutile production is from Australia.

Ilmenite is used in the manufacture of titanium dioxide for pigments in paints, lacquers, rubber, plastics, and textiles and for ceramics, fiberglass, and other products. It is also used in the production of alloys, carbide, welding-rod coatings, and titanium metal. The metal is most widely consumed in the space and aircraft industries. In airframe production and in aircraft powerplants it is used for landing-gear compo-

nents, fuel tanks, hydraulic tubing, fasteners, engine supports, jet engine components, and other parts. Most recently titanium has been used in connection with the missile and space program, and has been indispensable in many components of the manned orbital spacecraft.

Rutile is used in welding-rod coatings, alloys, carbide, fiberglass, chemicals, and ceramics. Some is also used for making metal and pigments.

MERCURY

Mercury (quicksilver) in one respect is unique— it is liquid at ordinary temperatures. Metallic mercury dissolves gold and silver and therefore is much used to recover these two precious metals wherever they are found in finely divided form. Nearly two-thirds of the gold produced in the United States is amalgamated with mercury at one stage in the recovery process. Mercury is resistant to corrosion and is a fair conductor of heat and of electricity. It has a high specific gravity and is fluid at normal temperatures.

Much of this metal is consumed in drugs, chemicals, and disinfectants. It is utilized also for dental amalgam and as an antifouling paint for ship bottoms. Its chief military use is in the manufacture of fulminate for detonating high explosives. Significant amounts are also used for electrical apparatus, industrial and control instruments, and in electrolytic preparations of caustic soda and chlorine.

Mercury is easily extracted from its ores and is shipped in iron flasks. The principal producing countries are Italy and Spain, which together supply about 53 percent of the world total. Other leading producers of mercury are the Soviet Union, China, the United States, and Mexico.

THE FERROALLOY METALS

A number of different elements, called ferroalloys, are used today to impart specific properties to steel. While steel was known to the ancients, it is believed that they did not understand its chemical nature. Prior to the nineteenth century, the making of steel on any large scale was very much a gamble.

Alloy steels are a response to engineering science's demand for steel that could do things that carbon steels could not do—steel that allows

Figure 35–3   World distribution of (1) iron ore (black dots) and the principal ferroalloy minerals: (2) manganese, (3) nickel, (4) chromite, (5) cobalt, (6) tungsten, (7) vanadium, and (8) molybdenum. Of these alloying elements, the United States is wholly or partially dependent upon foreign sources for all but molybdenum and vanadium. With the possible exception of the Soviet Union, no nation shows much promise of being able to even approach self-sufficiency in this group of metals.

an increase in loads and speeds on machine tools and on machines which supply power to mills and factories. Scientists wanted steels that would resist abrasion, shock, and fatigue; that would resist corrosion and high temperatures.

It was found that when metals such as chromium, cobalt, molybdenum, nickel, tungsten, and vanadium are added in small quantities (generally less than 1 percent) to plain carbon steel, it acquires certain new characteristics. Depending upon the materials added and the amount of each, the steel can be made stronger, tougher, harder,

more heat resistant, more resistant to corrosion, or it acquires some other property.

The ferroalloys, newcomers among the metals, are used in only small quantities and it is fortunate indeed that they are, because of their rarity (Fig. 35–3). Moreover, they are not equitably distributed—most of them not being found in the countries that lead in the manufacture of iron and steel. A single country may account for 75 percent of the world's production of a single one; in perhaps no other way is world interdependence more forcibly expressed.

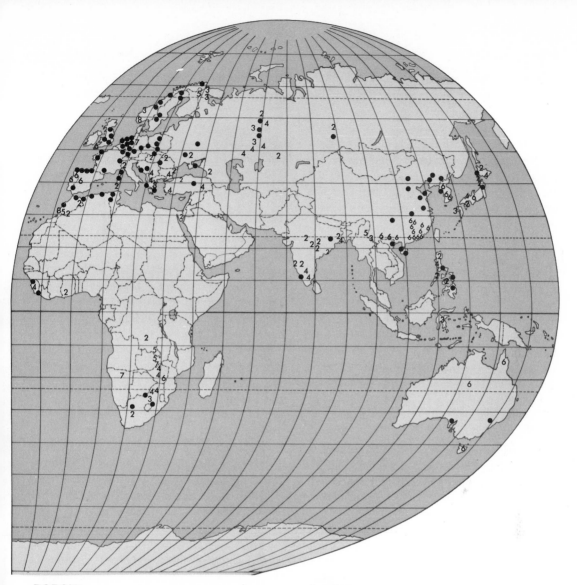

BORON[9]

Boron is an element that may be substituted satisfactorily for chromium, molybdenum, or nickel in an alloy. Because of its abundance, consumption is increasing.

Boron compounds, many of which are noted for their hardness, are used in atomic reactors, insulation materials, and abrasives. Boric acid is used in soaps, cleansers, detergents, fertilizers, and plant sprays. Other compounds have been utilized as catalysts, fuels, adhesives, solvents, deoxidizers, coatings, and lubricants.

The United States is the major world source of boron. She produces more than 85 percent of all output, most of this from Boron and Searles Lake, California. Nearly half the production in boron and boron compounds is exported. It is

significant that boron is plentiful since it helps conserve the scarcer alloying elements and, so far as the United States is concerned, lessens dependence on imports from abroad.

CHROMIUM

Chromium is one of the most indispensable of the ferroalloys. Chrome steel is essential where steel must be subjected to chemical corrosion at high temperatures.

Nearly 85 percent of the world output in chromite (the commercial ore of chromium) comes from six countries—the Soviet Union, the Republic of South Africa, the Philippines, Southern Rhodesia, Turkey, and Albania. In 1964 the

[9] Actually, boron is a nonmetallic element which does not occur by itself in nature.

first two countries supplied over half the total world production. Of an estimated 2,661 million long tons of world reserves in chromite ore, 2 billion are held by the Republic of South Africa, and 600 million by Southern Rhodesia. The Western Hemisphere is sadly lacking in chromite. The United States produces so small an amount that she must import virtually all her chromite, amounting to over 30 percent of world production in 1964.

In making steel, chromium has a wider application than any other alloy material. In fact, nearly all modern steels require it, for it imparts hardness and resistance to wear and increases resistance to corrosion. About four-fifths of domestic chromite consumption is by the metallurgical industry. Most of the chromite is converted into ferroalloys used in the production of stainless, high-speed, and alloyed steel. Chromite also has a variety of applications in the refractory and chemical industries.

COBALT

Cobalt, like tungsten, imparts the property of retaining a keen cutting edge to steel even at high temperatures. It finds much use in magnet steels. It is also an important constituent in alloys used in jet propulsion gas turbines.

About three-fourths of free world cobalt output comes from the Republic of the Congo and Morocco. Over three-fifths of the total is supplied by the Republic of the Congo alone. Other leading producers include Canada, Zambia, and Finland.

MANGANESE

This metal is more than an important alloy— *steel cannot be made without it!* It is used as a deoxidizer and desulfurizer in producing all grades of steel. Oxygen in steel makes for brittleness and porosity, while sulfur causes steel to crack during rolling and forging. About fourteen pounds of manganese, in the form of ferromanganese, are used in making every ton of steel and there are no substitutes for it for this purpose. It has therefore appropriately been called the "Achilles heel of the steel industry."

Normally more than 75 percent of the world's manganese comes from the Soviet Union, the Republic of South Africa, Brazil, India, China, and Ghana. Nearly half comes from the Soviet Union alone.

Although the United States has large reserves of low-grade manganese, it has almost none of high grade. Accordingly, she is forced to import approximately two-thirds of her requirements.

MOLYBDENUM

This metal is used mostly in the manufacture of stainless steel, where it serves to increase resistance to chemical attack. The United States produces over 70 percent of the world supply and consumes an estimated 54 percent. Although deposits are reported to be widespread, economical exploitation is possible in only a few places. Almost three-quarters of production and more than half the world output comes from the Climax mine in Colorado, an area of less than one square mile.

NICKEL

Nickel is a metal of the first importance. It gives toughness to steel; in fact it triples the strength of the iron that is in steel. It is little wonder then that it has acquired an importance all out of proportion to the amount used.

Although nickel-bearing deposits have been discovered in many parts of the world, actual mining is highly localized. Canada, the Soviet Union, New Caledonia, and Cuba account for more than nine-tenths of the world output and Canada alone contributes from 50 to 75 percent of the total. Almost all of the Canadian production comes from the copper-nickel ores of the Sudbury district, Ontario.

TUNGSTEN

This metal is particularly important because modern industry must have a steel that retains its hardness up to a red heat and can therefore be used at much higher speeds and for heavier cuts than ordinary tool steels.

The United States is the only first-rank iron-and-steel-producing nation with appreciable resources of tungsten. All others must seek their supplies from remote sources. The two leading producers are China and the Soviet Union, which

Metal	Principal Sources	Special Properties Imparted to Steel	Typical Uses of Alloy Steel
Boron	United States (California)	Strength, toughness, resistance to shock; increases hardness (boron carbide is the second hardest substance known)	Armor plate for battleships and tanks, projectiles, ball bearings, tools, machinery parts
Chromium	U.S.S.R., Republic of South Africa, Southern Rhodesia, Turkey, Philippines, Albania	Hardness and strength; resistance to heat, oxidation (more than 10 percent prevents rust), and corrosion	Armor plate, projectiles, guns, safes, ball-bearings, jet engines, turbine blades, thermocouples
Cobalt	Republic of the Congo, Morocco, Zambia, United States, Finland, Canada	Holds cutting edge at high temperatures	High-speed cutting tools, permanent magnet steel
Manganese	U.S.S.R., Republic of South Africa, Brazil, India, China	Toughness, resistance to abrasion, strength, hardness, ductility	Mining machinery, safes, rails for curves, frogs, switches, dredge bucket teeth, road working machinery, injection nozzles
Molybdenum	United States, U.S.S.R., Chile	Strength, toughness, resistance to repeated shocks	Tools, automobile parts, tubing for airplane fuselage
Nickel	Canada, U.S.S.R., New Caledonia, Cuba, United States	Toughness, stiffness, strength, ductility; resistance to heat, cold or corrosion	Tools, machinery parts, stainless steels, heat and acid-resisting steels, aircraft
Tungsten	China, U.S.S.R., United States, Republic of South Korea, Portugal, Brazil, Bolivia	Hardness at high temperatures	High-speed cutting tools, magnets
Vanadium	United States, Republic of South Africa, Finland, Peru	Strength, toughness, resistance to repeated shock	Tools, automobile parts and gears
Zirconium	United States, India, Australia, Brazil, Ceylon	Resistance to corrosion; can withstand high temperatures; toughness, strength	Axles, crankshafts, rock drills, nuclear reactors

Table 35–1.   Sources of ferroalloys and how they affect steel.

together supply about 50 percent of the total world output. They are followed by the United States, the Republic of Korea, North Korea, Portugal, Brazil, and Bolivia.

VANADIUM

This metal, though widely distributed, is found commercially in only a limited number of countries—the United States, the Republic of South Africa, southwest Africa, and Finland. Data are not available on the actual production of other countries known to mine vanadium including the Soviet Union, the Republic of the Congo, China, Mexico, Morocco, and Spain. The United States produces over 56 percent of the world's reported vanadium output.

ZIRCONIUM

Zirconium is obtained from zircon, a frequent by-product and coproduct of titanium minerals. Its strength, ductility, and corrosion resistance are among the properties recommending its use in atomic reactors. It is also used in concentrators, tanks, shafts, valves, and pipes in the chemical industry. In addition, zirconium compounds have been used in electrical insulators and resistors, glazes, enamels, steel coatings, and paints.

Major Free World producers of zirconium minerals are the United States, the Republic of South Africa, Australia, and Brazil. The United States, leading in production, is also a large importer. In 1963, of imports set at 52,543 short tons, 50,004 of them were from Australia.

THE PRECIOUS METALS

A small group of metals, particularly gold, silver, and platinum, is so highly prized and has been by so large a portion of humanity over so long a time as to have become known as the *precious metals*.

GOLD

Gold, probably the first metal to attract primitive man, still has the widest appeal to prospectors, and the search for it by peoples everywhere goes on continuously as it has for centuries. Gold is not only beautiful but it is workable. Its durability predestines it to use as a standard of value.

Gold is widely distributed and mined. It is found in places that are more accessible than are silver and platinum. Moreover, it can be exploited by primitive methods when necessary and its high value enables it to stand expensive means of transportation. Most of the world's supply comes from the Republic of South Africa, Canada, the Soviet Union, and the United States. The Republic of South Africa alone contributes over three-fifths of the estimated world production.

SILVER

Silver, like gold, has long been sought and is used for coin and in the arts. Of all the metals, it lends itself most readily to the craftsman's hand.

Silver occurs in less accessible places and requires more advanced methods of extraction than gold. Most of the world's richest deposits appear to be located in the Western Hemisphere; Mexico, Peru, the United States, Canada, the Soviet Union, and Australia are the leading world producers, accounting for over three-fourths of total world production.

Silver is unique in that more than half the amount recovered is from ores primarily mined for their copper, gold, lead, and zinc content. Mexico is an exception in this respect, for much of her production is from ores where silver is the chief element. Mexico is by far the largest producer.

PLATINUM METALS

This group includes besides platinum (the most widely used) several allied metals. Industrial uses and rarity give platinum a high value. For a long time the entire world supply came from Russia and Colombia but rather recently Canada and the Republic of South Africa have become even more important. In Canada most of the platinum is procured as a by-product of other ores—particularly nickel-copper ores.

SUMMARY AND CONCLUSION[10]

The high standard of living enjoyed by people inhabiting the so-called "developed" countries is owing in large measure to the availability and use of minerals, particularly the metals, with iron ore in the vanguard. The impressive industries and agriculture in such lands rest on the production of steel which in turn depends upon the availability of iron ore (and other resources[11] and circumstances). Countries lacking minerals or the means to purchase them abroad suffer from biting poverty. Such countries are called "underdeveloped." Thus the high level of living in developed countries rests largely upon the wide utilization of minerals and the low level of living in underdeveloped countries on the negligible use of them. No nation on earth, of course, is self-

[10] See W. H. Voskuil, *Minerals in World Industry* (New York, McGraw-Hill Book Company, Inc., 1955), Chap. I, "The Mineral Economy."

[11] Coking coal, ferroalloys, and limestone.

sufficient in minerals. Even the best endowed must purchase some minerals in remote quarters of the globe.

The machines and tools which characterize modern civilization and are a principal source of man's material welfare rest on a mineral base —particularly the metals. It is impossible to overemphasize this concept.

SUGGESTED USEFUL READINGS

Brooks, David B., *Supply and Competition in Minor Metals* (Baltimore, The Johns Hopkins Press, for Resources for the Future, Inc., 1965), 147 pp.

Courtney, P. P., "International Tin Restriction and its Effects on the Malayan Tin Mining Industry," *Geography*, 46, 1961, 223–231.

Crowder, Michael, "Aluminum, Metal of the Future," *Geographical Magazine*, 34, 1959, 42–52.

Engineering and Mining Journal, 97th Annual Survey and Outlook, Vol. 167, No. 2 (February, 1966), 77–164. This issue contains useful information on U.S. minerals self-sufficiency, the major metals, and the minor metals.

Kohn, Clyde F., and Raymond E. Specht, "The Mining of Taconite, Lake Superior Iron Mining District," *Geographical Review*, 48, 1958, 528–539.

Langdon, George, "The Mesabi Range—A Fabulous Iron Ore Producer Shows Evidence of Decline," *Journal of Geography*, LVII, 1958, 119–129.

Sutulov, Alexander, "Chilean Copper," *Engineering and Mining Journal*, Vol. 167, No. 7 (July, 1966), 71–76.

United Nations, *Survey of World Iron Ore Resources: Occurrence, Appraisal and Use* (New York, United Nations, 1955).

36

The Mineral Fuels

While it is generally conceded that no element of the natural environment is so important to human progress as climate, nevertheless coal, petroleum, and natural gas must be considered serious rivals as physical factors in the affairs of mankind.

Man, looking back to the Stone Age, may well feel that the Machine Age marks the apex of advancement in human welfare. But seldom does he realize the important role coal and petroleum have played in his progressive march upward. These two minerals became the mainsprings of the industrial world; and although today they are but parts of the source of total energy, they are still important parts (Fig. 36–1).[1]

COAL

Coal is the world's principal source of energy and upon it our present civilization depends to an amazing degree. In the United States, coal accounts for the generation of 27 percent of the total supply of energy; it sustains the entire iron smelting industry, and it is basic to the chemical industry (Fig. 36–2). In fact, it powered America's industrial revolution from the beginning.

COAL AND GEOGRAPHY

Coal is studied by the geologist, chemist, engineer, economist, political scientist, statistician, geographer, and others—each from a different point of view. Their studies are supplementary. Coal enters into the geographer's domain only insofar as its areal distribution, occurrence, mining, transportation, and utilization are concerned.

Although coal was in the earth long before the emergence of man, the geography of coal was unknown until the latter part of the eighteenth century, when human beings began to use it on a large scale.

DISTRIBUTION OF COAL

Coal, occurring in seams or sheets, is distributed in middle and high latitudes, largely between 35° and 50° N., though not to the exclusion of areas in lower latitudes. Of the world's total reserves of anthracite and bituminous coal, estimated at seven and a half trillion metric tons, the Soviet Union has 6.7 percent, the United States 14.7 percent, China 13.5 percent, West Germany 13.1 percent, the United Kingdom 2.2 percent, Poland 1.8 percent, the remainder being claimed by several other countries.

Two facts of distribution stand out: there is a dearth of coal in the Southern Hemisphere; and North America (Fig. 36–3) and Asia are the favored regions with the greater part of the exploitable deposits.

WHAT COAL IS

Coal deposits are old buried peat beds (*the carbonized residue of decayed vegetation*). The transformation came as a result of pressure from overlying strata, aided probably by heat from the interior of the earth. The moisture and gas were squeezed out, evaporated, or at least reduced. Thus peat was changed to lignite, and eventually to coal.

Let us try to picture the appearance of the landscape in those parts of the earth where

[1] See Hans Boesch, *A Geography of World Economy* (Princeton, N.J., Van Nostrand Company, Inc., 1964), Chap. 8, "Energy," for new insight on these and other sources of energy.

conditions were suitable for the formation of coal. There were great coastal lowlands and broad interior basins, bordered by adjacent areas of higher land which were being irregularly and progressively uplifted. Vegetation grew luxuriantly, though differing in character from place to place and from age to age, as indicated by the difference in the coals of eastern and western North America; in the East the vegetation consisted of trees closely resembling ferns, while in the West, at a much later time, it consisted of conifers and hardwoods.

Repeatedly the lowlands subsided and the adjoining highlands were uplifted. Then the gravel, sand, and mud eroded from the newly raised area swept down into the lowlands, burying the submerged vegetation, thereby building up and preparing the lands and depressions for a new cycle of peat formation. Seams of coal are invariably separated by earthy material. A cross section of a coal-bearing formation shows that the coal seams, varying in thickness from a fraction of an inch to many feet, are separated from one another by partings of fresh-water strata—sandstone, conglomerate, and shale—which are invariably thicker than the coal. In places, marine beds, including limestones, are interbedded with the fresh-water strata.

Geologists estimate that twenty feet of the original decayed vegetation are required to form one foot of coal and that each foot of thickness of a seam is the result of thousands of years of plant growth.

COALS DISTINGUISHED

The United States Geological Survey recognizes nine different kinds of coal which grade from slightly altered peat to graphitic anthracite. Space forbids treatment here of more than four broad classes.

Peat

Peat is a spongy, water-soaked substance of low carbon (or heat) content, generally regarded as the first stage of coal formation.

Lignite

Lignite, or brown-coal, is widely distributed and abundant. East Germany, the Soviet Union, and Czechoslovakia are leading producers. It is the least valuable kind of coal, having been least exposed to pressure and heat after the burial of the original peat. Moreover, it contains from 30 to 40 percent moisture, dries out rapidly, and suffers from heavy shrinkage. It also crumbles badly when exposed to the air and, hence, in transport moves via box car rather than gondola car. Since lignite frequently occurs in areas far removed from sources of high-grade bituminous coal, as in the Dakotas, it attains local importance because of heavy freight rates on fuel from distant sources.

Extensive and thick beds of lignite can be found in the lowland of northern Germany. In some places the coal seams exceed three hundred feet in thickness. Open-pit methods are employed in mining most of the fuel.

Bituminous

This type constitutes the bulk of the world's mined coal and upon it our civilization is largely dependent. It is superior in all respects to lignite but is considered inferior to anthracite for some purposes. It is a soft coal, is dirty, contains much volatile material, burns with a yellow flame, is economical. Bituminous coal is not uniform: that from relatively few fields is suitable for coking and hence certain phases of industrial development have become highly localized. For instance, the Pittsburgh District, a major fabricator of iron and steel, owes its beginning and present eminent position to its proximity to the world's best coking coal. Bituminous coal is used for metallurgy, heating, and power.

Anthracite

This variety is regarded by many geologists as the ultimate product in the conversion of vegetable matter into coal. It is almost pure carbon. The oxygen and hydrogen have been largely squeezed out. It burns with a blue flame, emits almost no smoke, and is very clean. It is so inactive chemically as to be used only as fuel. There is little anthracite in the world.

The above ranking of coal represents no strict chronological order, for different coals were produced by various conditions at widely different times.

Figure 36–1   World distribution of major mineral fuel deposits.

COAL PRODUCTION

The total output of anthracite and bituminous coal in 1964 was two billion metric tons.[2] The bulk of this is mined in leading industrial nations. The major producers, in order of importance, are the following: the United States (455 million metric tons),[3] the Soviet Union (409 million metric tons), the United Kingdom (197 million metric tons), West Germany (143 million metric tons), and Poland (117 million metric tons).

However, coal is in serious trouble the world over. In 1953, for example, the United States for the first time witnessed coal's drop from first to second place as a source of energy—34 percent of the nation's total B.T.U.'s (British thermal units) as compared with 39.4 percent for crude oil, 22.5 percent for natural gas, and 4.1 percent for water power.

[2] Statistical Office of the United Nations, Department of Economic and Social Affairs, *1965 Statistical Yearbook* (New York, United Nations, 1966), pp. 183–184.

[3] In 1964 also, coal supplied 22.5 percent of the nation's consumption of mineral energy resources and electricity in B.T.U.'s, crude petroleum and petroleum products supplied 40.3 percent, natural gas (dry and liquid) 33.5 percent, and electricity (hydropower and nuclear power) 3.7 percent. Figures are from U.S. Department of the Interior, Bureau of Mines, *Minerals Yearbook, 1964,* Vol. II (Washington, D.C., Government Printing Office, 1965), pp. 3, 7.

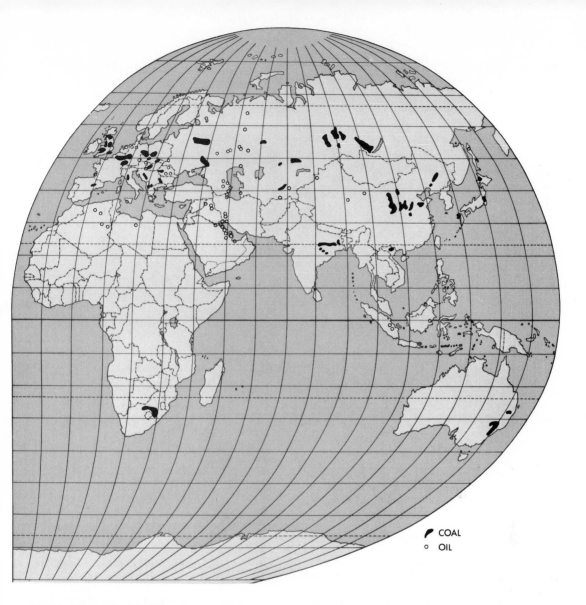

COAL

° OIL

HOW COAL IS MINED

Coal mining is carried on both above and below ground—the former being classified as *open-cut* or *surface mining* (strip mining), the latter as *shaft* and *drift mining* (Fig. 36–4).

Open-cut (strip) mining

Where the sedimentary rocks are little disturbed and where the seams of coal lie close to the surface (Fig. 36–5), the coal is often mined in open pits (Fig. 33–3).[4] In the United States this method of mining, known as *strip mining*, is gaining in importance, for it is the engineer's and operator's dream of efficiency, simplicity, speed, economy, and safety. Power shovels with as many as 140 cubic yards of bucket capacity remove the overburden (surface earth or rocks). There are no underground burrowing, no intricate and expensive underground rail system, no loss of coal, no flooded shafts, and no explosions. No pillars need be left standing to prevent the roof from caving in. Lignite, bituminous coal, and anthracite all are strip mined.

Underground mining

The great bulk of the coal is mined below the surface, where the location of the beds and the topographic conditions determine the feasibility of a vertical shaft or of a tunnel or slope. Amer-

[4] Where beds are not horizontal or when outcrops cut across hilly terrain, a form of strip mining known as contour stripping may be used.

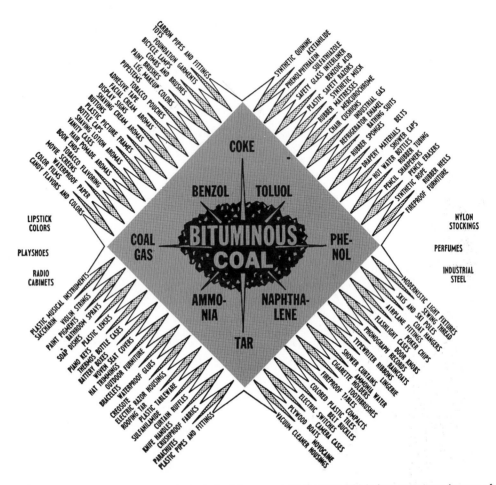

Figure 36–2 A few of the 200,000 products derived from coal. Coal enters widely into commerce by way of the chemical industry. (Courtesy of the National Coal Association)

ican coal mines, in contrast with those in Europe, are not deep, seldom exceeding four hundred feet.

American mining practice consists of the room and pillar method, wherein thick walls or pillars of coal separate adjoining rooms, in order to support the roof. In the rooms and entries, the miners remove the coal mostly with machine. The rooms are further protected by mine props vertically placed.[5] Tunnels or entries are driven from the bottom of the shaft or from the mouths of the drift and serve as thoroughfares for the mine; from them branch secondary entries.

As the mine becomes worked out, the pillars are removed, one after another, and either waste material is placed in the cavities or the roof is allowed to settle. As little coal as possible is left, but even so the waste is enormous; rarely is more than 60 or 70 percent of the coal removed.

The coal, as it is mined, is loaded into small cars (Fig. 36–6) and removed to a tipple where it is screened and sized and dumped into waiting railway cars beneath. Some deposits in the Appalachian field are trenched by navigable rivers. They are readily accessible by shallow borings or by adits from the sides of the valleys, and the coal may be dropped into barges.

Mining in an anthracite region is quite dif-

[5] A new method of supporting mine roofs known as roof bolting is being utilized either for reducing the number of timber supports or for eliminating them entirely. Long steel bolts are wedged into holes bored into the strata, forming the roof. These bind the rock strata together, making the roof self-supporting.

ferent, more complicated, and more costly. Folded beds multiply such problems as water, ventilation, timbering, and intermixed rock, besides reducing the opportunity for using machinery. For each ton of coal, half a ton of rock must be removed, eighteen tons of water pumped out, and seven board feet of timber placed. Moreover, the coal cannot go directly from the workings to a tipple and thence into railway cars as does bituminous coal; it must first be crushed in order to separate it from the bone, rock, and slate which are present as impurities. Since anthracite is costly to mine and sort, and since the deposits are restricted, its price to the consumer obviously is much higher than that of bituminous coal. This accounts for its diminishing role in use among all competing fuels to a mere 1.5 percent.

Coal mining in the United States is highly mechanized. Not only are machines used to mine the coal but machines also load it into mine cars. Prior to 1923, nearly all the coal mined underground was loaded by hand. Now, however, the bulk of it is loaded by machinery. This swing to mechanical loading in recent years has been the outstanding accomplishment of the industry. A typical large loader has a capacity of 240 tons per hour and requires only one man to operate it.

In some of the largest mines, conveyor belts are used instead of rail transportation. Such an installation has a carrying capacity of 1,000 tons per hour.

Europe is less efficient in its coal mining than the United States and hence employs a much larger working force. The output per man shift is considerably lower.

LIFE IN AN APPALACHIAN COAL-MINING TOWN

There is probably no such place as a "typical" coal-mining town, because nearly all coal camps differ one from another in location, topography, type of ownership, and in facilities. The old traditional coal-mining town was invariably isolated; it occasionally occupied a divide but more frequently nestled in a valley. Usually the valley was so narrow that it did not lend itself to "spreading out" a town (Fig. 36–7). Hence there could be but one or two principal streets.

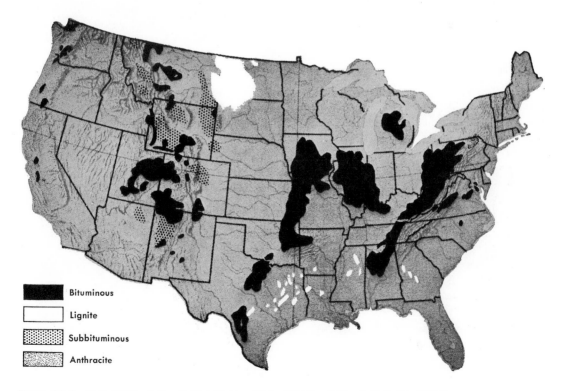

Bituminous

Lignite

Subbituminous

Anthracite

Figure 36–3 Coal fields of the United States. (Map after the National Coal Association)

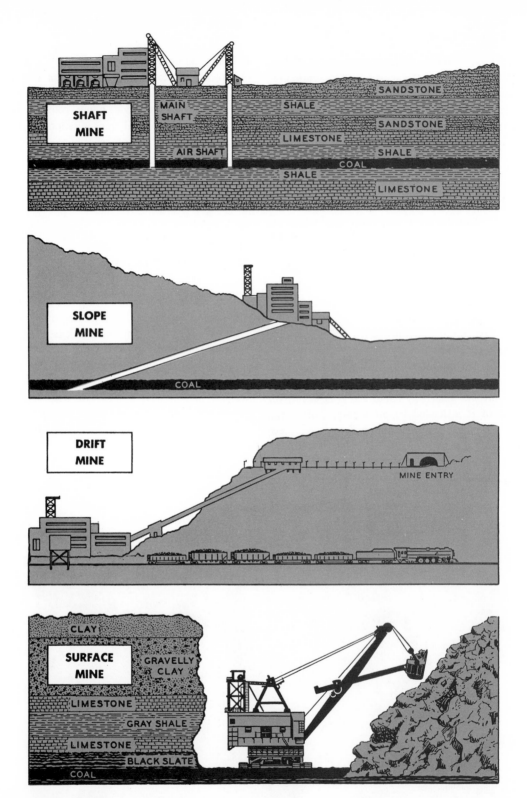

Figure 36–4 Four kinds of bituminous coal mines. Three of these are concerned with underground production: *shaft* mines are opened by sinking a perpendicular shaft through the layers of sedimentary rocks to the coal seam; *slope* mines are opened by driving an inclined entry through the rocks to the seam of coal; and *drift* mines are opened by driving horizontally into the seam of coal. *Surface* mining, commonly called *strip mining*, involves the removal of the overburden and the mining of the coal by power shovel at the surface. (Courtesy of the National Coal Association)

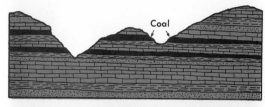
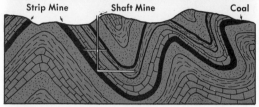

Figure 36–5 Cross section through coal seams: above, bituminous coal; below, anthracite.

Sometimes the valley was so narrow that the miners' shacks had to be perched on the sides of hills. Since at the beginning houses were located near the mine mouth and knowledge was lacking as to the permanency of the operations, little or no thought was given to such things as paved streets, sidewalks, sewers, or "city water." Often there were no trees, lawns, or gardens.

Nearly all the houses were identical in design. A house was little more than a box—a shelter from the elements. Often it was unpainted. The whole picture was drab and depressing. There still are some coal-mining camps that fit this description very well indeed, but the picture has been changing during the past

Figure 36–6 Electric locomotive pulling loaded coal cars through mine en route to the tipple where the coal will be cleaned and graded. (Photo courtesy of the National Coal Association)

few decades—rapidly in many places. Today, especially where well-established companies have large-scale operations which result in greater efficiency and in decreased cost of mining, there are modern mining communities where the inhabitants enjoy all or nearly all of the amenities of life which people do elsewhere in settlements of equal size. They have hotels, churches, hospitals, commissaries, post offices, and other buildings substantially constructed. Though most of the houses are apt to be small, they are trim and attractive (Fig. 36–8). Often they are owned by the families which occupy them.[6]

PETROLEUM

DISTRIBUTION OF PETROLEUM

Close study of a petroleum-production map indicates that while the resource is widely distributed over the earth, the product is, nevertheless, limited to rather definite zones. Efforts to find oil in areas of igneous, metamorphic, or pre-Cambrian rocks, which constitute some of the largest sections of the globe, must prove futile. Petroleum in commercial quantities never has been found in such regions and geologic science indicates that it never will be. Hence none of the great oil fields is located on either plateaus or lowlands of ancient rocks. Rather do they occur along the foot of the great mountain systems or in adjacent lowlands containing young sedimentary rocks—shales, sandstones, and limestones. A fundamental relationship apparently exists between mountain-building and oil distribution.

It is patent then that the geographic distribution of oil is the result of geologic processes and is only by chance related to political boundaries.

THE CONTINENTS AS SOURCES OF PETROLEUM

North America has enormous reserves and outranks all the rest of the world in production. Most of this oil emanates in the United States

[6] For new insights on mining activities and changing areal patterns in the Appalachian coal region, see three recent articles written by George Deasy and Phyllis Griess which are listed in the Suggested Useful Readings for this chapter.

Figure 36–7 An old traditional mining town. The narrow valley, so characteristic of the Appalachian region, precluded the town's spreading out. Built on two sides of the railroad track the miners' houses were perched on the sides of the hills. (Photo courtesy of *U.S. Steel News*)

Figure 36–8 Modern type of coal community—Kopperston, West Virginia. (Photo courtesy of the National Coal Association)

Figure 36–9   Oil derricks in California. (Photo courtesy of Standard Oil of California)

which contributes about 30 percent of the world output.

Fortunately for the United States, oil fields are well distributed over the country (Figs. 36–9 and 36–10). Because much petroleum has been found here, it is often assumed that this country is lavishly endowed with petroleum-bearing rocks. Actually, the petroleum resources outside the United States are so huge as to make our own appear meager (Table 36–1).

America's enormous production results from the following combination of conditions: (1) it has a large endowment, petroleum having been found in nearly every part; (2) the fields are connected with the refineries and markets by the most efficient and economical transportation facilities known; (3) Americans have been very resourceful in the exploration, exploitation, transportation, and utilization of oil; (4) American laws of property ownership have stimulated exploitation; (5) there is an availability of huge resources of capital.

Mexico at one time ranked next to the United States in production but declined greatly in importance following the government's expropriation of the holdings of foreign companies, particularly American, British, and Dutch.

More recently, however, both in the number of new wells drilled and production yielded, Mexico's petroleum industry has been growing.

Elsewhere in North America only Canada is impressive. Since 1947 when oil was discovered at Leduc in Alberta, Canada has vaulted from an oil-poor nation to eighth place among world producers. Reserves are enormous over a large area extending from the Rocky Mountain Front to the pre-Cambrian Shield and from the international border to the Arctic Ocean.

South America has one of the world's major oil regions. Lying within the Andes and especially on their east side, it extends all the way from Venezuela to Argentina and Chile including besides the three countries already named, Colombia, Ecuador, Peru, and Bolivia. Venezuela, largest producer of oil in Latin America, ranks third in world production and first in world exports. Although petroleum is found in several areas, the Lake Maracaibo basin is the most productive. Few countries rely so heavily upon petroleum for their economic life: more than 90 percent of

Figure 36–10   Giant offshore oil-producing platform in the Gulf of Mexico. Some such platforms reach down through as many as 210 feet of water and 40 feet of bottom mud to give the platform solid rock stability. Operating costs run upwards of $14,000 per day. Oil and gas wells now extend many miles into the Gulf whereas twenty years ago 50 feet was considered "deep water." Acreage is acquired through federal government lease. In 1962, for example, oil companies invested 450 million dollars just for a chance to probe the mammoth salt domes underlying the Gulf's northern waters. The oil and gas output of the offshore area is extremely important to the nation. (Photo courtesy of the Standard Oil Company, New Jersey)

Area	Barrels (Millions)	Percent	Ratio of Reserves to 1963 Production
North and Central America	38,455	11.8	12.3–11.3[1]
South America and Caribbean	22,885	7.0	15.8–8.7
Europe		10.8	
Western Europe	1,686		14.5
Eastern Europe (including U.S.S.R.)	33,441		20.9
Middle East	204,821	62.7	82.4
Africa	15,015	4.6	35.8[2]–23.4[3]
South Asia, Far East, and Oceania	10,322	3.2	24.0[4]–46.7[5]
World Total	326,625	100.0	34.5

[1] United States
[2] North Africa
[3] West Africa
[4] Asia, Far East
[5] Oceania

Source: *World Oil* (August 15, 1964).

Table 36–1.   Estimated world proved reserves of crude petroleum (1963).

Venezuela's exports, based on value, consist of petroleum. Isolation and transport difficulties have retarded development in parts of Bolivia, Colombia, and Peru and will continue to do so as long as fields more advantageously located with respect to large markets remain productive. Colombia became a world source of oil through the completion in 1939 of a spectacular pipeline that was built from a relatively low elevation in the oil fields east of the Andes to the port of Coveñas on the Caribbean. It had to cross the mountains at a height of more than 5,000 feet and then drop nearly to sea level. Petroleum is also produced near the Pacific Ocean in northwestern Peru and in southwestern Ecuador, on the east side of the Andes in Peru, and near the Atlantic Ocean in the province of Chubut in Argentina. Chile has a small producing area in the southern part of the country near the Strait of Magellan.

Relative to population and world importance, Europe has been comparatively poor in oil production. Of the five great powers in Europe at the beginning of World War II—Great Britain, Russia, France, Germany, and Italy—only Russia was a major producer. Although several of the countries—France, Germany, Italy, and the Netherlands—have recently made new discoveries and have increased production, the demand is so great that the continent's total output is internationally unimportant.

The Soviet Union has the largest area of all the nations in which there are oil possibilities (sedimentary basins). It has more than twenty such basins. This, of course, does not mean that it possesses the largest reserves. The Soviet Union has 150 developed oil fields, but most of the production comes from two fields. The ratio of production to reserves, about 25 or 30 to 1, is small. Although the U.S.S.R. ranks second in world output, the nation, nonetheless, badly needs more oil and some students believe that if the Soviet Union has an Achilles' heel, petroleum is it.

Asia's oil fields are in four widely separated regions: (1) Iraq, Iran, Kuwait, and Saudi Arabia with the largest reserves in the world, (2) the Republic of Indonesia, (3) the Soviet Union (scattered fields), and (4) Burma and India. Small amounts are produced also in Japan and Sakhalin.

The Middle East is fabulously rich in petroleum. Its reserves are the world's largest—62.7 percent as compared with less than 12 percent for North America, and only 10.7 percent for all of Europe. Development over most of the region is recent. The Middle East is noted also for the high capacity of its fields and of its individual wells.

Africa only recently has emerged as a major world oil producer. Algeria, Libya, and Nigeria all have become important. Advantages enjoyed by the petroleum industries of these nations are high yield per well, though not so high as in the Middle East, proximity to Europe, one of the world's major markets, and avoidance of passage and hence of tolls through the Suez Canal.[7]

Australia to date has been disappointing both in reserves and output, though the picture is brighter at present than for many years. Estimates of world reserves do not as yet even list Australia. Nonetheless, the powerful international oil companies continue exploring and drilling operations.

ORIGIN OF PETROLEUM

A detailed study of petroleum lies outside the realm of the geographer. Petroleum becomes geographic material only when man begins to seek, obtain, and utilize it. Nevertheless, it seems fitting to devote a paragraph to the origin of this product which today plays so potent a role in the lives of human beings throughout the entire civilized world. "What is petroleum?" and "how was it formed?" are the first two questions asked by nearly everyone interested in this resource. It seems justifiable, therefore, to present some of the salient facts in so far as they are known.

First of all, petroleum is a mineral. As to its origin, science has no final proof. Most authorities believe in the organic theory. According to this theory, organisms became embedded in marine sediments as they were formed and, being thus protected from decay, were subjected to slow decomposition, eventually yielding, among other products, the crude petroleum of commerce. The entombed life, *sea life*, is of the type that is most abundant in shallow waters close to shore. Oil fields then are in reality graveyards of marine life

which have been subjected to millions of years of heat and pressure beneath the earth's surface.

SOURCES OF SUPPLY

Most petroleum occurs in sedimentary rocks, particularly open-textured sandstones. The oil is held in pore spaces of the rocks, much as is water. Fairly productive sands may hold from two and a half to four quarts of oil per cubic foot of rock. Though oil men speak of "oil pools," they do not really mean this literally. They refer to a buried layer of porous rock of varying thickness which is saturated with oil and gas.

Sometimes the reservoirs of oil lie close to the surface but often they are at great depths. Wells have been drilled in recent years to depths exceeding 20,000 feet.

Often petroleum, gas, and water are found together. When this is the case, the gas rises to the top, the water sinks to the bottom, and the oil accumulates between them.

SCIENTIFIC VERSUS UNSCIENTIFIC SEARCH FOR OIL

Time was when some oil seekers used peach twigs and other magical devices on the pretense that they helped to find oil. In fact, a few men still occasionally seek petroleum on that basis. But geologists have utilized geologic principles in seeking petroleum almost from the beginning of the industry in the United States. Today the search for petroleum is in the hands of highly trained scientists who apply the principles of geology, paleontology, and geophysics to their problems and use instruments of great precision for measuring variations and differences from point to point in gravity, density, conductivity, magnetic susceptibility of the rocks comprising the earth's crust.

The most modern geophysical instruments now in use as a supplement to regional geologic studies are the gravity meter, the magnetometer, and the seismograph. The first two are capable of quickly measuring, in a given area, differences in

[7] For further information with regard to petroleum developments in Africa, see the several readings included in the Suggested Useful Readings at the end of this chapter.

the forces of gravity or the earth's magnetic field. Variations in gravitational pull or magnetic field (depending upon whether heavy or light rock formations are near the surface) provide a satisfactory general idea of the subsurface conditions. If the results obtained from these instruments seem to justify further exploration, seismograph crews take over. They set off charges of dynamite in shallow holes, which send vibrations downward; sound waves travel at different velocities through different types of rock—rapidly in highly elastic compact rocks; more slowly in less elastic and less compact ones. When they are bounced back to the surface, they are recorded upon moving film by instruments set at varying distances (usually several miles) from the explosion. Scientists then analyze the reflected sound waves and by matching results of their tests from several locations compile charts showing the presence or absence of structural traps which might contain oil. How accurate their deductions are in any specific instance, however, can be learned only by drilling. That they are highly

Figure 36–11 Pipelines of the Standard Oil Company of New Jersey. Enormous quantities of crude oil are transported by pipelines which thread their way over plains, deserts, and swamps, under rivers, and over mountains to refining centers located in some cases 1,500 miles away. Pipelines afford one of the easiest and cheapest means of transporting oil. Pumping stations are distributed along the line at intervals of forty to fifty miles. Pipelines are employed also for transporting refined products. (Photo courtesy of the Standard Oil Company, New Jersey)

efficient is attested by the fact nearly three-fifths of the 44,000 wells drilled in the United States in 1962 were productive and profitable. Nevertheless, the total outlay for dry wells during that same year was 847 million dollars.

The cost of drilling is so great that every means must be taken to avoid bringing in a dry hole. In 1962 the average productive oil well was 4,041 feet at an average cost of $13.41 per foot. Many wells exceed 5,000 feet in depth, however, and may even reach 25,000 feet.[8]

EASE OF TRANSPORTING OIL

Being a liquid, petroleum is easily and economically transported. It is moved by truck, rail tank car, river and lake barge, tank ship, and pipeline (Fig. 36–11). Trucks are employed on a large scale but mostly for short hauls. Rail tank cars, once important, are so no longer.

The bulk of America's crude oil flows from producing fields to ports and refineries by pipeline (Fig. 36–12). This is the most efficient form of *overland* transportation and costs about 5 percent of the average of movement by rail tank car. There is a system of trunk lines, hooked up to the wells by feeders known as gathering lines, which stretches across the country. Pipeline companies do not buy oil but serve as transport agencies for other companies. When there is a demand for such service, they function as common carriers. Nearly all countries producing petroleum make use of pipelines. One of the most famous is the Trans-Arabian pipeline, built across the Arabian desert to Sidon on the Lebanon coast. It handles more than 450,000 barrels daily. This 1,068-mile line shortens the sea route to Western Europe by 3,500 miles and avoids Suez Canal tolls.

Most of the oil moving through pipelines is in the crude state, though considerable gasoline is transported in some areas of the world. Pumping stations are spaced about forty or fifty miles apart, except in mountainous country or where heavy and viscous oil is being moved, when they are placed at more frequent intervals. The fluid oils of Pennsylvania are handled easily, while the

[8] Independent Petroleum Association of America, 1962.

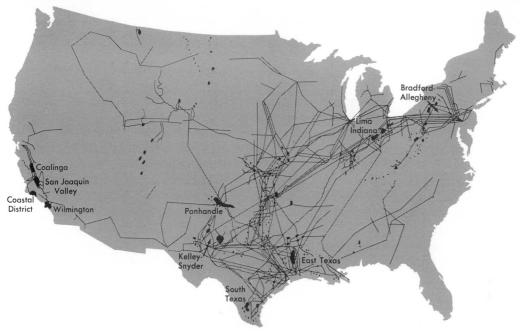

Figure 36–12   Network of major oil pipelines in the United States. (From *Alpha Map Transparencies—Mid-Continental U.S.A.* by Henry J. Warman, Consulting Geographer. © Copyright 1964 by Allyn and Bacon, Inc. Reprinted by permission of Allyn and Bacon, Inc.)

viscous, jelly-like crudes of California and Texas are moved with extreme difficulty.

Movement of petroleum by barge was not large for many years but during World War II, when the railways were straining under the burdens being put upon them, much crude oil and gasoline was shipped on the Great Lakes and on a number of our rivers and still is.

Most economical of all carriers, however, is the tank ship which is used to transport huge quantities of petroleum. In fact, more than half the traffic in refined products and nearly one-third of that of crude oil are via tanker.

The ocean tanker is one of the cheapest means of petroleum transportation. After pipelines, it is the most popular form of transport. The total number and carrying capacity of world tankers have risen steadily. Liberia, the United Kingdom, Norway, and the United States possess the largest tanker fleets in the world and account for nearly three-fifths of world total carrying capacity. The United States, ranking fourth, had a fleet numbering about 103 tankers in 1954. The largest of these, the SS. *Manhattan*, is a 108,590 dead weight tanker with a carrying capacity of about 910,000 barrels of heating oil.[9]

A TYPICAL OIL REGION

The typical oil region has all the earmarks of the boom town and like the latter is generally, though not always, far removed from large centers of population. It consists of a veritable forest of derricks. Occasionally these derricks are so closely spaced as to exclude almost all other objects of a cultural landscape.

Such a place may be disagreeable: the odor of oil permeates the air day and night, and dirt, grease, and slimy ditches and pools of oil abound. There is a constant chugging of engines and the clinking of drilling machinery. A floating population prevails, among whom are the many undesirable elements common to an industry where chance plays so important a role—gamblers, outlaws, shrewd and unscrupulous promoters, and others.

For a long time oil regions had no great industries as did the coal fields—no Pittsburghs, "Black Countries," or Ruhrs. Now many in-

[9] U.S. Department of the Interior, Bureau of Mines, *Mineral Facts and Problems,* 1965 ed., Bulletin 630 (Washington, D.C., Government Printing Office, 1965), p. 693.

dustries are locating on or near the oil fields of several nations. The chemical industry, particularly the petrochemical branch, is an example.

PETROLEUM VERSUS COAL AS A SOURCE OF POWER

Since the beginning of the twentieth century and especially since 1923, petroleum as a source of power has actively and successfully challenged the supremacy of coal. And in this relatively short period, it has become the most precious and most sought after of all the natural resources and has played the dominant role in many international skirmishes.

Petroleum and coal compete most actively in transportation. Petroleum is the principal fuel used by automobiles, airplanes, ships, and railroads. United States railroads are now almost completely converted to diesel motive power. Diesel locomotives are more efficient than coal-burning locomotives. The reasons why oil has largely replaced coal as steamship fuel are: it conserves space; is more economical; can be handled with a smaller crew, thus minimizing wages; and reduces bunkering time, since it can be taken on while loading or unloading cargo.

The reserves of coal will outlast those of petroleum. It would appear that so long as petroleum is abundant, easy to procure, and cheap in price, it will gain on coal but that when these advantages fade, coal may again dominate. But other fuels and energy sources, too, may complicate the picture.

POLITICAL ASPECTS OF OIL

Many international problems result from the great demand for petroleum and its concentration in production and probable occurrence. Frequently it is impossible to separate clearly the economic and political interests involved.

Even when strong nations are well endowed with petroleum reserves, they dare not be indifferent to the political distribution of the resource. Every great power desires to assure itself of important reserves for the future. The United States, for example, has supplied over half of mankind's oil in the past and produces now over three million barrels a year or 29 percent of the world total.

It appears that domestic oil will not be a factor in America's over-all energy supply for more than half a century. This does not mean that we shall have used up all our oil but rather that production can no longer supply a major portion of the national energy needs. Americans are active in the development of oil in Canada, southeastern Asia, the Middle East, North Africa, Nigeria, and South America.

The lands in the Middle East, poor and politically weak for centuries, have suddenly been plummeted into political and economic significance by the spectacular discoveries of oil there. The reserves are so huge and the production per well so high as to have set a new standard of oil richness. The region possesses three-fourths of the world reserves. It thus stands alone in oil riches. At the same time it is one of the smallest consumers. Until late 1956, when Israel, Great Britain, and France invaded Egypt, most of these countries leaned politically toward the Free World. The propinquity of the Soviet Union to this great oil region along with its frightening vulnerability poses, of course, a major international problem, for the vital role of petroleum in both peace and war makes the Middle East the greatest economic and military prize in the world.

There is also the continuous insistence by these nations that they receive a much larger share of the profits from the oil, despite long-term agreements with the foreign oil companies.

The Canadian oil resources also have political aspects. Already production exceeds domestic consumption. The Canadian market is limited and the oil, being almost in the center of the country and far from ports, is not well located. If too much is produced, it means competing at long range with sea-borne imported crudes. The markets for most crudes are determined by large ocean tanker rates; Canadian crude must adapt itself to pipeline transport costs which are about three times as high as those by large tankers. Thus the Canadian product carries a heavy transport penalty. In both peace-time and wartime, however, considerations of national defense must enter into the formulation of an oil policy, for the problems of Canada and the United States are similar. If overseas supplies of oil should be placed in jeopardy as they were during World War II, it might be essential to pool the resources of the two nations. Europe is far from self-sufficient and even with increased production finds it necessary to import nearly 2 million barrels of oil each day. If Middle Eastern and North African oil should be cut off, Europe would be badly off and would have to rely largely upon the Western Hemisphere. This actually has occurred twice in the wars between Israel and Egypt (the Arab nations in the second war of 1967).

The Soviet Union, with a large area where petroleum may possibly be found, does not appear to have as large reserves as the Middle East and the United States. Hers are estimated at 23 billion barrels. Russian production is inadequate —certainly well below the desired level. In 1957, a new fifteen-year plan set the 1972 goal for oil production between 350 and 400 million tons. In 1963, production had already risen from 98 million tons (1957) to 206 million tons.[10]

NATURAL GAS

A quarter-century ago, natural gas, for years the despised stepchild of the petroleum industry, was largely wasted—flared off at the oil fields. Very little indeed was utilized except in a few minor fields well located with respect to the large markets of the American Middle West. Now more than one-half million miles of pipeline carry this precious and desirable fuel to nearly every state in the Union. In 1964, over 15½ trillion cubic feet of gas, as compared with 8½ trillion cubic feet in 1954, were piped from a reported 103,084 producing wells.

Natural gas is a mixture of hydrocarbons of the paraffin series, mainly methane (CH_4). It is found in most oil fields, both in solution in the oil and as free gas trapped in the reservoir. Oil companies, wasteful of gas in the beginning, now use huge amounts to increase oil production: they pump it back into the depleted wells to build up pressure, thereby keeping the wells flowing and adding to their life span.

Though natural gas has been known for at least three thousand years, it did not break through the barrier of mystery and receive serious consideration as a fuel for household and industrial purposes until the early 1900's. The Chinese used it as long ago as 940 B.C., piping it through hollow bamboo rods for short distances and using its heat to evaporate brine in the production of salt.

Natural gas is the ideal fuel because of its cleanliness, great heating power, and economy. Once these properties were appreciated and once reasonably accurate estimates were available, indicating that the reserves for individual fields or local areas were sufficiently large to justify constructing a network of pipelines to specific markets, thereby guaranteeing profitable operations, it became the preferred fuel.

As we have already noted natural gas occurs both alone and with petroleum. Gas from oil wells is known as "wet" gas and is rich in volatile gasoline. It is run from well to gasoline plant where the gasoline is extracted. Some gas wells produce "dry" gas which is usually ready to go directly into pipelines. It is estimated that about one-third of all the gas now produced in the United States comes from oil wells.

While most of the petroleum-producing countries also possess natural gas, it is only the United States and Western Europe that as yet use very much. This results from the fact that pipelines are extremely costly to build (over $100,000 per mile) and distances usually are great between oil and/or gas fields and the densely populated, urbanized, industrial areas— often as far as two thousand miles.

In the United States it is the southwestern interior (largely Texas and Louisiana) that accounts for most of the natural gas. That region has 77.5 percent of the total reserves, 77.8 percent of the production, and 34.7 percent of the consumption.

The major uses of natural gas are for oil field operations, house heating, water heating, cooking, generation of electricity, and in the manufacture of carbon black, cement, clay products, aluminum, glass, and chemicals, and in oil refining. It is estimated that 40 percent of all petrochemicals are derived from natural gas.

Probably the most exciting aspect of the natural gas picture is the transportation from

[10] See Paul E. Lydolph and Theodore Shabad, "The Oil and Gas Industries in the U.S.S.R.," *Annals of the Association of American Geographers*, Vol. 50, 1960, pp. 461–486.

field to market. The gas moves in welded and seamless pipes eighteen to thirty inches in diameter which cost as much as $100,000 a mile to construct and which run over mountains, plains, swamps, and through forests. Today the United States has a network of natural gas pipelines exceeding 600,000 miles in length, which fan out in all directions (Fig. 36–13). During the ten year period from 1954 to 1964, production in the United States nearly doubled. With about two-fifths of the world's proved reserves, the United States produces about three-fourths of the world's marketed output.

Until quite recently little exploration or consumption of natural gas had occurred outside the United States. Today the situation is greatly altered and natural gas is becoming available to a growing number of countries widely distributed over the earth—the Netherlands, the United Kingdom, the Soviet Union, Canada, Mexico, Argentina, Venezuela, Algeria, Kuwait, and Saudi Arabia.

Proved world reserves of natural gas are placed at 800 trillion cubic feet, of which 281 trillion are in the United States. At current levels

of consumption, these reserves are estimated to be sufficient for 30 to 35 years; possibly a better estimate would be 50 to 60 years.

NUCLEAR MINERALS: URANIUM AND THORIUM

Among the most recent energy sources to appear in the modern industrial era are the two nuclear minerals, uranium and thorium. Both are radioactive elements, disintegrating to yield fissionable materials. Nuclear, or atomic, energy is derived from fission, the process by which a fissionable element divides into two new elements.

The nuclear minerals at present are used principally in the development of atomic weapons. A further application, and one which is becoming increasingly significant, is in nuclear reactors. Nuclear reactors are now being used in the production of electrical power, plutonium (for military stockpiles, and radioisotopes); in water desalting; and in research and development. The reactor itself is a combination of fuels, controls, coolant, and vessels designed to sustain the process of continuing fission (chain reaction)

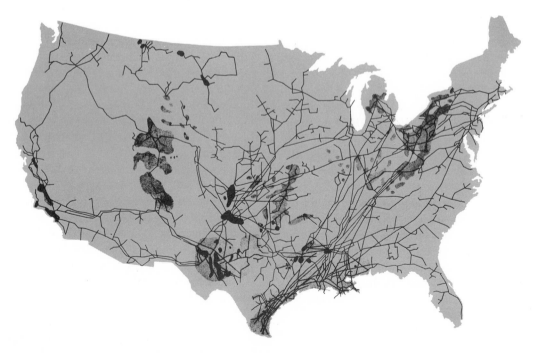

Figure 36–13   Natural-gas pipelines of the United States. (From *Alpha Map Transparencies—Mid-Continental U.S.A.* by Henry J. Warman, Consulting Geographer. © Copyright 1964 by Allyn and Bacon, Inc. Reprinted by permission of Allyn and Bacon, Inc.)

at a specific rate. A power reactor can provide an energy source for electrical power production, for space heating, and for propulsion.

With the supplies of conventional energy resources, such as coal, gas, and oil, being exhausted and world energy requirements still increasing, the future significance of nuclear minerals is sure to be enhanced. One pound of uranium produces energy equivalent to 1.3 million tons of coal, or 6,000 barrels of oil. Nuclear minerals are also superior sources of electricity, and are likely to supplant other sources as competitive minerals are depleted and power reactors are financed and installed.

Major deposits of uranium are found in seven major parts of the world: the Colorado Plateau, the rim of the Canadian Shield, eastern Brazil, western and central Europe, the Ferghana-Kara region of the Soviet Union, southern Africa, and eastern Australia. The largest reserves are in Canada, the United States, and the Republic of South Africa, which together possess about 85 percent of Free-World uranium reserves. Of a total of 612,000 tons of reserves reported in 1964, Canada was estimated to hold 210,000 tons, the United States 160,000 tons, and the Republic of South Africa 150,000 tons. The leading producers of uranium in the Free World are the United States, Canada, the Republic of South Africa, France, and Australia, in about this order of importance. About 85 percent of the uranium produced in non-Communist countries is acquired by the United States.

Thorium, the second nuclear mineral, often occurs with uranium and rare-earth elements, usually in association with monazite sands. Large reserves have been reported in India, Canada, the United States, the Soviet Union, and Brazil, with smaller amounts in West Africa, Australia, the Malagasy Republic, Nyasaland, and the Republic of South Africa. Leading world producers are Australia, the Republic of South Africa, the United States, and the Malagasy Republic. The Soviet Union is also thought to produce some.

THE MINERAL FUELS: AN ENERGY CRISIS?

The mineral fuels are expendable and the civilized world is annually making heavier drains on the reserves. Moreover, much coal and petroleum is left in the ground and much natural gas still is wasted. Only about 10 percent of the total coal deposits can be obtained at reasonable cost. Because of the importance of energy for political prestige and power and for industrialization, every outstanding nation desires and attempts to assure itself of reserves and production as far into the future as possible. It has been suggested that the world will run short of coal, petroleum, and natural gas in twenty-five to fifty years if population continues to increase as it shows every sign of doing, and if per capita consumption of energy continues to increase. If world population should reach the estimated six to ten billions by the year 2000, the energy situation would become critical unless technology learned how to tap new sources, for the yearly demand would by that time be many times what it is today. Some authorities believe that in a century mankind may be threatened by a real deficiency in energy. Nuclear power will no doubt contribute to the solution of the problem, for each year new discoveries of thorium and uranium are made and new techniques are developed for utilizing such energy. Only recently has it been proved that these deposits are enormous and widespread and should last for many years.

Atomic power plants will have one distinct advantage over all rival sources of energy—they can be set up anywhere, for the nearly weightless fuel can be easily transported.

It is possible that man has in the abundant deposits of thorium and uranium the requirements for his energy needs for thousands of years. Moreover, highly industrialized nations with small or dwindling supplies of conventional fuels, for example, Belgium, Britain, and Japan, are hard at work setting up atomic plants. Coal-, oil-, and gas-starved countries all over the globe, for instance, Brazil, see in atomic power a solution for their industrial backwardness.

Solar energy may ultimately prove to be the most promising source of power for the future, although no cheap method has yet been found for harnessing it. Hence at present very little is being utilized. Among the major problems are its variability due to the tilting of the earth, the interruption caused by darkness, and the non-cyclical variation caused by clouds. In order to use sun power, large interceptors will have to be installed and this will be costly. Moreover, the best sites presumably will be in deserts, far from sizable markets for the energy, the cost of whose transportation would be very great.

The dominance of the mineral fuels may not persist for more than a century. However, necessity plus man's growing ability to work with nature should save him from experiencing an energy crisis. Thorium and uranium along with the continuous sources—water, wind, tide, sun, and the earth's latent heat—will contribute notably to his ever-growing power needs, and it seems logical to believe that the transition from a mineral fuel energy economy to one of other sources will be gradual and orderly.

Another present-day trend which has not only local but worldwide implications is that of viewing future power and heating needs of mankind under the big heading of energy. Both the thermal and hydroelectric plants' contributions are viewed under the headings of actual and potential energy production. It takes but little insight on the part of a geographer to recognize the unbalanced energy equipment of mankind in the world today. How one man can enable his brothers to benefit from technical advances in the fullest measure poses economic, social, and political problems of the greatest magnitude. Perhaps the "number one region"—the earth itself as the home of man—may actually achieve that prime position through man's efforts to provide energy for all people through interconnecting systems of worldwide scope.

SUGGESTED USEFUL READINGS

Averitt, Paul, "Coal Reserves of the United States—A Progress Report," January 1, 1960, *United States Geological Survey Bulletin 1136*, 1961.

Clarke, John I., "Oil in Libya: Some Implications," *Economic Geography*, 39, 1963, pp. 40–59.

Cordry, Eugene, "Petroleum Developments in Central and Southern Africa in 1964," *Bulletin of the American Association of Petroleum Geologists*, 49, 1965, pp. 1257–1291.

Dalton, Howard, and William E. Humphrey, "Petroleum Developments in the Far East in 1964," *Bulletin of the American Association of Petroleum Geologists*, 49, 1965, pp. 1330–1348.

Deasy, George F., and Phyllis Griess, "Effects of a Declining Mining Economy on the Pennsylvania Anthracite Region," *Annals of the Association of American Geographers*, 55, 1965, pp. 239–259.

Deasy, George F., and Phyllis Griess, "Geographical Significance of Recent Changes in Mining in the Bituminous Coal Fields of Pennsylvania," *Economic Geography*, 33, 1957, pp. 283–298.

Deasy, George F., and Phyllis Griess, "Some New Maps of Underground Bituminous Coal Mining Industry of Pennsylvania," *Annals of the Association of American Geographers*, 47, 1957, pp. 336–349.

Ebel, Robert, *The Petroleum Industry of the Soviet Union* (New York, American Petroleum Institute, 1961).

Hagemeier, M. C., "Petroleum Developments in North Africa in 1964," *Bulletin of the American Association of Petroleum Geologists*, 49, 1965, pp. 1232–1256.

Hodgkins, Gordon A., *Soviet Power: Energy Resources, Production, and Potentials* (Englewood Cliffs, N.J., Prentice-Hall, Inc., 1961).

Hotchkiss, Henry, "Petroleum Developments in Middle East Countries in 1964," *Bulletin of the American Association of Petroleum Geologists*, 49, 1965, pp. 1292–1329.

Kamen-Kaye, Maurice, "Petroleum Development in Algeria," *Geographical Review*, XLVIII, 1958, pp. 463–473.

King, Robert, "Petroleum Exploration and Production in Europe," *Bulletin of the American Association of Petroleum Geologists*, 49, 1965, pp. 1176–1231.

Lydolph, Paul E., and Theodore Shabad, "The Oil and Gas Industries in the U.S.S.R.," *Annals of the Association of American Geographers*, 50, 1960, pp. 461–486.

Manners, Gerald, *The Geography of Energy* (London, Hutchinson University Library, 1964), 205 pp.

Miller, E. Willard, "Changing Patterns in the Mineral Economy of the United States, 1939–1954," *Professional Geographer*, 13, 1961, pp. 1–6.

Odell, Peter, *An Economic Geography of Oil* (London, G. Bell & Sons, Ltd.), 1963, 219 pp.

Parsons, James, "Geography of Natural Gas in the United States," *Economic Geography*, 26, 1950, pp. 162–178.

Pratt, Wallace E., and Dorothy Good, *World Geography of Petroleum*, American Geographical Society Special Publication No. 31 (Princeton, N.J., Princeton University Press, for the American Geographical Society, 1959), 464 pp.

Sass, Louis C., and C. H. Neff, "Review of 1964 Petroleum Developments in South America and Caribbean Areas," *Bulletin of the American Association of Petroleum Geologists*, 49, 1965, pp. 1112–1175.

Schurr, Sam H., and Bruce C. Netsschert, *Energy in the American Economy, 1850–1975; An Economic Study of Its History and Prospects* (Baltimore, Johns Hopkins Press, for Resources for the Future, Inc., 1960), 774 pp.

IX

Other Spatial Factors

The factors treated in the chapters following are taken for granted so often that many of their significant attributes are overlooked or slighted. Upon occasion, these factors assume leading positions in the lives of people, nations, and cultures. Size and shape express themselves in several geographic ways. Often the situation of a state or people, that is, their position with respect to physical, economic, social, and political situations of other peoples and places, may be crucially important, overriding the details of site. In some instances the site assumes proportions so ideal, or dismal, that the situation is of secondary importance.

The factors discussed are not static. Problems are solved, and created, when form or shape and size or space are altered. Sites and situations ebb and flow with the tides of history.

37

Areal Size or Space

The amount of arable land, forest, and other natural resources immediately available to a people is usually dependent upon the size of the area that contains them. Areal size or space, therefore, is a very important aspect of man's natural environment. In addition, it usually has a significant bearing upon human psychology. A people occupying a small area may think in restricted terms; one inhabiting a large area is apt to evolve far-flung and ambitious plans and strategies.

In one sense, therefore, space is the essence of geography in the same way that time is the essence of history. It is, consequently, an important criterion in the geographic evaluation of nations, regions, localities, and indeed all areal units.

UNITS OF AREA

NATURAL UNITS

In a spatial sense, size has no significance except in connection with definitely delimited areas or portions of the earth's surface. In geography, it is customary to deal with some three different kinds of delimited or demarked areas. The simplest of these are *physical areas*. They exist as entities because they have contiguity of surface extent, as for example, Greenland, Samoa, Long Island, or Africa. The concept of this type of spatial unit may be extended to include the so-called natural region which is demarked by its uniformity of natural landscape. The Paris Basin, the Plateau of Tibet, and the North Atlantic Coastal Plain are examples of natural regions.

GEOGRAPHIC UNITS

In contrast to such natural units of area are those which, for want of a better term, have been called *geographic regions. They are characterized by unity of human adjustment to the natural environment.* They are divisions of the earth's surface based upon ecological differences, and they may be recognized because *they possess continuity in their cultural landscapes.* The Cotton Belt, the North Central Dairy Belt of the United States, the Pampa of Argentina, and the Black District of England are approximations of geographic regions.

POLITICAL UNITS

The most common divisions of space, however, are political units. These vary in their order of magnitude all the way from nations, such as Mexico, Iran, or the United States, through provincial units such as New Jersey, Ontario, or Shantung, on down to minor civil divisions, such as the Department des Basses Alpes, Shizuoka Prefecture, or the Borough of Hackensack. Such spatial entities are delimited through their possession of *polity* and *territorial sovereignty* in varying degrees. Any area possesses a number of inherent qualities or environmental attributes, one of which is size or areal magnitude.

HOW SIZE IS EXPRESSED

Size may be expressed in one of two ways, statistically or geographically. The former, however, is much the more commonly used method. Moreover, extreme care usually is employed in order to make areal statistics as accurate as possible.

STATISTICAL EXPRESSION

Statistical expressions of size consist usually of mere statements of areal extent in terms of square miles, square kilometers, square versts, or some comparable unit. Where more than one area is being considered, the data may be arranged in tabular form so as to facilitate comparison, as follows.

Country	Area in Square Miles
U.S.S.R.	8,655,890
Canada	3,851,809
United States	3,615,211
Argentina	1,072,700
Mexico	758,259
France	212,659
Thailand	200,148
Japan	142,688
United Kingdom	94,209
Switzerland	15,944

Such bare statements of area are often rendered more meaningful by converting them into demographic ratios showing the number of people per unit of surface area. The following table shows the preceding list of countries converted into such man-land ratios.

Country	Population per Square Mile
U.S.S.R.	27
Canada	5
United States	54
Argentina	21
Mexico	52
France	228
Thailand	148
Japan	682
United Kingdom	574
Switzerland	368

Actually, the *crude density of population*, or the number of people per unit area, is often more revealing than mere statements of areal extent. Comparisons of areal units, particularly large ones, are less meaningful because of the considerable range and diversity of environmental features found within each unit. Furthermore, not all land is productive and equally capable of supporting population.

When the population densities of Thailand and Argentina are compared, the latter is seemingly five times as well off as the former. If the large areas of desert, mountain, and low-grade grassland in Argentina are deducted, however, Thailand is probably able to support somewhat more people than is Argentina. Actually, the number of people supported per acre of arable land is not very different in the two countries.

Besides a ratio of population to arable land, there is an index of population density per unit of cultivable land. If the density index is based on agricultural population, it is known as an *agricultural density*. Even these ratios are not too revealing, because they are based upon the assumption that arable land is always the primary resource supporting human life. Whole populations, however, can and do live in satisfactory relation to their environment with no arable land at their disposal. Furthermore, not all agricultural land is productive. Nor is nonagricultural land necessarily unproductive. They may support themselves through the utilization of their geographical location, grassland, fauna, minerals, or some other resources of their area. What is needed is a composite "use capability" formula for determining total areal productivity. Until such a formula is derived, statistical expression of spatial extent will continue to have limited value in human ecology.

GEOGRAPHIC EXPRESSION

No entirely satisfactory method of expressing size geographically has as yet been evolved, but for purposes of ordinary geographic analysis, a fairly acceptable method can be worked out by any student.

To be sure, areas are depicted with a high degree of accuracy on maps, but such cartographic pictures themselves require considerable interpretation and description when used for geographical purposes. Accordingly, such vague expressions as "a large region," "a tiny state," or "a small country," represent almost universal efforts to describe size in geographic terms.

Diminutive		Small		Medium		Medium (Cont'd)		Large	
Rhode Is.	0.03	Indiana	0.9	Wyoming	2.4	Illinois	1.4	Alaska	14.4
Canal Zone	0.01	Maine	0.8	Oregon	2.4	Iowa	1.4	Texas	6.5
Guam	0.005	So. Carolina	0.8	Utah	2.1	Wisconsin	1.4	California	3.9
V. I.	0.004	W. Virginia	0.6	Minnesota	2.1	Arkansas	1.3	Montana	3.6
Samoa	0.001	Maryland	0.3	Idaho	2.0	No. Carolina	1.3	New Mexico	3.0
Dist. Col.	0.001	New Hamp.	0.2	Kansas	2.0	Alabama	1.3	Arizona	2.8
		Vermont	0.2	Nebraska	1.9	New York	1.2	Nevada	2.7
		New Jersey	0.2	So. Dakota	1.9	Louisiana	1.2	Colorado	2.5
		Massachusetts	0.2	No. Dakota	1.7	Mississippi	1.1		
		Hawaii	0.2	Oklahoma	1.7	Pennsylvania	1.1		
		Connecticut	0.1	Missouri	1.7	Tennessee	1.0		
		Puerto Rico	0.1	Washington	1.7	Kentucky	1.0		
		Delaware	0.1	Georgia	1.4	Virginia	1.0		
				Florida	1.4	Ohio	1.0		
				Michigan	1.4				

Table 37–1.   Groups of states by sizes (using Ohio as a base).

These and similar attempts have been of minimum usefulness because they are based upon no definite scale. What is needed is a set of terms which when applied to an area, will immediately refer it to a definite category of size, and which will simultaneously imply a comparison with the sizes of other areas. Thus, the classification of areas into definite *orders of spatial magnitude* would seem to constitute the essence of expressing size geographically.

CATEGORIES OF SIZE

SIZE OF AMERICAN STATES

About four decades ago, Witham[1] undertook to develop a scale which would portray relative size or order of magnitude in space. As he pointed out, considerable difficulty is experienced by the average person in remembering the statistical sizes of any great number of areas. In dealing with the problem of learning the sizes of the states and territories of the United States, he proposed that the size of some one state be learned exactly, and used as a base for measuring the remaining states.

Table 37–1 gives the relative sizes of the states and territories *in terms of Ohio* whose area is a little more than 40,000 square miles.

Such indices are of great advantage, but they themselves of course present a problem in learning—although a somewhat lesser one than the original problem. The whole matter may be further simplified if the states are grouped into large descriptive categories as follows:

Order of Magnitude	Area in Square Miles		Geographic Size
1	less than	1,000	diminutive
2	1,000 to	40,000	small
3	40,000 to	100,000	intermediate
4	100,000 to	1,000,000	large
5	more than	1,000,000	gigantic

When arranged in this manner, the United States as a whole is gigantic or very large in size, eight states and territories are large, twenty-nine are intermediate, thirteen are small, and six are diminutive.

The superimposition of two or more maps of specific areas is often of considerable aid in developing definite concepts of size. Figure 37–1 shows by such a device the five orders of areal magnitude for the United States.

Obviously, a scale of relative sizes such as that just described is valid only if it is applicable

[1] E. C. Witham, "A Method of Teaching Large Geographical Areas," *Journal of Geography* (May, 1928), p. 185.

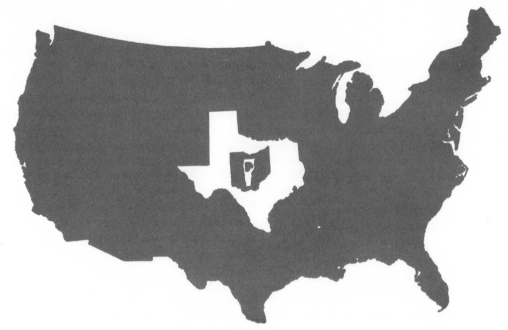

Figure 37–1   Cartogram to illustrate the five orders of size.

to the problem of describing the size of areas existing generally throughout the world, but for this it serves admirably.

SIZE OF EUROPEAN COUNTRIES

The continent of Europe currently contains thirty-one countries, and these are of very unlike sizes. At first glance, it is apparent that the U.S.S.R. is the largest, covering some 2 million square miles of the surface of Europe—an area comprising over one-half of the continent. Clearly the U.S.S.R. is an unusual case, and not representative of European countries in general.

A close inspection of the European map reveals the presence of six tiny states each of which has an area of less than 1,000 square miles. These are as follows:

Diminutive Countries	*Area in Square Miles*
Luxembourg	999
Andorra	191
Liechtenstein	62
San Marino	38
Monaco	½
Vatican	⅛

Diminutive		*Small*		*Medium*		*Large*		*Gigantic*	
Luxembourg	0.03	Hungary	0.9	Yugoslavia	2.4	France	5.3	U.S.S.R.	42.7
Andorra	0.005	Portugal	0.9	Romania	2.4	Spain	4.7	(European	
Liechtenstein	0.002	Austria	0.8	Great Britain	2.4	Sweden	4.3	portion)	
San Marino	0.001	Ireland	0.7	Czechoslovakia	1.3	Germany	3.4		
Monaco	0.0002	Denmark	0.4	Greece	1.3	Norway	3.1		
Vatican City	0.000004	Switzerland	0.4	Iceland	1.0	Finland	3.0		
		Netherlands	0.3	Bulgaria	1.0	Italy	2.9		
		Belgium	0.3			Poland	2.9		
		Albania	0.3						

Table 37–2.   European countries by sizes (using Bulgaria as a base).

These miniature nations are also exceptional cases and are not in any way typical of modern political states. After deducting these extreme cases, there are twenty-four typical countries remaining. The problem, therefore, reduces to that of classifying these into small, intermediate, and large sizes. If the same criteria be employed as were used in classifying American states, then Europe contains nine small, seven intermediate, and eight large nations. If the sizes of the thirty-one European countries be computed in terms of Bulgaria, whose area is 40,000 square miles (about the same size as Ohio), the indices are as in Table 37–2.

SIZE OF COUNTRIES IN GENERAL

This scale of areal magnitudes is as readily applicable to other continents as it is to Europe. It seems, therefore, adapted to the purpose of showing relative size on a worldwide basis.

Countries in the gigantic class occur on every continent, but they are not numerous. Only eight countries fall in this category:

Gigantic Countries	Area in Square Miles
U.S.S.R.	8,656,000
Canada	3,852,999
China	3,760,000
United States	3,615,000
Brazil	3,286,000
Australia	2,971,000
India	1,262,000
Argentina	1,073,000

Europe is the only inhabited continent which does not include at least one gigantic country in its entirety. By way of contrast, however, Europe contains all six of the world's diminutive states.

The remainder of the world's 86 sovereign or semisovereign national units vary in size from the Mongolian Republic (626,000 square miles) down to Lebanon (4,000 square miles).

SIZE OF REGIONS

The same scale of sizes may be used in describing and comparing natural areas, geographic regions, minor political divisions, and other types of areal units. For example, the Great Northern Forest Region of Canada, covering more than a million square miles, is gigantic in size. The American Corn Belt is large; the Winter Wheat Belt is intermediate; the Southern California Lowland is small; and the Pennsylvania Anthracite Region (480 square miles) is diminutive.

SOME GEOGRAPHIC EFFECTS OF SIZE

EFFECTS OF DIMINUTIVE SIZE

In antiquity, many areas of diminutive size, as for example, Tyre and Sidon, the Greek city states, the Hanse Towns, and Venice, achieved striking prominence. More recently, the Swiss cantons and the town units of New England similarly attained importance far out of proportion to their areal extent. Indeed, Aristotle specified that the ideal state should be small enough to be surveyed by the statesman's eye. The most obvious advantage of a diminutive area is that it is apt to be socially precocious. Precocity in most instances, however, has been offset by lack of longevity and by the restricted character of the civilization produced. The precocious and diminutive Athenian state still affords astonishment to the world because of the extent to which it emphasized the artistic and intellectual elements of civilization while totally neglecting the mechanical. Phoenicia and Venice, although they achieved enormous power, were mere commercial efflorescences without geographic bases wide enough to permit their survival. Tiny Sparta was as exaggeratedly militaristic as Judea was provincially religious.

Diminutive size may be a distinct disadvantage politically, although in the past, it has been less so than at present. When Europe emerged from the chaos resulting from the collapse of the gigantic Roman Empire, the first step was to develop thousands of diminutive fiefs and noble holdings. These served well the purpose of redeveloping civilization locally; but after this purpose was served, they were almost universally swallowed up in the growth of larger national units; a few have survived. Independent political units of diminutive size, however, are

today confined to Europe where they survive as
feudal relics. The independence of such units is
certainly more apparent than real, because they
possess an entirely inadequate areal basis for
genuine independent political existence. Luxem-
bourg has been attached first in customs union to
Germany and then to Belgium. Liechtenstein has
had customs union first with Germany, then with
Austria, and finally with Switzerland. Andorra
is dependent upon both France and Spain. San
Marino and Vatican City are as essentially Italian
as Monaco is French.

Along economic, as well as political lines,
diminutive size is disadvantageous. Certain urban
areas where the high value of geographic location has created commercial activity of a high
order are exceptions to this. But even in these
exceptional cases, the original tiny areas of many
cities reveal their inadequacy by the tendency of
metropolises to overflow their bounds. As an
example of the handicap of diminutive size upon
a metropolis, it may be pointed out that New
York City with its restrictive site has, in spite
of a superior location, developed far more pain-
fully and at vastly greater proportionate cost
than has Los Angeles in the midst of an unlimited area.

The strategic importance of diminutive areas
is sometimes so great as to cause them to assume
tremendous political significance. Port Arthur,
the Panama Canal Zone, Hong Kong, Gibraltar,
Malta, or Helgoland possess a significance not to
be measured in terms of areal magnitude. On the
contrary, their very ease of control and integration is considerably enhanced by reason of their
tiny area. In certain phases of political activity,
diminutive size is so desirable that such areas are
sometimes created artificially in order to form
wieldy units. The District of Columbia, the
federal districts of Mexico and Australia, and
Vatican City are examples of such wieldy areas
specifically created to contain central government
activities.

EFFECTS OF SMALL SIZE

All great nations have had their beginnings in
small areas. The Chinese Republic was cradled
in the Wei Valley, giant Russia arose from the
little Muscovite principality, and modern Ger-

many took its origins from the Prussian duchy
east of the Vistula. The Roman and British
empires in like manner had as their respective
nuclei the Tiber Valley and the London Basin.

Small compact areas are essential to the development of civilizations. Islands, valleys, oases,
peninsulas, and littoral strips have, therefore,
provided the loci of origin for most of the past
or present culture systems. Within a small area
there is usually a limited population consisting
of a single racial type, members of which early
develop both a group and an areal consciousness.
Moreover, they react upon one another in countless ways and so produce the elements of civilization. Concomitantly, the smallness of their en-
vironing area prevents the dissipation of their
energies. Thus comes early social and economic
maturity; the civilization produced, however, is
highly individualized and exaggerated along restricted lines.

If the bounds of a small area be too definite,
the smallness of its population, its limited resources, and its provincial outlook cause early
retardation and ultimate decay of its civilization.
It is only to the extent that a social group, upon
reaching maturity, bursts the bounds of its small
nurturing area and overflows, that it is able to
grow strong and survive. Otherwise it is almost
certain to be absorbed by a larger area.

Small countries are inclined to be weak
countries. As Semple[2] points out, "Belgium, Holland, and Switzerland exist as distinct nations
only on sufferance." To these might be added
Albania, Ireland, and Greece (prior to 1912).
Belgium has relied for national safety upon the
guaranties of friendly powers. Austria often
sought to attach itself to Germany as a com-
pensation for its small size. Denmark has permanently renounced war as a possible method of
settling external controversies.

Small areas are apt to be weak economically
as well as politically. To be sure, they manifest
a relatively large per capita foreign trade, but
this is actually no symptom of commercial vigor.
Their small area reduces domestic trade to a
minimum, and hence nearly all exchanges of

[2] E. C. Semple, *Influences of Geographic Environment*
(New York, Henry Holt and Company, Inc., 1911),
p. 177.

goods become visible as foreign commerce. Too often a small area is monotonous in resources with the result that it becomes asymmetrical in its economic life. Thus, Ireland, Denmark, and Hungary are too heavily agricultural, Belgium too highly industrialized, and Holland overdeveloped commercially.

EFFECTS OF INTERMEDIATE SIZE

Areas of medium or intermediate size are handicapped by some of the same restrictive factors which apply to small areas. Yet, at the same time they are extensive enough to contain large populations and may possess abundant and varied resources from which to forge military and commercial sinews. Countries of this magnitude are too large to be tolerated and preserved merely as desirable buffer states. On the other hand, they are too small to possess strength sufficient to assume a place in the ranks of world powers. Consequently, such countries are prone to combine themselves into alliances and ententes or to embark upon ambitious programs of expansion.

Countries of intermediate size, therefore, often constitute danger spots in the political pattern of the world. The medieval kingdom of Japan embraced a territory scarcely one-third that of the present area. Within this, the Japanese people rapidly multiplied in numbers, developed a strong group consciousness, and learned complete subordination to the state. Suddenly the sociostatic force of pent-up national energy burst its bounds, and Northern Honshu, Hokkaido, Formosa, and Sakhalin were added in rapid succession, bestowing large size upon the Japanese nation. Turning then to the mainland of Asia, Japan annexed Liaotung and Korea. Two decades later, Japan occupied Manchuria. After ten more years of consolidation, Japan undertook the conquest of practically all the eastern mainland of Asia and of all the islands of the western Pacific. Thus, an area originally of intermediate size was large enough to feel the stirrings first of a desire for growth, and finally for vast conquest. It was brought under control only by colossal efforts on the part of the United States, in collaboration with the other great powers.

Greece, prior to World War I, was a small nation existing only because of British influence.

It emerged from that war, however, augmented from small to intermediate size. This had the effect of changing Greece from a ward of the British Empire into an ambitious nation. At any rate, she quickly laid claim to Thrace, Constantinople, the Dodecanese, the Anatolian coast, southern Albania, and Cyprus. Only a renascent Turkey prevented the aggressive expansion of Greece.

EFFECTS OF LARGE SIZE

Other things being equal, ethnic, political, and economic strength are yielded by large area. During recent history, practically all world powers have been of large size. At present, of the ten nations which might be rated as world powers, half are large, while one more, Britain, very closely approaches that size.

Not only is there usually strength in large size, but a people occupying such areal dimensions possess an inherent security in the very extensiveness of their areal base. Perhaps this is best illustrated by the fact that there are more nations in the large category than in any other. Poland is a striking example: socially disunited, subjected to contrasting cultural influences, centrally located while devoid of natural boundaries, it has been repeatedly dismembered politically. But the Poles, occupying a large area, have been a persistent factor in European affairs.

World Powers	Area in Square Miles
Major Powers[3]	
U.S.S.R.	8,656,000
U.S.A.	3,615,000
China's (People's Republic)	2,279,000
France	213,000
United Kingdom	94,000
Minor Powers	
Brazil	3,286,000
Turkey	296,000
Japan	143,000
Germany (?)	143,000
Italy	116,000
Yugoslavia (?)	99,000

[3] Many geographers realistically insist that there are only two great powers—the U.S.A. and the U.S.S.R.

Germany affords an even better example. As long as Prussia was a small state, it was a relatively innocuous member of the European scene. When it grew to intermediate size, it became ambitious to exercise leadership in the German realm. When in 1871, Prussia attained that leadership, the German nation achieved large size. For the next seventy-five years, Germany remained a challenge to world security. During World War I, Germany received a crushing military defeat. Yet despite loss of both area and resources, it promptly became a world power once more. During World War II, it received the most crushing defeat ever administered to any modern nation. Despite this, the German people are spread over so large an expanse in central Europe that, united or dismembered, they possess tremendous strength.

EFFECTS OF GIGANTIC SIZE

Countries whose area embraces a million square miles or more are in the very nature of things possessed of a variety of resources. This, in turn, engenders great variety in industry and products and creates a domestic market almost sufficient unto itself. A gigantic country, therefore, is characterized by a huge internal commerce and a comparatively small per capita foreign trade. In order effectively to knit together its great expanse, ambitious transportation schemes come into being. The waterways of China and the roads of the Roman Empire find their modern counterparts in the vast nets of railways and arterial highways of the United States, Australia, and the Soviet Union.

The very extensiveness of gigantic countries makes them almost impossible to conquer, and, where they are invaded, their immense populations act as ready solvents for the invaders. Throughout history, China has thus absorbed one conqueror after another and emerged as Chinese as ever. Napoleon, in attempting the conquest of Russia, was defeated by the sheer distance through which he had to transport his army. In more recent times, Russia has been assailed by Japan on the east and Germany on the west. While both assaults were partially successful, neither penetrated to the heart of this vast country.

Under such conditions, the military is nor-

mally relegated to secondary importance in immense countries like China, Canada, the United States, and the U.S.S.R. In its stead, national energies are devoted to agricultural or industrial problems, or both, while schemes of reclamation, conservation, and internal development bulk large in national consciousness. It must not be thought, however, that gigantic size thus breeds exclusively an inlooking national viewpoint. Rather, the fact of mere size multiplies the number of international contacts between such a country and its neighbors. These continually engender new strength and promise much for a people so areally environed.

It is extremely significant that only three nations emerged from World War II with any real military and political power—the Soviet Union, the United States, and the British Commonwealth of Nations. These are political units of colossal size, and moreover they are not even nations in the customary sense; they are actually federal unions of sovereign nations. This suggests that in the modern world, people can find means for preserving and protecting their liberties only within the framework of gigantic political structures. Certainly, under nothing short of a sovereign government of the world, will most of the present nations find it possible to preserve their ultimate cultural existence.

IDEAS CONCERNING SPACE

GERMAN IDEAS

Toward the end of the nineteenth century, a German geographer, Friedrich Ratzel, advanced the idea that a human society (and more specifically—a political state) is an organism with a biological urge to expand. He pointed out that the culture of a people first spreads beyond its frontiers, and that this is followed by an expanding population; finally comes political consolidation. Moreover, Ratzel observed, the health and growth of a people depend largely upon its ability to think in terms of large space.

A little later Rudolf Kjellén, a Swedish geographer, further developed the organic concept of society. He reemphasized the idea that a nation is an organism and that political space or territory is its body.

In the early twentieth century, Karl Haushofer elaborated these earlier ideas and insisted that a nation must expand spatially or decline. He and other contemporary German geographers believed that strong peoples should encourage their birth rates, expand their cultures, and extend their economic enterprises in order to absorb smaller states. In a very important sense, World War II represented an attempt by the Axis nations (Germany, Italy, and Japan) to outbreed other nations, and then to use the factor of overpopulation as a reason for military, political, and economic conquest of neighboring peoples.

AMERICAN IDEAS

In answer to this thesis, the American geographer, Charles Colby,[4] pointed out that the "four freedoms" of the democratic world do not give any nation the right to overbreed at the expense of other peoples in a contest for the earth's space. By way of contrast, he felt that France, Switzerland, and the Scandinavian countries have gone a long way toward achieving a balance between population and space through birth control; and that the cure for many overpopulated areas may be a drastic reduction in the already existing population.

INEQUALITIES IN SPACE RESOURCES

Regardless of how one looks at space and the relations of peoples to it, there is no question that it constitutes one of the crucial natural resources for many nations. The Dutch and the Germans were originally two closely related tribes. The Dutch, however, were confined to the delta of the Rhine, while the Germans had a large area into which they could expand. In the same length of time, the Dutch have come to number about 10 million, whereas the Germans in Europe now number more than 80 million. In similar fashion, the Portuguese in their little homeland have increased slowly until they now number only about 9 million. Meanwhile, the Portuguese colonists in Brazil have become a nation of 82 million. The British in their island home and the British colonists in the United States repeat this same contrast.[5] Most of the nations of the world have had no definite theories regarding the rights of peoples to spatial resources. There is an almost universal tendency to assume that the amounts of area

seized by various peoples during the historical past shall constitute their shares through all future time, and that prolonged ownership confers ethical title to land and other resources no matter how unequal the division. It is certain that any major dissent from the doctrine of spatial status quo and historical precedent, such as the German demand for *Lebensraum* in the late 1930's, is promptly met by war.

The fact that certain peoples possess space wherein they can increase, while others do not, raises the very fundamental question as to whether there is anything either ethical or desirable in the present distribution of space resources in the world. For example, the Russians now number over 229 million. Their area is so large, however, that they are increasing at nearly 4 million per year. At this rate, they may number 500 million by the end of the next century. By way of contrast, the much more highly cultured Czechs are confined within the small Bohemian Basin and hence no such expansion is open to them.

The population density is particularly high in countries with high birth rates and limited areas for expansion. Already, the density of the United Kingdom has reached 574 persons per square mile. In England alone, it is over 850 persons per square mile. Japan, with a density of 682 persons, is another densely populated country. In Belgium and the Netherlands, two small, highly cultured nations, the relative densities are 775 and 920, respectively. The Americans, Brazilians, and African Negroes, however, inhabit enormous spatial areas with very low densities of population.

IMPLICATIONS

To accept the present distribution of space resources as final implies that the nations of the world are ready to assume that the Dutch, Bel-

---

[4] Charles C. Colby, "The Geographical Problem," *New Perspectives on Peace* (Chicago, University of Chicago Press, 1944), p. 36.

[5] There has been a great non-British immigration into the United States, but because the birth rate of British-Americans has declined in direct proportion to the influx of immigrants, there is reason to think that if no immigration had been permitted after 1800, the present population of America might have been about the same as at present.

gians, Swiss, Czechs, Danes, and Norwegians are entitled to increase not at all. Furthermore, it implies that the Germans, Italians, and Japanese are entitled to increase but little; but that the Brazilians and African Negroes are entitled to increase to perhaps a figure of 1 billion each, the Russians to about 700 million, the Malayo-Polynesians and the Americans to about 300 million each, and the Chinese to about 1 billion.

SPACE CONCEPTS AND CULTURE

Scant attention is usually paid to areal size or space in geographic analysis. Nevertheless, it unquestionably plays an important role in the ecology of human groups. The division of space resources, moreover, literally determines which peoples will eventually possess the earth in the biological sense of the term.

Man's concept of size and of the significance of space has varied widely through the course of history. One might almost say that the whole story of civilization is revealed in man's increasing space sense. This is true because mankind has progressed from knowing only its own isolated locality, up to a concept of terrestrial space as a whole. At any given time, however, man's idea of spatial magnitude was largely determined by the instruments which he possessed for overcoming time and space in travel and communication.

Primitive man had contact with only a very limited area, and hence his concept of space was restricted to his actual community of residence and its environs. Man under such relationships may be said to be in the *parochial* stage of culture. Gradually, in the course of social and mechanical evolution, man's consciousness of space was extended over the whole region in which his community lay. Thus *provincial* cultures developed. Nationalism is obviously only provincial culture in its most expanded sense.

With the Columbian discoveries, mankind became conscious of the unity of the world oceans, and other aspects of terrestrial oneness have been slowly realized by more enlightened minds over the earth. The development of cable, telephone, radar, radio, rapid transport, universal press, postal service, telestar, and orbiting laboratories has been fostering a global consciousness in the minds of many people, throughout most parts of the earth.

The advent of the long-range airplane and now rockets has suddenly rendered space three-dimensional. It is unfortunate that this abrupt change from a two-dimensional to a three-dimensional environment has occurred before mankind has completed its transition from a provincial to a global concept of space. The resulting strain is severe and widespread. World wars seem to be the inevitable result of mankind having in its hands the instruments of worldwide intercourse without having progressed from the stage of provincial culture to that of *global* culture.

SUGGESTED USEFUL REFERENCES

These three atlas-statistical sources are meant for Chapters 37 through 39.

Espenshade, Edward B., Jr., ed., *Goode's World Atlas*, 12th ed. (Chicago, Rand McNally & Company, 1964).
Steinberg, S. H., ed., *Statesman's Yearbook* (New York, St. Martin's Press, Inc., annual).
United Nations Statistical Office, *Demographic Yearbook* (New York, United Nations, annual).

38

Regional Form or Shape

In studying an area geographically, the form of that area is a characteristic so obvious as to receive usually little or no attention. The obviousness of a characteristic, however, is no reason per se for concluding that it is unimportant. Close inspection reveals, on the contrary, that the ecology of any human group bears significant relations to the areal form of the region which it inhabits. Probably the principal reason for the common failure to attach importance to this factor arises from the fact that it has not been analyzed from a really geographic standpoint.

FORM DEFINED

DESCRIPTIVE SHAPE

One frequently encounters attempts by lay observers to state regional form in purely descriptive terms. For example, Italy has been likened to a boot, Celebes to the handle of a saw, Greece to a hand and wrist, Ceylon to a pear, and Chile to a machete blade; or again, New Guinea has been described as a roosting turkey, Mexico likened to a leg of mutton, Germany to a knight's helmet, and Ireland to a bear cub. Such similes have no value at all, save perhaps as mnemonic aids for very young children.

GEOMETRIC SHAPE

Again, attempts are often made to classify areal or regional forms as regular or irregular, round, rectangular, triangular, spatulate, and so forth. Such terms are superior to the picturesque or whimsical similes mentioned earlier, but they have the fundamental weakness of being based upon purely empirical analysis. The shortcoming of all such classifications is that they deal with mere geometric shape or boundary delineation, while at the same time they ignore real areal form.

FORM DEFINED GEOGRAPHICALLY

If one accepts the theory that a political state[1] is an organism, then Ratzel's contention that its frontier or boundary is its end-organ appears plausible. Viewed in this light, a political boundary reveals the manner of a nation's growth or expansion. It also gives a clue to a nation's relations with its neighbors and a hint as to its security problems.

The specific pattern traced out by the boundaries of any spatial unit is of little moment (aside from the geopolitical considerations just mentioned) except as it affects the relation of the several parts of an area to the whole or to one another. Interruptions, projections, reentrants, and constrictions in boundaries are important, therefore, not because they trace out any specific shape, but because of the relations which they engender between the central mass or heart of a region and its outlying parts.

Any geographic method of classifying regional form must have for its purpose the devising of a set of terms which will describe the internal relations of an area created by boundary configuration. Any such terms when applied to an area should not only characterize it but should also afford a scale of comparison with other areas.

[1] The term *state* is here used not in the American sense (a synonym for province), but in the sense of national state, or nation.

GEOGRAPHIC TYPES OF FORM

From this standpoint, the following five geographic types of areal form may be recognized: (1) compact, (2) attenuated, (3) prorupted, (4) fragmented, and (5) perforated. These categories do not describe the shape of areas in the ordinary sense of the word, but they do denote the spatial nature of the various areal units with which the geographer has occasion to deal.

MEANINGS OF THE CATEGORIES OF FORM

An area is *compact* when all of its surface is contiguous and approximately equidistant from a common center.

It is *attenuated* or *elongated* if its surface is drawn out in one direction or extended along a single axis.

An area is *prorupted* when it exhibits one or more protuberances extending outward from its main central portion. Prorupted or tumoid form may also be engendered by constrictions or by reentrants of adjacent territory into its mass. These give to a region a jaculated, bulged, or sprawled appearance.

An area is *fragmented* in form when it is centrally broken into separate portions, or where the main mass possesses noncontiguous outliers.

An area is *perforated* in form if it does not include all the area within its outer continuous boundary; that is, perforation occurs where there are enclaves or inliers of another area within its boundary, in such manner as to interrupt the surface continuity.

GEOGRAPHIC RESULTS OF FORM
THE FORM OF SMALL LANDHOLDING UNITS

The effect of form may be seen clearly in connection with farms—one of the smallest social subdivisions of area. In the American Midlands, the early average farm was a result of laws passed by the Congress in an effort to encourage desirable land settlement. Because of these laws and because of the rectangular land survey inaugurated in the region, the usual farm was a nearly square area containing 160 acres.[2] This made a compact areal unit which allowed easy access to the individual fields and reduced transportation losses to a minimum (see Chapter 4). The form of such a farm encourages efficient land

[2] The United States is today in the throes of an agricultural revolution, the result largely of science and technology. There has been more change in American agriculture within the lifetime of men now living than in the previous 2,000 years of world agriculture. The economic upshot of this revolution is bigger farms and fewer farms and farmers. Technology in a sense forces up the size of farms in order to get greater utilization from farm equipment and reduces per unit overhead. In 1940, the average farm was 174 acres in size; in 1950, 215 acres; in 1956, 242 acres; and so it goes year after year. The nation loses roughly 125,000 farms annually through consolidation.

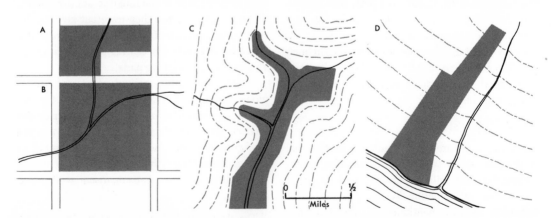

Figure 38–1 Geographic shapes in North American farms. A and B are prorupt and compact farms from the rectangular survey area of the Middle West. C is a creek-bottom farm from the Kentucky hill country. D is a river-fronting farm from Quebec. Compare this with Figure 38–2.

utilization and crop rotation, as well as the effective use of labor (Fig. 38–1B).

Farms which were originally compact have often assumed a prorupted form through acquisition by the owner of a tongue of adjacent creek-bottom pasture, or through mere desire on the part of the proprietor to add a neighboring 20–, 40–, or 80–acre tract (Fig. 38–1A). Of necessity, proruption in form reduces the labor efficiency of the farm, increases difficulty of interfield communication, and augments fencing costs.

In the Appalachian hill country, farms are commonly attenuated in form. A single landholding may be confined to a narrow stream bottom and extend along the watercourse for a considerable distance. Cornfields are sometimes a mile long and perhaps only ten rows wide (Fig. 38–1C). In Quebec, farms are in many instances attenuated at right angles to the St. Lawrence. This has resulted from the fact that the original land grants were laid out in such manner as to insure that each would have river frontage. This provided the owners with hay from the river marshland, fishing rights, and riparian rights for landing boats. When a farmer died, his land was divided, each heir getting a strip (a new farm) fronting on the river (Fig. 38–1D). Hence, by reason of division and subdivision, farms came to be several rods wide and perhaps a mile long.

Fragmented division of land is well illustrated by the manorial or *vill* system of medieval Europe. Under this system, a peasant cultivated parcels of land located in various parts of the lord's estate. Such land subdivision discouraged individuality, prohibited proper rotation of crops, and set a minimum valuation upon time and labor. In part, the system of land subdivision practiced in the average vill was an attempt to give each villein two or more pieces of arable land, a piece of woodland, a piece of permanent pasture, and a piece of what other kind of land lay in the locality. It also was designed to encourage the fallowing (resting through noncultivation (of each arable piece during an-occasional year. But there is no question but that it was also designed, in many instances, to prevent the villein from becoming attached to any one piece of land so firmly as to encourage him to

demand ownership, or even to feel a vested interest in the land on which he labored.

Fragmented landholding survived in France, Russia, Romania, Switzerland, and a few other countries even into modern times (Fig. 38–2). In Russia, the system was so firmly embedded that even the Bolshevik revolution failed to dislodge it. At first, the Soviet government established large model farms (*sovkhozes*) in order to demonstrate to the peasants the economic desirability of land consolidation. When this largely failed, the government undertook a program of forcible consolidation into *kolkhozes* or huge collective farms.

THE FORM OF URBAN AREAS

Cities fall into distinct types in regard to their geographic form. Buffalo is a typically compact urban area, the city centering on the waterfront furnished by the artificial harbor at the mouth of the Niagara River (Fig. 38–3). From this focus, railways lead outward like the spokes of a wheel. The arterials, Niagara, Main, and Genesee streets, Broadway, and Delaware Avenue, facilitate rapid movement into and out of the city center. These are intersected at intervals by circumferential streets and boulevards, and by belt-line railways. The total is such as to give compactness to the urban area. The city of Duluth shows a pronounced attentuation between Lake Superior and the uplands a short distance inland.

Los Angeles, formerly a compact city, has developed a markedly prorupt form. From the central city area, a narrow fifteen-mile corridor extends to the harbor unit at San Pedro. Lesser proruptions project outward to Santa Monica, Pasadena, and Glendale. A suburban extension is now growing eastward along the Foothill Boulevard toward San Bernardino.

Officially, San Francisco is a compact city situated at the end of a small peninsula. The geographic urban area is actually fragmented in the extreme, for Oakland, Alameda, and Berkeley on the eastern shore of the bay are integral parts of the city. South San Francisco, Sausalito, San Rafael, and Richmond are smaller outliers. All told, more than two million inhabitants are included in this fragmented urban formation.

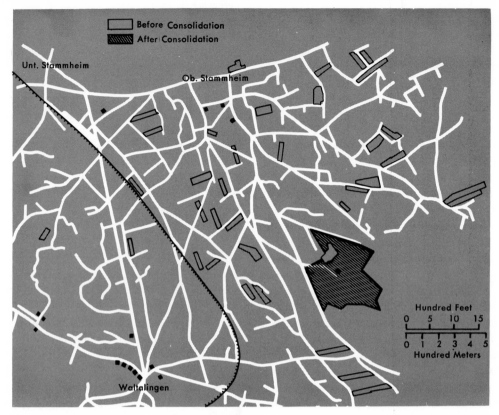

Figure 38–2 A Swiss farm before and after consolidation. This farm, covering a total area of 40.2 acres, was composed of thirty-nine separate fragments (small rectangles). In 1923, exchanges were made and the farm consolidated into one fairly compact piece (diagonally-ruled area). The usual Swiss farm consists of an average of 14.3 strips each of which averages 1.5 acres of land. This system, which is a relic of the Middle Ages, is a great handicap to agricultural progress over much of Europe. There is much waste of time and loss of efficiency in going from one parcel of land to another because these frequently lie several miles apart. It is seldom possible to consolidate a fragmented farm into a single piece and hence little progress has been made toward this end in many European countries. (Map after USDA)

Seattle may be cited as a representative example of attenuated form. The city originated as a bay-head village on Puget Sound. It rapidly expanded so as to occupy the entire isthmus between the Sound and Lake Washington, and thus confined, it could grow farther only by north-south attenuation. Aside from awkward ferry service, ingress to the city was long to be had only from the north or south, and hence railways, arterial streets, and bus lines show a north-south axial alignment. Since the advent of the Pacific Highway, there is a tendency for the cities of Everett, Seattle, and Tacoma to coalesce along this axis. There are, thus, symptoms of the evolution of an attenuated "City of Puget Sound" more than sixty miles in length and with a maximum width of five miles.

The form of an urban area is more than a mere curiosity, for it controls, in large measure, the transportation web and street pattern of a city. In addition, it creates problems in water supply, fire control, police supervision, and commercial integration. In one way, this is aggravated by modern transportation. Most cities show a radial pattern of main highways leading outward from their center, and over these move daily streams of commuters. In growing outward, cities tend to expand more rapidly along these arterial routes, thereby developing long outward-reaching arms like the points of a star, separated by embayments of rural landscape. Thus a compact form is converted to a markedly prorupted form, with numerous resulting problems.

A few city areas display a perforated form. In the process of growth, a metropolis often engulfs sizable suburban cities. Customarily these latter are incorporated into the metropolis, but occasionally they possess enough "personality" to withstand absorption. Thereupon, they remain independent political units, "islands" of territory perforating the area of the metropolis. An outstanding example of this is afforded by Highland Park and Hamtramck in the Detroit area.

THE FORM OF AMERICAN COUNTIES

The great majority of counties in the United States are geographically compact, whether they be the rectangular units of the West and Middle West, the irregular divisions of the East and South, or the peculiar circular areas of Tennessee.

Attenuation of counties is fairly common and, in most instances, gives rise to peculiar problems of communication and administration. For example, the counties of Kansas are for the most part compact square or rectangular areas of generally similar size. Finney County, however, is a noteworthy exception. It is L-shaped with the county seat, Garden City, lying in the main western section. At one time the eastern projection constituted the separate county of Garfield. This latter was the only Kansas county which did not have a railroad, and hence it was joined to Finney County. Its former county seat, thus deprived of all political significance, dwindled rapidly until the farmers of eastern Finney now have no real shopping center.

As originally planned, Iowa was to have 104 counties, but because some counties were made longer than average, the total declined to 99. One of the attenuated counties, Pottawatomie, is twice as large as its neighbors. Council Bluffs, the county seat, is located at the western extremity, further aggravating the attenuated form. To offset this, Avoca in the eastern portion is maintained as a minor county seat. Many of the counties in western United States show attenuation. Usually this has resulted from organizing a well-settled area into a county unit and then attaching, for administrative purposes, a long strip of unsettled land to it. When the latter was eventually settled, its inhabitants usually have experienced considerable inconvenience in traveling to and from the county seat; sometimes, the unwieldly unit was subdivided and a new county created, but more often, political inertia thwarted such reforms. Perhaps the most severe example of elongation is furnished by Arapahoe County in Colorado. It is about seventy-two miles long and some twelve miles wide, with Littleton, the county seat, near the western end (Fig. 38–4).

Numerous American counties (and also the subprovincial units of Canada) exhibit considerable fragmentation in their form. Usually this occurs in coastal counties which consist wholly or in part of islands. San Juan County, Washington, consists of three large and many small islands. Its fragmentation is so severe as almost completely to destroy its social and political unity. In one instance, namely, Norfolk County in Massachusetts, fragmentation was created by de-

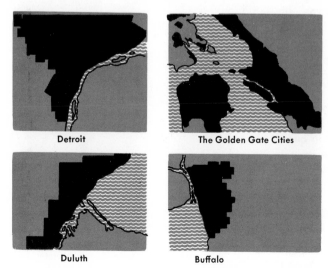
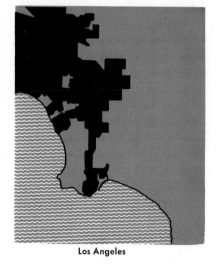

Figure 38–3   Geographic forms as illustrated by some American cities.

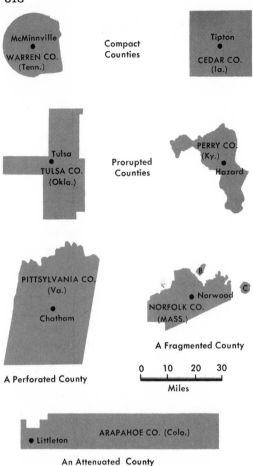

Figure 38–4 Sketches of seven American counties to illustrate geographic forms.

liberate political intent. This was done by the inclusion of the detached outlying "towns" of Brookline and Cohasset. Citizens from these outliers must traverse Plymouth or Suffolk territory in order to visit their county seat (Fig. 38–4).

Perforation of county form occurs only in Virginia. Cities in that state may, upon reaching proper size, assume independent "county" status of their own. When a city lying within a county assumes such status, it leaves the county in question with a "hole" in its territory. The several categories of form as illustrated by American counties is shown in Figure 38–4.

THE FORM OF STATES OR PROVINCES

Many American states, as for example Iowa, Ohio, and Wyoming, are very compact. California, in contrast, is so attenuated as to extend from the subtropics to the upper middle latitudes. The economic-geographic contrasts produced by this latitudinal elongation have led to striking political disaffection between the northern and southern portions of the state. Tennessee, whose length in an east-west direction is nearly five times its width, suffers acutely from its attenuation. Within the state, there has developed a remarkable tripartite sectionalism. While the capital is located at Nashville, the supreme court sits in rotation at Knoxville, Nashville, and Memphis, and many state institutions are, of necessity, repeated in triplicate.

Fragmented form is perhaps best illustrated by Michigan. That state is completely separated into two parts by Lake Michigan. The northern part is a large peninsula projecting eastward between lakes Superior and Michigan. The southern part is an even larger peninsula projecting northward between lakes Michigan and Huron, and is the more populous portion of the state. By all geographic logic, the northern portion should have been made a part of Wisconsin. So complete is the separation of the two sections that sectional consciousness largely eclipses state consciousness. An inhabitant of Michigan almost invariably identifies himself as hailing from either the "Northern Peninsula" or the "Southern Peninsula" (Fig. 38–5).

Figure 38–5 Sketches of some American states to illustrate geographic forms.

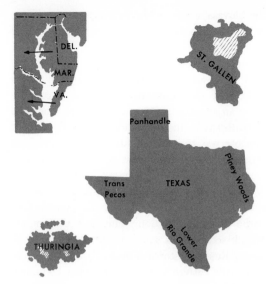

Figure 38-6 Sketches of some unusual provincial forms.

and dry-farmed winter wheat and sorghums. Hence the citizens of these prorupt portions have almost nothing in common with those of the cotton-growing and general farming central portion, except that pride of state which is strong in all Texans.

No American state, with the possible exception of Hawaii, exhibits a perforated form, but perforation is not unknown in other parts of the world. The Spanish state of Alava, for instance, completely surrounds a portion of the state of Burgos. In Switzerland, the canton of Appenzell takes a piece out of St. Gallen much like the hole in a doughnut (Fig. 38-6). In Germany, perforation of state forms was quite common before the Nazi reorganization of the internal divisions. There, the case of Thuringia was probably the most striking: three inliers of Prussian territory created gaps in the Thuringian area. To further complicate matters, there were four outliers of Thuringia in Prussia and Bavaria.

NATIONAL FORMS

Form is a much more important consideration to a nation than it is to a geographic region, or to a province, county, city, or any other variety of areal division. The reason is, of course, that nations are competitive units and hence basically inimical to one another. Accordingly, they are compelled to think in terms of military defense. Regional form is a not unimportant factor in defense. The importance of form in national life is reflected in constant attempts by nations to accomplish what is known in diplomatic language as the "rectification of boundaries." The fact that many wars have been fought in order to "round out" national territory, suggests that regional form is a much more important environmental factor than has been commonly supposed.

Compactness

Romania being nearly circular, had the best shape of any nation; postwar Romania is slightly prorupted, but it is still relatively compact or blocklike (Fig. 38-7). Hungary, France, Uruguay, and Ethiopia are also well-shaped nations. Compactness of form is a distinct asset to a nation. It means that the frontier is reduced to a minimum length, that there are no long bulges

Virginia has two detached and badly isolated counties, Accomac and Northampton, lying east of Chesapeake Bay. Maryland also has nine detached counties on this "Eastern Shore" of Chesapeake Bay. The eleven Virginia and Maryland counties have much closer ties with Delaware than with the main portions of their own states. Indeed, the thirteen counties of southern Delaware, eastern Maryland, and eastern Virginia tend to regard themselves as an unofficial state called Del-Mar-Va (Fig. 38-6).

West Virginia, Idaho, Oklahoma, Texas, and Alaska reveal long proruptions or projections popularly known as *panhandles*. The most interesting of these is perhaps the Oklahoma Panhandle: the three western counties—Cimarron, Texas, and Beaver formerly constituted a long strip of land left over after Texas, New Mexico, Kansas, Colorado, and Indian Territory were formed. When Oklahoma, the last continental state, was organized, this residual three-county strip was attached to it.

Texas possesses not only a panhandle but two additional protuberances as well, making that state markedly prorupted in form. The lower Rio Grande extension is interested in orcharding and irrigation horticulture; the trans-Pecos lobe is arid ranch country; and the northern panhandle is concerned with petroleum, natural gas, cattle,

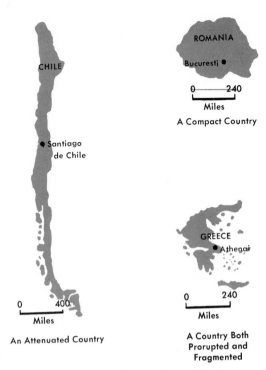

Figure 38-7 Sketches of countries to illustrate geographic form.

or outlying areas to defend, and that a relatively simple system of roads and railways will serve commercial needs. Other things being equal, the more compact a country, the fewer are the number of adjoining countries; and hence the fewer minority problems are likely to exist, and the fewer points of dispute are apt to arise. Many nations have, through the process of military and diplomatic abrasion, achieved approximate compactness.

Elongation

In ancient times, folk migrations tended to flow along river valleys, coastal strips, and other well-marked natural corridors. Today, some ethnic groups show the influence of their ancient migration by being distributed over elongated areas. Nations which have arisen from such ethnic groups consequently tend to assume attenuated form. Czechoslovakia is a good illustration; its people long ago migrated into central Europe along the Carpathian piedmont. The Czechs and Moravians occupy the nearly inclosed but compact Bohemian Basin and Moravian Plateau, but

the Slovaks were pushed back against the Western Carpathians by later invaders. The union of these three West Slav peoples after World War I produced a country which was markedly attenuated. This was further aggravated by the treaty-makers of Versailles, who extended Czechoslovakia an additional 150 miles eastward along the Carpathians to the boundary of Romania. Their purpose was to wall out Russian influence from central Europe. The new nation within such frontiers was, however, largely indefensible. In 1938, Germany annexed the western Czech portion, while Hungary annexed the eastern Carpatho-Ukrainian section. This left the middle Slovak section as a small puppet state. In 1945, when Russia restored Czechoslovakia, she annexed the eastern section to her own Ukrainian state (Fig. 38-8).

Chile is the classical example of attenuation, since it is 2,500 miles long and only 110 miles in average width (Fig. 38-7). The form of the country makes central governmental management difficult. The federal authorities are unable to comprehend the problems of the northern and southern extremities and legislation appears to be mainly for the benefit of the central provinces. For a century, Chilean railways were limited to short transverse lines which acted as feeders for the trunk line of communication—the ocean. Recently, at great cost and effort, the 1,900-mile Longitudinal Railway was constructed to supplement the feeble unifying influence of the ocean.

Figure 38-8 German partition of the attenuated country, Czechoslovakia.

Fragmentation

Ancient Greece (insofar as it may be regarded as a country in the modern sense of the word) was badly fragmented in form. A certain unity was maintained by maritime activity, but when this diminished, the Grecian world collapsed almost completely. Even Greek culture practically vanished because there was no strong central area to supply a nucleus for its preservation.

Among modern nations, Greece, Britain, New Zealand, the Republic of the Philippines, Italy, and Denmark are excellent examples of fragmented or broken units. Japan is a classical representative of fragmented form. It consists now of just the four "home" islands, but before its defeat following World War II, it comprised chains of islands, archipelagoes, and a vast continental hinterland in eastern Asia. It was able, during World War II, to defend itself against enormous armed power. As long as the Japanese air force was intact, Japan was able to make the American conquest of even tiny outlying islands costly and bloody beyond belief. Behind this inter-island shield of air power, the Japanese navy and merchant marine were able to unify and supply a colossal fragmented empire. When their air power was weakened, the Japanese bridge of ships was quickly destroyed. Thereupon, Japan's fragmented form ceased to be an advantage and created insuperable problems of supply and the deployment of men and weapons. American naval vessels and airplane carriers were able to penetrate to the very heart of the Japanese homeland, and collapse came with astonishing suddenness.[3]

Proruption

Prorupted form in national states results from a number of causes. Most protuberances or extensions in the form of a country occur through the movement of its people in search of commercial advantages. The Soviet Union, for instance, thrusts out nearly a dozen prongs or extensions— most of which are the result of Russia's thousand-year search for a satisfactory outlet to the ocean.

The Panhandle of Alaska, the Tenasserim Coast of Burma, and the 500-mile Kansu extension of China Proper are examples of proruptions of form resulting from commercial causes. Unlike these, the eastern prong of Afghanistan resulted

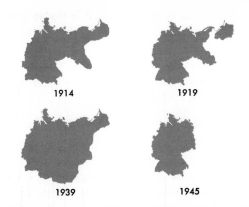

Figure 38–9   Forms of the German Reich from 1914–1945.

from the deliberate creation of a narrow buffer zone between Russia and British India.

At one time in American history, northern Mexico formed an embayment into United States territory, severing the direct land route between Texas and southern California. Accordingly, the United States made the Gadsden Purchase, in order to correct this.

Germany from 1871 to 1914 was extremely prorupted. Schleswig-Holstein, Alsace, Bavaria, Silesia, and East Prussia gave to Germany a quinque-radiate shape, into which foreign territory penetrated dangerously. The need to protect such a preposterous periphery was beyond doubt a factor in German militarism. After World War I, the Polish embayment into eastern Germany was increased. To make matters worse, the Treaty of Versailles cut a Polish "corridor" between East Prussia and the main area of the Reich (Fig. 38–9).

A glance at the post-1918 map of Germany also shows that Czechoslovakia cut an enormous bite out of what would otherwise have been the fairly compact area of Germany. The Czech "bite" and the Polish "corridor" disrupted trade and transportation and made Germany difficult to defend militarily.

It was, therefore, not without reason that the first two German moves in World War II were the conquest of the Czech and Polish "em-

[3] The invention of a new instrument of warfare by America (namely, the atomic bomb) greatly hastened the debacle, but the process of collapse was far advanced before its use.

bayments." By 1940, as indicated in Figure 38–9, Germany had achieved an almost ideally compact form. After World War II, the cure employed for the problems of German proruption was to lop off the Silesian and East Prussian bulges and give them to Poland.

Perforation

Perforated or "punctured" form is unusual in nations. It is, however, not unknown. Perhaps the best illustration of it is the Republic of South Africa, within which lies in its entirety the native state of Basutoland. In similar fashion, British India was long perforated by a large number of surviving native states and by the French colonial city of Chandernagore. Within Switzerland are two tiny inliers of German territory. These and the small autonomous republics within some of the federal republics of the Soviet Union are illustrations of somewhat different kinds of punctured form. Perforation in general would seem to be a mark of political immaturity.

Form, then, plays a significant part in national development. Upon this factor are dependent problems of communication and transportation. Matters of internal administration, political unification, and social provincialism are also related to it. National aims and policies are, indeed, partially traceable to a country's form.

39

Natural
Site
and Situation

SITE AND ITS SIGNIFICANCE

In examining the natural environment of any community, one of the more significant aspects to be noted is the *site* of the community in question. It is customary to say that a city, village, or other community is situated on a level lowland, a water front, a river terrace, a rocky eminence, a swamp or marshland, a foreshore, a ridge crest, a mountain valley, a hill top, an alluvial slope, and so forth. Such brief characterizations can of course be expanded by the addition of a great amount of detail, but even without elaboration, they are useful in characterizing the site upon which the human settlement in question stands.

Such site terms as the preceding, however, are usually applicable only to a single community. They are not applicable to an extensive pattern of settlement covering a large region (or in some instances, an entire nation), because a region comprises a great many dissimilar local sites. It is desirable, however, in studying an extensive pattern of human occupance, to describe the physical-occurrence aspect of its region in the same way that one describes the site of a single community. This large-scale descriptive aspect is usually termed *natural situation*. In other words, *natural situation* is to the region or other large area what *site* is to a single locality. For example, the site of the city of Cincinnati is the river terrace and bluff on the outside of a great bend of the Ohio River; the natural situation of the Republic of Panama is an isthmus connecting the two American continents and separating the Atlantic and Pacific oceans. Man has turned the latter into an important maritime bottle-neck and a possible bridge for inter-American land routes, by digging a canal.

TWO TYPES OF SITUATION

The land surface of the globe is composed of seven continents and numerous islands, all disposed rather irregularly through the world ocean. This division of the earth's surface into land and water bodies is the prime factor underlying the distribution of human society over the earth. Since this is true, the natural situation[1] of any area may be expressed in terms of whether it is part of the heart of a continent or whether it lies in or adjacent to the ocean. Where a place or an area occurs upon a great land mass in such manner that it has a minimum of contacts with the sea and where its regional relations are principally land relations, its situation is said to be *continental*. Where it occurs upon an island or upon the margin of a great land mass in such manner that its regional relations are mainly with and by way of the sea, its situation is said to be *maritime*. Each of these two major types of natural situation may be subdivided into several categories or classes.

CONTINENTAL SITUATION

All continental regions have one thing in common, namely, a preponderance of land relationships over water relationships. The results of this are that land interests, land trade, and problems

---

[1] The term *situation* is derived from the Latin word *situs* meaning permanent placement, fixation, or site. In geography, therefore, the term *situation* is applied to the occurrence of a place in regard to fixed features made by nature. It thus stands in contrast to *position*, which is mathematical occurrence (see Chapter 4), and to *location*, which is occurrence in relative spatial terms (see Chapter 5).

of military defense eclipse maritime interests, ocean trade, and problems of naval defense. Continental situation, however, is not a fixed quantity; several varieties may be noted, chief among which are the following: (1) *intermontane*, (2) *midland*, (3) *piedmont*, and (4) *riverine*.

INTERMONTANE SITUATION

Interior regions lying between two mountain ranges, or nearly enclosed by highlands of one sort or another, may be described as having intermontane or closed continental situation. Such a region often forms a citadel of great natural strength. An excellent example of this is furnished by the Aar Basin of Switzerland between the Jura Mountains and the Alpine Oberland. Although the seeds of Swiss national existence germinated in the mountain valleys along the eastern edge of the Aar Basin, nevertheless it was the Basin itself which was the cradle of the Swiss nation. It is that small enclosed lowland which today constitutes the economic, cultural, and political heart of the nation. Moreover, it is Switzerland's strong site which has enabled that country, alone among the small continental states of Europe, to maintain an uninterrupted national existence since medieval times. The prestige of Swiss national stability and continuity has helped to give Switzerland a considerable importance in modern European affairs. It has been the headquarters of the International Red Cross, it was the capital of the League of Nations, and it has long served as a clearing house for both diplomacy and espionage (Fig. 39–1).

MARITIME TYPES
- Littoral
- Insular-peninsular
- Isthmian-pontine

CONTINENTAL TYPES
- Midland
- Intermontane
- Piedmont
- Mesopotamian

Figure 39–1 Natural situation in Europe.

At the eastern end of the central European highlands stands the natural citadel of Transylvania. This upland basin is surrounded by the Bihar Mountains, the Transylvanian Alps, and the Eastern Carpathians, in such manner as to form a landlocked site of great strategic importance. This bastion of southeastern Europe has been fiercely contested by Roman and Barbarian, Austrian and Turk, Hungarian and Romanian. It is inhabited by Germans, Hungarians, and Romanians, with the last-named preponderating. At present, it is held by Romania, and it is safe to assume that as long as she holds it, her position in southeastern Europe will be a relatively strong one.

A third intermontane site in Europe is that of western Czechoslovakia. The Bohemian, Ore, Giant, and Sudeten mountains and the Moravian Hills form an almost complete rim about an upland known as the Bohemian Basin. This was long a very strong site; within it the Czechs, a western branch of the Slavs, were able to maintain their language and ethnic character relatively intact amidst the rising intrusion of Germanic culture.

During the age of land warfare, the Bohemian Basin was perhaps the strongest natural situation on the continent. Indeed, it was often called the "Citadel of Europe." Austrian power in central Europe was in the ascendancy after the Hapsburg dynasty gained control of Bohemia. Austrian decline was assured when Czech independence was achieved at the close of World War I. From 1918 to 1938, Czechoslovakia was the keystone of political stability in central Europe. In the modern age of aerial warfare, which began during the 1930's, natural citadels such as the Bohemian Basin have lost much of their military (and hence political) significance.

In north central Asia, the intermontane area between the Sayan and Altai mountains is a natural fortress of considerable strength. Although claimed politically by China, the inhabitants achieved independence under the name of the Republic of Tannu Tuva. Later they joined the Soviet Union. Similarly, the strong intermontane areas of Anatolia, Abyssinia, Dasht-i-Lut, and Seistan have made it possible for the relatively weak nations of Turkey, Ethiopia, Iran, and Afghanistan to survive.

One of the most interesting examples of the values of an intermontane site comes from China. In 1937, the Japanese invaded China and overran large areas. The Chinese government promptly retired to the Red Basin, a large area walled in by the Ta-pa, Yünling, and Taiping mountains and the Yünkwei Plateau. Although Japanese planes bombed it unmercifully, the Japanese armies were unable to follow the Chinese into this great natural citadel.

In the United States, the "Intermountain West," between the Sierra-Cascades and the Rockies, forms a vast natural citadel. Like most intermontane situations it suffers from relative isolation and poor access (Fig. 39–2).

MIDLAND SITUATION

Most continental areas are, in contrast to the intermontane sites just described, very open, exposed, and easily traversed. To such areas is often applied the term *midland* or open-continental situation.

Probably the classical example of continental situation of the midland type is afforded by Poland. That nation sprawls vaguely over the drainage basin of the Vistula River in almost the exact center of Europe, the world's most troubled continent. Poland has no natural boundaries and has at times extended as far west as the Elbe, and as far east as the Dneiper. After World War I, she occupied the area from the Netza River to the Pripet Marshes. After World War II, she was given the area between the Oder and the Bug rivers. At times she has disappeared from the political map. Invariably she has reappeared— sometimes as a small state; sometimes with a seacoast, sometimes without.

In South America, Paraguay, with her weak midland situation, shows certain resemblances to Poland. In North America the great colonial domain of New France finally succumbed to the weakness inherent in a midland site, and was inundated by the inland spread of the Anglo-American people.

To a certain degree, most of the middle European countries show the effects of their midland continental situation. Germany, Austria, Hungary, Romania, and Yugoslavia are curious mixtures of eastern and western European civilizations. Almost every military, commercial, and

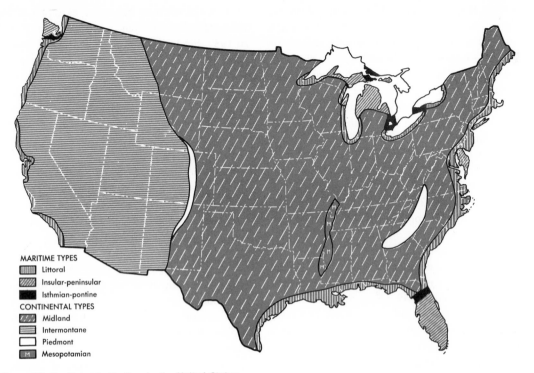

Figure 39–2   Natural situation in the United States.

religious misadventure of the continent has washed over them and left its ruthless imprint upon them. Their political boundaries have expanded, contracted, and wandered over the map like amoebae when viewed under a microscope.

PIEDMONT SITUATION

Where a lowland area lies against the base of a mountain range or some other considerable highland mass, it is said to have *piedmont* or foreland situation. Such areas are deviations from general continental situation because they possess unique environmental characteristics which tend toward special geographic results.

Piedmont areas often become the sites of important lines of travel and traffic moving parallel to the nearby mountains. At intervals these longitudinal routes intersect transverse routes through the mountain passes—a circumstance which often creates a long line of trading cities along the foot of the highlands. In humid regions, a piedmont area often becomes the site of manufacturing because of available water power in the nearby highlands. This may be aided by supplies of coal,

metal ores, timber, and other raw materials yielded from the mountains as well as agricultural and pastoral products from the plains. Examples of this are furnished by the Piedmont Upland along the edge of the Appalachians in eastern United States, the Piemonte at the base of the Alps in northern Italy, and the Romanian-Russian-Polish foreland of the Carpathians in Europe.

In arid regions, piedmont zones take on exceptional importance because generally they are sites where underground water is obtainable. In addition, mountain streams debouching on the piedmont slopes supply surface water for irrigation. Since remote antiquity, therefore, caravan routes have traversed these foreland sites, thereby skirting the rugged mountains and avoiding the desert plains.

One of the best examples of the importance of this type of natural situation is furnished by the so-called "Fertile Crescent" of the Near East. Two of the earliest loci of civilization developed in the Tigris-Euphrates Valley of Iraq and the Nile Valley of Egypt. These areas were separated by the Syrian section of the Arabian Desert. The only easy route from one to the other was by way of the crescent-shaped piedmont zone lying north of the area. Probably as early as 6000 B.C., therefore, this zone had become an important passageway from east to west. Trade cities grew up at the sites of Mosul, Diarbehr, Hama, Homs, and Damascus. Perhaps no site on earth has been fought over more, or has changed hands more often, than this narrow strip of land.

In modern times, railroads and major highways have tended to follow piedmont zones for reasons similar to those which gave them importance in earlier times. An excellent example may be seen in Turkestan where the new Russian Central Asian Railway connects the mountainfoot cities of Askabad, Merv, Bokhara, and Tashkent. Similar to this is the piedmont of the Southern Rockies with its line of cities—Cheyenne, Greeley, Denver, Colorado Springs, Pueblo, Walsenburg, and Trinidad.

RIVERINE SITUATION

One of the most interesting of continental positions is riverine or mesopotamian situation. Sites of this kind consist of lowlands lying between large rivers. Some are often so nearly enclosed by rivers as to be, for all practical purposes, inland or epicontinental "islands." Frequently they are rather isolated and hence have tended to develop a marked provincial individuality. The natural protection enjoyed by such areas caused some of them to become the sites of early civilizations—despite their liability of flood and their poor drainage.

The classical example of between-river sites is Mesopotamia, lying between the Tigris and Euphrates rivers. Farther eastward, the area between the Amu Darya and the Syr Darya is occupied by Uzbekistan, Tadzhikistan, and part of Kazakhstan. Pakistan supplies a striking example in the Punjab (land of five rivers) with its almost incredibly ancient civilization.

Other continents also supply good examples. Australia has its Riverina lying between the Murray and Murrumbidgee rivers. Europe contributes the central Hungarian region between the Tisza and the Danube. Africa exemplifies it in the Ubangi-Congo area; South America with the Entre Rios province of Argentina (between the Uruguay and Parana rivers). In the United States, there are four good examples within the lower Mississippi Valley, namely, the St. Francis, Yazoo, Tensas, and Atchafalaya basins. These riverine areas are enclosed between the Mississippi and tributary streams which parallel it for long distances before effecting a confluence.

MARITIME SITUATION

In marked contrast to continental regions, all maritime areas have in common proximity to the sea. They are subjected to influence by the sea and they are characterized by the adjustments and adaptations which their inhabitants make to this great element of the natural environment. Accordingly, the peoples of maritime areas commonly exhibit a marked interest in the sea, are preoccupied with the seafaring industries of fishing, shipbuilding, marine trading (and sometimes piracy), and participate in naval diplomacy and war.

Maritime sites, however, do not exhibit these traits in equal amounts. The influence of the sea is, at most, only a relative thing. It laps over the margins of the land masses, here strongly, there weakly. Inland, it fades rapidly as the shoreline is left behind and the forces of continentalism are encountered. Coasts, peninsulas, offshore islands, and remote islets far out in the ocean spaces are maritime situations which differ in degree rather than in kind. Isthmuses and narrow straits, however, differ somewhat in kind. In general, some six varieties of maritime situation may be recognized, as follows.

1. Coastal   4. Pelagic
2. Peninsular   5. Pontine
3. Insular   6. Isthmian

COASTAL SITUATION

Littoral situation is possessed by most coastal portions of the continents.[2] Not all coasts, however, are maritime in a geographic sense. Where mountains reach the sea, they may destroy littoral character, as in north California. Desert coasts, as those of western Africa and Australia, also

---

[2] The traits, advantages, and disadvantages of coasts are discussed at length in Chapter 27.

frequently show few littoral characteristics. Land bordering upon frozen oceans, as for instance northern Siberia and northern Canada and most of Antarctica, exhibit few if any of the traits characteristic of coastal situation.

None of the great modern nations has arisen wholly upon a littoral site. The margin of a continent is too narrow a local base, too meagerly equipped in agricultural and mineral resources, to permit the development of great national strength. Portugal, occupying the western coast of the Iberian Peninsula, well illustrates the feeble geographic base supplied by this type of situation. Norway has fared somewhat better, partly by reason of its nearness to rich fishing grounds, and partly by reason of the exceptional energy of its inhabitants. The Netherlands has reclaimed its wet deltaic lands and capitalized upon its location at the mouth of the Rhine, thereby developing notable commerce; but it possesses little national power.

The United States and Brazil are the only examples of large modern nations which have arisen from coastal or seaboard sites. The thirteen American colonies were entirely littoral in situation, but they developed into a great American nation only after they expanded inland and achieved a magnificent continental base. Brazil took its origin in a line of Portuguese settlements on the long narrow littoral of northeastern South America. Eventually, these expanded onto the interior plateau and up the vast Amazon Valley. From this new continental base, Brazil is now developing into a great nation.

The examples of the United States and Brazil are, however, unusual. The case of Phoenicia is more typical. Between 4000 and 2000 B.C., several Phoenic (or Punic) cities arose along the coast of Syria. Collectively, these cities—Tyre, Sidon, Byblos, and others—are usually referred to as Phoenicia. Their sites were for the most part rocky promontories and tiny offshore islands. Behind them rose the wall of the Lebanon Mountains, leaving only a narrow, dissected, overpopulated coastal strip to support these cities. The Lebanons were difficult to cross and were backed mainly by desert areas. Because of this limited hinterland, no strong Punic state developed. The cities became only entrepôts and trade emporia,

unable to maintain control over even such colonies as Carthage, Dreparum, and others. Eventually Phoenicia disappeared and its coastal area was absorbed by an interior Syrian state.

Phoenicia was not an unusual example; indeed, coastal strips are frequently absorbed by continental states behind them. Such has been the fate of Frisia, Dalmatia, Dobruja, the Greek coast of Asia Minor, Esthonia, Latvia, Lithuania, and many other seaboard states. In almost as many instances, however, areas so situated have been invaded by foreign states from overseas and held as colonies or dependencies.

PENINSULAR SITUATION

The principal characteristic of peninsulas is their semidetachment from a continent, without the handicap of extreme isolation. They are areas of relative safety because they lie off the main channels of continental migration and war. Hence, they form areas of refuge and provincialism. Peninsulas, therefore, frequently contain decadent human stocks which have retreated to their semiseclusion before the pressure of more vigorous continental groups of people. The Cornish and Welsh in the peninsulas of western England, the brunette Gaelic-speaking Irish in the peninsulas of Kerry, Galway, Mayo, and Donegal counties, and the Bretons of Brittany illustrate this principle. The Tatars of Cape Apsheron, the Australian aborigines of Cape York and Arnhemland, the pre-Aryan peoples of the Indian Peninsula, the Amerinds of Lower California and the Olympic Peninsula, the Lapps of the Kola Peninsula, and the numerous small ethnic groups of the Balkan Peninsula also illustrate the museum aspect of *peninsular* situation.

When a seafaring nation invades a large land mass, it frequently does so by first occupying the out-thrust peninsular areas. In World War I, Britain invaded Turkey via the Gallipoli Peninsula. In World War II the United States invaded Europe via the Calabrian (Italy) and Cotentin (France) peninsulas. Japan, in her forty-year war to overrun eastern Asia, occupied successively the Liao Peninsula (Kwantung), the Korean Peninsula, Shantung, the Shanghai Promontory, and the Malay Peninsula.

Because of their relative ease of conquest,

small peninsulas are often detached politically from mainland countries and held by outside nations. Spain long held the Florida Peninsula, as Denmark did the Skåne Peninsula of Sweden, Italy the peninsula of Istria, and Britain the Malay Peninsula.

In contrast to these small examples, large peninsulas tend to develop independent national status. Illustrations of this are Korea, Arabia, Greece, Italy, Spain, Denmark, Norway, and Sweden.[3] Even where peninsulas are part of a larger political unit, they are apt to form state or provincial subdivisions of such large units. Examples are supplied by Florida, Nova Scotia, Brittany, Skåne, Baja California, Shantung, Cornwall, Apulia, and Calabria.

INSULAR SITUATION

Islands lying along coasts or upon shallow continental shelves are said to possess *insular* situation. Their principal trait is almost complete detachment from the continent without the handicap of any serious isolation. Islands lying near a continent receive numerous ethnic and cultural contributions from the mainland. Often these ethnic additions are refugees from the continent who, seeking to escape extinction or absorption, find harborage in an insular site. Whereupon, within narrow island confines, these are often nurtured and welded together to form a distinctive racial type and often a superior cultural composite.

Nowhere is this better seen than in Britain. She has been close enough to Europe to permit her to receive promptly the inventions and innovations, and the latest advances in science, literature, and human thought from the continent. Leaders in every line of endeavor have visited her shores. To all intents, she has been a part of Europe during times of peace. During war, however, her insularity has been of immense significance. If she participated in Europe's wars, she was able to choose the time and place of her entry. And in any event she was spared the destruction attendant upon invasion. Only once within the last millennium has Britain been heavily invaded. Through all that period she has been practically free of even the fear of invasion. Thus, she was spared the crushing tax load of maintaining a huge standing army like that of most European states. She was spared, too, the need of oppressive and strong centralized government. Hence, British society was free to evolve in the direction of personal rights and civil liberties.

Many other islands show the melting pot action as well as does Britain. In Sicily, Malta, Madagascar, and Japan, very diverse racial elements have been amalgamated. The result in each case has been to produce a new ethnic type and a somewhat provincial attitude of mind. In the cases of Japan and Britain, this latter has taken the form of a feeling of superiority—doubtless a result in part at least of long freedom from foreign invasion.

The effect the "Air Age" has upon the psychology of island peoples is as yet problematical. During World War II Britain, although actually not invaded, was so thoroughly bombed from the air that her old feeling of security was largely shattered.

Japan, although practically free from invasion for three thousand years, has not been the recipient of much stimulation from the hermit nations which faced her from the continent of Asia. Consequently, she had not evolved much beyond medievalism in her thinking, although she had, after the middle of the nineteenth century, made more progress along material lines than any other Asiatic country. The eventual effect of her defeat in 1945 by American aerial warfare is as yet imponderable.

Small coastal islands are even more easily detached from political control by the mainland than are peninsulas. Japanese seizure of Formosa off the coast of China is an excellent illustration of the ease of such detachment. The Greek islands off the coast of Turkey, French control of Corsica off the coast of Italy, Italy's erstwhile control of Lagosta and other islands along the coast of Yugoslavia are other illustrations. French retention of St. Pierre and Miquelon off the coast of Newfoundland, prolonged holding by Americans of the Isle of Pines off the Cuban coast, Spanish control of Fernando Po off Nigeria and Dutch ownership of Curaçao off Venezuela are further examples.

---

[3] Norway and Sweden formed one nation up to 1905.

Britain, for long the dominant sea power, accumulated a number of coastal islands along the shores of other nations. Hong Kong Island along the China coast, Penang and Singapore off Malaya, the Channel Islands off France, and Pantellaria off the coast of Italy are a few examples.

PELAGIC SITUATION

Tiny islets, atolls, island chains, and other remote bits of land far out in the oceanic expanses illustrate *pelagic* situation (Fig. 27–3). Continental man is a land animal. On coasts, peninsulas, and islands, he becomes somewhat amphibian. In pelagic situations, however, he is almost a completely marine creature.

For instance, inland Afghanistan has no navy, but every Afghan from the cradle is a soldier. The coastal Dutch and the insular English are equally good fighters on land or sea. The pelagic South Sea Isles, however, have produced no armies; every Polynesian is a congenital sailor, able and eager to man a war canoe.

At its worst, this type of natural situation is manifested by St. Helena, Tristan da Cunha, and Easter Island; at its best by the Azores, Bermuda, and Hawaii. Intermediate are the Faeroes, the Galapagos, and Mauritius Island. Sometimes pelagic islands serve as penal or exile sites. In the days of sailing vessels they served as watering and victualing points. Today, they are valued chiefly as fueling, radio, or cable stations, or as airplane landing points.

PONTINE SITUATION

Narrow waterways or straits connecting seas or oceans have been important sites since the dawn of ocean navigation. They are the jugular veins of sea trade. Their importance stems from the fact that they act as constrictors of seaways, and from the ease with which they may be controlled by the nation holding them.

In ancient Greek times, navigation centered in the eastern Mediterranean and the Black Sea. Accordingly the Greeks colonized and held the shores of the Strait of Messina (Scylla and Charybdis), the Strait of Otranto, the Dardanelles, the Bosporus, and the Strait of Kerch. Such localities may be said to be *pontine* or bridge sites.

After the time of Columbus, commerce moved out onto the oceans, whereupon a new set of points possessing pontine situation came into importance. At present the principal "bottlenecks" of ocean traffic are the straits of Gibraltar, Bab el Mandeb, and Malacca, the Dardanelles-Bosporus Passage, Öresund-Kattegat-Skagerrak Passage, the English Channel, the Tunisian Channel, and the Shetland Passage. To these may be added the Antarctic passages around the ends of the three southern continents.

It is significant that Britain, which was long the world's dominant sea power, has a naval base on or near most of these sites. At the Strait of Gibraltar, one side is controlled by Britain, the other by the international zone of Tangier. At the Bosporus-Dardanelles, international control was tried once and may be tried again. International control may be the eventual fate of most, if not all, such pontine sites.

ISTHMIAN SITUATION

A natural situation consisting of an isthmus is uncommon but one which may be fraught with considerable significance. Its significance arises from the fact that an isthmus is a portion of a continent so narrow that maritime influences may lap clear across it.

The isthmuses of Panama and Suez are among the world's most significant commercial sites. Their significance has been enhanced by the fact that canals have been cut through them. Indeed, the first navigation canal in the world was probably an ancient Egyptian waterway constructed about 2000 B.C. not far from the location of the Suez Canal.

Germany, in order to obtain control of the Kiel Isthmus, attacked Denmark, annexed Schleswig-Holstein, and dug the Kiel Canal. This she protected by the Kiel naval base at one end and the island fortress of Helgoland near the other. The Isthmus of Tehuantepec in Mexico is crossed by a rail route, but it fails to be of great importance chiefly because of the nearby narrower Panamanian Isthmus. Similarly, the Kra Isthmus is eclipsed by the Strait of Malacca.

France might be said to possess *isthmian* situation on a grand scale but admittedly only to a relatively weak degree. Lying athwart the isthmus of western Europe, she faces two great

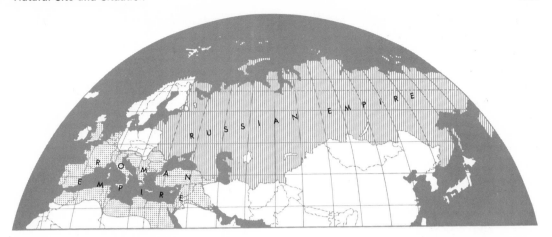

Figure 39–3   The ancient Roman and the modern Russian empires contrasted as to natural situation.

bodies of water. Facing the Atlantic and the North Sea, France developed strong interests in fishing and maritime commerce. Facing the Mediterranean, she crossed that narrow sea and developed a huge African land empire. Situated so as to intercept all traffic between Spain and central Europe, France was also crossed by the ancient trade routes running overland from the Mediterranean to the English Channel. In modern times, these routes are marked by trunk railways and a system of canals connecting the Rhone River with the Garonne, Loire, Seine, and Rhine. Perhaps largely because of these reasons, France was the first modern nation to emerge from medieval chaos, and today occupies what is perhaps the most advantageous situation in Europe.

OBJECTIVES OF NATIONAL EXPANSION

CONTINENTAL NATIONS

The U.S.S.R. may be regarded as the epitome of continentality. In climate, race, culture, and economic interests, she reflects her continental situation. Comprising approximately half of Europe, Russia long constituted a bulwark of western culture against the adjacent continent of Asia. For more than a thousand years, however, the Russians have sought to obtain a satisfactory coastal outlet to the ocean. Thwarted in this by the powers of western Europe, the Russian Empire expanded some 4,000 miles across Asia to achieve a rather unsatisfactory outlet on the Pacific. Within this magnificent transcontinental situa-

tion the modern Soviet Union has slowly developed enormous power.

This perhaps illustrates the tendency of all strong continental nations to achieve a transcontinental situation (Fig. 39–3). The United States, starting from the Atlantic Seaboard, followed her "manifest destiny" across North America to the Pacific. Brazil expanded nearly 3,000 miles across South America, but was stopped some 350 miles from the Pacific by the wall-like Andes. Germany expanded southward into Europe as far as possible and then achieved transcontinental power through her "Axis" alliance with Italy. Not content with this, she allied herself with Japan and attempted to extend her power clear across Eurasia.

MARITIME NATIONS

In contrast to the *transcontinental* goal of all continental powers, the ultimate goal of all maritime nations would seem to be expansion in such a way as to achieve *circum-marine* situation. This type of situation comprises all the margins of a sea together with the included peninsulas and islands.

Ancient Greece was a growth about the Aegean Sea, and later the Ionian and Black seas also. The Roman Empire circled the entire Mediterranean Basin (Fig. 39–3), in much the same manner as the Spanish colonial empire circled the American Mediterranean (Caribbean) some 1,500 years later.

Sweden, under King Gustaf Adolf, in the seventeenth century, attempted to convert the

Baltic into a Swedish lake. Denmark, Britain, and Germany have variously tried to become circummarine about the North Sea. The primary expansion aim of Japan after the main islands were consolidated was first to expand completely around the Sea of Japan. Later, she attempted to encircle all of the East Asiatic seas.

The situation of Italy is a complex one: the northern part is continental, the Riviera is littoral, the southern part is peninsular, Sicily and Sardinia are insular. The annexation of Rhodes, Zara, Lagosta, Albania, and the contraposed coast of Libya, together with a demand for Nice, Tunisia, Corsica, and Dalmatia, indicate that, prior to World War II, Italy intended to convert the entire central Mediterranean into an Italian lake —a circum-marine or perithalassic site of superb proportions.

Out of World War II emerged three preeminent world powers. Among these, Russia with most of her coasts bordering on seas frozen during much of the year, is the greatest of all military land powers. Britain with the open sea on all sides of her island site has, through most of modern times, been the greatest of all naval powers. The United States, extending across a continent, and fronting on two navigable oceans, is both a great land and a great sea power. Their spheres of surface power are well defined. The great contest at present is over control of the world's airways.

X

Perpetual Trans- formation

The trilogy of geography, namely, the physical impactors, the cultural impactors, and people, discussed and portrayed diagrammatically in Chapter 1, are in continual flux, separately and collectively. Maps really need dates on them for they represent but "snapshots" in the long corridor of time. On such portrayals one finds landmarks of the present and the past, depicted in their distributional patterns at the times selected. The persistence of some natural and cultural creations may be shown for successive periods. However, the dynamics of change are striking, be they physical, economic, social, or political. One important aspect of such change, often overlooked, is that man himself with the power of volition, the power to choose, has enacted a big role. With the recognition of such a concept, that man is the ecological dominant, plans for future development of the environment in its broadest sense become imperative.

40

Ecological Succession Within the Region

No two localities possess identical natural and cultural environments. In traversing any considerable expanse of the earth's surface, it is evident that the appearance and character of the landscape vary markedly from place to place. In spite of this, large areas are sufficiently homogeneous in many of their characteristics to possess geographic unity in general terms. Such areas are usually known as regions.

One of the principal functions of geography is to recognize, describe, and analyze the regions of the earth's surface. Into the analysis of any region, there invariably enter three factors: (1) the natural environment, (2) the population—its character, race, and numbers, and (3) the regional ecology with its geographic relationships and its expression in a cultural landscape. Any given geographic region is distinguished and set off from other adjacent regions by three things: (1) a natural environment distinctive in character and appearance, (2) a population manifesting a characteristic density, distribution, and racial make-up, and (3) a specific geographic adjustment of that population to the physical milieu. These three traits of regions—natural environment, population, and ecological arrangement— are unlike in their degree of fixity or permanence.

Except when viewed over a long period of time, the natural environment of a region is in most respects comparatively fixed and unchanging. This is true regarding certain of its broader aspects such as position, relief, general soil type, and, to a lesser degree, climate. The biota and its ecology, are, on the contrary, subject to marked change. Throughout recorded history, almost every region has exhibited significant changes in the number and content of its plants, lower animals, and human population. Similarly, the ecological relations to environment by which this population has maintained itself have changed. As a consequence, the cultural landscape, which is the tangible expression of such ecological relations, has evolved, undergoing progressive or retrogressive evolution. The evolution of the cultural aspects of a region may be called its *ecological succession*, and the various local sequences occurring in the evolution of any region may be termed its *sequent occupance*.[1]

ECOLOGICAL SUCCESSION

Many economists hold that there is a tendency for society to pass through an economic cycle wherein more complex forms of industry constantly replace simpler and more lowly forms. This process is often regarded as a normal result of man's more or less spontaneous cultural development.[2] This explanation may be challenged for a number of reasons, chief of which is the observed reluctance of peoples to change their basic ways of doing things. Witness the attempt of colonists to transplant the economic patterns

[1] D. S. Whittlesey, "Sequent Occupance," *Annals of the Association of American Geographers*, Vol. 19, 1929, pp. 162–165.

[2] Anthropologists look upon culture as a mode of life —the aggregate of the thoughts and deeds of a people. This round of life in its entire sweep of individual activities is the basic phenomenon to which the historian, the sociologist, and the anthropologist give the name, *culture*.

of the mother country to their new environment. Regional change is a reality, but the explanation for its occurrence would seem to be geographic rather than primarily economic.

The inhabitants of any region support themselves by exploiting or capitalizing certain elements of their physical milieu, and they tend to maintain this relation as long as it will support them. Whenever the resource basis of the relationship is changed, a new set of industries comes into existence and with it certain resulting social changes. Before long the occupance pattern of the region is recast and remotivated.

Ecological succession or geographic readjustment in the past seems to have occurred in one of two ways: (1) it may have been accomplished through invasion by a people from the outside who possessed a different culture; the region's inhabitants may have been exterminated to make room for the invaders, as was the case of the Argentine Pampa or they may have been absorbed by intermarriage with their conquerors as in Chile with the Araucanians and Spaniards, or symbiotic relations may have been worked out wherein the two groups remain distinct but mutually assisting inhabitants of the area, as with the Boers and Kafirs in Transvaal; or (2) it may have been accomplished from within, through an increasing pressure of population upon the particular resources being used, as in Great Britain.

Throughout human history, increase in population pressure has tended to produce regional saturation unless drained away by disease, famine, or war.[3] India is a case in point. In a total area less than half the size of the United States live about 532 million people—a population density five times the world average. India faces a future population growth of nearly 75 million per decade. Moreover, one-third of the people dwell on a mere 6 percent of the land: average densities in such areas exceed 800 persons per square mile and in some places the densities are from 1,200 to 2,250 per square mile. Each farmer averages only four-fifths of an acre of land. Thus it is clear that the country is overpopulated. A high death rate accompanied by a high birth rate; the recurrence of epidemics of plague, cholera, smallpox; occasional epidemics, such as that of influenza in 1918–1919, when at least 8.5 million

people, or five or six times the rate in the United States, died; the prevalence of malaria,[4] typhoid fever, hookworm; and the periodic visitation of famine—all these point clearly to the operation of the natural checks on the growth of population.

Where saturation has occurred under any given form of geographic adjustment, stagnation in the life of a region has ensued and with it at least a temporary decline in the level of living. The advent of timely and significant inventions and technological improvements tends to stave off a falling level of living. Some of these may do more; they may so change the economic process as to call into use hitherto unutilized resources, with the result that new ecological relations are set up. Eventually the geographic basis of society is shifted and a new stage of occupance initiated.

IS THERE A GEOGRAPHIC CYCLE?

This suggests that there exists a geographic cycle, wherein certain socioeconomic forms tend to replace one another as the environmental basis of society is shifted from one resource to another. Generally, the most accessible and attractive resources are exploited first and the less accessible and attractive ones left for a later date. Consequently, the sequence of occupance in any region will be a resultant of the resource equipment of the environment as balanced against the cultural equipment of the population. An arid area may, depending upon the culture of its occupants, engage only in grazing; later people may enter who have machinery for tapping relatively deep-lying sources of water and grazing may be replaced by irrigation agriculture. In the Occident many areas

[3] Frequently emigration is considered a factor contributing to the solution of population pressure. Generally speaking this is fallacious, though in the case of Ireland it is true. Elsewhere in Europe, "emigration has been accompanied by a growth in population at home." See Warren S. Thompson, *Danger Spots in World Population* (New York, Alfred A. Knopf, Inc., 1939), p. 133.

[4] Malaria was virtually eliminated through the splendid work of the World Health Organization during the 1960's.

have passed through mining, irrigation agriculture (supplemented by dry farming), and commerce in the order named; some have progressed omitting either mining or irrigation agriculture. The Mormon pioneers, for example, did not engage in mining, though rich deposits of metallic minerals were present in the Wasatch and Oquirrh mountains which border the Salt Lake Oasis on the east and west respectively. Fearing that mining would break down their plan of systematically colonizing the Great Basin, the Mormon leaders so discouraged prospecting that minerals were scarcely touched until 1862—fifteen years after the pioneers entered the region, and then only by the soldiers (non-Mormons) stationed at Fort Douglas. The Mormons refrained from prospecting until the Church approved it following completion of the Union Pacific Railway in 1869.[5] On the other hand, when mining was booming at Virginia City in west central Nevada after 1859, agriculture was not even attempted. The site lacked both water and timber. Every necessity of life and luxury was brought from the outside. Central Colorado today is in the throes of an interesting succession. The processions of ore trains that once rumbled out of the rich canyons of Boulder Creek, the Platte, and the Arkansas are memories, and hundreds of miles of track have been torn up and sold for scrap. The leading railroad from Leadville to Denver has been abandoned. Denver, however, has not become a decadent mining town with grass growing in many of its streets as in the case of Leadville and Cripple Creek. The water and fertile soils in many of the valleys of its tributary area have permitted the development of agriculture which gives employment to more people than the mines ever did. Denver has become the center of a great agricultural region. There are areas in the arid West that have passed through the hunting, pastoral, agricultural (dry land), mining, industrial and commercial stages. Therefore, in arid regions human culture rather than physical environment appears to be the decisive factor in determining the mode of occupance.

Thus it appears that generalizations prescribing specified orderly stages in ecological succession have many exceptions. According to Whittlesey,[6] "normal sequences are rare, perhaps

only ideal, because extraneous forces are likely to interfere with the normal course, altering either its direction or rate, or both." He suggests that these breaches may be brought about either by some element of the natural environment becoming abruptly and profoundly modified as by severe earthquakes, floods, insect pests, volcanic eruptions, and the like or they may be induced by man-engendered interruptions in the cultural order. He writes that

. . . shifts in political boundaries, revolutions, or often mere enactment of laws; movements of population which carry with them mores and attitudes novel to their new habitat, or create social friction; the introduction of new technology; changes in means of communication which alter physical and mental contact with outside regions; all these are capable of breaking or knotting the thread of sequent occupance.

The following cycle, nevertheless, has characterized a number of areas in the humid Central Lowland of the United States. The first inhabitants were Indians who were hunters but who supplemented their hunting activities by a little hoe agriculture. On the prairies this stage was often followed by the pastoral stage wherein white men grazed their domesticated animals directly upon the grassland. Where forest was the natural vegetation, white men did not engage in pastoralism but went directly into agriculture after first clearing the tree cover or at least parts of it. They planted cereals, especially corn. This they marketed principally in the form of swine and cattle. Since the animals could furnish their own transportation, large numbers of them were driven over the Appalachian Mountains to Philadelphia, Baltimore, and other eastern cities and south into the Cotton Belt. The first cattle were driven from the Ohio Valley to Baltimore in 1805. They went in droves of 150 to 500. Hogs were driven from the region soon after 1812. Slaughtering for shipment down the Ohio and Mississippi rivers began about 1820 and Cincinnati became a great pork-packing center. As transportation facilities developed in the Middle

---

[5] See footnote 4, Chap. 35.
[6] Derwent Whittlesey, *op. cit.,* pp. 164–165.

West, the market for live animals became much better and grain could be grown for export. Canals (1830–1850) and railroads (1840–1860), along with the public land policy, ushered in the era of extensive agriculture.[7] In many areas this era was dominated by grain farming. The year 1850 is the date usually accepted as beginning the forty-year period "during which time the great grain fields were brought under cultivation."[8] Per capita wheat production during much of this period was about 50 percent above normal consumption. Eventually, grain farming was superseded by general or mixed farming over the greater part of the region. This is a type wherein the production of hay and feed crops and the fattening of livestock or even dairying are balanced against cereal production. The American Corn Belt is essentially this type of region today and it will probably remain so in areas some distance from large urban agglomerations. Near cities, dairying replaced general farming, less land and more labor being used in production. Dairying persisted while farms shrank in size. This brings us to the present. With increasing population land becomes too valuable for this type of farming and is given over to market gardening, both out-of-doors and under glass. Dairying then shifts into the next outlying belt, gradually displacing general farming which locates in the zone adjoining but farther from the city (Fig. 40–1). Ultimately, urban expansion may so enhance land values in the immediate environs of the city that no kind of agriculture is really profitable. Greenhouses tend to move out into the dairying belt providing, of course, that good hard-surface roads connect them with the city markets. This succession is excellently illustrated in the Indianapolis and the Cleveland areas.

In the Midwest, if a district becomes dominantly manufactural and commercial in its interests, cities, towns, and villages dot the land thickly. Between the urban areas, some of the land is utilized by commercial dairy and poultry farms and by market gardens. An increasing proportion of it, however, is occupied by families, members of which commute daily to offices, mills and factories in nearby cities and towns. Thus the face of America is changing. Suburban growth has been spectacular, with population increasing

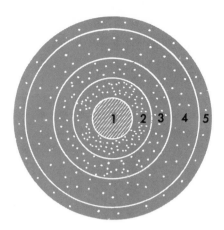

1. The City Itself
2. Greenhouses and Market Gardens
3. Market Gardens and Fruit Farms
4. Dairying and Intensive Agriculture—Potatoes, etc.
5. General Farming—Grain, Hay, Livestock

Figure 40–1   Idealized zones of agricultural production about a city in the United States.

several times the rate for urban areas. New York City suburbs have grown more than five times faster than the city. Thus, tens of millions of American adults use passenger cars on an average day. American workers are transported to and from work primarily by automobile. In a study of workers in a Chicago plant, it was found that a considerable number lived sixteen to sixty-seven miles from the plant, commuting daily in their own cars. They greatly preferred to live outside the big city.

In urban centers everywhere, the influence of population growth is apparent, and the sequent occupance has frequently been almost dramatic. For example, some areas which have become cities have been in turn the scene of (1) hunting and fishing (Indian and pioneer), (2) agriculture, (3) commerce, (4) manufacturing, and (5) sometimes mining. Cleveland, Ohio, exemplifies the urban phases of sequent occupance very well indeed.

CLEVELAND, OHIO

When Moses Cleaveland, head surveyor for the Connecticut Land Company, reached the site on

[7] B. H. Hibbard, *A History of the Public Land Policies* (New York, The Macmillan Company, 1924), p. 544.
[8] *Ibid.*, p. 539.

July 22, 1796, he learned that seminomadic Chippewa, Delaware, Ottawa, and Seneca Indians made their winter camps along the Cuyahoga River and lived by trapping and hunting. As white settlers supplanted the Indians, the area was cleared of its forest growth and planted with corn and wheat. Thus agriculture was the second stage of succession. The town grew very slowly. In 1800 it had 25 inhabitants; in 1820, 600; and by 1850 only 17,034.

Its strategic location on natural routes of travel, however, assured it a place in the commercial sun as soon as transportation should be developed in the trans-Appalachian region. It borders Lake Erie at the mouth of the Cuyahoga River and is on the best through-route between eastern and central United States; it is also the northern land terminus of the principal lowland route connecting the coal fields of Pennsylvania with the Lake Superior iron ore region. Hence it is at the intersection of two heavy lines of traffic. In short, Cleveland is located where it is easily accessible to many large markets of the country, to the important raw materials producing section of the nation, to the chief coal field, and to the most productive iron ore region. Cleveland received its first impetus to prominence and began the third stage of its evolution (commerce) when the Ohio Canal, connecting it with central and southern Ohio, was opened in 1834. As the northern terminus for the canal, the city soon became the most important transshipping port between the Ohio country and the eastern markets via Lake Erie, the Erie Canal, and the Hudson River. Then came the railroads; the lake shore favored east-west lines and the wide valley offered a splendid opportunity for the easy approach from the south. Already a lake-canal port, its strategic position along the railway "water-level route" from Chicago to Buffalo placed Cleveland in a still more favorable position for commerce and industry.

After 1850, manufacturing, the fourth stage, became important. Orth[9] points out:

Graphically the steps have been as follows: two decades of hand industry, two decades of [simple] manufacture, preparing products of the farm for the market, followed by two decades of the development of iron and steel, which development is continued to the present day. The decade of 1870 was the decade of oil; the decade of 1880 that of meat packing and electrical appliances; the decade of 1890 that of clothing and paints, and the decade of 1900 has been the decade of the automobile.

The decades since 1910 have been characterized by *diversity*.

POPULATION SUPPORTING CAPACITY

Except where superimposed from the outside, changes in a region's ecology are closely tied up with changes in its population density. Indeed, this latter may frequently be the major cause for ecological succession. This is because a region tends to increase in population until saturation is reached, whereupon it must choose among (1) a decline in the level of living which means hardship and catastrophe, (2) birth control, (3) a geographic readjustment in economy, or (4) war. The various countries facing this problem have accepted one of these alternatives. India and China are examples of the first; France is of the second (its population is essentially static); Great Britain, Germany, and Japan are of the third; and Germany, Japan, and Italy are of the fourth. It should be realized, however, that no real relief can come to any overpopulated country today except by the restriction of births. England, which has run almost the entire known gamut of sequent occupance, is overpopulated and like most of the countries of western Europe is practicing birth control. And Japan, which until her defeat in 1945 was desperately attempting to solve her population problem by more intensive tillage, by reclaiming more land, by improving methods of farming, by selecting better yielding varieties of seed, by embracing industry, by engaging in commerce, and finally by resorting to war, at last appears to realize that birth control is the ultimate solution of the problem.

Often there arises the question, "What density of population represents saturation for a region?" The answer to this query hinges upon two factors: the richness of the natural resources, and the kind of geographic relations under

[9] S. P. Orth, *A History of Cleveland, Ohio* (Cleveland, S. J. Clark Publishing Co., 1910), p. 638.

which the population lives. Where the former can be precisely evaluated, the latter remains a variable factor. Consequently, no one degree of population density represents permanent saturation for a region.[10] In fact, overpopulation in one stage of ecological succession may be underpopulation for the following stage. Stated another way, population tends to increase up to the limit of the supporting power of the environment (land), on a given stage of the arts, and for a given standard of living.

As long as a region is occupied by people who obtain their sustenance by hunting, fishing, and gathering wild fruits and seeds, there is a definite upper limit to its population supporting capacity, a limit which may not be exceeded without conspicuous misery and threat of famine. While regions differ markedly in their wealth of native game and fruits, even the richest areas are able to support only a sparse population by these resources alone. On the outskirts of the habitable areas, perhaps seventy to two-hundred square miles are required to maintain one person under primitive food-gathering adjustments to the environment; extremely favorable circumstances allow of a population of only one to several per square mile. As a consequence, barbaric populations never achieve any noteworthy density of numbers.

In the pastoral stage, the population supporting capacity of land is appreciably greater than in the wild-food-gathering stage. A square mile area, however, when used pastorally, is compelled to do double duty in that it must nourish both man and beast. Grass is a far less efficient product of the soil in terms of nutriment than are grains. It is no wonder, then, that 2 to 5 persons per square mile represent a heavy population for a strictly pastoral area.

Agricultural adjustment to the physical environment permits a manifold increase in population as compared with the pastoral stage. The population which can be supported by agriculture varies with the natural environment, the level of living, and the cultural milieu. For example in Iowa, perhaps 20 or 25 persons per square mile are maintained by agriculture, but in Denmark or Romania perhaps twice that number. Agricultural China supports an average popula-

tion of no less than 1,500 persons per square mile of farm land, portions of the Ganges Valley in Eastern Bengal average from 1,200 to 2,250, and the cultivated and settled parts of Egypt average about 1,800.

These high Oriental densities have been achieved, however, only at great sacrifice in level of living—in fact, by reducing life close to the most meager existence. Consequently, they are to be regarded as undesirable. Moreover, such population densities are by no means entirely the product of agricultural adjustment. In considerable measure they are supported by auxiliary cottage industries, trading, and other forms of adjustment. This leads one to suspect that under socially healthful conditions, agricultural populations cannot well exceed 500 per square mile if, indeed, they can reach this figure.

The industrial stage, in turn, ordinarily brings a greatly augmented capacity for supporting human numbers. The Saar Basin with approximately 1,100 persons to the square mile is said to have 70 percent of its population engaged in coal mining, iron and steel making and in numerous finishing industries. The number estimated as being dependent upon manufacturing is about 500 persons per square mile. From the large population in the Saar, as in the Ruhr Valley and Lancashire, one may conclude that 500 to 800 people per square mile may be supported in the industrial stage of development.

In the commercial stage, area loses most of its significance and the quality of geographic location becomes the dominant factor. Vast populations, if adjusted commercially to their environment may, therefore, be crowded into very small spaces as in London, New York, or Hamburg. Manhattan Island sustains nearly 2 million inhabitants on about 22 square miles, an average of approximately 100,000 per square mile, and this on an area where once only a few hundred

[10] The culture of a people must enter into any consideration of this problem. It has been said that it is not easy to decide at what point a given country becomes overpopulated, though that point has obviously long since been reached in India and China. But in the Western world the prevailing conception seems to be that population is too great when its size begins to lower the standard of living to which it is accustomed.

Indians could exist. The ecological capacity of a commercial location, therefore, is evidently not limited by area and local resources, but by volume of trade which depends in large measure upon the hinterland served.

From the foregoing it is evident that "every advance to a higher state of civilization has meant a progressive decrease in the amount of land necessary for the support of the individual, and a progressive increase in the relations between man and his habitat."[11] The relation of population capacity to area in the several stages of ecological succession may be summarized as follows.

Hunting Stage

"Hunter tribes on the outskirts of the habitable area as in Arctic America and Siberia require from 70 to 200 square miles per capita; in arid lands, like the Kalahari Desert and Patagonia, 40 to 200 square miles per capita: in choice districts and combining with the chase some primitive agriculture, as did the Cherokee, Shawnee and Iroquois Indians, the Dyaks of Borneo and the Papuans of New Guinea, ½ to 2 square miles per capita."

Pastoral Stage

"Pastoral nomads show a density of from 2 to 5 to the square mile; practising some agriculture, as in Kordofan and Sennar districts of eastern Sudan, 10 to 15 to the square mile."[12]

Agricultural Stage

Extensive—26 to 125 to the square mile.
Intensive—125 to 500 to the square mile.

Industrial Stage

Five hundred to eight hundred to the square mile in industrial districts in modern Europe—Belgium, France, England, Germany.

Commercial Stage

Several thousand to the square mile.

REGIONS OF ARRESTED DEVELOPMENT

From what has been said, it might be supposed that all regions have exhibited a conspicuous succession in their geography. This, however, is not always the case. Some areas, especially those in restrictive environments, manifest much the same human ecology today as must have characterized them generations ago. This does not mean that they have not experienced some change; in every case they have come into contact with European civilization and this has invariably meant some alteration in the mode of living of the inhabitants; what it does mean is that nature is so hard and unyielding as to present positive checks to ecological succession. That this is so will be noted from the following two examples.

NORTHWEST GREENLAND

The Polar Eskimo, a group of about 270 persons living in northwest Greenland, are the northernmost people in the world and are separated by hundreds of miles from their nearest neighbors. Their relation to the natural environment is simple and direct. W. Elmer Ekblaw[13] wrote:

A chain of favorable conditions, unusual for regions so far north, permits continuous human occupancy of their country. The racing tides through Smith Sound . . . prevent the formation of ice even in coldest and calmest winters; the open water in relative proximity to the land tempers the circumpolar cold; at the near-freezing temperature of the water the carbon dioxide content is high. The rich store of carbon dioxide and the continuous sunlight for four months of the year favor the growth of an abundant phytoplankton, the ultimate source of food of all the higher forms of life. Numerous birds and animals frequent the adjoining seawaters. A few species of land animals, vitally critical in the domestic economy of the Polar Eskimo, feed on the sunny grass covered slopes enriched by the guano from the bird-rookeries. The land and sea-animals supply the Eskimos with all resources necessary for life.

Consequently the Polar Eskimo are hunters, not because of low mental capacity but because they have no other source of food, clothing, fuel, light, or material for artifacts. They are entirely and exclu-

[11] Ellen C. Semple, *Influences of Geographical Environment* (New York, Henry Holt and Company, Inc., 1941), pp. 64–65.

[12] *Ibid.*, p. 65.

[13] W. Elmer Ekblaw, "The Geographic Response Complex of a Primitive Polar People," *Annals of the Association of American Geographers*, Vol. 17, 1927, pp. 25–26.

sively carnivorous, their sole food being the flesh and blubber of the animals they hunt and kill. Their fuel and light come from blubber burned in their small lamps. Their clothing is made from furs and skins and feathers, all tanned soft and pliable by chewing. Practically all their equipment for the trail, the chase, and the home is from animal parts.

The sites of their villages both summer and winter are determined by conditions of relief, exposure, temperature, wind, snowfall, and ice-lay. They must be near, and seasonably accessible, to the haunts of the game. Their winter houses are of stone, their summer tents of sealskins, and their temporary shelters on the trail or in the hunting camps are of wind-packed snow. Their trails and travels are dependent upon the condition of the sea—whether open or covered with ice. Their sole means of transportation on land and ice is by dog-sledge, and the sledges and the methods of harnessing, hitching, and driving the dogs have been adapted to the physical conditions of the trail. The kayak, distinctly constructed in response to local conditions, is their one way of transportation over open sea.

When first discovered by John Ross in 1818, the Polar Eskimo had lived in isolation so long that they had forgotten their origin and believed themselves to be the only people in the world. They displayed amazement and terror at the sight of white men.

While they were visited by later expeditions and occasional whalers, the next event of outstanding importance was the arrival of a small number of Eskimo from North Baffinland who had learned of them and had set out to join them. After a migration lasting several years during which they suffered terribly, a few survivors finally arrived and were adopted by the Polar Eskimo.

When Peary made his dash to the Pole, he received invaluable assistance from the Polar Eskimo. As a means of expressing his gratitude, he furnished them with firearms, steel knives, files, and wool. Some years later a trading station was established at North Star Bay, thus terminating the long dominance of solely local conditions. It cannot be denied that native culture has been profoundly modified by the introduction of foreign equipment and customs. But northwest Greenland will not experience any pageant of sequent occupance; in this respect it must forever

be a retarded region. Nature has reserved it for the occupancy of hunters and fishers.

NORTHWESTERN AMAZONIA

In northwestern Amazonia just beyond the borders of Brazil and between the Yapurá and Putumayo rivers (73° to 75° W. and 0° to 2° S.) dwell the Witotos. The region is claimed by both Colombia and Peru but is administered by neither.

The Witotos are omnivorous; they collect wild fruits, nuts, and the tender shoots of the cabbage palm; they catch insects, lizards, snakes, turtles, rats, and mice, all of which they eat with avidity. They also gather honey from hollow trees. Of domesticated animals they have none save the dog. They are hunters par excellence, procuring large game-deer and tapirs with light spears of cane equipped with barbs and poisoned points, and birds and smaller mammals—peccaries, sloths, monkeys, and others—with darts from blowguns. They also employ nets, traps, snares, deadfalls, and concealed pits. The Witotos supplement game with fish which they catch in dip nets and traps but which they procure mostly by poison.

A primitive type of agriculture is carried on; the men clear the forest but the women actually grow the crops of corn, peanuts, peppers, pineapples, plantains, sweet potatoes, coca, and tobacco. Yucca is their staple crop.

The Witotos store no food for times of scarcity; when food is available, they gorge themselves; when it is scarce or absent, they endure hunger philosophically.

They build their houses away from the rivers (the chief highways) and conceal the approaching paths in many crafty ways. They do not work stone, leather, or metals.

Each clan has its own community dwelling, a chief, and recognized hunting and fishing grounds, and it guards these against encroachment by neighboring groups.

The Witotos had no contacts with white people until the beginning of the automobile era. The demand for rubber for tires caused Amazonia, the original habitat of *Hevea brasiliensis*, to boom. Labor, of course, was scarce. Hence the ruthless white exploiters forced the Indians to gather rubber. Though the Witotos were terribly abused, the world did not learn of it until 1909, when the "Putumayo atrocities" acquired a notoriety paralleled only by that of the Belgian Congo. During the dozen years from 1900 to 1911, the Putumayo output of four thousand tons of crude rubber cost thirty thousand native lives.

The rubber industry here is no longer of major importance and the Witotos once more dwell in comparative isolation in the rain forest. They cling tenaciously to their traditional manner of life and, if primitive man survives anywhere unaffected by modern civilization, it is here.

REGIONS OF CHANGING ECOLOGY

Although some areas have suffered arrested development and the adjustments of man to environment therein have long remained nearly static, most regions have experienced a veritable pageant of geographic adjustment and readjustment. The following rather detailed examples may advantageously be given as a supplement to the brief accounts presented in the earlier pages of this chapter.

THE HIGH PLAINS (LLANO ESTACADO) OF TEXAS

Northwestern Texas consists of an upland plain from three thousand to five thousand feet above sea level. It is primarily a vast slope covered with unconsolidated silt with smaller quantities of sand and gravel which have been spread over it by overloaded streams from the Rockies. The land surface (one of the flattest in nature) slopes almost imperceptibly toward the east until the "break of the plains" is reached. This "break" forms a ragged escarpment which descends abruptly to the rolling lowlands on the east.

The plains are virtually unscored by erosion except where the Canadian River and a few minor streams cross from west to east in broad, deep valleys. The Canadian River has cut a valley nearly one thousand feet deep and five to twenty miles wide at the top.[14]

This area, clad with an even cover of grama and buffalo grass (short grass), was originally the feeding ground of vast herds of bison. Antelope and smaller forms of steppe life were also plentiful. Indians possessed the region, depending for a living on the great herds of buffalo,

though they supplemented the meat diet with a few roots and berries. The bison was a general purpose animal supplying, besides food, clothing, shelter, and fuel.

Early in the nineteenth century, there was some travel across the Southern High Plains by white men enroute from Arkansas to the Southwest via the Canadian River. During the period 1840–1865, the Santa Fe Trail crossed the Great Plains just north of the Llano Estacado. These routes, however, had little effect upon the economy of the Indians, and the region was little disturbed by the white man until after the Civil War. Shortly after 1865, white hunters began the wholesale extermination of the bison, killing huge numbers for food for railroad construction gangs and for hides which were in great demand in the East for coats, robes, belts for machinery, and other purposes. The buffalo robe became a common sight in the average home throughout the East.[15] Within twenty years the buffalo was exterminated in the wild state. With its disappearance, the Indians lost their chief support and became dependent on the white man. Soon they were rounded up and removed to reservations elsewhere.[16]

[14] Nevin M. Fenneman, *Physiography of Western United States* (New York, McGraw-Hill Book Company, Inc., 1931), p. 22.

[15] "Among the earliest freight shipments from the rail heads of the continental railroads were bales of buffalo skins that could now for the first time seek a remote market. The swain of the seventies did his winter courting in the moderate space afforded by his cutter, and warmed by the generous thickness of the buffalo robe." From Frederic L. Paxson, *History of the American Frontier* (Boston, Houghton Mifflin Company, 1924), p. 535.

[16] Thus contact with the white race changed everything for the Indian. The following quotation dealing with the Omaha tribe is applicable to possibly all Great Plains Indians:

"The environment was changing rapidly, and the changes brought confusion of mind to the old people as well as to many in mature life. The beliefs of the fathers no longer applied to the conditions which confronted the people. All that they formerly had relied on as stable had been swept away. The buffalo, which they had been taught was given them as an inexhaustible food supply, had been destroyed by agencies new and strange." From A. C. Fletcher and F. La Flesche, "The Omaha Tribe," *Twenty-seventh Annual Report* (Washington, Bureau of American Ethnology, 1911), p. 29.

During the last third of the nineteenth century the second stage of succession became important—that of cattle-rearing. Texas was the chief center of the Great Plains industry because cows could calve at any season and care for their calves. This was not true in the north. In summer, Texas longhorns were driven northward over the plains to "cow towns" which arose at different points in Kansas and Nebraska on the various railways. Since such drives put the cattlemen at the mercy of the cattle buyers from Chicago, Kansas City, and other stockyards centers, they established ranches where they could hold and sell their cattle when the market was most advantageous.[17] In 1884, four thousand men drove a million cattle out of Texas. Soon after this, drives were rendered unnecessary by the extension of railroads into the region. Up to the early eighties, herding was universal and cowboys were employed to guard the herds and grass; but soon Yankee ingenuity contributed barbed wire and fencing of the range became the rule. Since 1886 the cattle industry has witnessed considerable improvement; up to that time Texas cattle had the reputation of providing "substantial chewing," but as soon as a good market appeared, steps were taken to improve the breed. Imported bulls were introduced—Herefords, Durhams, Shorthorns, and Galloways.[18] The growing of forage crops was also initiated.

Owing to the semiaridity and the unreliability of the rainfall, as well as to the lack of fuel and building materials and to the scarcity of surface waters, agricultural inroads were made slowly. Poor transportation and the opposition of those interested in pastoralism were additional discouragements. As late as 1880 the Llano Estacado as well as other parts of the Great Plains west of the 98th meridian (except along some larger valleys) were occupied only by scattered stockmen. During the last half of the eighties, however, the cow country began to disappear. Overstocking was among the major causes. About this time, too, thousands of land-hungry settlers poured into the region and began to grow wheat. Thus began the third stage of succession—growing wheat for export. The newcomers used the same seed and the same methods they had used when living in the better watered lands to the

east.[19] They did not know that they had come to a strange land as far as farming was concerned. Close on their heels came the town builders and boomers and soon Amarillo, Dalhart, Clarendon, and other towns were laid out. The first years were encouraging because of abnormally abundant rains, but before long drought and other discouragements appeared. Finally, prolonged drought in the early nineties brought a series of almost complete crop failures. Thousands of settlers were starved out and forced to migrate, and millions of acres of land returned slowly to grass. Within a few years the sites of many towns were marked only by parallel rows of cellar excavations, iron hydrants at corners, and the like.

The depopulation of the area was, however, not complete. The vast stretches of level land with deep fertile soil continued to invite large numbers of farmers; attempt after attempt was made only to be blasted by the tragedy of drought. But the drought had taught some of the leaders one great lesson, the need of experimentation. By successive trials man finally triumphed. Success was largely owing to the adoption of dry farming and to the introduction of foreign drought-resistant crops. Thus year by year the tillable area expanded while the area devoted strictly to ranching shrank. Between 1925 and 1930, the cultivated area almost doubled.

But this expansion served as only the immediate prelude to the devastating dust storms that accompanied the drought of the 1930's. Farming, overgrazing, and drought together conspired to create the Dust Bowl.[20] In 1935 and

---

[17] James Truslow Adams, *The Epic of America* (Boston, Little, Brown and Company, 1931), p. 291.

[18] More recently Brahma and Zebu stock have been introduced.

[19] It has been said that though the homesteader failed, he did so through no fault of his own. Congress had failed to appreciate that 160 acres were not enough land for a farm in a region of little and uncertain rain. Moreover, agricultural experiment stations were not established to gather facts until decades after the homesteaders first needed them.

[20] James C. Malin, a long-time student of dust storms, believes they are among the natural phenomena of the Great Plains—that they were frequent and severe prior to white settlement and the plowing of the sod. He does not think they are in themselves necessarily abnormal, at least not in the sense in

1936, more than six million acres of land in this area were subject to severe wind erosion. Crops were devastated, livestock died, and farms by the hundreds were abandoned. Surveys in 1939, however, revealed that the Dust Bowl had shrunk, with less than one million acres subject to severe blowing and these mostly on the fringe of the area. This shrinkage resulted mostly from increased precipitation as compared with the drought years, but conservation practices also played an important role. Severe and widespread dust storms were plaguing the region again in the middle 1950's.

Agriculturally, the region is now characterized by wheat north of the east-west tier of counties southwest of where the Red River cuts the one hundredth meridian to form the southwest corner of Oklahoma, and by cotton south of it. The drought resistant grain sorghums—milo maize and Kaffir corn—are widely distributed throughout the entire region and are of great importance. These grain sorghums have gone far to transform the Llano Estacado from a grazing region to a farming region. They constitute the *dependable* grain and feed crops of the Southern High Plains. They are consumed mostly on the very farms where they are grown, and they enable the area to support more cattle now than it did in the day of the cattle barons.

The fourth and present revolutionary stage of sequent occupance—that of natural gas and oil—was ushered in when natural gas was discovered in 1918. Three years later oil was located in the area, though some distance from the first gas well. Subsequent drilling has indicated that areally the Amarillo District is one of the largest oil and gas pools in the world. These important mineral adjustments have stimulated urban development and have produced considerable capital. Refineries, carbonblack plants, a zinc smelter, and other factories have arisen. These, together with packing plants, grist mills, and cotton gins, present a noticeable industrial element in the regional economy. During World War II this area, a part of the so-called West South Central States Region, got the greatest relative benefit in proportion to its prewar share of United States manufacturing activity. Whereas before the war, this region contributed about 3.34 percent of the

country's manufacturing activity, it received 10.94 percent of the total war plant or about 328 percent of what could be considered its share on the basis of the prewar industrial record. Most of this activity is close to the Gulf of Mexico in Texas and Louisiana. The High Plains, however, can not yet be said to have entered a fifth stage (manufacturing) of sequent occupance. Although considerable natural gas is being utilized in the Panhandle, much also is being sent by pipeline to distant markets.

INTERIOR ARABIA

Among the sun-baked, hard gravelly plains, rocky hills, and sand dunes of interior Arabia, nomadic herding was formerly almost the exclusive mode of land occupancy. Because of the low rainfall, the vegetation is sparse and harsh. Perennial rivers are nonexistent; drainage lines consist of dry stream beds with an occasional water hole. In this inhospitable environment dwell numerous small tribes of Semitic peoples who follow herds and flocks of camels, sheep, and goats from place to place. Even the worst of the forage is utilized; thus prickly and thorny bushes are browsed by camels without injuring their mouths. Interior Arabia is reputed to be the world's leading camel-breeding region.

The Bedouins' whole existence centers about their domesticated animals and it is through these that they adjust themselves to the natural environment. The herds and flocks provide them with food, clothing, shelter, transportation, fuel, and utensils. Hence, the needs of the animals determine the mode of life. The sparse vegetation necessitates constant moves; accordingly the people are mostly pastoral nomads. Each day the flocks and herds are grazed in a different tract from that of the previous day. Since within a few weeks all the forage is consumed on those grazing grounds readily accessible from the encampment, frequent moves must be made to new localities some miles distant. The migrations are also seasonal. Hence a tribe must have jurisdic-

---

which the subject was exploited during the drought decade of the 1930's. See James C. Malin, "Dust Storms: 1850–1900," *The Kansas Historical Quarterly*, Vol. XIV (May, 1946), pp. 1–71.

tion over an immense tract of land, even though occupying but a fraction of it at any given time.

As the tribes arrive in the desert again from their migration, let us say, into Iraq, they split up into family groups and disperse far and wide.

Because of the continuous wanderings, there is a definite limitation on the type of dwelling and upon the possessions of the people. Homes are tents made of wool or hair. Most of the equipment is obtained from the animals. Every item can be readily packed and moved with facility. Property consists of livestock and portable chattels; wealth in the European sense is scarcely known.

All the nomads of interior Arabia belong to tribes, each of which is widely separated from its neighbors. Members of a tribe must act in concert in all affairs. Life, which is simple and austere, is regulated entirely by traditional rules strictly enforced. Each tribe is under the leadership of a chief who is both capable and responsible; he makes the important decisions for the entire group; it is he who determines when and where the group will move.

For the most part life here had not changed for millennia: the natural environment had remained much the same and the Bedouins had adjusted themselves as perfectly to it as their culture would allow. Thus, long before Mohammed, long before recorded history, the nomads and their animals had wandered in search of water and herbage. Home to them was wherever they pitched their tents. Scholars who knew Arabia best anticipated no major change in the way of life in the future.

Then came the discovery of oil and with oil came the great pipeline across the desert from the Persian Gulf to the Mediterranean Sea. Water had to be provided for the oil pumping stations and for what they anticipated would be modest numbers of people. Scores of wells were drilled along the 1,100 miles of pipeline. With permanent sources of water, Bedouins by the hundreds converged on the wells, bringing thousands of camels with them. Now more and more Bedouins are forsaking the traditional migrations and are encamping near the new sources of water. When the animals have assuaged their thirst, they move into the desert, finding what scant grass and

thorny scrub they may before turning back three or four days later.

Thus amazing changes are taking place in the manner of life of the people: a way of life that was built around the camel is shifting over to one based on the mineral, petroleum. Here as in few places on earth can be seen in swift progress the vast social revolution that comes with oil.

Many camel herders' sons, most of whom had never seen modern tools, are learning to drive trucks, repair diesels, and operate lathes! Thousands are now employed by the oil industry. Thus each year there are fewer foreigners employed by Arabian American Oil Company and more and more Bedouins getting jobs.

Each year, too, the number of nomads declines a little, for the camel is losing his place in the Arab way of life. It is no longer the only means of transport. In fact a 50 million dollar railway now runs the 350 miles from the port of Dammam on the Persian Gulf to the capital city of Riyadh on the high pleateau. Its trains make the fastest time of any in continental Asia. Highways, too, are being extended and thousands of trucks and automobiles travel over them daily.

Finally, agriculture is being taught to many former nomads. Three one-thousand-acre farms comprise an experiment at Al Kharj in the heart of the desert. The oil company supplies twelve thousand gallons of water per minute to the project and the fields yield bountifully. To thus anchor his restless nomads to the soil by means of irrigation was one of the dreams of Ibn Saud, who successfully welded together the present kingdom of Saudi Arabia.

CONCLUSIONS

Ecological succession is a reality and tends to manifest itself in most regions, although slowly in areas where definite retarding factors predominate. Progress and change are incited by population pressure but become realities largely through contact with outside peoples and cultures. Innate inventive genius is perhaps an added factor to be considered.

Intense cold, inadequate rainfall and, under some conditions, alkaline soils present almost insurmountable obstacles to succession in many parts of the earth, for they can produce no higher economic and social groups than pastoral hordes.[21] Extreme isolation, which minimizes culture transfer, is a powerful retarding factor. Continuously hot humid climate (Rainy Tropical) or exceedingly rugged terrain also act as checks to transition.[22] Poor endowment of domesticable animal forms is still another factor. Thus Australia, without a single animal fit for domestication, was occupied by aborigines who could not get beyond the hunting stage. Accordingly, inferior or marginal lands everywhere are likely to exhibit a rudimentary sequence of regional occupance.

In many favored areas, a cycle of geographic evolution exists. In the primary stages of human occupation, a region, unless its culture be superimposed from the outside, is characterized by simple adjustments to the physical milieu, but these are eventually replaced by more complex adjustments. As the pressure of population becomes greater, these more advanced types of adaptation, in turn, give way to adjustments of still greater complexity and intensity. So-called normal sequences, however, are by no means regular in occurrence. In fact, one or more of these types of societal economy may appear occasionally out of what is generally considered the normal order. Moreover, certain stages may be elided or omitted altogether.

Thus as stated earlier in the chapter, generalizations prescribing definite, orderly, identical sequences on a worldwide basis should be made with great caution. Such sequences could exist only if all habitable land were almost tantamount in quality, equal in accessibility, and occupied by people similar or identical in cultural level. Where such similarities do exist, the several types of geographic adjustment have tended to follow a rather definite sequence. Save in the most restrictive environments, then, every region is somewhere along the cycle of geographic change and its cultural landscape exhibits marks of transition along a morphological scale. The recognition and

understanding of ecological succession not only constitute one of the means for historical analysis, but provide an effective tool for use in regional planning, where efforts are made to anticipate and provide for future changes in human economy.

From what has gone before in this chapter it is apparent to the reader that the stages of development are not the same worldwide. It has been suggested that maps be drawn from time to time to show stages of development. Each map would have a legend as follows.

1. Regions which are undeveloped
2. Regions which are underdeveloped
3. Regions which seem to be fully developed for this time
4. Regions which are overdeveloped
5. Regions which are being redeveloped

The last item in the legend would include those placed in megalopoles where urban renewal is taking place. The first item would include the polar regions, the desert regions, and other regions which have been referred to as the "too" regions—too cold, too dry, too hot, too high, too rugged, too remote, and so on. The three middle categories, of course, would show the ecumene where mankind has obtained a fairly secure hold on his environment.

With such categories, world maps of Columbus' time, the Renaissance, pre-World War I, and the present, would provide ample source material for geographers as well as others to study and ponder on the theories advanced concerning ecological succession. Of particular significance would be thoughts about the role which man can and should play in that succession.

There is a geography for every time—past, present, and future.

---

[21] Mining, manufacturing, and commerce are not mentioned because they are indirect processes and cannot maintain a population by their own immediate winnings.

[22] C. Langdon White, "Storm Clouds Over the Andes," *Scientific Monthly*, Vol. LXX (May, 1950), p. 306.

Index of Illustrations

Index of Subjects

Classes, social, soils and, 491
Clay, 467, 468, 469
  as building material, 558
Cleveland, Ohio
  geographic cycle, 638–39
  navigable waters, 431
Climate, 5–6, 95 ff.
  air pressure and, 98–99
  altitude and, 98
  Arid Tropical, 141 ff.
  atmosphere and, 95
  average, 108
  barometer, 98–99
  classes, 109
  Dry Continental, 274 ff.
  Dry Subtropical, 223 ff.
  frost, 96
  human activity and, 300
  Humid Continental, 239 ff.
  Humid Subtropical, 208 ff.
  humidity and precipitation, 104, ff.
  "ideal," 300
  isotherms, 98
  latitude and, 97–98
  marine vs. continental, 110–12
  mediterranean, 190 ff.
  Monsoon Tropical, 164 ff.
  mountains and, 373–74
  oceans and, 101 ff., 448, 456
  plains, 365
  Polar Ice Cap, 330 ff.
  Rainy Subtropical, 180 ff.
  Rainy Tropical, 115 ff.
  regions and man, 112–13
  Semiarid Tropical, 180 ff.
  Subpolar, 312 ff.
  Temperate Marine, 295 ff.
  temperature, 96–97
  "tropical," 141
  types, 112
  wind and, 99 ff.
    continental system, 104
  zones, 112
Climax vegetation, 495
Clothing, animals and, 519
Coal, 580 ff.
  definition, 580–81
  distribution, 580
  mining, 583 ff.
    town, 585, 587
  oil vs., as power source, 594
  producers, 582
  types, 581
  water vs., as power source, 439–40
Coast, 7. See also Coast zone.
  windward, Rainy Tropical, 115
Coast Guard ice patrol, 332

Coast zone, 448 ff.
  compound shorelines, 454–55
  emergent shorelines, 451–53
  neutral shorelines, 453–54
  political detachment, 455
  racial contrasts, 455
  struggles for, 455–56
  submergent shorelines, 448 ff.
Coastal plains, 359–60
Coastal situation, 627–28
Coastline, 448
Cobalt, 576, 577
Cocci, 525
Coffee, 176, 177
Colby, Charles, 611
Cold front, 254–55
Collective farming, 260–61
Collinson and M'Clure, 336
Colombia
  economy, 403
  oil, 590
Colonialism, Rainy Tropical regions, 137
Colorado, geologic succession, 637
Colorado Plateau, 399
Colorado River, 154
Columbia Basin soils, 481
Columbia Plateau, 401
Columbus, Christopher, 458, 459
Commerce
  Arid Tropical, 155–56
  Dry Continental, 291–92
  ecological succession stage, 640, 641
  forests and, 509
  Humid Continental, 250, 262–63
  mediterranean, 203–4
  Monsoon Tropical, 177
  ocean, 457 ff.
  Rainy Tropical, 136–37
  Subpolar, 323
  Temperate Marine, 309
Commercial industries, 15
Commercial subregion, 83–85
Communication, mountain, 377 ff.
Communism, 221. See also Union of Soviet Socialist Republics.
Community
  site, 623
  water supply, 415–16
Compact form, 614, 615, 617, 619–20
Compound shorelines, 454–55
Condensation, dew point and, 105
Configuration, 351, 357
  water table and, 410
Congo
  native inhabitants, 124, 125
    Pygmies, 130
  water power, 439

Conic projection, 55
Coniferous forest, northern, 500–501. See also Taiga.
Connate ground water, 409
Conservation
  forest, 258–59, 304–5
  game, 183–84, 520
  mineral, 552
Continental climate
  dry, 274 ff.
  humid, 239 ff.
  marine vs., 110–12
Continental shelf, 445–46
Continental wind system, 104
Continents, 345–47
  area of, 346
  continual processes, 347
  expansion objectives, 631
  global pattern, 346–47
  land arrangement, 346
  location, 65–67
  petroleum sources, 587 ff.
  situation, 623 ff.
  size, 346, 604
  surface features, 347
Control relationships, 16–17, 72–74
Convectional precipitation, 106
Cook, James, 337, 338
Coolgardie, 150
Coordinates, global, 46
Copper, 570–71
  ancients and, 540
  Montana, 81–82
  Utah, 568
Coral reefs, 453–54
Cork stripping, 202
Corn
  European, 248
  hill country, 392
  Humid Subtropical, 214–15
  soils, 488
Corn Belt, 259
  Crop production, 247–48
  ecologic succession, 638
  livestock, 249
  moraine, 363
  social adjustments, 251
  subregions, 88–89
Correction lines survey, 46–47
Cotton, 177, 214–15
  boll weevil and, 515
  Russian, 287
  soils, 488
Cotton Belt, 208, 215, 216
Country location, 63
County forms, 617–18
Cowlitz River, 393
Crevasses, 334
Crop rotation, 484–85

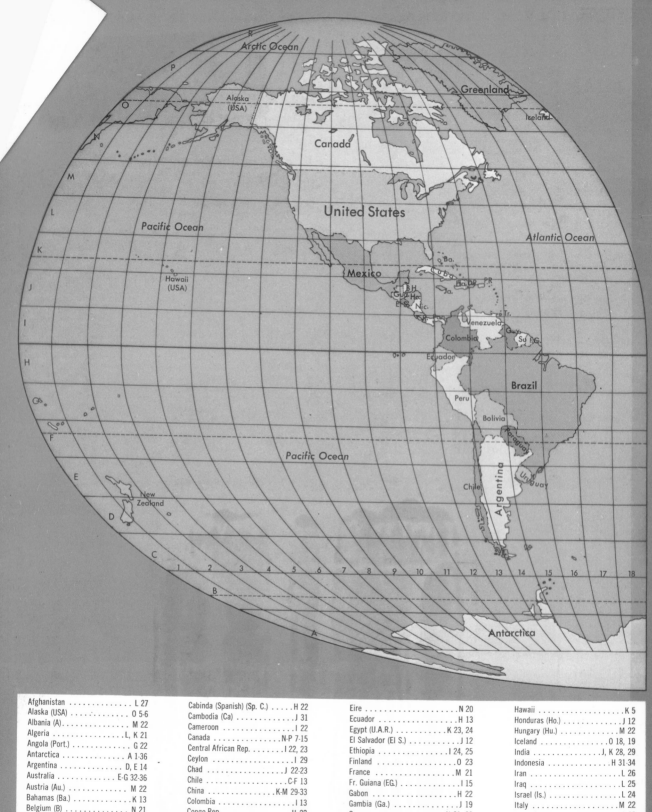